1980

Management of
Industrial
Enterprises

MANAGEMENT OF INDUSTRIAL ENTERPRISES

by Richard N. Owens, Ph.D. C.P.A.

VISITING PROFESSOR OF BUSINESS ADMINISTRATION

LOS ANGELES STATE COLLEGE

FOURTH EDITION • 1961

RICHARD D. IRWIN, INC.

HOMEWOOD, ILLINOIS

FOURTH EDITION
First Printing, January, 1961

Library of Congress Catalogue Card No. 61–6321

PRINTED IN THE UNITED STATES OF AMERICA

Preface

SINCE Frederick W. Taylor began his work in management about 1880, men have attempted to make the subject more exact by developing a body of proved techniques and by formulating principles of management that might be regarded as scientific. Companies and individuals have conducted numerous experiments, studied the experiences of others, and examined specific situations in an attempt to derive management principles. This study continues unabated.

In the first studies of management, attention was centered upon problems of production at the plant or worker level. Managers concerned themselves with technical processes, the selection and care of machines and equipment, the flow of materials through the plant, the organization of the work, and the supervision of workers. In the plant, management has continued to be interested in the basic problems pertaining to the volume of production, the cost of the product, human relations, and safety. The problems remain the same, although the emphasis has shifted.

The discussion of management problems requires attention to the manner in which people co-operate to produce goods and services. This discussion requires attention to the three levels of organization which present different types of problems: the executive level, the supervisory level, and the worker level. These three levels are separately treated in this book. Since the organization for production requires certain staff services, attention is also directed to the development of staff and its proper relationship to the line.

Problems of physical equipment also require study. Such problems pertain to plant location, machinery and equipment, the increased mechanization of production, automation, methods of materials handling, and maintenance of machinery and equipment. At the workplace, the work of production brings together the machine, the tools, the materials, and the worker who tends the machine and fashions the product. Relevant techniques of management at this stage include methods of dealing with increasing mechanization, reducing the costs of materials handling, setting standards for the amount of production, and planning and controlling production. In fact, Taylor found that all of the problems of management could be traced to the methods of organizing and controlling the work at the machine or the work center.

In the discussion of management problems in this book, attention is necessarily directed to some of the broader problems that affect the activities at the work level. During recent years, production plans and programs have been affected by the prospects of inflation or deflation. For example, the decision to construct or rent a building and to buy or lease machines depends in part upon the prospect of inflationary trends. Other developments outside the company which affect production plans include government programs for national defense, the emphasis upon the dispersal of the facilities of production, new highway construction, changes in competition from other companies and other industries, and the attitude of governmental agencies toward size and the expansion of the product line through mergers. Reference is made to these changes at various places throughout the text.

The subject of management may be studied and taught in formal courses of study in any one of three ways. First, certain techniques or methods of carrying out a program or plan may be explained. Examples are methods of computing costs with a new machine in comparison with costs for an old machine, methods of revising the layout of the plant, the procedure for setting work standards by motion and time study, and the way to interview an applicant for a job. Much of the discussion throughout this book is concerned with such techniques and the methods of conducting various programs.

Second, a better understanding of management may be developed by a discussion of the work of various divisions or departments of an enterprise, the relationships of departments and divisions to each other, and ways of co-ordinating their activities with each other and with institutions outside the company. For example, quality control is achieved through the co-ordination of product research, product design, standards for purchasing and storing materials, the manufacturing processes, and inspection. Human relations problems affect decisions as to building construction, plant layout, physical equipment, and working conditions. At various places in the discussion in this book, reference is made to the need for co-ordinating production activities.

Third, the student may be prepared for work in management by developing his ability to analyze a business problem and to arrive at a logical solution. This phase of student development may be furthered by a discussion of the philosophy of management in relation to specific problems and by questions and cases which call for new applications of principles. In a text like the present volume, only a beginning can be made toward this aspect of the development of the student, but it is hoped that the book can make a contribution toward this objective.

It may be assumed that the manager is required to have a knowledge of the technical processes of production in the company or the plant which he is called upon to manage. In this book, illustrations are drawn from a great many industries, including metal working, glass, soap, book publishing, and automobile. The discussion is not intended to make the reader an expert in any field of production. It is intended to illustrate that management principles are of general application and can be useful in any area of activity.

RICHARD N. OWENS

Los Angeles, California
October, 1960

Table Of Contents

PART I. INTRODUCTION

CHAPTER   PAGE

1. THE DEVELOPMENT OF MANAGEMENT   3

EARLY DEVELOPMENTS IN MANAGEMENT: Early Industrial Management.
Beginning of Work Measurement. Standardization of Product. Develop-
ment of Manufacturing Methods. Development of Management Methods.
SCIENTIFIC MANAGEMENT: Frederick W. Taylor. Summary of the Taylor
Principles. Name of the System. Management as a Science. Henry L.
Gantt. The Gilbreths. Comparison of the Gilbreths and Taylor. Other Lead-
ers in Management. MANAGEMENT FROM 1910 TO 1920: Adaptation of the
New Methods. Use of Management Consultants. Society for Discussion of
Management Problems. Effect of World War I. Developments after the
War. DEVELOPMENTS SINCE 1920: Emphasis on Engineering. Changing
Attitude toward the Worker. Growth of Unions. Legislation Affecting
Management. Management at the Higher Levels. Adaptation to Change.
Preparation for Management. Operations Research. Use of Machines for
Data Processing.

2. PRODUCTION PROBLEMS AND POLICIES   32

SOME PROBLEMS OF ORGANIZATION: Organization of the Board of Di-
rectors. Flat or Steep Organization. Extent of Delegation. Development of
Staff. PROBLEMS OF PHYSICAL EQUIPMENT: The Problem of Size. Num-
ber of Plants. PROBLEM OF THE PRODUCT LINE: Question of Leadership.
Question of Buy or Make. Horizontal and Allied Expansion. Sell or Rent.
Dropping a Product. PERSONNEL PROBLEMS AND POLICIES: Attitude to-
ward Workers. Attitude toward Unions. FINANCIAL PROBLEMS AFFECTING
PRODUCTION: Problems of Inflation. Sources of Funds. STABILITY WITH
FLEXIBILITY.

PART II. ORGANIZATIONAL PROBLEMS

3. ORGANIZATION FOR PRODUCTION   49

ORGANIZATION IN A SINGLE-PLANT COMPANY: Line Organization. Ad-
vantages of Line Type. Disadvantages of Line Type. Development of
Staff. Authority of Staff. Staff Functions in Industry. Functional Organ-
ization. Advantages of Functional Plan. Disadvantages of Functional Plan.
Importance of Functional Plan. Relation to Line and Staff. ORGANIZATION
IN A MULTIPLANT COMPANY: Co-ordination of Plant Activities. Effect of
Number of Products.

4. PRINCIPLES OF ORGANIZATION   68

Provision for Essential Activities. Authority to Act. Assignment of Re-
sponsibility. The Scalar Chain. Channels of Communication. Lines of
Promotion. Logical Assignment of Duties. Regard for Personal Capacities.
Distribution of Work. Proper Placement of an Over-all Service. Centralized
Authority. Co-ordination. Use of Committees. Use of Charts in Organiza-
tion Planning.

CHAPTER   PAGE

5. PROBLEMS AT THE EXECUTIVE LEVEL 85

WORK OF THE EXECUTIVE: General Administration. Talking with People. Delegation of Authority. Judgment by Standards. PREPARATION FOR EXECUTIVE WORK: Education for Executive Work. Training of the Executive. Growth and Development of Executives. Organization of a Development Program. Requirements for Success.

6. PROBLEMS AT THE FOREMAN LEVEL 100

TECHNICAL RESPONSIBILITIES OF THE FOREMAN: Responsibility for Directing the Work. Responsibility for Working Conditions. Maintaining Quality. Controlling Costs. RELATIONS WITH WORKERS: Nature of Employee Relationships. Communication with Workers. Handling Worker Complaints. RELATIONS WITH OTHER MANAGEMENT PERSONNEL: Transmitting Information. Relations with Staff. COMPENSATION OF FOREMEN. TRAINING OF FOREMAN: Selection for Training. Training in Management. Training in Company Organization. Technical Training. Training in Human Relations. FOREMEN'S UNIONS AND CLUBS: Reasons for Foremen's Unions. Legality of Unions. Foremen's Clubs. JUDGING THE WORK OF FOREMEN: Desirable Qualities of a Foreman. Rating of Foremen. Reviewing Ratings with Foremen.

7. PROBLEMS AT THE WORKER LEVEL 120

WHAT THE WORKER EXPECTS FROM HIS WORK: Satisfactory Compensation for Work. Security. A Feeling of Belonging. Organizational and Social Status. Treatment as an Individual. Individual Attitudes and Social Relationships. Differences between Workers. Handling Morale Problems. Human Aspects versus Work Aspects. MEASURING WORKER ATTITUDES: Opinion Surveys. Using the Information. Value of the Survey.

PART III. EQUIPMENT AND WORKING CONDITIONS

8. CHOOSING A LOCATION 137

PLANNING FOR PHYSICAL EQUIPMENT: The Problem of Location. FACTORS INFLUENCING LOCATION: Nearness to Market. Nearness to Raw Materials. Transportation Facilities and Costs. Labor Conditions. Power and Fuel. Vulnerability to Air Attack. Cost of Land. Water Supply. Waste Disposal. Building Costs. Service Industries. Taxes. Industries Which Use By-products of Others. Climate. Financial Aids. Civic Values. CHOICE OF TOWN OR CITY: Suburban Location. Small-Town Location. Location on a Superhighway. The Industrial Park. The Company Town. DECIDING UPON A LOCATION: Data Required. Comparison of Different Sites. The Break-Even Point. Limitations of a Cost Analysis. DEVELOPING FAVORABLE PUBLIC RELATIONS.

9. THE BUILDING AS PRODUCTIVE EQUIPMENT 159

PLANNING FOR THE BUILDING: The Decision to Build. Sale-and-Lease-Back Arrangement. Effect of Inflation. Tax Considerations. The Building Plan. TYPES OF BUILDINGS: Single-Story Buildings. Multistory Building. Number of Buildings. Types of Construction. Floors. Roofs. ADAPTATION OF THE BUILDING PLAN: Employee Comfort. Built-in Safety. Provision for Expansion. External Appearance. Maintenance Program. Renovation of Building and Equipment.

CHAPTER   PAGE

10. MACHINERY AND EQUIPMENT   181

EQUIPMENT FOR PRODUCTION: Manually Operated Machines. Semiautomatic Machines. Fully Automatic Machines. Automation. General-
Purpose Machines. Special-Purpose Equipment. Factors in the Selection
of Equipment. EQUIPMENT FOR HANDLING MATERIALS: Costs Resulting
from Poor Methods. Principles of Materials Handling. Factors in the
Selection of Equipment. Types of Materials-Handling Equipment. Overhead Conveyors. Trucks. Responsibility for Improving Materials Handling.
THE REPLACEMENT OF EQUIPMENT: Continuous Replacement. Effect of
Rising Prices. Estimating Savings from Replacement. Lease or Buy. Re-
sponsibility for Selection of Equipment. LABOR AND MACHINE PRODUC-
TION.

11. LAYOUT OF THE PLANT   213

PHYSICAL REQUIREMENTS: Layout by Processes. Layout by Products. Work
Centers. Changing the Basis of the Layout. Relation of Layout to Other
Problems. Production Planning. MAKING THE LAYOUT: Information Required. The Process Chart. Planning for Equipment. Special Requirements
of Machines. Service Departments. Review of Space Allocation. Choosing
the Best Layout. Completing the Plan.

12. MAINTENANCE OF MACHINERY AND EQUIPMENT   235

ORGANIZATION FOR MAINTENANCE WORK: The Maintenance Department.
Relation to Operating Departments. PLANNING FOR MAINTENANCE: Problems of Scheduling. Determining the Work Load. Following the Progress
of the Work. Management of Maintenance Stores. CONTROL OF MAINTE-
NANCE PERFORMANCE: Standards of Performance. Management Reports.

13. WORKING CONDITIONS: LIGHT AND COLOR   249

LIGHT: Advantages of Good Illumination. Phases of Illumination. Essentials of Good Lighting. The Intensity of Light. Effect of Building Construction. Cleanliness of Walls and Windows. Methods of Lighting.
The Source of the Light. Type of Lamps. Maintenance of a Lighting System. USE OF COLOR: Some Effects of Color. Color for Safety.

14. WORKING CONDITIONS: AIR, NOISE, MUSIC, MONOTONY   262

AIR CONDITIONING: Temperature. Humidity. Smoke and Dirt Removal.
Movement of Air. Relation to Building Construction. NOISE: Nature of
Noise. Effect of Noise. Control of Noise. MUSIC AND BROADCASTING SYS-
TEMS. MONOTONY: Nature of Monotonous Tasks. Worker Attitudes to-
ward Monotony. Reducing the Effect of Monotony. FATIGUE: Nature of
Fatigue. Reducing Fatigue.

PART IV. THE PRODUCT

15. PRODUCT RESEARCH   283

NATURE OF INDUSTRIAL RESEARCH: Types of Research. Who Conducts
Research. DEVELOPMENT AND CONTROL OF RESEARCH PROGRAMS: Co-
ordination of Research Programs. Location of Research Laboratory. Re-
search a Staff Function. Organization for Research. Planning the Research
Program. Organizing for Production of the Product. Budget Control of
Research. Patenting of a Product or a Design.

CHAPTER   PAGE

16. DESIGN OF THE PRODUCT 299

INFLUENCES UPON DESIGN: Service Expected. Weight of the Product. Appearance. Shipping Costs. Cost of Manufacture. Consumer Ideas. Nature of the Competition. Functional Design. Manufacturing Design. The Lag in Product Design. Design of Container. DEVELOPMENT OF DESIGN: Specifications. Permissible Variations. Development of Standards. Limits of Standardization. Design a Staff Function. Importance of Timing. ELIMINATION OF UNPROFITABLE DESIGNS: Pressure for New Designs. Effects of Overexpansion of the Product Line. Elimination of Unprofitable Items.

17. INSPECTION OF THE PRODUCT 321

PURPOSES OF INSPECTION. WHEN TO INSPECT. WHO INSPECTS: Worker Inspection. Automatic Inspection. Machine Inspection. HOW MUCH TO INSPECT: Partial or Complete Inspection. Use of Statistical Methods in Inspection. WHERE TO INSPECT. KIND OF TEST IN INSPECTION: Accuracy of Dimensions. Profile Inspection. Strength of Material. Smoothness of Surface. Chemical Composition. Color. Inspection for Internal Faults. MANAGEMENT OF INSPECTION.

PART V. PRODUCTION STANDARDS

18. METHODS IMPROVEMENT 343

MOTION STUDY: Purposes of Motion Study. Analysis of Motions. Therbligs. Principles of Motion. The Methods Improvement Program. Training the Worker. Economies of Motion Study. Objections to Motion Study. Effect upon Employment. WORK SIMPLIFICATION. HUMAN ENGINEERING. WORK SAMPLING: Initiating the Program. Information Gained by Work Sampling. Uses of Work Sampling.

19. TIME-STUDY TECHNIQUES AND PROCEDURES 362

THE TIME-STUDY PROGRAM: Uses of Time Study. Relation of Motion Study to Time Study. The Time-Study Man. Personal Qualifications. MAKING THE TIME STUDY: Selection of the Department and the Task. Selection of the Worker. Time-Study Equipment. Recording the Element Times. Other Types of Equipment. Number of Observations.

20. SETTING THE STANDARD TIME 378

DETERMINING THE STANDARD: Exceptional Observations. Computing the Time for an Element. Performance Rating. Allowances. ESTIMATING THE TIME STANDARD: Standard Element Times. Predetermined Time Standards. REVISING WORK STANDARDS: The Tight Standard. Revising Loose Standards. Criticisms of Time Study.

PART VI. WAGES AND INCENTIVES

21. THE PROBLEM OF WAGES 397

THE ECONOMICS OF WAGES: The Marginal Productivity Theory. The Commodity Theory. The Functional Theory. Relative Bargaining Strength. WAGE CRITERIA FOR THE EMPLOYER: What Is Necessary to Get Workers. Cost of Living. Ability of the Employer to Pay. Effect of Work Conditions. Nature of the Job. Ability of the Worker. BARGAINING ON WAGE RATES.

CHAPTER PAGE

22. WAGE SYSTEMS. 413

SYSTEMS THAT GRANT NO BONUS: Advantages of the Hourly Rate. Disadvantages of the Hourly Rate. The Measured Day Rate. Annual Wage. SYSTEMS THAT PAY A SMALL BONUS: Halsey Plan. Rowan Plan.

23. WAGE SYSTEMS—CONTINUED 424

SYSTEMS THAT PROVIDE FOR PAYMENT IN PROPORTION TO OUTPUT: Piece-Rate Plans. Bedaux Plan. Group Piece Rates. Attitude of Labor Unions. INCENTIVE WAGE SYSTEMS: Basic Principles. Gantt Task and Bonus Plan. Emerson Efficiency Wage. Requirements of a Successful Plan. Maintenance of the Plan. Evaluation of Incentive Plans. PROFIT-SHARING AND BONUS PLANS: Disadvantages of Profit Sharing. Christmas Bonuses.

24. JOB EVALUATION 438

INFORMATION FOR JOB EVALUATION: Types of Job Information. METHODS OF JOB EVALUATION: Job Ranking. Job Classification. Factor Comparison. Point System. MAKING THE PLAN EFFECTIVE: Disseminating Information as to the Plan. Maintaining the Plan. LIMITATIONS OF JOB EVALUATION: Need to Get Workers. Relation to Employee Rating. Attitude of Unions.

PART VII. PERSONNEL RELATIONS

25. PERSONNEL ACTIVITIES 457

PERSONNEL FUNCTIONS: Development of Personnel Function. Relations with Unions. Organization for Personnel Relations. PERSONNEL OBJECTIVES AND POLICIES: Furthering Company Objectives. Developing an Efficient and Loyal Work Force. Statement of Personnel Policies. Responsibility for Human Relations. Qualities of Personnel Manager. Index of Employee Relations.

26. EMPLOYMENT OF PEOPLE 471

SOURCES OF LABOR SUPPLY: Inside Sources. Outside Sources. Requirements for Good Sources. METHODS OF SELECTING WORKERS: Preliminary Interview. Application Blank. Letter of Application. Employment Interview. Recommendations. Personal Investigation. Mental Tests. Special Aptitude Tests. Trade Tests. Situational Testing. Testing the Test. Physical Examination. Use of Selection Methods. INTRODUCING THE WORKER TO THE JOB. EVALUATION OF SELECTION METHODS.

27. CHANGES IN THE WORK FORCE 489

TRANSFER OF WORKERS. PROMOTION, DEMOTION, AND LAYOFF: The Promotion Chart. Basis of Promotion. Merit Rating in Promotion. Seniority Rights. Demotion. DISCHARGE: Attitude of the Union. Reasons for Discharge. Company Rules Concerning Discharge. Proof of Violation. The Preclearance Interview. Report of Termination. INDEX OF CHANGES: Indexes of Separation. Using Turnover Rates.

28. EMPLOYEE TRAINING 507

OBJECTIVES OF TRAINING: The Training Program. TYPES OF TRAINING PROGRAMS: Vestibule Training. Apprenticeship Training. On-the-Job Training. Training for Upgrading. Training in Safety. MANAGING A

CHAPTER   PAGE

TRAINING PROGRAM: Determining the Need for Training. Determining
Objectives. Obtaining Instructors. Responsibility of the Personnel Department. Rewards for Course Completion. Checking the Value of the Training Program.

29. EMPLOYEE SERVICES 520

HEALTH SERVICES: Improvement in Working Conditions. Medical Services.
Group Hospitalization and Surgical Benefits. Group Life Insurance. RECRE-
ATIONAL SERVICES. FINANCIAL BENEFITS: Retirement Plans. Employee
Stock-Purchase Plans. Credit Unions. SERVICES TO ESTABLISH CLOSER
RELATIONSHIP WITH EMPLOYEES: Employee Publication. Plant Food Serv-
ices. Company Stores. Suggestion Systems. Accident Prevention Programs.
Employee Counseling. Other Services.

PART VIII. PROCUREMENT AND STORAGE

30. PURCHASING 541

TYPES OF PURCHASES: Materials for Fabrication. Merchandise for Resale
without Fabrication. Machinery and Equipment. Supplies. THE WORK OF
PURCHASING: The Timing of Purchases. Organization for Purchasing. Purchasing a Service Function. PURCHASING PRACTICES AND POLICIES: Developing Sources of Supply. Selection of Vendor. Reciprocal Buying.
Commercial Bribery. What to Buy. Checking for Quality. How Much
to Buy. The Purchase Order. One-Year Contracts. INFORMATION USED
IN PURCHASING.

31. INVENTORY STANDARDS AND CONTROL 561

Purpose of Inventory Management. Standard Quantities. Determining
the Quantity to Order. Reorder Point. The Balance of Stores Record.
Pricing of Materials Issued.

32. STORING AND ISSUING MATERIALS 574

RECEIVING AND STORING: Receiving Stores. Use of Space. Method of
Storing. PROTECTION AGAINST LOSS: Protection against Deterioration. Pro-
tection against Damage and Fire Loss. Prevention of Waste and Theft.
THE ISSUING OF STORES: Ease in Issuing. Handling and Moving. Preven-
tion of Accidents. SOME INVENTORY PROBLEMS: Keeping Inventories at a
Minimum. Constant Supply. Ease in Taking Inventory.

PART IX. PLANNING AND CONTROL OF QUANTITIES

33. THE PROBLEM OF PRODUCTION PLANNING AND CONTROL 595

Development of Production Control. Scope of Planning and Control. An
Illustration of Planning and Control. Advantages of Production Planning.
Relation to Other Management Problems. Departments Affected by Production Planning. Production Control Methods. Centralized or Decentralized Control. Effect of Method of Manufacture.

34. ROUTING AND SCHEDULING 609

ROUTING: Parts Necessary for Assembly. Sequence of Parts Completion.
Materials Necessary. Operations Necessary. Preparation of Forms. Division

CHAPTER   PAGE

of Work into Batches. SCHEDULING: Nature of Scheduling. Purposes of
Scheduling. Information Necessary for Scheduling. Bulletin Boards for
Machine Loads. Scheduling the Order. Centralized or Decentralized
Scheduling. Adaptations of Scheduling Methods.

35. DISPATCHING AND FOLLOW-UP 629

DISPATCHING: Issuance of Orders. Following the Progress of the Work.
Changes in Machine Loads. Communication between Departments. FOL-
LOW-UP.

36. PLANNING AND CONTROL IN CONTINUOUS MANUFACTURING . . . 637

Characteristics of Continuous Production. Routing. Preparation for Production. Scheduling Production with Demand. Scheduling Monthly Deliveries. Scheduling Production of Parts and Assemblies. The Factory Float.
Keeping the Factory Float Low. Scheduling Daily Runs. Dispatching.
Follow-Up.

PART X. FINANCIAL PLANNING AND CONTROL

37. BUDGETARY PLANNING AND CONTROL 655

NATURE OF THE BUDGET: Relation of the Budget to Management. Static
or Flexible Budget. Length of Budget Period. The Budget Officer. PREP-
ARATION OF THE BUDGET: Development of the Estimates. Relation of
Budget to Control. THE SALES BUDGET: Information Needed. Preparation
of the Sales Budget. Importance of Sales Estimate. MANUFACTURING
BUDGETS: The Production Budget. Purchases Budget. Plant and Equip-
ment Budget. Maintenance Budget. The Labor Budget. Manufacturing
Expense Budget. THE EXPENSE BUDGETS: Planning for Advertising Ex-
penses. Selling Expense Budget. Administrative Expense Budget. BUDGET
SUMMARIES: Cash Budget. Estimated Financial Statements. EXECUTION
OF THE PLAN: Effect upon People. Advantages of Financial Planning.
Limitations of Financial Planning.

38. PLANNING AND CONTROL THROUGH COSTS 672

NATURE AND USES OF COST INFORMATION: Some Uses of Cost Data.
Kinds of Cost Systems. Elements of Cost. DETERMINING THE COST OF A
UNIT OF PRODUCT: Determining Material and Labor Cost. Purposes of
Manufacturing Expense Accounting. Allocation of Service Department Ex-
penses. Allocation of Expenses to the Product. SOME PROBLEMS OF COST
DETERMINATION: Costs Based on a Predetermined Rate of Production.
Cost Based on Normal Rate of Output. Standard Cost. Differential Cost.
Total Cost. Replacement Cost. Opportunity Cost. Disseminating Cost In-
formation. A PROGRAM FOR COST CONTROL: The Question of Objectives.
Standards for Costs. Action on Cost Information.

39. GENERAL PLANNING AND CONTROL 691

THE OBJECTIVES OF THE ENTERPRISE: Social Objectives. Adaptation to
Change. The Profit Objective. Obligations to Other Groups. Establishing
Company Objectives. DIFFICULTIES OF ACCOMPLISHING COMPANY OB-
JECTIVES: Overemphasis on Profit. Attitude of Specialists. Empire Build-
ing. The Play-Safe Attitude. Bureaucracy. Personal Objectives. METHODS
OF CO-ORDINATION AND CONTROL: Divisional Profit and Loss Statement.

CHAPTER   PAGE

Cost Information. Use of Statistical Data. Measuring the Effectiveness of Staff. Profit-Sharing and Bonus Plans. Effective Employment of the Work Force. Work Stoppages. Unemployment. MANAGEMENT AS A SCIENCE: Management as a Body of Principles. Continuous Research as an Attribute of Science. Willingness to Accept New Ideas. SUCCESS OF MANAGEMENT IN ACCOMPLISHING OBJECTIVES: Private Objectives. Public Objectives. Other Reasons for a High Standard of Living.

INDEX

INDEX 715

PART I
INTRODUCTION

1 The Development of Management

WHENEVER people work together for the accomplishment of a common objective, some persons need to give attention to the problems of planning what is to be done, making provisions for physical facilities, assigning duties or tasks to the people, and directing and co-ordinating the various activities. As the work progresses these same persons may receive reports of work done, inspect the results, compare accomplishment with some predetermined standards, and take such corrective actions as may seem desirable. These principles of organization and management may be applied in industry, commercial enterprises, and other types of group activities.

EARLY DEVELOPMENTS IN MANAGEMENT

Even in ancient times, attention was given to management methods in the conduct of the government, organization for war, construction projects, and other work where co-operative endeavor was required. The book of Genesis[1] in the Bible tells how Joseph foretold the seven years of famine and then suggested to Pharaoh a plan for preparing for it in order that the people might have food during the years of scarcity. His plan was accepted, and he was put in charge of the project. With the assistance of supervisors, he collected grain, stored it, protected it against deterioration and loss, and dispensed it during the years of famine. This project required attention to many methods of organizing,

[1] Genesis 41:44.

3

supervising, providing warehouse space, collecting and transporting grain, reporting on the progress of the work, checking on results, and taking corrective action.

Later the Israelites followed other practices resembling the methods of modern management. Moses was required by the burden of his work to delegate authority to certain subordinates, to establish control techniques, to limit the number of subordinates reporting to him, and to establish a chain of command.[2] Joshua sent spies into Jerico to appraise the strength and weaknesses of the enemy.[3] This practice bears certain resemblances to methods sometimes used in a competitive economy. In ancient times, the kings sometimes sought the advice of prophets, whereas executives now may seek the advice of consultants.[4]

Many other examples of management methods in ancient times might be cited. The Carthaginians were particularly proficient in technical methods of maneuvering ships at sea and in the organizational aspects of maritime warfare. The Romans studied and applied methods of conducting land warfare and constructing and managing public enterprises, such as roads, aqueducts, public entertainment, buildings, and monuments. The Romans were able to establish an empire of great territorial extent and to rule it for several centuries because they mastered the techniques of organizing through the use of the chain of command and of controlling the work of persons to whom authority was delegated.

No attempt will be made here to trace the changes in the problems and methods of management throughout history. To give a meaningful treatment would require extended discussion of the manorial system of the Middle Ages, the feudal system, the revival of trade and commerce following the Crusades, the increased activity in business activities following the discovery of America, the methods of production and sale in the handicraft system, and the rise of the factory system. The discussion will be limited to the beginning of the modern management movement and a few of the more recent developments.

Early Industrial Management. In industry, methods of organizing, planning, supervising, directing, and controlling the flow of production were developed at least as early as the days of Adam Smith. Writing in 1776, he described the process of making ordinary brass pins.[5] The work involved eighteen distinct operations. In some factories, he

---

[2] Exodus 18:22.
[3] Joshua 2:1-24.
[4] II Chronicles 18.
[5] *The Wealth of Nations* (London: George Bell and Sons, 1899), Book I, chap. i.

said, the number of workers was more than eighteen, and more than one worker was assigned to some operations. In other factories, fewer than eighteen workers were employed, and one worker would perform more than one operation. In either case, a production line existed, although the materials were not moved by conveyors. Adam Smith found that the division of labor in pin making, and also in other industries, substantially increased production through various economies which he enumerated.

Another interesting observation of Adam Smith was that the division of labor led to the need for an entirely new trade or occupation of managers, to whom he gave the name of philosophers. He described the new developments as follows:

All the improvements in machinery, however, have by no means been the inventions of those who had occasion to use the machines. Many improvements have been made by the ingenuity of the makers of the machines, when to make them became the business of a peculiar trade; and some by that of those who are called philosophers or men of speculation, whose trade it is not to do anything, but to observe everything; and who, upon that account, are often capable of combining together the powers of the most distant and dissimilar objects. In the progress of society, philosophy or speculation, becomes, like every other employment, the principal or sole trade and occupation of a particular class of citizens. Like every other employment too, it is subdivided into a great number of different branches, each of which affords occupation to a peculiar tribe or class of philosophers.

In the foregoing paragraph, Adam Smith makes a distinction between the production-line worker, the person who designs the machine and handles other engineering problems, and the managers who plan, organize, supervise, observe, and control the operations. These distinctions are basic to much of modern management.

Beginning of Work Measurement. Studies in work measurement were made from time to time in both the United States and England. Some of these studies included the use of the stop watch. An interesting study of this nature was made by Thomas Jefferson in 1769 as he began to dig the foundation of his new home near Charlottesville, Virginia, which he called Monticello. He observed that "four good fellows, a lad, and two girls of about sixteen" dug a hole of $14\frac{2}{3}$ cubic yards in $8\frac{1}{2}$ hours. As a modern time-study man would do, he observed and recorded all the circumstances which affected the amount of work done, such as the weather, the time taken to eat breakfast, the crowding of the workers in the hole being dug, and the necessity for one or two persons to haul away the dirt to prevent it from rolling in again. From such observations he estimated the amount of dirt that one person could dig and haul away in a day of twelve hours.[6] Standards of this kind constituted the essential feature of the Taylor system of management which was developed later. Such standards are still very important.

Standardization of Product. Another early development was the production of parts according to specifications in such manner that the parts were interchangeable. As a result of this development, any part could be used in assembly without being machined to fit other parts. This advance permitted the production of parts in quantity, the division of labor with smaller and smaller work assignments to any one person, and the establishment of an assembly line with all that this technique implies. Eli Whitney is credited with having developed the principle of interchangeable parts in the manufacture of muskets.

Development of Manufacturing Methods. The beginning of the modern era about 1500 was marked by a number of inventions, of which the most significant were the printing press, the lens, the compass, and various uses of gunpowder. Beginning about 1775, a number of machines were developed for the manufacture of cloth, which was one of the most important industries. These inventions were so significant that the beginning of the industrial revolution is usually dated from this period. The changes in methods of production soon extended to other industries with the invention of the steam engine, the cotton gin, the steamboat, the reaper, and other machines. The inventions not only revolutionized methods of production on farms and in factories that used the machines but also gave rise to new industries for the manufacture of machines and the materials and parts used in their production.

With the introduction of new machines, larger factories were built to employ larger numbers of people. The work of production was further subdivided into smaller tasks to provide for greater specialization among the workers. Attention was directed to such problems as plant location, plant layout, methods of moving materials, and the design of factory buildings. Machines were gradually improved and new machines were invented from time to time.

Development of Management Methods. During the first half of the nineteenth century, attention began to be directed toward such management problems as personnel relations, hours of work, fatigue, and market relationships. Not much was written on the subject of management, but each company seems to have worked out its own techniques. The attitudes gradually changed after 1850 and management

---

[6] *Thomas Jefferson's Garden Book,* quoted by Albert Lepawsky, *Administration* (New York: Alfred A. Knopf, Inc., 1949), p. 120.

began to be a subject for discussion in magazines and professional meetings. The management of production gradually came to be regarded as something more than engineering.

The new emphasis is illustrated by a paper written by Henry R. Towne entitled "The Engineer as an Economist," which he read before the American Society of Mechanical Engineers in 1886. He stated that the manager needed to know much besides the technical information pertaining to production methods. He said:

The organization of productive labor must be directed and controlled by persons having not only good executive ability, and possessing the practical familiarity of a mechanic or engineer with the goods produced and the processes employed, but having also, and equally, a practical knowledge of how to observe, record, analyze, and compare essential facts in relation to wages, supplies, expense accounts, and all else that enters into or affects the economy of production and the cost of the product.[7]

To meet the requirements of the changing environment of business, Towne recognized the three basic requirements or skills of business management. First, the manager needed an understanding of the technical problems of production, such as the processing of the product, the machines used, the layout of the plant, methods of inspection, and maintenance and repair of equipment. Second, he needed an understanding of people, including methods of selection, placement, training, communication, and motivation. Third, he needed an appreciation of the industry and the economic system in which the business bought its raw materials, sold its products, procured funds for financing, and maintained various other contacts.

SCIENTIFIC MANAGEMENT

Scientific management is the name given to a new movement which began in a small way in the latter part of the nineteenth century and received national prominence in the first two decades of the present century. The new system was characterized by a spirit of inquiry, the questioning of all conventional management methods and techniques, and an attempt to promulgate basic management principles. Probably the best known of the persons associated with the new movement were Frederick W. Taylor, Henry L. Gantt, and Frank B. and Lillian M. Gilbreth.

Frederick W. Taylor. Scientific management is usually associated

---

[7] Quoted by Lepawsky, *op. cit.*, p. 115.

with the name of Frederick Winslow Taylor (1856–1915). After an early life in a sheltered environment of study and travel and a period of apprenticeship as a machinist, Taylor entered the employ of the Midvale Steel Company at Philadelphia in 1878. He worked as laborer, clerk, machinist, and foreman. His interest in management was strongly influenced by his observation that, throughout the plant, workers took more time to perform any task than they needed to take. Furthermore, the management had not developed any standards by which the efficiency of a worker at a task could be judged. When Taylor was made a foreman, he obtained the permission of the management to develop standards and to improve production with a view to reducing the labor costs. The standards would be set for tasks after timing workers with a stop watch.

As might have been expected, the effort to establish a standard time for each task aroused the strong opposition of the workers. In an effort to gain their co-operation, Taylor developed a piece-rate system which was intended to share the savings with them. However, the opposition was never fully overcome.

The attempt to set a standard time eventually led to a complete study of all phases of plant management because all plant activities were developed to aid production at the workplace. The repair and maintenance of machines required attention because the speed of any machine depended upon its condition. Belts and their tension received special study because the way the machine performed depended upon the transmission of the power to operate it. Machine tools required managerial control. In order that the proper tools would be available when they were needed, a toolroom was established to make or purchase tools, repair and store them, and issue them. Standards for materials were developed in order that materials used in the work would be uniform in quality and would be the same as the materials used when the standard time was set. Studies were also made to determine the optimum hours of work, the proper number and length of rest periods, the weight of the load that a worker should be expected to lift, the percentage of time that a worker could be under load, and the time that might be required for walking, standing, or sitting. Control over the flow of work throughout the plant was established through a special assistant to the superintendent to plan for production, issue orders for work to be done, follow the progress of the work, and take such corrective action as might be required.

As the studies in management continued at the Midvale Steel Company, Taylor was joined by a number of other persons. This group later assisted in introducing the new methods at other plants and also in publicizing the ideas of the movement. They remained at Midvale until 1890 when the company discontinued the studies. Members of the group then took up the work with other companies either as members of the management or as consultants. From 1898 until 1901, Taylor and some others of the original group continued the studies at the Bethlehem Steel Company. From 1901 until his death in 1915, Taylor devoted himself to writing and lecturing on the subject of management.

Summary of the Taylor Principles.   While Taylor summarized his principles in several ways, the following statement of the responsibilities of management personnel under the new system is suggestive:

First, they develop a science for each element of a man's work, which replaces the rule-of-thumb method.

Second, they scientifically select and then train, teach and develop the workman, whereas in the past he chose his own work and trained himself the best he could.

Third, they heartily co-operate with the men to insure all the work being done in accordance with the principles of the science which have been developed.

Fourth, there is an almost equal division of the work between the management and the workmen. The management takes over all work for which it is better fitted than the workmen, while in the past almost all of the work and the greater part of the responsibility were thrown upon the men.[8]

Name of the System.   The integrated system of management has sometimes been called the Taylor system, or more simply, Taylorism. Taylor did not like either of these names because he did not believe that the new movement should be so closely associated with himself. The first name which he gave the system was "a piece-rate system," in 1896. However, he was surprised that many people regarded the method of wage payment as the essential feature, and some people were opposed to the idea of a piece rate.

The next name which he gave the system was "the task system." This name indicated that each man would be assigned a daily task which would be clearly defined and difficult of accomplishment. Management would be responsible for providing standardized conditions to enable the worker to accomplish the task. The responsibility of management embraces the various features of the system as previously indicated. Further, the system would provide for high pay for success and a severe penalty in case of failure. This name also aroused opposition and caused the system to be criticized because, as Taylor said, the name

---

[8] Taylor, *Scientific Management*, p. 36.

"sounded as though you were treating the men severely, whereas the whole idea underlying our system is justice and not severity."

In his book, which was published in 1903, Taylor used the name "shop management." This name failed to describe the system accurately. It suggested a particular kind of work, whereas the system was supposed to be of general application. In fact, the emphasis throughout Taylor's writings is placed upon the activities of a metalworking establishment, and most of the illustrations are drawn from experience at the worker level.

The name "scientific management" was agreed upon at a meeting of a group of management people in the apartment of H. L. Gantt in New York City. Taylor was not present at this meeting, but he readily adopted the name.[9] His next book was called *Scientific Management*. His explanation of the name of the system is as follows:

> The development of a science . . . involves the establishment of many rules, laws, and formulae which replace the judgment of the individual workman and which can be effectively used only after having been systematically recorded, indexed, etc. . . . . All of the planning which under the old system was done by the workman, as a result of his personal experience, must of necessity be done by the management in accordance with the laws of the science.[10]

Management as a Science.   Science is defined as a branch of study which is concerned with an organized body of demonstrated truths or facts systematically classified in relation to general laws. A science also implies trustworthy methods of research for the discovery of new truths within its usual scope of interest. On both of these grounds, Taylor believed that his system qualified as a science. He regarded the system as more than a collection of techniques or procedures, such as time study, wage incentives, and the planning of the flow of work. Most significant, in his opinion, was the spirit of inquiry, the discovery of the facts and principles of work, and the classfication of data.

Although the break with traditional or conventional methods of management represented a distinct advance, the principles of management can hardly be said to have the exactness of natural laws. The amount of work that can reasonably be expected of an individual cannot be determined with the same degree of accuracy as the output of a machine. While scientific management attempted to select for each task the person best suited to do the work, the results were affected by such important factors as the age of the worker, his strength or physical con-

---

[9] See Albert Lepawsky, *op. cit.*, p. 122.
[10] Taylor, *Scientific Management*, p. 37.

dition, the hours of work, his motivation or willingness to co-operate, social pressures within the plant, and the attitude of the union.

Management has never been able to devise a scientific formula for paying wages that are "fair," for paying a bonus for the co-operation of the worker, or for dividing the increased production resulting from better management methods between workers, management, stockholders, and customers. Although the principle that such savings should be divided is generally accepted, the basis of the division is determined in part by collective bargaining. No final solution can be reached because conditions change so much from year to year.

Henry L. Gantt. One of the associates of Taylor at the Midvale Steel Company and also at the Bethlehem Steel Company was Henry Laurence Gantt (1861–1919). Gantt joined the group in 1887 for the purpose of working out solutions to certain formulas that were used to determine the proper method of cutting metal. He worked with several other companies after 1901 in introducing the methods and principles of scientific management. He regarded his original contributions to management as less significant than his work of introducing the new system. As he said, "We have today so much undigested and unutilized knowledge that I am inclined to think that the man who shows us how to use it satisfactorily is quite as important as he who discovers it."

Gantt differed from Taylor in his emphasis upon leadership and motivation. He placed less reliance upon financial incentives. His attitude is clearly expressed in the following statement:

The general policy of the past has been to drive, but the era of force must give way to that of knowledge, and the policy of the future will be to teach and to lead, to the advantage of all concerned. . . . People learn but little from what they are told, but they readily imitate what appeals to them. If, therefore, a man would be a leader, he must know thoroughly the people whom he would lead, and be able to shape his actions in such a manner that he will not only be understood but thoroughly appreciated by his followers.

. . . .

Twenty years ago the financier thought he had found a panacea for most of the evils which the new development began to show, in his combination of industrial plants into large organizations. . . . But the most important problems, those concerning the relationship of employer to employee, have not been solved any better by the large corporation than by the individual employer. In fact the larger corporation seems in many cases to have accentuated the troubles which had arisen.[11]

Gantt is probably best known for the development of a chart for the

[11] Henry L. Gantt, *Industrial Leadership* (New Haven: Yale University Press, 1916), p. 2.

control of production schedules, which were a part of the Taylor system. Although the principles of the planning and scheduling of work were simple, the planning was complicated by the large amount of detail, the difficulty of comparing performance with the original plan, and the necessity for revising the schedules because of delays and interruptions. Gantt designed a chart that would show the work that had been performed and the work remaining to be done. On this chart, which is now widely used for a variety of purposes, the lines are always drawn horizontally, never vertically. The spaces on the horizontal scale represent the months or weeks and the quantity planned for sales, production, orders to be received from customers, or other data. The actual data are recorded on the same chart in a heavier line, and the chart is brought up to date from time to time. The planned and the actual data are shown for comparative purposes in such a manner that management can easily compare plans with accomplishment.[12]

Gantt was much interested in cost accounting, which in his day was not very far advanced. The methods of scientific management were designed to reduce labor cost but would be ineffective unless total cost could be reduced. Because cost might be computed in any one of several ways, Gantt assisted in the development of procedures and techniques for determining cost. Materials and labor cost computations involved a minimum of difficulty, and the principal question was the determination of the proper amount of manufacturing expenses to include in the cost. When the plant stands idle a part of the time or is used to only part of its capacity, the question of how much expense to include as cost of the product is not easily determined. To illustrate, suppose that the plant operates for seven months of the year and is closed down for the other five months because of a lack of orders. Gantt argued that the cost of the product manufactured during the seven months should include only the expenses incurred during that time and that the fixed expenses incurred during the five months of suspension, such as property taxes, insurance, depreciation, and maintenance, should be charged to idle time rather than to the cost of the product. This theory is now generally accepted by cost accountants.

Gantt also is well known for his development of a new method of wage payment which is known as the "Gantt task and bonus plan." Perhaps an important reason why this plan became so well known was that Taylor described it and spoke favorably of it in his writing. This plan provides for a guaranteed hourly wage but increases the pay by 25 per

---

[12] The chart is described in Wallace Clark, *The Gantt Chart* (3d ed.; New York: Ronald Press Co., 1942). For illustrations of the chart, see Chapter 34.

cent of the wage for the standard time at that point where the work is completed within the standard time. For example, if the wage is $2.00 per hour and the standard time is 30 minutes, the worker is paid at the hourly rate if he takes more than 30 minutes for the task. If he does the work in 30 minutes, he is paid $1.00 plus a bonus of 25 cents. The total pay is $1.25, and the rate remains at this same amount for any performance of 30 minutes or less. In effect, the plan provides for an hourly rate for the worker who requires more than the standard time and a piece rate for the worker who can do the task in the standard time or less. It provides a substantial reward for the co-operation of the worker but protects him against serious penalty in case of failure. Because of worker and union opposition, the Gantt plan of wage payment is not widely used.

The Gilbreths. Frank Bunker Gilbreth (1868-1924) is best known for his work in motion study, fatigue study, and related phases of management. After his marriage to Lillian Moller in 1904, he was assisted by her. Mrs. Gilbreth became an outstanding authority in the field of management.[13]

Gilbreth's interest in management began in 1885 when, at the age of seventeen, he accepted a job as an apprentice bricklayer. The employer placed him between two bricklayers who were to teach him as they worked. He immediately observed that the bricklayers taught different methods. Much confused, he changed his position to work between two others; and he was surprised to find that they used methods that were different from those of either of the first two. Moreover, he observed that the bricklayers did not themselves follow the methods which they had explained. In fact, each bricklayer used three sets of motions—one when he was working slowly, a second when he was working rapidly, and a third when he was teaching someone. Gilbreth reasoned that the motions could not all be correct; and since other workers used still different motions, it was possible that no set of motions made by any worker was best. His investigations soon convinced him that every worker made some unnecessary and wasteful motions.

Gilbreth first undertook to find out why so many motions were used.[14] He found that the bricklayers did not think of their work as consisting

[13] The best treatment of the work of the Gilbreths is Edna Yost, *Frank and Lillian Gilbreth, Partners for Life* (New Brunswick, N. J.: Rutgers University Press, 1949). An interesting popular account is Frank B. Gilbreth, Jr., and Ernestine Gilbreth Carey, *Cheaper by the Dozen* (New York: Thomas Y. Crowell Co., 1949).

[14] Frank B. Gilbreth and Lillian M. Gilbreth, *Applied Motion Study* (New York: Sturgis & Walton Co., 1917). Also Frank B. Gilbreth, *Bricklaying System* (Chicago: M. C. Clark Publishing Co., 1909).

of a series of motions or motion elements. Their emphasis was upon the quality of the work. They had been taught such things as the proper consistency of the mortar, the amount of mortar to spread on the wall, the way to break a brick, and the way to keep the wall plumb. The motions made when the worker was working rapidly differed from those made when he was working slowly because of the difference in the tension of the muscles and because of the effect of centrifugal force, inertia, and momentum. Gilbreth found that the motions made while the bricklayer was working rapidly were usually the most efficient.

Gilbreth found that one part of a task could not be perfected without standardizing the entire system of work. First, the scaffold on which the bricklayer stood while working was changed to enable the helper to raise it without interfering with the progress of the work. He could do so by turning a crank. Then the scaffold was so constructed that the helper could walk on the side opposite the wall, and he could place bricks on a board which ran parallel to the platform on which the bricklayer stood. The bricks were properly positioned so that the bricklayer did not have to stoop to pick them up or turn them over to examine their edges for defects. The helper was also instructed to keep the mortar at the right consistency. Other improvements were the selection of the worker, standardization of the motions performed, and the training of the bricklayer in the improved methods. Incentive methods of wage payment were used to secure worker co-operation.

The Gilbreths introduced the practice of taking motion pictures of the worker as he performed his task. The pictures could be projected on the screen, rerun as many times as necessary, and stopped at any point for study. A clock which recorded time to fractions of a second was shown in the picture. This device made possible an accurate check on the timing of the operation. The picture machine was also improved to show more frames per second. Still cameras were used to make time exposures on a plate showing the path followed by the hand in the performance of the task. The path of the hand was recorded on the plate by using a small electric light attached to the hand. The light was equipped with an interrupter to break the current. The result was a line of dashes on the plate, the length of the dashes indicating the speed of the hand. After the methods had been improved and the worker had been photographed while he was using the standard methods, a motion model was made. The motion model consisted of a wire which was attached to a wooden platform. The course of the wire on the motion model indicated the path of the hand of the worker. The model was also equipped with an upright cross-sectioned board at the back which was used to indicate the height of the hand above the level of the bench or machine when the work was being done. The model was used to instruct workers in the proper way to do the task.

Improvement of the motions performed at one task required attention to the operations at other work stations preceding and following any operation and to the methods of moving materials and work in process. The Gilbreths therefore studied the layout of the plant and the flow of work from one department to another for the purpose of eliminating unnecessary operations, combining and simplifying different tasks, reducing the distances required for the movement of materials, and perfecting better methods of material handling. They originated the method of listing all operations performed in processing the material, including transportation, inspection, and storage. The list of operations and the incidental activities is called a "process chart." This method of studying the flow of work for the purpose of introducing improvements has now received general acceptance.[15]

The Gilbreths made extensive studies for the purpose of eliminating unnecessary fatigue and providing ways for overcoming unavoidable fatigue. They devised improved footrests and chairs, comfortable shoes, and clothing which gave freedom of movement to the arms and other parts of the body. They experimented with rest periods and provided comfortable rest rooms. They improved the workplace to eliminate unnecessary bending or twisting of the body, made provision for proper working conditions, and reduced fire and accident hazards. One purpose of controlling accident hazards was to reduce fatigue by relieving the mind of worry. To control fatigue, every phase of plant activity was studied and brought under control.

Comparison of the Gilbreths and Taylor.   In some respects, the work of Mr. and Mrs. Gilbreth was similar to that of Taylor. Both worked on methods improvement and time study, fatigue, shorter hours of work, selection of workers for the task, improvement in working conditions, and other such techniques. Both were primarily interested in what went on at the worker level rather than at management or executive levels, although Gilbreth wrote a book called *Field System* which described the methods and organizational relationships as practiced in his offices. Both attempted to develop principles of management by observation and experimentation. Both tried to interest others in the new movement and to disseminate information concerning its methods.

The work of each person was also distinctive in several respects. Tay-

---

[15] For illustration of the process chart, see Figure 23, Chapter 11.

lor began his studies when he became a foreman and was therefore a part of management. Gilbreth began his experiments while he was an apprentice bricklayer. Taylor was primarily interested in time studies, and he became concerned with methods improvement principally because such studies were a prerequisite to accurate work standards. The Gilbreths were principally interested in finding the best way to perform a task, and they used the stop watch to measure performance by different methods. Taylor emphasized soldiering and attempted to induce workers to follow a faster pace. The Gilbreths attempted to increase production by improving motions and by eliminating delays that were attributable to various causes.

Taylor alienated workers by his superior attitude and his autocratic approach. The Gilbreths were more successful in gaining worker cooperation. Taylor's system encompassed broader phases of plant management, while the Gilbreths developed intensively the more limited area of motion study and fatigue. Taylor did his experimentation largely in the metal industry, and he drew his illustrations principally from that field. The Gilbreths showed that the new methods could be successfully applied in such fields as building construction, concrete work, textile manufacture, lumber and paper production, home management, surgery, and merchandising. Taylor's work was widely publicized because he worked with a group of managers and experimenters. While Mr. and Mrs. Gilbreth wrote a number of books and articles, they worked more independently of others and were slower to receive recognition.[16] Each of these three persons made significant contributions to management.

Other Leaders in Management. In the present discussion, the work of four influential persons in management has been considered. It should not be inferred that others did not make significant contributions.[17] Carl G. Barth (1860-1939), who became an assistant to Taylor at the Bethlehem Steel Company in 1899, developed a formula for an easy solution of the problems arising because twelve variables affected the method of cutting steel. The formula made possible the application of the best method of steel cutting in the shop. He developed an improved slide rule for solving other problems in work methods and conducted valuable research in time study and the effects of fatigue.

Sanford E. Thompson (1867–1949) worked with Taylor in his early

---

[16] Their most significant publications have been reproduced in William R. Spriegel and Clark E. Myers, *The Writings of the Gilbreths* (Homewood, Ill.: Richard D. Irwin, Inc., 1953).

[17] For brief biographical sketches of the work of many of the leaders in management, see *The Golden Book of Management* (London: Newman Neame, Ltd., 1956).

studies and applied the new techniques to work in the building industry. He made significant contributions to the development of time study. Horace K. Hathaway (1878–1944) worked with Taylor at the Bethlehem Steel Company and then went to the Tabor Manufacturing Co. Later he became the vice president of the company. As a result of his work with this company, his system came to be regarded as a model in management methods. Harlow S. Person, who was for many years director of the department of business administration at Dartmouth College, took a conspicuous part in the development of the new techniques in industry. He made many contributions to the literature of management and became the first managing director of the Taylor Society. Harrington Emerson, a management consultant, is well known for his book *The Twelve Principles of Efficiency,* which was published in 1919. Morris Llewellen Cooke (1872–1960) served as a consultant and thereby encouraged the improvement of management methods in industry. He also demonstrated that the new methods could be adapted to other fields of activity. In 1910 he made a study of management methods in universities and prepared a report which indicated many areas where improvements could be made.[18] From 1911 to 1915 he was director of public works for the city of Philadelphia, and a book which was published by him in 1918 drew attention to the wasteful management of city government.[19] In various other ways, the scope of the management movement was gradually widened.

When the management movement began to be popularized after 1910, the leaders included Richard A. Feiss, general manager of Clothcraft Shops; Ernest M. Hopkins, manager of the employment department of Curtis Publishing Company; Meyer Bloomfield, director of the Vocational Bureau of Boston; and Henry S. Dennison, treasurer of the Dennison Manufacturing Company. The work of some of these men will be referred to in later chapters.

MANAGEMENT FROM 1910 TO 1920

The year 1910 became a landmark in the development of management as a result of the publicity resulting from hearings before the Interstate Commerce Commission in that year. Testifying before the Commission concerning an application for increases in freight rates, Louis D. Brandeis, later a member of the United States Supreme Court, presented

[18] Morris L. Cooke, *Academic and Industrial Efficiency* (New York: Carnegie Foundation for the Advancement of Teaching, Bulletin No. 5, 1910).

[19] Morris L. Cooke, *Our Cities Awake,* (Garden City: Doubleday, Page & Co., 1918).

much data in support of the argument that the railroads would not need the increases if they would adopt the new principles of management. Harrington Emerson, who had done some pioneering work in management with the Santa Fe Railroad Company, estimated that the railroads could reduce their operating expenses by $1,000,000 per day if they would eliminate waste in materials and labor.[20] The hearings were widely publicized at the time. Taylor's *Scientific Management* appeared shortly thereafter, first in a popular magazine by installments and later (1911) in book form. Widespread interest was immediately manifest.

Adaptation of the New Methods. In the United States prior to World War I, the number of companies using scientific management methods was not large; and most companies using the system adopted only certain parts of it. Writing in 1916, Robert F. Hoxie estimated that not more than two hundred shops scattered through various industries and in various sections of the country were using scientific management.[21] He believed that relatively few of the companies using the system would be regarded by the followers of Taylor as valid examples of the new system. Hoxie, who was by no means an advocate of the new methods, declared that the significance of the movement could not be measured by the number of shops using the system, for he found that its principles and methods were permeating the whole business world. This appraisal seems to have been correct. In a report prepared for the International Management Congress in 1938, Henry S. Dennison (chairman) stated that many of the original techniques were used daily in most of the well-established plants in America.[22] The methods used included time study, planning, scheduling, inventory control, and the manner of organizing the departments or divisions of the business.

Employment departments began to be established in a few companies about 1911. In that year, an employment managers' association was organized at Boston.[23] Its purpose was the discussion of methods and problems arising in the selection of workers at the employment office. However, many companies were slow to take away from the foreman the right to hire and fire. The following statement was made in a symposium on management methods in 1919:

The best selection method from all standpoints is to let the applicants "sell themselves" by direct personal appeal to the foreman under whom they are to

[20] Henry S. Dennison *et al.*, "History of Scientific Management in America," *Mechanical Enginering*, Vol. LXI (1939), pp. 671–75.
[21] Robert F. Hoxie, *Scientific Management and Labor* (New York: Harper & Bros., 1917), p. 296.
[22] Dennison, *op. cit.*, p. 672.
[23] Meyer Bloomfield, "The Aim and Work of Employment Managers' Associations," *Annals of the American Academy of Political and Social Science*, Vol. LXV (1916), pp. 76–87.

work. Let him take them on trial. A well trained, responsible foreman will keep the ones he wants and will know how to direct the others into the arms of one of his fellow-foremen, or out through the front gate of the plant, as may be best for all concerned. . . . Select your workers by the ordinary common sense method of clean cut, personal contact between the man who will rank above the applicant and the applicant himself.[24]

Even where employment departments had been established, selection in the days preceding World War I was often made on the basis of palmistry, phrenology, hunches, general impressions, and other unreliable methods.

Use of Management Consultants. Frederick W. Taylor was consultant in management for several companies during the years 1890–98. Gantt and other associates of Taylor advised with various companies on their management problems at a later date, and the Gilbreths did much consulting work after 1911. Both Taylor and Gilbreth worked at the plant level on production planning, plant layout, worker incentives, inventory control, and other such problems. Gilbreth extended the work of the consultant to include office management. Immediately after World War I consultant firms began to advise managements on their personnel problems in the areas of interviewing and testing, training, and merit rating. The scope of the work of the consultant has since been further enlarged until at present management may seek and obtain advice on any of the major problems of administration, including market or product research, public relations, budgeting, system building, organization planning, and financing. Many firms provide a variety of services, while others limit their work to one or a few areas of business problems. Many consulting firms are nationwide or international in their work.

The consultant can often render valuable services to management because of his detached position. He can look at problems from the point of view of the company as a whole rather than a single department. He has the time to study management problems because he is not subject to the pressure of routine duties. In many cases, he can obtain more information about the attitudes and opinions of employees and management personnel than would be available to a member of the company. His work with many companies equips him with a varied experience and assists him in advising with managements. For these reasons, consultants have assisted in improving management methods and techniques.

Society for Discussion of Management Problems. Until 1910

---

[24] James M. Boyle, "The Selection, Discipline, Training, and Placing of Workers," *Annals of the American Academy of Political and Social Science*, Vol. LXXXIII (1919), p. 113.

the principal forum for the discussion of management problems was the American Society of Mechanical Engineers. Before that society, the papers of Taylor, Gilbreth, and Gantt were read. In 1910, several members of the engineering society began to meet separately for the discussion of management problems; the group included Gilbreth, Barth, Cooke, and Hathaway. In 1912, they formed the Society to Promote the Science of Management. In December, 1914, the society began the publication of a bulletin. Its membership increased to more than a hundred by 1917. During World War I the name was changed to the Taylor Society, and in 1936 the Taylor Society amalgamated with the Society for Industrial Engineers to form the Society for the Advancement of Management. The American Management Association, another society, was formed in 1922 as a consolidation of three previously existing organizations. In the meantime, several other societies had been formed in related fields, such as personnel, safety, and industrial research. These societies publish magazines and books or pamphlets reporting on special studies in management. They hold national forums for the discussion of current developments and problems. They have local chapters which organize their own programs according to the needs and interests of the local membership.

Effect of World War I. During World War I, government, industry, and labor were alike interested in increased production, the elimination of waste in manpower, and the saving of materials. Consequently, the introduction of management methods was generally encouraged. Many companies adopted the new methods for the first time under the guidance of consultants. By the close of the war, many additional companies were using such management methods as incentive wage plans, balance of stores record for the control of inventories, purchasing according to the requirements of the manufacturing department, planning of production, and motion and time study. The greatly increased turnover of the labor force caused many companies to establish employment departments, and some organized complete personnel departments.

Probably the greatest effect of the war was the development of methods of dealing with personnel. The first such development was a better method of selection and training, which was emphasized by practices in the armed forces. The selection of men for training was made through specially designed trade, mental, and aptitude tests; and training programs were devised and put into practice. The success of the program indicated that such tests were valid for selection and that the long period of apprenticeship formerly required could be dispensed with in many trades. Similar methods were, in fact, used in many war industries, particularly shipbuilding. Riveters, for example, were trained within a few weeks instead of the years formerly required.

The second management development advanced by the army was in methods of rating people. The army instituted a plan for rating officers on the basis of loyalty and certain other qualities. The method was man-to-man rating, that is, the comparison of one officer with another. Points were assigned on each of the various qualities. Rating systems had been used before, but the difference was in the number of persons rated and the number of persons who became acquainted with the technique. Improved systems have since been developed.

Developments after the War.   Management methods were widely copied after the war. The new techniques included parts of the Taylor system and also various tests for the selection of workers. Many systems were introduced without the necessary modification to suit the requirements of individual companies and without regard for the wishes or attitudes of foremen and workers. Gantt and Gilbreth had both observed in 1916 and 1917 that poor methods were sometimes introduced as scientific management. In an address at Yale University, Gantt characterized the persons who were calling themselves efficiency engineers as mere "stunt peddlers." He declared that time studies were made of tasks which were being improperly performed. He said that clerks with stop watches were allowed to go into factories to study operations about which they were ignorant. This practice, he said, should be severely condemned, for it was largely responsible for the storm of opposition to the stop watch on the part of the workmen.[25] Such unsound practices greatly increased in 1919 and 1920. The name "efficiency men" is still associated with the mistakes of that period.

The use of tests for the selection and placement of workers had a similar development. Too much was claimed for the tests; and when the performance of workers did not correspond closely with their test ratings, managements were inclined to reject the whole idea of tests. Time was required to establish the fact that tests are of much value, provided that they are properly designed and used.

DEVELOPMENTS SINCE 1920

Management methods have greatly improved since 1920. Significant developments have been made in such fields as personnel, industrial re-

---

[25] Henry L. Gantt, *Industrial Leadership, op. cit.,* pp. 45, 46.

search, methods of moving and handling materials, design of product to suit the needs and the demands of consumers, budgeting, and laborsaving machinery. However, in recent years the contributions of individuals are not easily distinguished because so many persons have participated in the developments. Studies in management methods have been made by private corporations, professional societies, university and college teachers, business consultants, and various agencies of the government. Several magazines now regularly discuss management subjects, and information is made available in leaflets, pamphlets, books, and special research publications. For this reason the paragraphs which follow indicate principally the general trend.

Emphasis on Engineering. The engineer has consistently made contributions to many phases of the management movement. The building is now regarded as a part of the equipment with which management works and not merely as a shelter for people and equipment. It has been steadily adapted to the well-being of employees. Machinery and equipment have been improved to lighten the burdens of workers, to permit better working conditions, to increase output, and to lower costs. Especially in the field of materials-handling methods and in the design of equipment that requires less attention of workers, engineers have made significant contributions. Other improvements have been made in such areas as the reduction of waste, the utilization of what would otherwise become scrap and waste, plant layout, and manufacturing processes. Following the suggestions made by Henry R. Towne in 1885, many engineers have added to their technical training an understanding of communication, human relations, organization, and other requirements of the executive.

Changing Attitude toward the Worker. In an effort to narrow the gulf which had admittedly come to exist between top management and employees, many companies undertook extensive investigations of their labor problems. Typical of the new point of view was Whiting Williams, who gave up his position as personnel director of the Hydraulic Pressed Steel Company to live among workers. Keeping his identity a secret, he lived and worked with day laborers in steel mills, coal mines, and factories. He described his experience and his observations in a book entitled *What's on the Worker's Mind*, published in 1920.[26] Williams declared that it was impossible to understand the

---

[26] Published by Charles Scribner's Sons, New York. Later Whiting Williams made a similar study of conditions in western Europe published under the title *Horny Hands and Hampered Elbows: The Worker's Mind in Western Europe* (New York: Charles Scribner's Sons, 1922).

problems of the worker without seeing the world through the eyes of the man to whom the daily job means daily bread and daily hope. He described the feelings of the worker who stood before the factory gates in the cold of a February morning, the heartsick dejection of the worker who was looking for a job, the demoralizing loss of standing as a man, and the paralyzing fear of the bread line which filled the mind and soul of the man who had no job and no hope of finding one. Williams found that three things were uppermost in the mind of the worker: first, the security of the job, which meant his daily bread; second, fatigue, which resulted in a constant effort to stretch out the work and to make it last; and third, uncertainty as to the future plans and purposes of the employer. The observations which a person would make under similar circumstances at the present time would probably be different, particularly because hours of work have been shortened and machines have lightened the manual labor required of workers. The investigation made by Williams is significant in indicating the growing recognition of the importance of personnel problems and a new spirit of inquiry.

The effort to discover facts as a basis for personnel policy was manifest in elaborate studies made by the Western Electric Company in cooperation with the National Research Council and a group of psychologists and technicians. In 1924 the company began to experiment to determine the effect of changes in illumination upon production and fatigue. The scope of the inquiry was broadened in 1927 to include many other phases of production and also of personnel. At its plant in Cicero, a suburb of Chicago, the company tried out the effect upon production of changes in the hours of work, the introduction of rest periods of varying length and at varying intervals, the providing of refreshments at rest periods, and other such changes. At times the workers were told that they would be given more illumination or less illumination when one light bulb was replaced by another of the same wattage. The peculiar feature of the research was that two groups of workers were used in the experiments. Conditions were changed for one group, called the "experimental group," and were kept unchanged for the other group, called the "control group." The experiments, usually referred to as the "Hawthorne experiments" from the name of the plant, revealed that the innovations in the methods in work caused relatively little variation in the production rate as between the experimental group and the control group but that both groups substantially increased production. The conclusion was that illumination, rest periods, midmorning or midafternoon refreshments, and other conditions of work are not the only important factors in worker performance but that attitude is equally important. Slight variations in working conditions are important only to the extent that they indicate that the management is interested in the welfare of the worker and that they succeed in gaining his co-operation. The workers in the Hawthorne experiments were willing to co-operate because they were the center of attention from top management and from the persons in charge of the experiments, because they were made to feel important, because they believed that increased production was to their personal advantage, and because they themselves were interested in the experiment. Production increased in the control group because the workers in that group wanted to show that they were as good as those in the experimental group.[27] In both cases, the human element was the controlling factor. The Hawthorne experiments, like the studies of Whiting Williams, are significant both because of the factual knowledge of worker feelings and attitudes and because of the new method of approach to personnel problems which they represented.

Growth of Unions. The decade of the 1920's was marked by the growth of the company union, a labor organization in which membership was restricted to the employees of one company. The union was usually formed as a result of the suggestion and encouragement of management. It provided sick or other benefits for the members to which the company made a financial contribution. Joint relations between the company and its employees concerning wage rates, hours, conditions of work, employee grievances, and other personnel problems were conducted between the management and the officers of the union. Company unions of this type are not permitted now by federal law. The National Labor Relations Act of 1935, sometimes called the Wagner Act, made it an unfair practice for the employer to dominate a labor union or to interfere with the unionization of its employees. The same provision was included in the Labor Management Relations Act of 1947. It means that a company cannot contribute financial or other support to a union. The establishment of company unions was a part of the growing desire of managements to learn of the grievances of the workers and to give them a voice in matters closely concerning themselves. It also reflected an attempt to head off the unionization of workers by outside unions.

After the enactment of the National Industrial Recovery Act in 1933 and the National Labor Relations Act in 1935, membership in national

---

[27] The Hawthorne experiments are described in National Research Council, *Fatigue of Workers in Its Relation to Industrial Production* (New York: Reinhold Publishing Corp., 1941) ; Elton Mayo, *The Human Problems of an Industrial Civilization* (New York: MacMillian Co., 1933) ; F. J. Roethlisberger, *Management and Morale* (Cambridge, Mass.: Harvard University Press, 1941) ; F. J. Roethlisberger and W. J. Dickson, *Management and the Worker* (Cambridge, Mass.: Harvard University Press, 1939).

and independent unions increased rapidly. This development was significant for management in that many companies which had not previously bargained collectively with their workers were now compelled to do so. Equally significant, however, was the fact that the unions demanded a voice in decisions which managements had previously thought were their own prerogatives. Union contracts contained clauses relating not only to wages and hours but also to promotions, layoffs, spreading of work during slack periods, methods of handling grievances, the introduction of laborsaving machinery and other technological improvements, motion and time study, and accident prevention.

Legislation Affecting Management.   The requirement that managements do certain things in the interest of the health or safety of their workers is not a recent development. Many years ago the states established maximum hours of work and minimum wages for certain industries. The railroads, for example, have been required to grant relief for trainmen after a limited number of hours of work or after the train has moved a stated number of miles. However, the trend toward the regulation of industry by government was sharply accelerated after 1933. Some of the more significant federal laws relating to personnel relations are:

Social Security Act of 1935, which provides for old-age and survivors' benefits and unemployment compensation. This law was amended to increase the benefits and extend the coverage in 1939 and again in 1950, 1952, and 1956.

Walsh-Healy Act of 1936, which provides minimum wages and maximum hours and prohibits child labor for work on government contracts of more than $10,000.

Fair Labor Standards Act of 1938, which provides minimum wages and maximum hours and regulates child labor in industries in interstate commerce. Both the Walsh-Healy Act and the Fair Labor Standards Act permit labor in excess of the hours specified, provided overtime payment is made.

Labor Management Relations Act of 1947 (Taft-Hartley Law), which regulates certain phases of the relations of management and labor.

Landrum-Griffin Act of 1959, which establishes numerous detailed requirements for the management of labor unions and their relations with management in an effort to correct abuses in the labor-management field.

Management at the Higher Levels.   In the United States, the early attention to management problems was confined largely to problems of plant organization and management, with particular reference to the workplace and the motivation of the worker. However, Frank B. Gilbreth published a description of his general organization in 1904 in a book called *Field System,* and Gantt was interested in such problems as the growth and development of executives, leadership in industry, democratic methods throughout the organization, and cost control in its relation to selling prices. Probably the most significant early contribution to management and administration at the higher levels was made by Henri Fayol, a French mining engineer and business executive. Fayol, like Henry R. Towne in the United States, recognized the need for developing executives in the use of administrative techniques and skills as distinguished from the technical phases of mining or manufacturing. His ideas were set forth in papers which he read before mining engineering societies in 1900 and 1908. They were summarized in a small book in 1916, which was called *General and Industrial Management*.[28] Fayol's discussion was brief and concise, but he stated his principles in general terms with a minimum of reference to mining companies. His classification of the elements of management as planning, organizing, commanding, co-ordinating, and controlling constituted a particularly significant contribution.

In the United States during recent years, an increasing amount of research has been devoted to the problems of administration and management at the higher levels. Attention has been directed to policy formulation and administration, the growth and development of executives, profit-sharing and bonus plans, the employment of assistants for the performance of staff functions, cost and budgetary control, product research, market research, and many other such problems.

Adaptation to Change.   Perhaps management has always found adaptation to change to be a major requirement, and risk is recognized as an inherent element in every managerial undertaking. However, the rapidity of change and the extent of the risks appear to have increased since the decade of the 1930's. During the New Deal era much legislation affecting business was enacted. Labor unions increased in membership and power. The government became an important purchaser of many of the products of industry. Business has been required to adapt its programs to changes from peace to war conditions with its wage and price control and other problems. After the war business management was affected by numerous developments, such as increasing mechanization, increasing population, shifts in age groups, payroll and other taxes, greater application of science to industrial processes, the greater menace of international communism, and the remarkable recovery of industry in western Europe. In an economy such as that of the United States, industry adapts to such changes under the direction of private business management with a certain amount of assistance from the government.

---

[28] This title was given to the English translation as published by Sir Isaac Pitman & Sons, Ltd., 1949.

Preparation for Management. Business has been giving an increasing amount of attention to formal and informal programs for the growth and development of executives or managers. Some such programs are concerned with the methods or techniques that other businesses have found to be successful, such as methods of supervision, morale building, discipline, safety and accident prevention, motion and time study, and the care and maintenance of plant and equipment. This type of program may be designated as training because it attempts to assist the manager in handling a specific problem or meeting a definite situation.

A second type of program attempts to broaden the understanding of the manager in such fields as labor law, commodity prices, business cycles, channels of distribution, international relations, electronics, and business organization. This type of program is educational in nature.

Some programs attempt to assist the manager in making decisions and in meeting new situations. Such programs assume a variety of forms, such as job rotation, a discussion of cases which describe business situations requiring the making of decisions, participation in conferences at which current problems are considered, and the assumption of increased responsibility in making decisions. These programs do not attempt to give the manager a ready-made solution to his problems but are based upon the recognition that the manager will be required to face ever-changing situations.

Operations Research. During the decade of the 1950's, renewed emphasis was placed upon the scientific approach to management problems. The new methods, which were given the name of operations research, represented a refinement and an extension of the best management and engineering practices to include mathematical and statistical techniques. They sought to provide a way of taking into consideration all of the various factors or forces affecting a problem and to provide a solution that would be most economical or most profitable in the light of all of the various considerations.

Operations research includes such work as fitting trend lines to statistical data, projecting trend lines to provide information as to future conditions, converting data to percentages and averages, determining average and standard deviation, determining the proper size of a sample to be inspected where complete inspection would be too costly, and estimating the probable number of defective items in an entire lot on the basis of sample inspection.[29] Operations research may assist management

---

[29] See Alexander Henderson and Robert Schlaifer, "Mathematical Programing," *Harvard Business Review,* Vol. XXXII, No. 3 (1954), pp. 73–100.

in handling such problems as the following, in addition to the problems previously mentioned:

Determining the best plant layout where one arrangement of machines, workplaces, passageways, and storage areas will afford certain economies and another arrangement will have other advantages.

Determining the most economical quantity of materials to buy on one order when larger quantities will result in the increase of some costs and expenses and the decrease of other outlays.

Determining the most economical quantity to manufacture on any one production order when all or a part of the product will be placed in the storeroom in anticipation of future orders.

Dividing a production order among two or more machines for processing where several machines are available for similar work.

Determining the most economical number of machines one worker can operate or supervise when additional machines per worker will increase the probable downtime of the machine but reduce the labor cost.

The use of statistical and mathematical methods in the solution of managerial problems is sometimes called "mathematical programing." Another name for the new method is "linear programing," although this method is merely one phase of operations research.

Operations research is not expected to reduce management to the point where decisions become automatic or mechanical. It merly affords some additional summaries of facts which can be useful to management. In mathematical formulas, allowance cannot be made for certain intangible factors, such as the attitudes of people or future changes in the situation. A decision may be sound only if allowances have been made for the future development of new products, shifts in the population in certain areas, changes in the price level, changes in the competitive situation, and the like. Management will still be required to use judgment and the results of experience in the making of decisions.

Although many people have regarded operations research as a new technique, it really represents only an extension or an elaboration of methods long in use by some managements. In the 1880's, Frederick W. Taylor and his associates used mathematical formulas in the solution of certain problems. One problem of particular importance to Taylor pertained to the method of cutting metals under different conditions. He found that the best method depended upon the thickness of the metal, its hardness, the temperature of the material, the temperature of the tool used in cutting, the speed of the tool, and other factors. Solutions to this problem were determined by means of a slide rule. Other management people have used mathematical formulas in the solution of other problems. However, operations research represents a significant trend in management thinking and has made important contributions to management methods.

Use of Machines for Data Processing. The increased use of factual data in the making of decisions has resulted in large part from the development of electronic tabulating and computing machines. These machines are available from several manufacturers and can be used in a variety of ways. However, all of them provide for three essential steps: input, storage and processing, and output. In the first step, data are put into the machine from a keyboard or by means of tabulating cards, magnetic tape, or other method. The information that is put into the machine includes any data pertaining to the activities of the business, such as materials on hand, the unit price of materials purchased, and standard costs. The data can be put into the machine at great speed. In the second step, the machine stores the data by means of drums, cylinders, or cores; and it retains the information until it is required to reproduce it. The machine will accumulate, add, subtract, divide, and compute and record new balances, such as the balance owed by a customer or the balance of materials on hand.

The output depends upon the type of machine and the data desired. The machine may print the information on a tape or an invoice, record totals, or produce other types of reports. A principal advantage of such machines is that the information becomes immediately available.

By enabling businessmen to base decisions on factual information, tabulating and computing machines have reduced the area of opinion or judgment in decision making. The trend is toward increased reliance upon machines.

QUESTIONS

1. What principles of management may have been applied in the building of the pyramids?

2. In what respects are the problems of public undertakings such as construction similar to the problems of business management? In what respects are they different?

3. What was the function of the philosophers as described by Adam Smith?

4. Explain the meaning of work measurement. What is its significance in management?

5. Show the importance of the standardization of the product to the management of an enterprise.

6. Taylor relied in large part upon a piece rate as a means of gaining worker co-operation. In what respects might a piece rate fail to provide the proper incentive?

7. What did Taylor mean by the statement that his system provided for a proper division of work between management and the men?

8. Explain the limitations of the different names that were given to the new system.

9. Explain how a policy of leadership as advocated by Gantt would affect management methods.

10. Compare and contrast the work of Taylor with that of the Gilbreths.

11. How was the management movement affected by World War I?

12. Does technological change affect management methods? Explain.

13. How may electronic data processing affect management methods?

CASE

1. PROPOSED STANDARDIZATION OF AUTOMOBILE DESIGN

Wallace Clark, a well-known management consultant in the United States, went to France and other countries of western Europe in 1926 to advise with managements concerning their production problems. He worked with various companies in several countries until 1939 when the German armies invaded Poland. One of his French clients was a large automobile manufacturer. Clark found that the manufacturer was in financial difficulties largely because he had failed to standardize the design of the car. The company had established a reputation for making a luxury automobile for a small group of customers of considerable wealth. All cars were made to the specifications of the customer with regard to such features as horsepower of the motor, length of wheel base, body and fender design, color, arrangement of instruments on the dashboard, and type and color of upholstery. As a car was being built, the customer might inspect it and change the specifications as suited his preferences. In many cases, the changes were extensive. The manufacturer himself frequently suggested changes because he prided himself on his artistic ability.

Clark advised the manufacturer that he should adopt a standard design at the beginning of the year and make all cars in accordance with the standard, regardless of customer preferences. He might make provision for a few colors and two or three body styles, but these variations would be included in the original designs. The only changes that should be introduced during the year, according to Clark, would be made for the purpose of eliminating mechanical defects that were found to exist in the original design. The practice of making cars according to the order of the customer should be discontinued as soon as a standard could be perfected, specifications stated, and production lines set up.

The standardization of the product would make possible various savings. Layout of the plant could be built around the processes necessary to the manufacture of the standard design. The parts could be manufactured on lines of feeder machines or made in advance of final assembly and stored at the proper places along the assembly line. The inventory of raw materials and parts could be standardized and the investment in inventory would be reduced. The uninterrupted flow of the product along the assembly line would reduce the value of the inventory of work in process. The degree of skill required of workers and foremen would be reduced because each worker would be required to perform only one simple operation. Processes formerly performed by manual labor could be mechanized. Workers would derive more personal satisfaction from their work because they would always have the proper machines and tools for each task and they would not be required to rework a product where the work was done properly in the first place. Production costs would be reduced to such an extent that wages could be increased, prices could be reduced, and profits would become satisfactory.

The manufacturer refused to accept the advice of Wallace Clark. He said that the French people were too artistic and too individualistic to be satisfied with an automobile of standard design. The company continued to make automobiles according to the specifications of the customer, and it continued to lose money. Eventually, the plant converted to war production with the aid of a government subsidy.[30]

Questions:

1. To what extent should an automobile company permit a customer to specify design?

2. Why is the plan of individual design disadvantageous to the customer?

3. What is necessary to the standardization of a product?

---

[30] The experiences of Wallace Clark are described in Pearl Franklin Clark, *Challenge of American Know-How* (New York: Harper & Bros., 1948).

2 Production Problems and Policies

THE objective of the management of production should be to produce the right goods and services of the right quality in the right varieties, with the right materials, machines, and labor. Management should also attempt to maintain the proper relations with customers, the government, financial institutions, and the public. Most companies attempt to produce at a cost that will enable them to sell the product at a fair price and to earn a reasonable profit.

This summary of objectives may seem to leave most questions unanswered. However, each company should define or establish for itself the proper standard with respect to each of the aspects of the work of production in the areas suggested. Such standards, which are called policies, serve as guides to the persons in the management in planning, co-ordinating, and controlling the activities of persons at the various levels throughout the organization. The determination of policy requires that the problems in each area of management be defined, that the alternatives or possible courses of action be compared, and that a decision be made to follow a certain course. The decision should be made known to subordinates through the proper channels of communication, and controls should be established to see that the standard is being met or the policy is being followed.

Any policies that are established should be stable but flexible. Stability is required in order that people may know what is required of them and what they are permitted to do. They can plan their own courses of action with the assurance that their actions will be approved by their supervisors. Without policies, the activities of a group cannot be unified and directed toward the common objectives. Other requirements include organizational relationships, position descriptions, systems, and rules and regulations, all of which should be relatively stable.

Flexibility is required because the economic and industrial organization is constantly changing. Although the economic system has never possessed the attribute of certainty, the rate of change has been accelerated in recent years, particularly since the close of World War II. Changes are constantly demanding the attention of business management in such areas as media of communication, mechanization, foreign trade, and prices of individual commodities, as well as the price level, labor relations, and manufacturing processes. Flexibility has become as necessary to success as stability.

Changes are made within the company from time to time as a result of management changes. When a new executive joins the organization or persons within the organization are promoted to higher positions, changes in policies and methods may be expected. However, the changes are often made gradually in order that subordinates may not be unduly disturbed or alarmed and that orderly processes may continue to function. Such changes are introduced while the business continues to produce and sell goods to customers and to maintain the usual relationships to persons outside the company. At times, however, the position of a company may deteriorate to such an extent that rapid changes become necessary. The two methods are described as evolutionary changes and the "earthquake approach."

In the present chapter, some of the areas in which policies should be established for the guidance of persons in the production division will be briefly discussed. No attempt will be made to prescribe a set of basic policies because different policies are required by each company whose situation differs from others; and for any one company, changes will be made as the circumstances require. Some important problems demanding attention will be briefly considered. Most of these problems are considered at greater length in later chapters.

SOME PROBLEMS OF ORGANIZATION

Organization constitutes the plan for the assignment of duties and responsibilities to the various positions within the enterprise and the delegation of authority to people who are placed in the positions. The duties and relationships indicate to each member what is expected of him, the extent of his authority, the persons who are responsible to him, and the associates with whom he is to work. Methods and policies of organization are therefore of vital importance to each person.

Organization of the Board of Directors. The organization of a company is usually assumed to start with the board of directors because the stockholders are regarded as legal owners or investors rather than an active force in administration. The board is described as an outside board if a majority of its members come from outside the company and hold no other position in the organization. It is said to be an inside board if all or a majority of the members hold positions as officers of the company. The outside board has the advantage of providing a general or balanced point of view, and it may afford a better protection of the interests of stockholders and bondholders. In other words, it may emphasize the trustee function. The inside board is composed of persons who are well informed about the problems of the industry and the individual company, and it is therefore more likely to emphasize the managerial function.

The board of directors does not usually undertake to supervise company activities but limits itself to the giving of advice, the adoption of the financial plan as stated in the budget, approving plans for expansion or merger, and reviewing results as reflected in the financial statements. When the situation requires such action, the board may select a new president, and it may request the resignation of a president. For some stockholders, the declaration of dividends constitutes the major function of the board.

In some companies, the board of directors does much of its work through committees. An executive committee may advise with the president and otherwise act for the board between meetings. Other committees may handle problems of finance, pensions, labor relations, and bonus plans. The actions of a committee are subject to approval by the board. In each case, the board and its committees deal with general rather than detailed problems. However, the effects of the actions of the board are reflected in the work of people at all levels throughout the organization.

Flat or Steep Organization. With a given number of employees at the work level, a company may assign a large number of employees to each supervisor; and if it does so, it is said to have a wide span of control. The organization is described as flat because a relatively small number of levels of supervision is required from bottom to top. If the company assigns a smaller number of employees to each supervisor, it is said to have a narrow span of control, and the organization is described as steep.

In a flat organization structure, the supervisors can give less time and attention to each subordinate than would be possible in a steep organization. The supervisor is required to leave each person to work out many problems for himself. Although the span of control may vary with the level of the organization, the trend is toward a wide span of control.

Extent of Delegation. A closely related problem pertains to the extent to which the executives and supervisors at the intermediate and lower levels are to be permitted to make decisions in matters affecting them and their work. At one extreme is a plan which is called "bottom-up management." This plan allows executives at the lower levels to make many decisions within the limits of company objectives and policies with only that degree of supervision which may be necessary to protect the company from serious loss due to mistaken judgment. At the other extreme is the plan of "benevolent autocracy," which requires that most important decisions be made by the top executives. The term implies that top executives will make decisions in the interest of the company and its members rather than their own personal interests. A third plan would require that all important decisions be made by top executives but provides a procedure for consultation with subordinates and for the transmission of their ideas and suggestions to their supervisors.

Development of Staff. Business problems have become more and more complex as a result of increasing mechanization, the application of science to methods of production and research, the wider extent of markets, the growing importance of governmental activity, and other developments. The chief executive and other top executives have been required to deal with a wide variety of problems in the technical, the human relations, and the organizational fields. New problems of external relationships have also arisen. To deal with such problems, the executives need persons to conduct research and to render advice. Such services may be rendered by staff personnel within the company or by consultants who are called in from the outside. Many companies, both large and small, employ outside consultants on a per diem or fee basis, and all companies include some persons in their organization whose work can be described as largely advisory.

PROBLEMS OF PHYSICAL EQUIPMENT

Although conditions have been changing rapidly in the area of physical facilities, management needs to establish policies and methods of dealing with such problems in order that people may work together

effectively. Any decision in regard to physical equipment requires periodical review.

The Problem of Size. The management of each company decides
how large it wants the company to become. Size is measured by the number of plants or sales branches, the amount of the dollar investment in
plant and equipment, the number of units of product made and sold, the
number of people in the organization, and the dollar amount of sales.
The growth of a company may be limited by the lack of good managers,
the territorial extent of the market, or the funds available to the company.

As the company increases in size, as measured by the number of employees, it is required to increase the number of levels in the organization or to widen the span of control. Problems of supervision, communication, and co-ordination are increased. New and improved methods of
reviewing and controlling activities are required, and the management
must place increased dependence upon written and oral reports, statistics,
cost analyses, expense schedules, budgetary control, profit and loss statements, and other financial reports. Some executives find that the
planning and controlling of production becomes more difficult when
more of the work must be accomplished through the services of other
persons.

If a company limits its size and the scope of its activities, the management must decide what plan will be followed when the demand for the
product exceeds the capacity of the company to produce. Any one of
several plans may be adopted. Production might be increased during
the dull season to produce for stock, which could be drawn upon to meet
the greater demands of the busy season. Orders beyond current capacity
might be accepted during the busy season and scheduled for production
and delivery at a later date. Contracts for the purchase of additional
quantities of the product might be negotiated with other manufacturers
who would produce additional supplies. The company might decline to
accept additional orders during the busy season, or it might refer its
customers to other sources of supply. Still other plans might be followed.

If plant facilities and personnel are increased to meet the maximum
seasonal and cyclical demands, the company will have excess capacity
and unneeded personnel during the slack season. Additional costs for
idle equipment will have to be absorbed, and some plan for handling
the personnel problems will be necessary. If size is increased to meet
the greater demand for the product, the company will be required to
increase the management personnel, the size or number of buildings, the

extent of borrowing or other financial activities, and other aspects of management. It should maintain a balance between physical equipment, personnel, organization, finance, and customer relations. Decisions in each area should be made with reference to other problems.

Number of Plants. As the production facilities increase and the market expands, larger numbers of workers are employed and additional plants may be built or otherwise acquired. Several plants might be operated if a different line of products can be made in each plant. Raw materials may be bulky and require processing near the source of supply. In some cases customers can best be served from a plant that is located near them. Labor conditions may be better in several plants in small communities than in one large plant in an industrial area. The decision to operate one plant or several plants is basic to the planning of production.

PROBLEM OF THE PRODUCT LINE

A major problem of a business pertains to the development of the product line. This problem requires constant attention because far-reaching changes can come quickly as a result of the introduction of new materials, new electronic devices, new types of synthetic fibers, new types of weapons for national defense, and various other innovations. Because the changes can be rapid, the present discussion can only indicate some of the areas requiring attention.

Question of Leadership. A company may seek to become a leader in industry by developing and introducing new products and new materials. Leadership may require an extensive program of research in an effort to discover new scientific principles or to find practical applications of principles that are already known. The attempt to lead involves considerable risk because the results of a project may not be known for many months or years. Although some projects will fail to produce a profitable product, a research program may be worth its cost if the program as a whole results in a sufficient number of new and profitable products.

If the company decides not to attempt to become a leader, it may use the accepted methods and products and seek merely to distinguish its product by varying the style, the container, or other feature. In some lines of product, a company may contract with another company to make certain parts according to specifications prescribed by the principal manufacturer. Either the attempt to lead or the plan to follow may be profitable under certain circumstances.

Question of Buy or Make. Each manufacturer must determine the extent to which it will make parts or materials and the extent of its purchasing program. Although every company will probably buy some of its materials and supplies, some buy a larger percentage than others. A company may make some materials of a certain variety and buy additional supplies of the same kind of materials to meet peak requirements. A shirt manufacturer, for example, may make a percentage of the cloth used for making shirts and purchase the remainder. The manufacturer might purchase all of its buttons, thread, stationery, repair parts for machines, and other supplies.

One reason a manufacturer might purchase the parts or the materials is that the machines used in production and the manufacturing methods differ from methods of manufacturing the main product. The volume of parts and materials may not be sufficiently large to justify the installation of the equipment needed. An expansion of facilities and personnel at one stage of production might result in a lack of balance with facilities and personnel at other stages. Expansion also creates problems of financing, organization structure, size of plant, and planning and controlling.

Several reasons may be advanced in favor of making some or all of the parts needed in production. In busy seasons, the manufacturer may be unable to purchase the parts needed and to obtain prompt delivery to meet an increase in demand. Quality may be more easily maintained when the principal manufacturer can directly control the quality of the materials and the manufacturing processes. If some parts are made and others are purchased, the manufacturer can more easily determine the fair cost or purchase price of the parts that are bought on contract. In many cases the buying of all or some of the parts and materials is good policy.

Closely related to the policy to buy or make a part is the policy of integration, which means the carrying of the materials through two or more stages of manufacture. Complete integration would mean that the materials are processed throughout all stages from raw materials to finished product. Sometimes integration is accomplished by reaching backward in the manufacturing processes to acquire the plant or the company in the earlier stages of production. For example, a can-making company might purchase machinery and equipment to put the coating of tin on the steel that it uses, or a fruit-packing company might purchase machines for making the cans that it needs. Integration may also be accomplished by the purchase of equipment for processing the material through later stages of production. A manufacturer may obtain control of retail or wholesale establishments for the distribution and sale or the servicing of its products.

Integration gives a company much the same advantages as the manufacture of parts: an assured source of supply, better control of production schedules, more effective control of quality, and the elimination of sales and purchasing activities at the various stages of production. Similar disadvantages arise. The demands upon the management are increased, and balance may not be easily maintained at the different stages. Integration requires more financing and more attention to organizational problems.

Horizontal and Allied Expansion. The management may decide to add additional product lines that are related to the present line because they are made of the same raw materials, are manufactured by similar manufacturing processes, or can be made with the same machines in their present location. In some cases the additional product lines are advertised through the same media, can be distributed through the same distributive facilities, or can be sold by the same sales organization as the existing product line. Some product lines have been developed because the products are made from waste or scrap. New products may be developed as a result of scientific discoveries in the laboratory.

If the new products are closely related to existing lines, the expansion is said to be *allied.* If no relationship exists, the product line is said to be *conglomerate* or *polygot.* A conglomerate product line may result from corporate mergers. Sometimes expansion is designed to reduce dependency upon one market. For example, a company making a product used for national defense might acquire a product line that is sold to civilians or to manufacturers in industries that serve the general public.

Sell or Rent. A machinery manufacturer is required to adopt a policy of selling its product or leasing it to users on a long-term lease or rental contract. As a result of a number of court decisions interpreting the antitrust laws, many manufacturers who formerly leased their machines but refused to sell them are now required to give the customer the option of buying or leasing. The maintenance of the machines being used under lease arrangement is covered by special provisions of the contract. The sale of a machine also raises the question of the acceptance of a trade-in of an old machine, and the trade-in arrangement involves the manufacturer in the problem of selling used machines. Under the provisions of the Clayton Act of 1914, a manufacturer cannot require that the customer or lessee use the supplies of the lessor in the operation of the machine.

Dropping a Product. The management should establish criteria for deciding when a product should be dropped. The proposal to drop a product will usually encounter opposition because it may result in the loss of some jobs to both employees and management personnel, and the discontinuance of a line may also create difficulties for the sales force and others in the sales division. Suggestions may be made that, before the line is dropped, efforts should be made to increase sales or reduce manufacturing cost. The argument may also be made that the product should be continued as long as it pays the direct costs of production and sale and contributes something to the overhead. The product may be retained in the hope that it will yield a profit at some later period. For these reasons, management requires definite criteria for determining the necessary rate of profit and the period of time that an unprofitable product will be carried before it is finally discontinued.

PERSONNEL PROBLEMS AND POLICIES

Relations with employees and with unions constitute an important phase of company problems and policies. The material is processed at the machine, which is operated or tended by a worker. Efficiency in production depends in large degree upon the technical competence, dependability, and co-operation of the worker. The methods of dealing with workers concern not only the workers themselves but also the supervisors, the personnel manager, the inspector, and others in the management group.

Attitude toward Workers. The general attitude of the management toward workers underlies the methods of handling many problems. According to one point of view, the workers are people with personal interests, family relationships, financial problems, prejudices, educational accomplishments, limitations, and other attributes of people in general. Each person has his own peculiar personality and his own problems. If management takes the human relations approach, it will seek to help people with their personal difficulties and will appreciate the need for different methods of financial and nonfinancial motivation. Overemphasis of the human relations point of view may cause the management to neglect the objective of producing and selling goods and services at a profit.

The management might regard the worker as a factor in production along with land, capital, and management. If management takes this point of view, it would seek to produce the maximum amount of goods and services and to utilize the services of the worker to the fullest extent to accomplish this objective. While labor is necessary to production, the management should not look upon its employees as a means of producing the maximum amount of goods.

A third point of view regards the worker as a source of profit for the company. According to this view, management hires the worker at a wage which is something less than the value of his contribution to the product and makes a profit from his employment. If management takes this point of view, it would hire workers when a profit can be made by doing so, and it would dismiss a worker when he ceases to make a contribution that is equal to his wage. Overemphasis of the profit point of view would cause management to be ruthless in its program of hiring, firing, training, paying, and otherwise dealing with workers. This attitude has characterized some managements during an earlier period. It resulted in labor trouble and eventually led to the enactment of legislation which was intended to assure fair treatment for employees.

Managements have sometimes adopted a paternalistic attitude toward their workers. They have regarded workers as a parent might regard his children. They sought to grant benefits and render services of various kinds because the workers could not be depended upon to provide such services for themselves. One difficulty with such programs was that the management gave them and could take them away. At the present time, unions bargain for financial and other services and they remain alert to see that the services are not discontinued.

Attitude toward Unions. The law now requires that management refrain from interfering with the unionization of workers and that management bargain with the union when it has been organized. However, some companies co-operate with unions to a greater extent than others do. The management may take the initiative in developing programs, or it may co-operate only to the extent that it is required to by law and by union pressures. In developing the personnel program, the management cannot adopt any methods that are intended to weaken the position of the union or to destroy its influence with the workers.

FINANCIAL PROBLEMS AFFECTING PRODUCTION

Although the methods of financing an enterprise are beyond the scope of this book, certain financial policies should be taken into consideration in planning and organizing a production program. The company may buy its building and certain units of machinery and equipment, or it may lease them under a long-term contract. The decision to buy or lease is primarily financial, but certain phases of the production program are affected, such as plant expansion, the replacement of machines, and the morale of management personnel and employees. Financial planning also affects the program for machine replacement, increased mechanization, and the automation of production. The financial strength of a company may affect the plans for carrying larger inventories of materials and especially key items of which a short supply could delay production. Although mergers are primarily a problem of finance, they may increase the extent of the product line or the degree of vertical integration. Mergers also require revisions of the organization plan and shifts in management personnel.

Problems of Inflation.   The policy of the company in meeting anticipated "creeping inflation," rapid inflation, or perhaps deflation would also affect the production plans and programs. Anticipated inflation might be a factor in increasing the facilities for production and in buying buildings and machinery rather than leasing them. If deflation is anticipated, the management might decide to postpone an expansion of facilities, the replacement of equipment, or the automation of production. All phases of the management of an enterprise are, in fact, closely related.

Sources of Funds.   The method by which a company raises the money for the financing of the enterprise will affect the plans and policies for production. For an established company, some of the money is made available through profits and also through funds withheld or retained in the business as a result of the annual depreciation charge. Other funds may be provided through bank loans or the sale of stock or bonds. At times, conditions in the money and securities markets may make borrowing difficult, and the lack of funds may limit expansion or modernization that might otherwise be desirable. Likewise the poor credit rating of a company may prevent the acquisition of more efficient equipment or other facilities.

STABILITY WITH FLEXIBILITY

The foregoing pages have attempted to suggest some important problems where guidelines are desirable in order that people throughout the organization may know how to plan their work and to co-operate with other persons. Unless the guidelines or policies have a measure of stability, persons within and without the organization cannot know what to expect or what is expected of them. Both the individual enterprise and the economic system require stability for efficient operation.

Flexibility is also required because constant change has become a characteristic of the economic, political, and social system. Change in company organization and policy is necessary in order that the enterprise may adapt itself to new scientific discoveries, shifts in population, changes in customer demand, political changes at home and abroad, and other movements. In a system of private enterprise, adaptation to change results largely from the decisions of businessmen, although the government also exerts an important influence upon the direction and the rate of change. Thus, both stability and flexibility are required.

QUESTIONS

1. Distinguish between policies, rules, and practices. Illustrate.

2. A reason sometimes given for failure to establish policies is that the management wishes to be free to meet new situations as they arise. Does this reason justify refusal to formulate policies?

3. Is flexibility consistent with stability?

4. Show how technological changes may require changes in organization and in policies.

5. The vice-president of a large corporation has said that his company has established a wide span of control in order that executives may be required to delegate substantial authority to subordinates. Explain why delegation is necessary in such an organization.

6. Under what circumstances might a company employ outside consultants instead of developing its staff personnel to perform advisory services?

7. When might a company plan to provide less plant capacity than would be required to meet peak demands for its products? How might it provide for filling the orders of customers at the peak season?

8. What considerations enter into the decision to buy parts or accessories instead of making them?

9. How are costs or expenses reduced by the integration of the facilities for production?

10. It has been said that managements have less difficulty in adding products than they have in dropping unprofitable items in the product line. Explain why this should be true.

11. Can management be too human in its approach to personnel problems? Can management place too much emphasis upon profit in its handling of personnel problems? Explain.

12. If management should decide that the level of commodity prices will rise 10 per cent per year during the next ten years, how might it change its production plans and programs?

CASE

2. PLANNING FOR PRODUCTION IN AN EMERGENCY

The Rowell Spring and Wire Company owns and operates a plant in a small city in Indiana for the manufacture of automobile seats, chair cushions, and other wire products, mostly for other manufacturers. The company employs 450 persons. It buys steel rods which it makes into wire of various sizes. The wire is used largely for making springs, frames, and other parts for assembly to make the finished product. Wire not needed by the company is sold to other manufacturers of wire products in the area. The steel is purchased in Pittsburgh, Wheeling, and Chicago.

On July 1, all of the major steel companies were required to cease production because of an industry-wide strike which was called by the steelworkers union. During the first half of the year, the possibility of a strike had been widely discussed, and the Rowell Company had purchased enough steel to enable it to continue operation for several weeks. By the first of September, however, the company had used the greater part of the steel and had a supply for only two more weeks of production. The president of the company called a meeting of the policy committee, which included all of the top executives, to discuss methods of meeting the emergency.

The director of sales contended that some departments of the plant should be kept operating as long as they had the materials and parts. After the wire-making department had processed all of the material on hand, the wire should be further processed in the other departments, and products should be assembled for shipment to customers as long as the parts were available. When steel could again be obtained from the iron and steel companies, operations could be resumed in the wire-making departments for later processing in the remaining departments.

The personnel manager agreed with the director of sales because employment would be provided for workers in each processing department as long as any materials were available. Any other plan, he said, would throw a great many employees out of work and cause hardships for them as well as for merchants and tradesmen in the city.

The controller thought that when the supply of steel was exhausted, the entire plant should be closed immediately. He said that if some of the workers were kept at their jobs after the first department was closed, they would practice slowdowns to make the work last and that wage costs would mount rapidly. Workers might even damage their machines intentionally in order to delay production and make the work last. If the entire plant was closed, workers and residents of the town would not blame the company because the difficulties would be attributed to the steel strike.

The plant manager also thought that the entire plant should be closed but his reasons were different. He stated that the plan urged by the sales director and the personnel manager would "empty the pipe lines" and leave the plant without any work in process when production was resumed. The workers could not all be called back at the same time, but a few workers in a department would be called each day as the materials being processed were moved along from one department to another. The planning of the flow of work would be difficult because some workers could not be reached just at the time they were needed. If the entire plant were closed at one time, all workers could be called back by general announcements in the newspaper, on the radio, and on television. All workers could pick up the processing at the point where they had left it.

The plant engineer argued that keeping the plant open with only a few departments in operation would increase expenses for heat, light, and power and for various employee services, such as cafeteria, storeroom, and toolroom. Furthermore, he thought that the company would have difficulty in holding the workers until all of the material had been processed because they would start looking for part-time jobs elsewhere before they were laid off.

The president thanked the members of the policy committee for their opinions. He said that he would discuss the problem with the board of directors and notify the members of the committee as soon as a decision was reached.

Questions:

1. Did the president follow the proper procedure?
2. What would be the proper decision in this case?

PART II

ORGANIZATIONAL

PROBLEMS

3 Organization for Production

PRODUCTION requires the use of machines and equipment, materials to be processed, and workers to attend the machines or man the workplaces. Each of these three factors in production raises a series of problems for the management. The assignment of duties to people requires that the total work of making the product be subdivided into tasks which can be performed by each person according to his training and ability. As the number of workers required to perform the various tasks may be too great to permit of effective supervision by one person, additional intermediate supervisors may become necessary. Organization is concerned with the division of tasks necessary to the total work of production and the assignment of the tasks to the various jobs or positions to be manned by employees, supervisors, assistants, and executives.

Organization is defined as a system or a plan for the co-operation of individuals in an enterprise for the accomplishment of the objectives. The organization is properly regarded as a system because the work of more than one person is involved. Organization comes into existence at any time when two or more people work together in a common endeavor because the essential tasks must be divided between them.

ORGANIZATION IN A SINGLE-PLANT COMPANY

The problem of organization in a single-plant company differs in several respects from that of a multiplant company. Problems of planning and co-ordinating the various activities are somewhat less complex, and fewer management people at the higher levels may be required. Some management functions that might be well developd in a large company may be combined with other functions to form a single position, and some functions may be neglected. In some cases, outside consultants, tax experts, research specialists, accountants, or attorneys may be engaged to perform certain services which in a large company would be performed by specialists within the company. In a small company, relationships may be conducted on a informal basis and, because the management may not have devoted sufficient attention to problems of organization, an illogical and unbalanced structure may have been permitted to develop.

In a small single-plant company, any one of three methods of organization may be used. They are the line method, the line and staff method, and the functional method. Although the method of line and staff is commonly employed, the other two methods require attention partly for the light they throw upon the line and staff method by way of contrast and partly because they may occasionally be encountered.

Line Organization. A line organization is based on relative authority and responsibility rather than on the nature of the activities. In the line organization, authority flows directly down from one level to another; and each person is responsible to the one directly above him. The name of this type of organization is borrowed from the military services, which designate the fighting branches as the line organization. In a pure line organization, no divisions or departments are organized or equipped to provide service or render advice only, but each department is engaged in performing an activity or function that is necessary to accomplish the objectives.

In a very small enterprise, all of the work may be performed by the manager and members of his immediate family. An organization would exist if the owner performed certain functions himself and assigned other functions to the wife and the children. If he employed still other persons as salesclerks, bookkeepers, or delivery assistants, the organization would continue to be a pure line organization. The owner-manager might decide to devote more time to general problems, banking relationships, planning, and supervision and to assign routine work to others. Until the proprietor employs an assistant to advise with the supervisors or to render certain services to them, the organization continues to be strictly the line type.

If the proprietor found it necessary or desirable to distinguish more clearly the duties of the various departmental managers, he might designate one for welding, another for sheet metal work, another for machining, and so on. This basis of organization is called organization by functions, and the authority of each department head would be that of a line executive. If the proprietor placed each department head in charge of the manufacture of a product, the basis of organization would be that of products. In a container factory, for example, one department manager might supervise the work of making round metal cans, another flat or oblong metal containers, another round containers made of paper, and another cardboard milk containers. To organize on the basis of products would require that the machines in the plant be arranged in a similar manner with all of the machines for making any one product grouped together in one part of the plant.

As the number of persons and the volume of work increase, the proprietor will probably find it necessary to assign to certain executives the work of selling, financing, and accounting. This type of organization would still be classed as line since no divisions or departments exist solely for formulating plans or giving advice to other executives or rendering a service to foremen and workers. The line organization is illustrated in Figure 1. Taylor found this kind of organization being

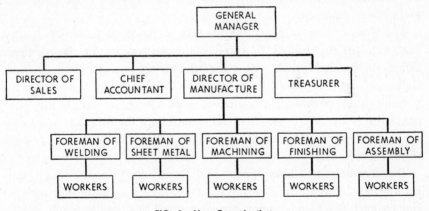

FIG. 1. Line Organization

used at the Midvale Steel Company when he started his work in management there in 1880.

Advantages of Line Type. The line organization has certain definite advantages over any other method of organization. Each person is made responsible for the management of a department or a phase of the work, and he presumably is given sufficient authority to achieve the desired results. If the authority is commensurate with the responsibility, he is not able to shift the blame for poor results. Consequently, he may be expected to do all that he can to accomplish any tasks that may be assigned to him.

Another advantage of the line organization is that authority and responsibility can be clearly defined. Each person in the organization receives instructions, orders, or commands only from his immediate superior. The line organization provides for the final centralization of authority in the person at the top.

In the line organization, the principal direction of communication is vertical, that is, from superior to subordinate and from subordinate to superior. Some horizontal communications, that is, with associates at the same level, may be necessary and desirable for purposes of co-ordinating the work; but in any case of misunderstanding or disagreement, any person could ask his supervisor for clarification. Since lines of authority and responsibility and vertical channels of communication are indicated by the organization chart and since each person is responsible to only one supervisor, the organization chart is easily understood. It involves a minimum of confusion to all persons concerned. For this reason also, the line organization is most effective in time of emergency because each person can take whatever action seems desirable without the necessity of consulting any person except his immediate superior and his subordinates.

If the supervisor or executive handles a variety of activities as they pertain to his department, he receives a broad training in management. For example, the foreman of a manufacturing establishment as illustrated by Figure 1 would be required to handle a variety of problems pertaining to planning, organizing, supervising, co-ordinating, and controlling. Experience of this kind should help the foreman to qualify for a position of greater authority and responsibility if the occasion should arise.

Disadvantages of Line Type. In a large enterprise the line organization has decided limitations. Because it makes no provision for specialists, each foreman or supervisor is required to attend to many details. The pure line organization therefore tends to overload executives. The foreman has so many duties that he may be inclined to leave workers to their own devices in such matters as methods of work, care and maintenance of equipment, and economy in the use of materials.

The duties of the foremen not only include a large amount of work, but also require that he have a variety of talents and abilities. Taylor listed nine qualities of a good foreman, some of them having to do with training and experience and some with personal traits. He said that the foreman should have education, technical knowledge, and manual dexterity. Necessary personal traits, according to Taylor, are brains, tact, energy, grit, honesty, judgment or common sense, and good health. Taylor said that it was difficult to find a man who had as many as five or six of the necessary qualities and impossible to find anyone who had all of them.[1]

Another weakness of the line organization is that it emphasizes individual action to the neglect of co-operation. The foreman or supervisor may attempt to handle a problem through vertical relationships rather than horizontal. He may feel that he has sufficient authority and does not need to co-operate with other persons at the same level. This tendency, to be sure, may be overcome by indoctrination, training, or proper supervision from higher levels.

Another possible limitation is that transfers of either workers or foremen to other positions are not easily arranged. No separate department has the authority to arrange transfers, and a foreman may prefer not to transfer a good worker to a job outside his department. For this reason, in the line organization transfers are seldom made at the lower levels. The worker may quit a job in one department and seek employment elsewhere in the same company, but this practice is wasteful.

Development of Staff. Military organizations long ago developed special units to assist the line in the handling of certain problems or in making important decisions. Philip of Macedon (died 336 B.C.), for example, is known to have surrounded himself with a group of competent men who advised him on military and political affairs. His son, Alexander the Great (356–323 B.C.), depended upon his associates for assistance in appraising the strength and weaknesses of the enemy, determining the time and the method of attack, and developing various phases of strategy. His eventual failure was due largely to his disregard of their advice. Gustavus Adolphus (1594–1632) made very effective use of staff for planning and organizing his campaigns, and his methods were later adopted by most of the military commanders of western Europe. George Washington was most effectively aided in planning his military strategy by several competent European generals who supported the American cause, particularly Marquis de Lafayette and Baron von Steuben. However, the concept of a general staff was not fully developed by the United States Army until after the Spanish-American War.

Although the kinds of staff are not clearly differentiated, they may be classified under three heads. The *general staff* exists principally for the

---

[1] F. W. Taylor, *Shop Management* (New York: Harper & Bros., 1903), p. 96.

rendering of advice and the formulation of plans for carrying out a program. If the plans are accepted by the line executive, the staff may assist in putting them into effect by explaining how the program should work, checking on the progress of the program, and conferring with the line executives on the operation of the plan. The general staff derives its name from the fact that it may assist the commander in handling any problem which he is required to handle. It should not be inferred that the giving of advice is limited to the general staff as any person can give advice to the chief, and any supervisor can counsel with his subordinates or his associates.

Special staff is the term used to designate the department or other unit that renders a service to the line or aids in co-ordinating its activities. In the military, such services include medical services, supply, transportation, psychological warfare, public information, and the work of the chaplain. Because the head of a department which renders a staff function has direct or line control over his own subordinates, the word *staff* might properly be used to describe the function of serving the operating departments. A term that is more descriptive, although it is not commonly used, is *the facilitating function.* If this term is adopted, the line departments might properly be described as operating departments.

The term *personal staff* is used to describe the work of persons who perform services of a personal nature for the commander. Examples are the services of the receptionist, the secretary, the orderly, and the chauffeur. The personal staff is often omitted from the organization chart, which shows only the principal positions.

Authority of Staff. The supervisor of a department that performs a staff function exercises direct or line control over his own subordinates only, and he has no authority to give orders to workers in other departments. To illustrate, an inspector has no authority to order a worker to stop work on a machine even though he finds that the quality of work being produced does not meet the required standard. Instead, he is expected to inform the foreman of the situation and the foreman would decide what should be done. If the foreman refuses to take satisfactory action, the inspector would report the difficulty to this own supervisor, and the problem could be reported up the chain of command until it reaches a supervisor who is in charge of both production and quality control. This supervisor might be the plant superintendent. His decision would be transmitted down the chain of command until it reaches both the foreman and the inspector. Because line foremen or supervisors know that this solution is possible, also because staff recommendations are usually good, most difficulties are settled without the necessity of appeals up the line. For this reason the question of whether the persons performing staff functions have authority over the line may seldom be raised.

Staff Functions in Industry. The three types of staff are usually found in larger industrial organizations although they may not be labeled as staff. The extent to which the staff functions are developed will vary with the size of the enterprise, the nature of the business in which it is engaged, and the ideas of the proprietor or general manager.

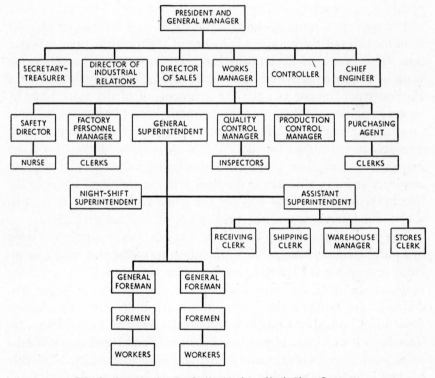

FIG. 2. Organization for Production in a Single-Plant Company

A possible organization for a single-plant company is shown in Figure 2. The top executives who perform line or operating functions in this company are the secretary-treasurer, the director of sales, and the works manager. The executives who perform a facilitating or staff function are the director of industrial relations, the controller, and the chief engineer. All of the executives at the level of the general superintendent except for that executive himself perform a facilitating or staff function. The persons reporting to the assistant superintendent on the chart also perform a facilitating or staff function.

Staff functions that may be separately organized at the plant level but are not shown on the chart include industrial engineering, plant transportation, the manufacture and maintenance of tools, tool storage, power in case the company has its own power plant, maintenance of plant and equipment, and product engineering. However, in the organization as shown in Figure 2, these functions may be handled by the chief engineer. Another peculiar feature of the organization as depicted in the chart is that the safety function is separately organized under the direction of a safety manager. Safety is frequently considered to be a part of the personnel function, or it may be combined with engineering.

The nature of most of the staff functions may be sufficiently clear from the titles of the positions, but some of them require brief explanation. The personnel department has been developed to assist in the work of employee activities and employee relations. The work of the personnel department includes the maintenance of the work force by encouraging persons to apply for jobs and by interviewing, testing, and investigating applicants. It recommends to supervisors the persons it considers best qualified for jobs. It makes recommendations for training courses throughout the organization and it assists in planning for employee training although it does not give the training. It assists the line by providing various services for employees, such as recreation, sports, food services, and the publication of a plant magazine.

The work of purchasing materials, supplies, and equipment is done by a purchasing department under the direction of the purchasing agent. He is responsible for knowing markets, interviewing salesmen, making purchase contracts, and following up the purchase order to see that deliveries are made on time. Inspection work is done by an inspection department headed by a quality control manager or by a chief inspector. This department inspects purchased materials and supplies, purchased parts, work in process of manufacture, and finished products. The title of chief inspector is probably more appropriate for the head of this function because quality control includes the original design of the product, the setting of standards to be observed in the manufacture of the product, the work of production itself which builds the quality into the product, and inspection for the purpose of seeing that standards have been adhered to.

The plant engineer is responsible for machine design, the selection of machinery for purchase, the installation of machinery and equipment, and the replacement of machines. He supervises the operation of the power plant and the toolroom which stores, repairs, and issues tools for use in the manufacturing departments. The industrial engineer, whose position is not separately shown in the chart, determines the methods by which work is to be done at the machine or workplace. By means of time studies, he sets standards for the various tasks. Such standards, sometimes called *production standards,* indicate the proper time to be required for each task as performed by the worker and may be the basis for the setting of a piece rate or the determining of a bonus.

The product engineer, another position which is not separately shown in Figure 2, is responsible for the design of the product. In some companies, his position may be regarded as a top function and he may report directly to the president and general manager. In other companies, the position may be placed at the plant level and he may report to the works manager. This function may also be combined with the work of the chief engineer. Product engineering includes the preparation of drawings showing the general design or appearance of the product; the accessories, parts, and subassemblies of which it is made; and the dimensions, contour, lines, shape, and other qualities of each part. It also includes the setting of any other qualities or requirements of the product and of each part, such as color, texture, tensile strength, capacity as in jars and bottles, and ability to withstand internal pressure or wear and tear.

In the organization chart as shown in Figure 2, four plant services have been grouped together under the direction of an assistant superintendent. This position is sometimes given the title of *plant service manager.* The work of the service department includes the receiving and unpacking of incoming shipments. It routes incoming freight shipments for materials and parts, checks freight bills, and traces delayed or lost shipments. It supervises the storing of materials, parts, and supplies. It issues stores upon requisition, and it transports materials inside the plant. It may provide for the shipment and routing of goods sold to customers.

The production planning department is responsible for routing production orders through the plant. It determines the department and the machine to which the work should be assigned. It schedules starting and completion dates at each phase of production and also final completion dates for finished products. The department dispatches the orders to workers through the office of the foreman, and it follows up the work to see that the schedules are met or that appropriate corrective action is taken.

Functional Organization. The word *function* means an activity or a group of related activities. In the functional organization, each executive is made responsible for a function and is given authority to supervise and direct persons in the organization who perform the activity. Since a workman may at various times perform more than one activity, he would be subject to more than one supervisor or foreman. The functional organization represents an extension of the principle of providing the services of specialists on which the line and staff organization is based. In the functional organization, the specialists become executives in charge of functions with authority to see that their recommendations are put into effect.

The functional plan of organization has been developed largely at the lower levels. It has been used principally in the shop, where it is known as "functional foremanship." It was popularized by Taylor and his associates, who contrived the system to correct the weaknesses of the line organization at the level of the foreman. Taylor began by providing the foreman with an assistant; then he added other assistants, each in charge of a certain phase of the work. Finally, the assistants were made foremen with the same rank as that of the original foreman but with a very different assignment of duties. The complete plan provided for eight foremen, four in the office and four in the shop. The eight foremen were as follows:

Foremen in the shop:	*Foremen in the office:*
Gang boss	Route clerk
Speed boss	Instruction card clerk
Repair boss	Cost and time clerk
Inspector	Shop disciplinarian

The duties of the foremen are partly, though not fully, indicated by their names. The gang boss had charge of the work up to the time it was placed in the machine. He was responsible for seeing that the workers were provided with the proper machine tools and that the machines were correctly adjusted. If necessary, he demonstrated the correct method of setting up and adjusting the machine. However, he had nothing to do with the processing of the materials. His work ended when the machine was ready to operate. The work of the gang boss at the present time is performed by the setup man and the move man, whose work is regarded as a staff or service function.

The speed boss supervised the operation of the machine. He saw that the cuts in the metal were started in the right part of the piece, that the machine was run at the proper speed, and that the depth of the cut was correct. Like the gang boss, he might be required to demonstrate how the work should be done. The name "speed boss" is not particularly appropriate and is often erroneously associated with the idea of speeding up the worker. The name merely refers to determining the correct speed of the machine and to supervising the flow of work through the shop. In the line and staff form of organization, the work of the speed boss is performed by the foreman.

The repair boss was responsible for the repair and maintenance of equipment. He was expected to see that the machines were kept in proper working condition and not merely to repair equipment after a breakdown. He could best meet his responsibility by periodical inspection, regular adjustment and lubrication, and overhaul before breakdown. Emergency repairs would be made under the direction of the repair boss when necessary. In the line and staff organization, the work of the repair boss is done by a repairs and maintenance department. This staff function is performed under the direction of the chief engineer.

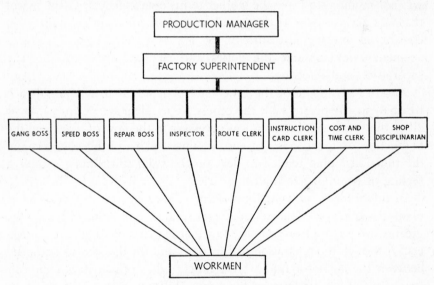

FIG. 3. Functional Foremanship Organization

The inspector was responsible for seeing that incoming materials met the specifications as set forth in the purchase order or in the contract with the vendor, that parts and accessories met the established standards, and that quality requirements were maintained throughout all phases of production. His work was similar to that of the chief inspector and the plant inspectors at the present time. The difference is that under the functional type of organization the inspector was considered a boss with a line relationship to the worker, whereas in the line and staff type of organization he performs a staff or service function and has a functional relationship to the foreman and the worker. The organization of a plant under the functional foremanship plan as developed by Taylor is shown in Figure 3.

Advantages of Functional Plan. The functional plan of foremanship was designed to reduce the span of training and skill required of the foreman. It accomplished this result by permitting each supervisor to become a specialist in a function of limited scope. The sphere of work of each foreman was so narrowed that properly qualified persons could be found or could be developed for each position. The special abilities of the functional foremen were continuously utilized in work for which each was especially fitted. Each foreman always performed the type of work for which he was best qualified.

The functional plan also reduced the span of operations of each foreman sufficiently to enable him to perform the duties of the position. He was not required to leave the worker to his own ingenuity to the extent that was necessary under the pure line type of foremanship. This plan constituted an essential feature of the Taylor system under which management would assume the duties and responsibilities of adequate supervision and direction.

Another advantage of the functional plan was that it required each foreman to co-operate with the others. The adequate performance of all of the functional foremen was necessary to the flow of work and the production of the goods. In encouraging and requiring co-operation, the functional plan tended to develop the team spirit and to foster a feeling of belonging to the company.

Disadvantages of Functional Plan. The functional foremanship plan was found to be subject to several serious limitations. Perhaps the greatest weakness arose from the fact that it was confusing to the workers. Although the separation of functions and the division of authority between the eight foremen were clear-cut and distinct, it was difficult for the worker to understand his responsibility to each of the foremen. In a stable working force the workmen might in time learn for what purposes and in what types of activities they are subject to each foreman. When labor turnover is high and many employees are new, workers are confused by this type of organization. The employee finds it much more satisfactory to work under the same boss all the time. Likewise, the workers feel less secure when they are subject to many foremen. They cannot be sure that their work is satisfactory when they have many persons to please. They may lose their jobs if any one of the eight foremen disapproves of their work.

Among the foremen themselves, responsibility for failure cannot be easily placed. If, as a group, they do not co-operate as they are expected to do, each one may blame the others for any difficulty that may arise. No one person assumes the final responsibility for failure to produce goods of the right quantity and quality at low cost according to a fixed schedule.

While the functional plan provided for specialization by functions, it did not provide for specialization by manufacturing operations or by products. For example, the gang boss would be responsible for the selection of the proper tools and for the adjustment of the machine whether the work was done in the drill press department, the finishing department, or assembly. He might be required to supervise the setting up of one machine for the production of parts with a tolerance of 0.001 of an inch and of another machine for the production of parts with much closer tolerance.

A high degree of specialization in any function at any level in the organization is desirable for the performance of that specialty, but it fails to develop people for a wider range of duties and for advancement to positions of greater responsibility. If a functional foreman confined his work and his interests to a single function as the plan contemplated, he might never qualify for a higher position such as that of plant superintendent.

Importance of Functional Plan. The functional form of organization was never widely used in industry. Experience showed its weaknesses, and by 1920 it had been abandoned by the few plants which used it. The significance of the functional plan is that it emphasized the idea of placing a specialist in charge of each function. While its strength lay in its provision for expert service, it violated the basic principle that each person should be made responsible to only one boss.

The functional plan hastened the development of the line and staff form of organization, which makes provision for specialists or staff departments to perform the work of Taylor's functional foremen. The work of the gang boss is now performed by the setup man, who may be in the engineering department. The work of the repair boss is now delegated to the maintenance department and that of the inspector to the inspection department. The work of Taylor's route clerk is performed by the planning or the production control department. The work of the instruction card clerk is performed by the standards and methods department, and the cost and time clerk has become the cost accounting and payroll department. The personnel department renders a wide range of services which replace but also go far beyond the work of the shop disciplinarian. The present-day foreman retains the authority of the speed boss and is in other respects the direct supervisor of the workers.

Relation to Line and Staff.   The line of demarcation between the functional organization and the line and staff is, in practice, often indistinct.   If a person who serves as a staff officer assumes the authority of giving orders directly to the subordinates of a manager in a different department, he becomes a functional executive and the organization becomes functional.   For example, a personnel officer might issue reprimands or take disciplinary measures without consulting with the foreman.   The maintenance man might tell a worker to operate a machine in a prescribed manner.   The wage and salary administrator might allow wage increases or transfer workers to other jobs or other departments.   The difficulties that would arise in such cases are obvious.   The worker would have many bosses just as he does in a functional organization.   However, a person in a staff position may at times act as though his authority is direct rather than advisory.

ORGANIZATION IN A MULTIPLANT COMPANY

If a company owns and operates several plants, additional levels of supervision become necessary in order that the work of production at the various plants may be properly integrated.   Some of the functions that would be assigned to the individual plant in a single-plant company might be performed at the main office for all of the plants.   Effectiveness of the organization might be increased by providing some uniformity of methods, procedures, or programs by means of a central staff in the main office.   The central staff would devise the most desirable or the most efficient methods which would be used throughout the organization.

Co-ordination of Plant Activities.   The method by which the work of many plants may be co-ordinated is illustrated by Figure 4, which shows the top organization of a large can-making company.   This company owns about sixty factories which are located in all parts of the United States.   It has the dual problem of performing certain services centrally in the interests of efficiency and also of supervising the various plant operations to see that general company plans and procedures are being followed.   The staff functions which are performed centrally are engineering, industrial relations, public relations, legal advice and litigation, purchasing and traffic, and research.   These activities include the giving of advice to the chief executive officer and to the operating executives.   They would propose to the chief certain general plans and policies to be followed throughout the company.

The vice-president for manufacturing would be expected to manage the operations for production in accordance with the company programs. Since he could not supervise directly the operations of sixty factories, he

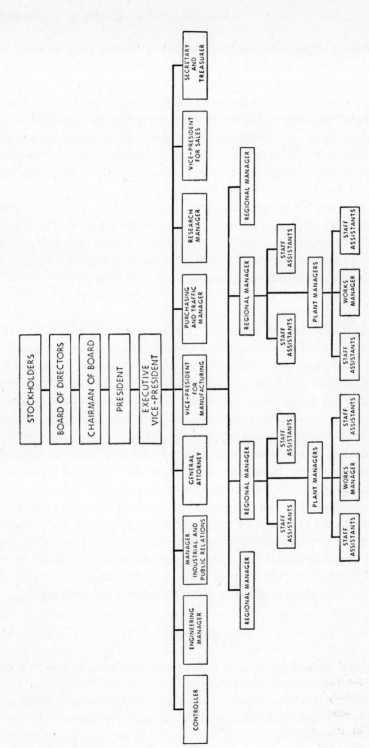

FIG. 4. Organization of a Multiplant Company

is assisted by regional managers who report directly to him. (Not all regional positions are shown on the chart.) The managers of plants in a defined area of the country would report to each regional manager. Reporting to each regional manager also are certain staff assistants whose functions correspond with the functions of the staff as organized at the main office. Each staff assistant at the regional office would have a line relationship with the regional manager and a functional relationship with the corresponding executive at the main office. In the same way, each plant manager is assisted by certain managers who perform staff functions. The staff personnel at the plant have a line relationship with the plant manager and a functional relationship with the corresponding staff executive at the regional office. The line relationship is indicated by the solid lines on the chart. A functional relationship, if it were to be shown, would be indicated by broken lines. In most cases, functional relationships are not indicated on organization charts because they would be so numerous as unduly to complicate the chart.

Effect of Number of Products. Organization necessarily depends upon the variety of products made and sold. A few companies produce a single product or one line of closely related products. Examples are sugar, soft drinks, college textbooks in business, and lumber. In such companies, one person may be placed in charge of each major activity, such as sales, production, purchasing, engineering, and finance. Some companies produce a variety of products. One company, for example, might produce and sell coffee, salt, frozen foods, gelatin, margarine, and other food products. In such a company, any one of several methods of organization is possible. The organization might follow the lines previously suggested for a company having a single product; or one person might be placed in charge of the production and sale of each product, together with related activities such as engineering, purchasing, and product research. Another possible organization is for sales to be organized by products, with all production activities centralized under one executive. Still other methods will be found in some companies.

QUESTIONS

1. Explain the meaning of organization. Show its relation to people, duties, position descriptions, and objectives.

2. For what type of enterprise is the line organization best suited?

3. Why is a staff especially needed in military organizations as a supplement to the line?

4. Explain the proper relationship of a person who performs a staff func-

tion to the persons engaged in production at machines. Illustrate by reference to the personnel director or the purchasing agent.

5. If an inspector finds that a machine is producing parts that do not meet the required standards, should he order the foreman or the worker to stop the machine? If not, what should he do?

6. Has the development of departments performing staff functions simplified the work of foremen and workers, or has it increased the difficulties of their work? Explain.

7. How does the line and staff type of organization differ from the functional organization?

8. A large company has sixteen plants located in various parts of the United States. At the home office is a director of industrial relations who reports directly to the president of the company. At each plant is a personnel director who reports to the plant manager. Explain the relationship of the two personnel managers to each other and to their respective supervisors.

9. The director of industrial relations referred to in Question 8 sent an assistant to a plant to confer with the local personnel director. If he finds that the practices at the plant do not conform to company policies and practices, what should he do?

10. If a company manufactures and sells several lines of products which are sold through different sales outlets, how might it gain by placing both manufacture and sale of each line of products under a separate manager?

CASES

3. CHANGE IN FORM OF ORGANIZATION

The Union Wire and Cable Company was incorporated in 1950 to acquire the stock of two other companies engaged in the manufacture of various kinds of wire and cable. It immediately issued all of its stock in exchange for 100 per cent of the stock of the two companies. During the remainder of the year, Union Wire and Cable functioned as a pure holding company. Its officers consisted of a president, a secretary, and a treasurer.

One of the subsidiaries owned two plants in Ohio. The main office of that company was in Cleveland. Top management of the company included the president, a market manager, a treasurer, a vice-president in charge of manufacturing, and a vice-president in charge of engineering. Plant superintendents reported to the vice-president in charge of manufacturing. Under each plant superintendent were the following executives: works manager, personnel manager, service manager in charge of purchasing and stores, plant engineer, and the cost accountant.

The other subsidiary had only one plant. The top management of the company consisted of the president and nine vice-presidents in charge of sales, finance, controllership, public relations, manufacturing, personnel, engineering, purchasing, and traffic.

The president of Union Wire and Cable Company was convinced that the management of the company was top-heavy and that substantial savings could be effected by reorganization. He proposed to the board of directors that the corporate charters of the subsidiaries be surrendered to the state and that their assets and liabilities be taken over directly by the top company. Central offices would be maintained only for sales, manufacturing, finance and accounting, purchasing, personnel, and engineering. A plant manager under the supervision of the director of manufacturing would be placed in charge of each plant. Under each plant manager would be a works manager and local staff departments for personnel, plant services, maintenance, costs and payrolls, and production control. In the office of the president and acting as his staff assistants would be a public relations manager and the secretary of the corporation.

Required:

1. Draw up an organization chart of the company immediately after the holding company was formed.

2. Draw up an organization chart of the proposed organization.

3. Explain what difficulties may be encountered in putting the reorganization into effect. What provisions should be made for persons holding office in the present subsidiary corporations?

4. AN ORGANIZATION PROBLEM

The Fenn Manufacturing Company was organized by Forrest A. Fenn during World War I to manufacture electric appliances needed by the armed forces. After the war, the company shifted its work to make and sell similar products needed in homes and factories. The founder of the company died in 1935, and his son, Mr. James B. Fenn, is now president. The company has only one plant. It employs 1,200 men and women. Recently much of the work has been done on subcontracts with larger corporations having contracts directly with the government.

As the company has increased in size, the president has endeavored to keep in close touch with its affairs. He believes that he can know what it going on throughout the company if he has the head of each important division reporting directly to himself. Directly under the president are fourteen executives in charge of the following activities: production, sales, purchasing, finance, controllership, product research, advertising, public relations, labor relations, market research, engineering, office management, budgetary control, and overseas activities.

Mr. Fenn says that he never seems to get caught up on his work, and the heads of the divisions complain that they experience undue delay in getting decisions from Mr. Fenn concerning important questions. The difficulties are increased by the fact that Mr. Fenn insists upon having all important questions referred to him for decision. Considerable dissatisfaction exists among the top executives, and three of them recently resigned to accept positions elsewhere. Mr. Fenn believes that his total salary cost is too much. He attempts to keep secret the salary of each top executive, but according to rumor, considerable differences exist in the top salaries.

The principle of wide span of control as followed by Mr. Fenn is followed also by executives at the next level below him. The director of production has reporting directly to him executives in charge of the following activities: plant management, plant maintenance, industrial engineering, traffic, storeroom, toolroom, plant accounting, production planning, safety, employment management, employee services and clubs, plant cafeterias, and plant protection. The director of production, like the president, Mr. Fenn, feels that he is overworked and that decisions are often unduly delayed. He has suggested to Mr. Fenn that a revision of the organization should be effected. However, Mr. Fenn believes that no reorganization is needed.

Required:

1. Criticize the plan of organization of the company.
2. Suggest possible changes in the organization.

CHAPTER

4 Principles of Organization

No one plan of organization is satisfactory for all enterprises, and a plan that is workable for any company at one time may not be satisfactory for the same company as conditions change. As explained in the preceding chapter, the organization will vary with the legal form, the number of employees, the variety of products manufactured and sold, the services rendered to customers, the extent of the span of control, and other factors. However, some principles that are of general application can be suggested.

Provision for Essential Activities. The organization chart indicates the positions within the company, and position descriptions would indicate the duties assigned to each position. New positions are added as the situation requires, and some positions may be eliminated if a product is discontinued or a plant is sold. During slack periods, some unprofitable activities may properly be continued temporarily in order to hold the working force intact. In time of depression or in periods of technological change, persons who might otherwise be dismissed are given make-work jobs until the slack can be taken up. Such activities may be discontinued as soon as the situation can be righted through the normal labor turnover or transfer of persons to other work.

Another factor in the decision to continue certain activities is the effect upon community or public relations, employee attitudes, and management development. Most companies conduct some activities and programs that do not contribute directly to profit. For example, a company might arrange for visitors to tour the plant or it might sponsor a program of musical concerts by the local symphony orchestra, even though they may not contribute directly to profit. The stability and strength of the system of private enterprise depend in part upon the fact that private corporations do not measure the desirability of every activity by the amount it directly contributes to profit. However, this situation creates the problem of distinguishing between desirable and undesirable activities.

Authority to Act. Two kinds of authority may be distinguished: delegated authority and earned authority. Delegated authority is the right to make decisions affecting people, money, or property, and to take such measures as may be necessary to see that the decisions are carried out. This kind of authority is delegated by each person to his subordinates from top to bottom throughout the organization. Earned authority refers to the ability of a supervisor to make his decisions effective because of his personal influence. Earned authority is gained through such qualities as knowledge of the technical aspects of the work, good communication, understanding the personal attributes of subordinates, and proper use of incentives. Earned authority is sometimes called the authority of leadership. The following discussion pertains to delegated authority.

The organization chart should provide for the delegation of authority to perform all work which should be done. Every activity necessary to the operation of an enterprise should be definitely assigned to someone. Moreover, the line of demarcation between the divisions and departments should be definite, in order that each person may know who is expected to act in certain cases. A corollary to this proposition is that the duties should not overlap.

The work of each position includes the making of decisions within a certain range. From the top of the organization chart to the bottom, each person is authorized to work out certain programs, to decide upon methods and work assignments, to check performance, and to take corrective measures within a specified range of authority. Each person can make decisions as they relate to certain problems. Other problems must be referred up the line for decision, and more detailed problems may be assigned to subordinates for investigation, the rendering of decisions, or the execution of a plan. Still other problems or questions may be referred horizontally to persons in other departments or divisions. The essential requirement is that each person should know the kind of problems to be handled by him and the persons to whom questions beyond his authority are to be referred.

The most important attribute of an organization pertains to the amount of authority in decision making which the executive delegates to his subordinates. At the top of the organization, the chief executive may require that decisions in certain areas be made by himself, and he authorizes the major executives to make decisions on questions of somewhat lesser importance. A similar problem of the amount of authority delegated arises at every level. If the organization is decentralized at the top level, it may be either centralized or decentralized at lower levels. However, if authority is centralized at the top, it is likely to be centralized at lower levels also. The amount of delegation in any company depends upon such factors as the span of control, the number of important decisions to be made, the nearness of the offices to each other, the speed in decision making that may be required, the ability of executives at the lower levels, and the attitude of the management.

Assignment of Responsibility. When any authority is delegated to a subordinate, responsibility for performing the duties is assigned to him. The assignment means that the subordinate is informed as to the nature of his duties, the extent of his authority, and the manner in which the work is to be done. A time limit for completion of any task may also be indicated. Incentives for proper performance, both financial and nonfinancial, may also be instituted, and the subordinate may be informed as to the nature of the rewards or disciplinary measures to be used. An assignment of responsibility is not complete until methods have been established for checking on performance and taking corrective measures.

In assigning responsibility, the executive does not relieve himself of his responsibility for the larger task. When he delegates authority and assigns responsibility, he retains the responsibility for seeing that the work is properly done. He cannot abdicate or delegate to any one his own responsibility to his chief.

The Scalar Chain. The successive levels of executives or supervisors to whom responsibility is assigned and through whom control is exercised constitute the scalar chain. The relationship of the various levels is also called the chain of command or the chain of authority. The principle of the scalar chain requires that each person know to whom he is responsible and who is responsible to him. A lack of understanding by any person of his position in the scalar chain indicates confusion in organizational relationships and in authority. The failure to define the place each person holds in the organization will result in conflicting orders and ineffective performance. Violations of the principle of the scalar chain are most likely to occur at the lower levels in the relations of the staff to the line.

Observance of the principle of the scalar chain does not lessen the need for co-ordination between the various units of the line or between line and staff. Co-ordination is essential to effective group effort. Moreover, communications can properly bypass the direct chain of command, although orders and commands should be transmitted only from supervisor to subordinate.

Channels of Communication. Each position serves not only for the making of decisions but also for communication. Since every person, except possibly the one at the top, is under the supervision of another, and since the final authority rests with the top executive, the channels of communication must permeate throughout the length of the scalar chain. The lines of communication should be kept open for the flow of information, instructions, orders, and commands from above and the flow of reports, comments, and suggestions from below. The supervisor should be available to subordinates for consultation whenever they require assistance or need to render a report.

Communications begin at the top level as stockholders receive various financial reports from directors and officers and convey instructions to directors through resolutions and other actions at stockholders' meetings. Directors receive reports from officers and informally discuss problems with them. The chief executive communicates with divisional executives through committee meetings, written memoranda, informal conferences, and other means. The subjects of such communications include budget requirements, expense and cost information, planning for physical facilities and executive personnel, and the co-ordination of various activities. The chief executive seeks not only to impart information concerning programs and plans but also to receive information on current developments and problems throughout the company.

Within each division, channels of communication are established for the transmission of information to and from the lower levels. Communication for any one person begins when he is appointed to a position and is informed of his duties and responsibilities. The newly appointed person is informed as to duties in order that he may know how to meet recurring problems without the necessity of consulting with his superior each time. Media for such communications include a written description of the position, together with a personal conference. Subsequent information on changes in plans and new developments may be transmitted by personal interviews, monthly or weekly discussion meetings, executive orders, and written notices. Luncheon meetings of committees and other groups are frequently used for communications. These methods may be used to reach all levels of the organization. New employees may be informed of company programs affecting them through their employment interview, talks as a part of the induction procedure, booklets on company rules and employee services, and interviews with the foreman. In some companies, each new employee is placed under the sponsorship of a dependable employee who assists him in using plant services such as the plant cafeteria and answers his questions concerning routine procedures. After his induction the employee may be informed of later developments through such media as discussion meetings, announcements on bulletin boards, conferences, counseling interviews, and annual reports to employees.

Many persons feel that the problem of communication from the upper levels to the lower is less difficult than that of communication from the lower levels to the upper. In upward communication the information may be incomplete or too condensed. Persons at the lower levels may hesitate to communicate unpleasant information, and they may omit details that might reflect discredit upon themselves or their subordinates. A foreman, for example, might hesitate to report differences between himself and an employee if he thinks he might be held at fault. At times, his chief concern may be that his superior may learn of the difficulty in some way not under his control.

For effective communication, each person should report to only one boss or supervisor. If orders are received from two or more bosses, the subordinate may receive conflicting orders, he may be confused over the priority to be given different assignments, and he will have no one person whom he may consult to correct difficulties. If one job does not keep a person busy all of the time, he may properly be assigned to different supervisors or departments on different days, provided the assignments do not overlap.

Lines of Promotion. The organization plan may indicate some though not all lines of promotion. If a person is promoted to a higher position in the same department, the normal direction of advancement may be considered to be the next higher level in the organization. Each person should be informed of the duties of the positions at the next higher levels and the qualifications required for promotion to them. It is a mistake, however, for the management to hold out to every person the possibility of promotion because some persons are not suited in temperament, emotional traits, or intellectual ability for advancement beyond a certain point. Some persons cannot acquire the necessary technical skill, and at the higher levels they may be unable to make the decisions required of a top executive. Many employees do not seek promotion to positions of increased responsibility.

The lines of promotion may lose significance in an expanding organization because new positions may be created. As branches are established, new plants are constructed, additions are made to an existing plant, or new products are added to the line, the organization chart must be adapted to meet the changing conditions. Furthermore, executives may be developed by transferring them from one position or one plant to another. In such cases, the regular lines of promotion may be disregarded.

Logical Assignment of Duties. The work assigned to a division or a department should be logically related. Each division manager should be in charge of a major activity, such as production, sales, finance, or accounting. Each person reporting to an executive should be in charge of a logical subdivision of the major activity. The same principle should be followed at other levels in the organization. One person may be placed in charge of each activity or subdivision of an activity. No person should be overloaded by having to manage functions requiring varied capacities; and all positions at the same level should require ability, training, and experience of comparable degree. Although this goal cannot always be achieved, it is a desirable objective.

Regard for Personal Capacities. The ideal situation exists when persons holding positions all along the line have the ability to perform their duties, have had sufficient training and experience to equip themselves for the work, and are interested in the things they are expected to do. However, if all people have just the ability necessary for their present positions, promotion to positions carrying greater responsibility will be difficult. On the other hand, if their positions do not require their best efforts, they may become discouraged and seek employment elsewhere before they receive promotion. It is the responsibility of executives to see that this does not occur, although no attempt should be made to hold a person within the organization when he can better himself by going elsewhere.

The principle of awarding promotions on the basis of ability, training, and interest is often violated in practice. The initial placement may be based on some principle other than merit, and methods of judging people for both employment and promotion are often faulty. Once a person is intrenched, and particularly after a long period of service, it may be better to leave him where he is rather than to remove him to make way for a more capable person. Deserving employees may therefore be required to await the promotion or retirement of a superior before they are placed in the positions for which they are best fitted. A favorite device is promotion to a newly created position with a high-sounding title but with few responsibilities. This method is popularly known as "kicking a person upstairs." The organization may be a compromise between an ideal logical assignment of duties and an assignment based upon personal capacities. The management may plan for an organization as they think it should be and gradually work towards it by shifting assignments of work as people develop or receive training for new responsibilities. The need for reorganization also arises with changes in personnel due to retirement or other causes and changes in the work to be done.

Distribution of Work. If possible, the work should be so divided that all persons at each level have approximately equal loads, with no person overloaded. This requirement is not easily met. If work is assigned by functions, the result is usually an uneven distribution. It can hardly be expected in a manufacturing enterprise, for example, that production, sales, and finance would make the same demands upon the executives in charge of each of these divisions. The same is true of the allocation of duties at other levels. The burden of the work would also be unequal because of differences in the ability, training, and experience of the executives and because of differences in their capacity to get things done.

A common reason for inequality of burden within an organization is the difference in the temperament and disposition of executives. Some people get things done, while others may appear to be busy without actually accomplishing a great deal. When new functions are undertaken and new duties assigned, the additional work may be given to people who have succeeded in keeping their desks clear and their work up to date. In time, this method results not only in the overloading of capable executives but also in an illogical assignment of tasks and functions.

An unbalanced work load may be caused by the failure of some executives or supervisors to delegate authority and assign responsibility. If a person attempts to attend to a mass of detail and to insist that he make all of the important decisions, he may have more work to do than his associates even though the organization chart would indicate a proper distribution of work. Each supervisor should check to see that his subordinates have delegated the proper amount of authority.

Work loads may also be improperly distributed if some executives have too many subordinates reporting to them. The smaller number of subordinates would mean fewer conferences and fewer problems of coordinating the work. However, a larger number of subordinates might require that more authority be given to each person and that few problems be referred to the chief by each subordinate. No definite number of subordinates can be said to be proper for all companies and all levels within the organization.

A lack of balance in an organization may be suggested by an improper designation of titles or the use of assistants. For example, five of the subordinates of a superintendent might be given the title of section head while the sixth might be called assistant superintendent. This type of organization would be confusing because it would suggest that one subordinate held a more important position than the others, whereas the organization chart would indicate that all subordinates are on the same level. The role of the assistant in this case should be more properly defined.

In practice one subordinate will exercise more influence upon the management of the enterprise than another and the recommendations of one subordinate are more likely to be accepted than those of another. The organization will not function in the way a formal chart might suggest because the positions are filled by people of varying personalities, experience, ability to communicate, and other traits. The working relations between the people in an enterprise constitute the informal organization.

Proper Placement of an Over-all Service. The organization is likely to operate with a minimum of friction if a service department is placed on a co-ordinate position with the departments it serves rather than in a subordinate position to one of them. For example, the personnel department might interview and recommend for employment applicants for jobs in the manufacturing division and also for positions in the sales, advertising, and controllership divisions. If the employment department is a part of the manufacturing division, the employment manager might be inclined to pay special attention to the needs of that division and to neglect the needs of the others. A similar situation might arise if a secretarial pool or a duplicating department is made a part of one of the divisions which it serves. One solution in such cases would be the authorization for each department to provide the special services it needs.

Centralized Authority. Centralization of authority means that final responsibility for the success of the enterprise has been placed in one person and that he has been given the authority to see that the objectives are accomplished. It does not mean that the head of the organization attempts to make all decisions or to attend to details. According to legal theory, final authority in the corporation rests with the stockholders who establish the framework of the enterprise and delegate authority to a board of directors elected by them. In small corporations the theory is valid; but in large corporations the stockholders are unable to perform this function because of their large number, the expenses of holding meetings attended by them in person, and their willingness to trust others to act in their behalf. Occasionally, a few stockholders owning substantial blocks of stock take an active interest in corporate affairs. More often, the policy-making function and the final authority rest with the directors. However, the board of directors may leave many important decisions to the officers, for the board of directors meets infrequently and many members of the board may be less familiar with corporate problems than are the officers. In any case, the essential requirement of a good organization is that final authority should be definitely placed, whether in the general manager, the president, the board of directors, or the stockholders.

The principle of centralization of authority implies that the number of persons reporting to any one executive should not be so large as to make it impossible for him to exercise control over the various activities. If the span of control is too great, the executive may be unable to supervise his subordinates effectively. He may be compelled to permit them act too much on their own initiative.

Co-ordination. To establish an effective organization, vertical and horizontal co-ordination is required. Vertical co-ordination means that the persons at the various levels work together without friction. Each executive gives his subordinates the proper supervision and knows what is being done by each subordinate. Vertical co-ordination also means that established lines of communication are observed and that an executive does not bypass his subordinates by giving orders to persons at the lower levels. Likewise, junior executives do not attempt to bypass their supervisors by reporting directly to executives at the higher levels. Problems requiring solution are handed down until they reach the proper executive, who proceeds to take the necessary action. In the same way, questions requiring decision are passed upward within the organization until they reach the executive in whose province the decision lies. This procedure cannot properly be called "passing the buck." It is merely the referring of a problem or question to the person who has been authorized to handle it. An executive may properly be said to "pass the buck" if he refers to another person a problem or a question which is within the range of his own authority.

Horizontal co-ordination means that persons in the various departments at each level work together effectively. For example, the enterprise is co-ordinated at the top level if the sales division directs its efforts to sell the type of goods made by the production division in the quantities it can economically produce and the finance division raises just the amount of funds necessary. This principle is closely related to that of balance in organization.

Horizontal co-ordination is achieved in part by communication. To avoid bypassing an executive and to assure that the organization is co-ordinated vertically, it is important that all communications move upward to a common executive and then downward again to the proper level, as shown in Figure 5. However, this procedure is time consuming,

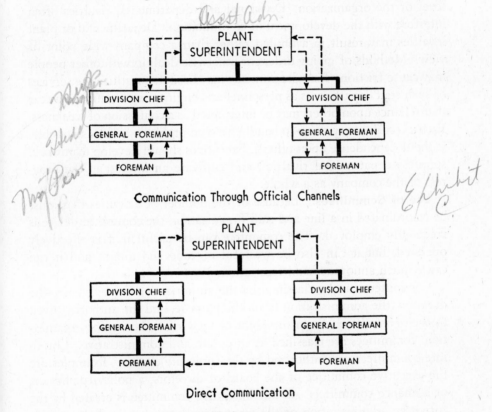

FIG. 5. Methods of Communication

adds to the work of the executive, requires more oral and written reports, and is likely to result in a less satisfactory solution than would be achieved by direct communication. Frequent lateral communication occurs between the foreman and the personnel department, between the production control department and the purchasing department, between the standards and methods department and the foremen of manufacturing departments, and between various other departments at the same level.[1] Consequently, it is much better for people to confer directly and to work out their problems by personal contact, provided that the persons conferring are able to agree as to what should be done, that the immediate supervisors know that personal conferences are being held, and that supervisors are kept informed as to what agreements are reached or what new programs are initiated. If these requirements are not complied with, direct conferences should be discontinued; and the questions should be taken up through the official channels of communication.

The problem of developing horizontal co-ordination exists at each level of the organization. Divisional and departmental rivalries often interfere with the development of co-ordination. Departmental or plant loyalties may result in a limited rather than a company-wide point of view. Methods of giving orders or otherwise dealing with other people may cause friction. Line departments may hesitate to utilize the services of such staff departments as personnel and engineering because of a fear that reliance upon others may be interpreted as a confession of weakness. Each executive may strive to handle his own problems as far as possible, without dependence upon others. Executives should develop teamwork, suppress departmental rivalries, and cultivate an interest in the progress of the company as a whole.

Use of Committees. Because of the number of activities that must be co-ordinated in a line and staff organization, the committee device is frequently employed. The committee can be useful if it is effectively operated, but it can also be wasteful of time and money and it can cause much annoyance and frustration.

Committees can be classified by the authorization for existence, the duration, the administration level, the purpose, and the authority given to each committee. From the point of view of authority for organization, committees are classified as corporate and administrative. Corporate committees are authorized by the corporate charter. Examples are the executive committee of the board of directors, a policy committee, or a finance committee. An administrative committee is created by the corporate administration or the management to meet a need not contemplated by the charter. From the point of view of duration, committees are permanent or temporary. Temporary committees are sometimes designated as *ad hoc,* which means "for this specific purpose." A temporary committee is sometimes permitted to become permanent because the executive who created it failed to define precisely the work to be performed.

---

[1] Henri Fayol referred to direct communication as the "gang plank." See his *General and Industrial Management* (London: Sir Isaac Pitman & Sons, Ltd., 1949), p. 35.

Committees may be organized at any level from the board of directors to the workers. In some cases, membership is limited to persons at one level, but it may include persons at two or more levels. In some cases, the membership will be rotated from time to time. The level in the organization and the membership will depend upon the purpose and the duration. At the top level, a committee might consider such problems as budgets, methods of financing, sales policy, public relations, retirement plans, salaries and executive bonuses, and research programs. At the lower level, committees may deal with such problems as accident prevention, employee recreation and clubs, reduction of waste, quality control, and employee complaints and grievances.

The objectives of a committee vary considerably. In some cases, a committee may be established for the purpose of improving communications from the chief to the subordinates, from subordinates to the chief, or between executives at the same level. Committees may be asked to discuss a problem and to make recommendations. In some cases, committees whose membership is composed of branch managers may work out methods of handling problems that are common to all of them. Committees can best review information that is already available. They are least suited to making investigations or making decisions on management problems.

The authority given to a committee will depend upon the objective. The authority may be limited to listening, discussing, or making a recommendation. Usually the committee does not have authority to make a decision or to handle a problem in management, though some committees do have such authority.

Committees are most successful when they are used for the purpose of advising an executive, for the exchange of ideas, for keeping the members informed, and for unifying points of view. For making decisions, the committee may be effective in combining different points of view. However, the decisions of a group may represent compromises, and the committee may be dominated by the more talkative persons. Decisions may not be the best because some members may be unqualified. The committee also results in a division of responsibility. It does not possess the means for carrying out a decision or for supervising the activities of the members of an organization. The success of a committee for any purpose will depend upon the size, the nature of the membership, and the qualities of the chairman.[2]

Use of Charts in Organization Planning. Many companies make

---

[2] Estill I. Green, "The Nature and Uses of Committees," *Advanced Management*, Vol. XXIV, No. 7 (1959), pp. 24–28.

much use of organization charts which show formal positions, titles, and perhaps the names of the persons occupying various positions. Such charts are useful in the development of the organization and also in instructing new members of the management group of their relationship to other persons in the company. The charts serve a useful purpose in disclosing defects in the assignment of duties and responsibilities. When an enterprise which has developed without reference to an organization chart draws up such a chart, undesirable features are usually found to exist. Activities may not be logically arranged. Certain functions may have been separated with a part of the function assigned to one department and another part to another. Duplication of work assignments may have been made with the result that two or more departments are performing the same work. Unrelated activities may be grouped together, and specialized departments may have been assigned varying duties which they are not qualified to handle properly. Some departments become overdeveloped in relation to the others, with consequent waste of money and effort on unprofitable activities. At various levels in the organization, the number of persons reporting to one supervisor may exceed the number that can be effectively supervised. The undesirable features in an organization may continue indefinitely unless a chart brings them into focus. However, all weaknesses should be corrected before the chart is set up in final form. It should be a cardinal principle that the chart is not rigid or fixed and that no one acquires a vested interest in his position.

Organization charts are subject to certain limitations. Although they show the vertical relationships of each position, they do not show all horizontal relationships. For example, they do not show the relationship of the purchasing agent to the cost accountant, the storekeeper, the standards and methods engineer, and other members of the organization. A further limitation of charts is that they do not show the authority associated with certain positions because of the personal influence or prestige of the persons holding the positions. An aggressive or competent person may exert much greater influence than his position seems to bestow upon him. He achieves his influence by his ability to help people and by the force of personality. Practical relationships in such cases do not conform to the chart or to organization theory. Furthermore, the chart cannot show the extent to which authority has been delegated and the level at which various decisions are made. As previously indicated, this attribute is probably the most important feature in any organization.

Another difficulty with organization charts is that of keeping them up to date. This problem is particularly acute when the names of persons holding the various positions are shown on the chart. Organization charts may also tend to make the organization inflexible because management may strive to maintain the relationships that the charts portray. Because of theoretical objections, and also because of operating pressures, some companies have not prepared charts or have not keep them up to date.

QUESTIONS

1. Distinguish between authority and responsibility.

2. Distinguish between delegated authority and earned authority, also called organizational authority and authority of leadership. Why are both necessary to effective management?

3. Chester I. Barnard, a well-known writer on management, states that the positions in an organization are centers for decision making and centers of communication. Explain the relationship of these two functions to each other.

4. Under what circumstances might an executive refer a question to his superior for decision? When might he refer a question to a subordinate? When might he refer a question to another executive at the same level in the organization?

5. Does the top executive design an ideal organization and require that all persons in the company adapt themselves to it, or does he adapt the organization to the persons who are to fill the positions?

6. Some executives seem to have difficulty in delegating authority. Explain how such delegation should be made.

7. Is the delegation of authority always downward in the organization, or may delegation be made upward?

8. Explain the importance of the scalar chain in management.

9. Why is communication upward more difficult than communication downward in the organization?

10. What is the importance of lines of promotion? Does promotion follow the line of authority and responsibility?

11. Explain the meaning of centralized authority.

12. What is necessary to the successful use of the committee?

13. Under what conditions is direct communication between executives at the same level in the organization permissible?

CASES

5. FUNCTION OF AN ORGANIZATION DEPARTMENT

A large corporation with a number of subsidiaries has established an organization department under the direct supervision of the president. The function of the department is described in the company manual as follows:

"The Organization Department is responsible for developing organization plans and policies which will be given company-wide application. These plans and policies are designed to assist members of management at all levels in the discharge of their primary responsibilities for the maintenance of sound organization; the active and effective control of methods, payroll expense, and manpower utilization; the proper evaluation of daily rate jobs and salaried positions; and the equitable administration of wages and salaries. The Organization Department furnishes assistance to the officers of the company and advice and assistance to departments and subsidiary management. The Department further provides functional guidance and assistance to executives who are responsible for organization and cost control in major departments. Periodically, the Organization Department appraises the effectiveness of the efforts of these divisions and positions, reviewing the results with the management concerned."

Usually the members of the organization department work at the main office in consultation with plant managers, the heads of divisions, and others who come in for consultation. The organization department has prepared a model organization manual for the use of all persons throughout the company for their guidance in preparing organization charts and position descriptions. The manual shows a typical organization chart for the top management of an entire company and more detailed charts of divisions and departments to supplement the main chart and to provide additional detail. Departmental managers are expected to use this manual in the preparation of charts and manuals for their own divisions, plants, or departments. Final responsibility for the organization of any such unit is placed upon the head of the unit and not upon the organization department.

Recently the manager of Plant A has been in consultation with the organization department concerning the organization of his plant. As the plant organization is now constituted, the manager has reporting to him the heads of the following departments: production planning, accident prevention, purchasing, maintenance, receiving and stores, payroll and costs, employment, plant cafeteria, plant engineering, and inspection. In addition, five general foremen report to the superintendent. Under the general foremen are forty foremen. The total number of employees is 560. The manager of Plant A is satisfied with his present organization. He believes that the number of persons reporting to him is about right and that the plant has about the right number of departmental managers.

In Plant B, the manager has only two persons reporting to him. One, who is called "staff manager," heads the staff functions which are the same as in Plant A. The other person is called "manufacturing manager." Reporting to him are three general foremen, and under the general foremen are fifteen foremen. The number of employees is 350. The manager of Plant B is satisfied with his organization as it stands and is opposed to making any changes.

Questions:

1. What changes do you recommend in the organization of each plant?

2. How should the manager of the organization department proceed to effect the changes he believes to be necessary?

6. ORGANIZATIONAL RELATIONSHIPS

Jane Winthrop accepted a position as bookkeeper and office manager with the Smith Clothing Company in 1940. She had graduated from high school and later had completed a course at a secretarial school. Jane's principal work was that of bookkeeper. She made all of the entries in the cash book, the sales journal, and the general journal. She posted the entries to the ledger, and at the end of each month she took a trial balance. She made the adjusting and closing entries as recommended by the auditor. She also supervised the work of three other young women on the secretarial staff and attended to various other details of the work in the office. She acquired a grasp of the details of the business and proved herself to be a capable office manager.

The volume of work grew steadily and, in 1957, Mr. Kendrick, the president, employed Mrs. Alice Sims as his assistant and private secretary. Mrs. Sims was 32 years of age. She was a college graduate in business administration with a major in sales management. Her salary was fixed at $6,500. Miss Winthrop was then being paid $6,200. Mr. Kendrick informed Miss Winthrop that the name of Mrs. Sims was to be placed on the payroll at that amount, adding the comment that Mrs. Sims had two children to support.

When Mrs. Sims reported for work, Mr. Kendrick talked with her and Miss Winthrop about the assignment of work in the office. He stated that both women would report directly to him. While he expected to make special assignments to Mrs. Sims from time to time, he did not expect her to direct the work of Miss Winthrop. As financial secretary, Miss Winthrop would supervise the work of the bookkeeper who recently had been added to the staff. She would buy office supplies, approve invoices for payment, and see that incoming and outgoing mail was properly handled.

Before long, friction began to develop between Miss Winthrop and Mrs. Sims. Miss Winthrop resented the fact that a younger woman had been added to the staff at a higher salary than she was being paid. Miss Winthrop thought also that Mr. Kendrick should have discussed the new position with her before Mrs. Sims was employed. She noted that Mrs. Sims was given an expense allowance for the entertainment of out-of-town guests while Miss Winthrop had no such allowance. Mrs. Sims seemed to think that she had a higher status than Miss Winthrop because she held a college degree and received a higher salary. She occasionally asked Miss Winthrop for an advance from the petty cash fund to pay for a luncheon to which she invited a visitor to the company. She disturbed the office routine by asking for reports of sales and expenses at odd times. Miss Winthrop was irritated not only by the requests but also by the manner in which the requests were made.

The local board of trade held a two-day meeting in January of each year. Speakers from banks and manufacturing companies discussed the outlook for finance and business in the area and in the industry. For many years, Miss Winthrop had made the arrangements for people in the management to attend the meetings, and she always included herself at the suggestion of Mr. Kendrick. She particularly enjoyed the luncheons and the banquet, and she found the discussion meetings to be very interesting. In January after Mrs. Sims was employed, Mr. Kendrick asked Mrs. Sims to make the arrangements. Mrs. Sims omitted the name of Miss Winthrop from the list of persons who were to attend. When Miss Winthrop heard of the omission, she went to Mrs. Sims who was seated at her desk, criticized her in a loud voice for omitting her name, mentioned other things that she did not like, and threatened to resign if she was not included in the group. She then went to the office of Mr. Kendrick and told him that she was being treated unfairly. Mr. Kendrick immediately called Mrs. Sims on the telephone and told her that Miss Winthrop was expected to attend the meetings of the board of trade.

Question:

What was the cause of the difficulty in this case?

5 Problems at the Executive Level

THE organization chart indicates the formal plan or system for the co-ordination of the activities of people in the enterprise. It suggests the basis on which the duties have been assigned to positions. It does not indicate how the organization employs the services of people and how the people work with each other. The problems and the relationships will vary with the organizational level. The levels may be roughly classified as the executive level, the foreman level, and the worker level. To develop a better understanding of the organization, these three levels will be treated separately.

WORK OF THE EXECUTIVE

The essential function of the executive is to unify the work of the people in his department, division, or company and to direct their energies toward the accomplishment of the common objectives. An important objective is the production of goods and services for sale in the market at a price which affords a satisfactory profit or possibly the maximum profit. Difficulties that may arise in the effort to gain co-operation include indefinite definition of the objectives, indifference, adherence to conventional methods, local or departmental ambitions, and attention to personal affairs.

The work of the executive is sometimes classified under three principal headings. First, he is concerned with the technical aspects of production or other activity that may be carried on. However, the technical work becomes less important as the executive advances to the higher positions in the organization because he relies more and more upon the advice of specialists. Second, he deals with people and gets the work done by directing and motivating them. Third, he attempts to get the enterprise to function as an entity or as a unit, to see that it accomplishes its main objectives, and to have it maintain its proper relationships with customers, vendors, banks, and other institutions in the economic system. All three of these phases of the work of the executive require attention to problems created by changes within and without the organization.

General Administration.   One of the best summaries of the phases of the work of the administrator or executive was made by Henri Fayol, the well-known French industrialist, in 1916.[1] He classified the work into five elements: planning, organizing, commanding, co-ordinating, and controlling. As these five steps indicate, the executive first plans what is to be done. In making the plans, he considers the various alternatives before selecting the best course of action. The plan also includes a statement of the physical facilities, the personnel, and the money that will be required to initiate and complete the planned program. The executive may divide the major task into the duties that will be assigned to each person. He makes the assignments and issues general or

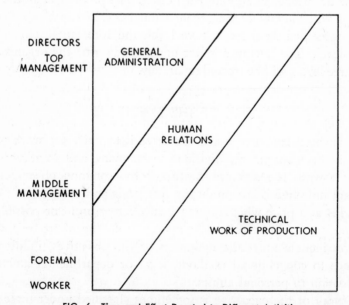

FIG. 6. Time and Effort Devoted to Different Activities

[1] Henri Fayol, *General and Industrial Management* (New York: Pitman Publishing Corp., 1949. Original in French, 1916).

detailed instructions depending upon the circumstances, and he delegates the necessary authority to each person. He co-ordinates their work as they carry out the plan, and he establishes methods of controlling or checking on the work done by each person and on the development of the work as a whole.

The various types of activities are shown graphically in Figure 6. This chart illustrates the fact that the percentage of time and effort devoted to the three types of work varies with the organizational level. At the lowest level, the worker is concerned largely with the technical aspects of production and his personal relationships with the foreman and other workers. The foreman devotes more attention to human relations but is still largely concerned with the technical aspects of production. At the top level, the technical aspects require less attention while general administration and human relations require a larger percentage of the time.

Talking with People. The president of a large manufacturing company, when asked by a worker what kind of work he performed, stated that he talks to people. The people with whom he talks include members of the board of directors, prominent stockholders, the heads of major divisions of the company, and some persons outside the company, such as lawyers, bankers, management consultants, and officials in the government. His direct contact with machines and the technical processes of production may be infrequent.

Because the executive gets his work done through other people, his ability to direct and influence others is important. He needs to develop an understanding of the meaning of reports and other methods by which information is communicated. He should be a good listener in that he should be willing to receive oral as well as written communications, and he should be able to evaluate the information received, relate it to the problem at hand, understand the need for more information as the situation requires, and make appropriate decisions. In making decisions, however, he should handle only those questions that fall within the limits of the authority that has been delegated to him.

The concern of the executive with general problems may cause him to develop a point of view that is different from that of the worker at the machine or even the foreman in the shop. As the executive considers such problems as rising costs of production, the difficulties of meeting the sales prices of competitors in the market, and the replacement of obsolete equipment with new and improved machines at higher prices, he may fail to appreciate the point of view of workers. The workers, on the other hand, may think largely of their own needs for money to meet the living expenses of themselves and their families or they may be concerned with such problems as working conditions in the department where they work or the discrimination of a supervisor. The foreman may direct his sympathies largely toward the workers because he knows them and their problems and because he needs their co-operation in order to maintain schedules.

The level in the organization at which the point of view shifts from the immediate and the specific problems of the day to the long-range and the general problems will vary with the company. However, it can be said that the vice-president for production and the plant superintendent must devote much of their thinking to general problems and to conditions outside the company. In order that executives may not become too far removed from the production line and may continue to understand the thinking of the workers and the foreman, most companies limit the number of levels in the organization.

Delegation of Authority. If the top executives are to perform their work effectively, they will not have time to handle detailed questions and problems but should delegate to subordinates the authority to dispose of many such matters. The principle of delegation with well-defined limits of the authority of each person is known as the *exception principle*. The executive establishes general objectives and programs for the guidance of subordinates, who can then dispose of routine problems. When some question of unusual nature arises, the subordinate carries that question to the executive for decision. When the decision has been rendered, the new rule is used as a guide until another exception occurs. Routine affairs disposed of by subordinates or assistants are summarized in periodical reports which enable the superior to know what has been accomplished. The principle was stated by Frederick W. Taylor as follows:

It is not an uncommon sight, though a sad one, to see the manager of a large business fairly swamped at his desk with an ocean of letters and reports, on each of which he thinks that he should put his initial or stamp. He feels that by having this mass of detail pass over his desk he is keeping in close touch with the entire business. The exception principle is directly the reverse of this. Under it the manager should receive only the condensed, summarized, and invariably comparative reports, covering, however, all of the elements entering into the management, and even these summaries should be carefully gone over by an assistant before they reach the manager, and have all of the exceptions to the past averages or to the standards pointed out, both the especially good and especially bad exceptions, thus giving him in a few minutes a full view of progress that is being made.[2]

---

[2] F. W. Taylor, *Shop Management* (New York: Harper & Bros., 1903), p. 126.

The principle that the executive should concern himself only with general policies and with exceptional cases is of ancient origin. When Jethro, the father-in-law of Moses, joined the Israelites in the wilderness, he found Moses undertaking to sit as judge of all the people. Moses worked from morning until night and still did not get all the work done. Jethro saw that this procedure placed too severe a burden upon Moses, delayed decisions, and required too much waiting upon the part of the people. Following Jethro's advice, Moses set up what seems to have been a line organization with rulers of thousands, hundreds, fifties, and tens. The plan was based upon the exception principle, which Jethro explained in the following statement: "And let them judge the people at all seasons; and it shall be that every great matter they shall bring unto thee, but every small matter they shall judge; so that it be easier for thyself, and they shall bear the burden with thee."[3]

In many companies, executives are overworked because they have failed to delegate authority or to train subordinates to make decisions, and they are required to attend to detailed problems to the neglect of larger issues. Even in a large company, for example, presidential approval may be required for purchases over a stated amount, salary changes above a stated minimum, public appearances of members of the management, and capital expenditures of more than a few hundred dollars. In smaller companies the president may approve grievance settlements that cost money, transfers of production workers, and awards made to workers for suggestions to management. In some small companies the chief executive opens all of the mail and signs all outgoing letters.

Several reasons may be given for the failure of executives to delegate more authority. Perhaps the principal reason is that the executive believes that he can do the work better than any one else or that his judgment is better than that of subordinates. He may find it easier in any situation to do the work or make the decision than to train someone. Another difficulty is that some executives enjoy handling detailed problems. A chief executive who has advanced by way of the sales division, for example, may feel that he knows more about sales problems than the present head of the division knows; and he may also derive a personal satisfaction from the handling of sales problems and the making of sales contracts.

An executive may hesitate to delegate because he is afraid that he may not receive credit for the results achieved unless he personally

---

[3] Exodus 18:22.

attends to numerous details. This fear is usually baseless. The head of any organization is credited with the success achieved because he selected capable persons for their positions, eliminated conflicts and difficulties, and directed the activities of the group toward the common goal.

In some cases the executive may have difficulty in delegating authority because the subordinate may prefer not to make decisions. A junior executive may insist upon taking his problems to the superior, with the excuse that he thought the chief executive would like to make the decision. If he does, the superior should decline to decide the question. He may properly assist the junior officer by suggesting possible lines of action, or he may inquire whether the subordinate has considered certain difficulties. However, he should leave the decision to the subordinate if it properly falls within the scope of his authority.

Judgment by Standards. The executive should have definite and reliable criteria by which to rate his subordinates and to determine which are the most valuable to the organization. The standards should be established in advance of performance, and they should be made known to the persons whose work is to be evaluated. If such qualities as punctuality, regularity of attendance, and personal appearance are important, the subordinate should know it in order that he may do what is expected of him. In making any judgment, the executive should make his ratings over a period of time which is long enough to permit a fair appraisal.

Three types of standards which may be employed in judging subordinates are standards of performance, financial standards, and standards of accuracy.

A standard of performance is a measure of the amount of output of an individual or a department. For example, the standard might indicate the number of units expected to be produced by the manufacturing division, the number of units to be sold by the sales division, the number of hours machinery is expected to be kept in operation, or the number and seriousness of accidents.

A financial standard is a measure of the success of an individual or a department stated in dollars and cents. The following are examples: sales made by each salesperson, sales returns in dollars and as a percentage of sales, and markdowns in prices stated in dollars and as a percentage of sales. The balance sheet and profit and loss ratios are financial standards. Comparison may be made with the performance of prior years, with averages for the industry, or with what is considered ideal performance.

A standard of accuracy is a measure of the quality of the work done.

An example is the amount of defective or spoiled work in a department. A standard of accuracy is often combined with a standard of performance.

In many cases the performance of last year or last month is used as a standard by which the performance of the present year is judged. Such a standard is easily constructed but its value is questionable. The performance of last year may have been poor, or it may have been good. Workers and foremen have been known to limit production in order that management may not use their performance to establish higher standards of output for other workers or for subsequent periods. The standard should represent efficient performance or perhaps performance under ideal conditions.

To be effective a standard should require consistent effort and reasonable efficiency on the part of employees or other persons. It should not be impossible of attainment. Moreover, it should not be changed if foremen or executives succeed in meeting its requirements. For example, a budget allowance should not be reduced if an executive fails to spend the entire amount for any one month or year. The standard cost should not be reduced merely because a foreman succeeded in keeping his costs within limits. The changing of a standard in this way destroys the effort to co-operate.

Both the superior and the subordinate would prefer that judgments be based upon standards. Partiality and favoritism may be avoided, and judgments are consistent from one time to another. The executive who has developed standards may more easily gain the good will and the co-operation of subordinates.

Reward should be related to accomplishment. Rewards may be financial or nonfinancial. Financial rewards are usually necessary, but nonfinancial rewards are also effective. Nonfinancial rewards include praise and commendation, increase in rank, additional authority and responsibility, and any recognition which increases the self-respect of the subordinate or the respect in which he is held by his associates. Recognition need not be given for each task successfully completed. It is sufficient if the subordinate knows that his superior is aware of meritorious service and ultimately rewards it. In the lower levels of the organization, however, rewards should be prompt if they are to be effective.

PREPARATION FOR EXECUTIVE WORK

The success of any enterprise will depend largely upon the competence of the people who provide for its management. While managers or executives must possess certain personal qualifications, they may also profit by both experience and formal preparation. A shortage of competent executives has existed for many years partly because the expansion of business and the increased size of the individual enterprise have created a need for more and better managers. Furthermore, business problems have been complicated by the increased application of science to production, the more direct interest of the federal government in business management, the greater power of labor unions, and other such developments. Businesses cannot expect to draw their executives from each other. They have been required to devote an increasing amount of attention to the preparation of people for executive work. This preparation has included education, training, and growth and development.

Education for Executive Work.   Education is defined as mental and moral discipline gained by study and instruction. It is also defined as the impartation or the acquisition of knowledge through a planned course of study or instruction. The need for education arises because of the complexities of modern industry, the territorial extent of markets and sources of supply of materials, and the application of science to industry. The relation of government to industry and the legal aspects of business raise additional problems. Most of the education of the executive may be acquired on his own initative before or after his association with the enterprise. Some of it may be acquired through a company program.

A part of the education of the executive is concerned with economic or political institutions. The institutions with which he deals are of two general types: institutions outside the company, and institutions within the company and its various divisions. Outside institutions include a variety of organizations because together they make up the environment in which the company operates. He should understand the industries and the companies from whom raw materials and supplies are acquired and the marketing agencies through which the company markets its product. Other types of institutions with which the executive should be familiar are in the areas of finance, competitive industries, competitor companies in the same industry, international markets, business counseling services, governmental agencies, and labor unions. The list could be extended indefinitely.

The company in which the executive works constitutes another institution that requires an understanding on his part. He should understand its place in the industry, the basis of its organization, the extent to which its facilities for production are decentralized, the extent to which decision making is centralized or decentralized, the product-line policy, the method by which the company is financed, the staff functions that are separately organized, and the relation of line and staff within the company. He needs to know the people who compose the executive group and the way they work together in practice as well as in formal relationships as prescribed by the organization chart. Many other details pertaining to the company organization could be indicated, but the foregoing list is suggestive.

Training of the Executive.   The word *training* means preparation for a specific contest, event, or position. Training programs are frequently organized for workers because their work is routine and definite, whereas the executive must be able to meet new situations, work out general problems, and transfer from one position to another. However, training programs for executives may deal with such topics as effective speaking, conference leadership, budgetary methods, cost control, production management, rapid reading, business writing, and human relations. The objectives of such programs depend upon the needs in each company.

Training also includes a study of methods and techniques that are used to adapt the enterprise to the industrial and economic system in which the company renders a service and performs a constructive role. They include methods of dealing with vendors and making purchase contracts, methods of dealing with transportation agencies, credit instruments for long-term or short-term financing, union contracts and their provisions, and methods of dealing with customers, competitors, governmental agencies, and the general public. The list merely suggests the breadth of such relationships.

Within his own company, the executive uses certain techniques to develop teamwork and to obtain a unified co-operative effort. Examples are found in the areas of cost and statistical reports, methods of communication, motion and time study, the preparation and use of budgets, the establishment of standards and ratios for the interpretation of financial statements, methods and procedures for the selection of employees, job evaluation, methods for determining fair wage rates, and the like. This list would include the various methods and techniques throughout the whole realm of business administration.

Growth and Development of Executives.   While a program of education or training might be expected to result in the growth and development of the participant, it does not necessarily do so. The development of executives depends upon certain inherent qualities, particularly balanced judgment, and also upon experience in the handling of various types of problems. Management may make a special effort to see that promising young executives are given an opportunity to learn how others handle such situations, and they may also participate in the discussion of cases drawn from business experience. The study of cases is most effective if classes are conducted at a university, a hotel, or a club which is removed from the day-to-day pressures of the work situation.

The most effective method of executive development may consist of active participation in decision making. A person may develop as a result of his being permitted to work out the details of a proposition. To assist in the development of subordinates, assignment of tasks may be made in general terms rather than in detailed instructions. In making an assignment, the executive should be sure that the subordinate understands what is wanted and how much authority he has in the matter. As illustrations of precisely what is meant by the assignment of a problem by an executive, the following are typical: plans for the sale of stock of the corporation to employees, development of a new type of advertising appeal, the inauguration of a plant periodical, a change in the safety program, or a system of merit rating for employees.

Organization of a Development Program. A formal program of executive development would begin with an inventory of the needs of the company at various levels and at new locations with particular reference to key positions. The requirements of such positions would be determined, and estimates would be made of the approximate dates when personnel will be needed. Persons within the organization who show promise of development would be rated, and their development needs would be appraised. Each person should be given such opportunities for development as he requires, but general programs given for large numbers of persons on the theory that some of the people need such development are wasteful of time and money and are also destructive of morale.

In an expanding organization, some persons will be brought into the company with the idea that they may be developed into executives as a part of a long-range program. Such persons would be selected on the basis of a review of their experience, education, and personal qualifications as determined by references, tests, and personal interviews. The personal qualifications are particularly important because the work of the executive requires certain personal traits. The company may plan a varied program according to the requirements of the positions and the qualifications of the persons being developed. The program might include position rotation, conferences, planned readings, lectures, and discussion meetings. The progress of each person would be watched. He would be rated by his immediate supervisor and other executives who may have occasion to work with him. Such a program may be continued indefinitely to provide a high level of proficiency among the executive group.

Requirements for Success. For an executive development program to be successful, the continous support of top executives is essential. A staff department, such as the personnel department, may suggest the program and take an active part in promoting it, but the line executives must also be convinced that the program is needed and they must assist in carrying it out. Opportunities for development and growth should be found largely in connection with the duties of a position. Emphasis should be placed upon experience and the bases for business decisions rather than upon lectures or reading assignments. Opportunities for development should be given to people within the organization as well as people who are hired for the express purpose of participating in an executive development program. Any idea that an executive is assisting in the development of a person to replace himself, except in case of his own promotion, should be dispelled. Continuous reporting on the operation of the program and control by top executives is also necessary. The program should not be forgotten after it is started. It requires continuous review from the top.

QUESTIONS

1. To what extent can it be said that the work of the executive consists of talking with people?

2. Why does the executive need an opportunity for growth and development as he advances within the organization?

3. In the rating of executives, should a distinction be made between performance in the present position and qualification for advancement?

4. Why may the executive fail to understand the attitude of the worker toward the company? Why may the worker fail to understand the attitude of the executive?

5. Why do some persons find it difficult to delegate authority?

6. Explain and illustrate different types of standards that an executive may use.

7. Distinguish between training and development. How does this distinction affect the program for the preparation for executive work?

8. How can a company know that a program for executive development is successful?

9. Do human relations problems exist at the top levels in an organization, or are they confined to the worker and foreman levels?

10. How may the development of electronic data processing machines be expected to change the work of executives?

11. The word *decision* formerly meant a cutting off or a separation. Does this meaning have any relation to the work of the executive?

12. What thought processes are required in the making of a decision?

CASES

7. PROBLEMS OF THE EXECUTIVE

The president of the United Chemical Corporation, Mr. J. C. Marsh, is disturbed about the downward trend in profits of the company during the last few years, and he has concluded that the cause is an excessive amount of overhead expense as a percentage of direct labor. However, he is unable to determine the items that are excessive or the causes, and he has decided to call in a consultant to study the problem. He was impressed by a talk on expense control that was given at a recent meeting of the trade association of the chemical industry, and he decided to engage the speaker to make a study of the company's problems. Before engaging the consultant, Mr. Reeves, he talked with the managements of some of the companies in which Mr. Reeves had worked, and he had reason to believe that Mr. Reeves was competent.

Mr. Reeves made a study of the company by studying its organization chart and by talking with people at all levels of management as well as with several employees. The company had no organizational manual, position descriptions, or policy statements. Mr. Reeves learned much about such matters from company correspondence, conferences with people, and general observations. In his conferences, he interviewed only one person at a time, and he gave assurances that no one would be quoted directly and that no names would be mentioned in any oral or written reports. He found several things that disturbed him.

The stock of the company is listed on the local stock exchange. The number of stockholders is 20,450; employees number 18,560. Except for the chairman of the board, all directors are executives of the company. Board membership is nine, and the term is three years. Three directors are elected each year. No fee is paid for attendance at meetings of the board. Meetings are always held during working hours, and all members are paid an annual salary. The salary of the chairman of the board is $50,000 per year. The company owns and operates three manufacturing plants, all of them in West Virginia. One plant produces commercial fertilizers, another dyestuffs, and another a miscellaneous line of products.

Mr. Marsh was promoted to the presidency after working his way up in the sales division. He is very good at establishing and maintaining outside contacts. He has been very successful in obtaining some very lucrative sales during recent months. However, his action has caused the director of sales and some of the salesmen to feel that the president is obtaining the large easy-to-get contracts and leaving the more difficult sales promotion work to them.

Reporting directly to the president are the directors of the following major divisions of the company; finance, controllership, domestic sales, foreign sales, purchasing, production of fertilizers, production of dyestuffs, production of miscellaneous chemical products, research, office management, engineering, public relations, industrial relations, and secretarial work of the corporation. Advertising in the domestic market is considered a part of the work of domestic sales, and advertising abroad is considered a part of the work of foreign sales. The chairman of the board, who was formerly director of domestic sales, is much interested in the advertising program. At his invitation, the advertising manager of the domestic sales division attended a recent meeting of the board for the purpose of supporting an increase in the advertising appropriation in which both persons were interested. Mr. Marsh did not object to this procedure, though he thought that the invitation should have been extended by himself or the director of domestic sales.

Negotiations with the union are conducted by Mr. Marsh himself, because he believes that the union contract is vital to the success of the company. In the conduct of the negotiations, he relies heavily upon the advice of an attorney who has specialized in labor law. The legal terms that are introduced into the contract through the influence of the lawyer protect the company from inaccuracies, although the precise meaning of many words and phrases is not always clear to the industrial relations director and the line personnel of the plant.

Mr. Marsh is proud of the close personal relationships between himself and the workers. He maintains the "open door" policy and encourages people to come into his office. However, they are expected to come at convenient times and to make appointments with his secretary. Mr. Marsh also has monthly meetings with the foremen of each plant. All foremen are invited to dinner, and after dinner Mr. Marsh opens the discussion by stating that all of the discussion is "off the record" in the sense that nothing said there will be held against any person. Middle management, including division chiefs and the plant superintendent, are not invited to these meetings. Mr. Marsh is of the opinion that the discussion is free and open and that he learns of the intimate details of plant operation and plant problems.

The president is very solicitous of the welfare of the workers in the plants. Recently, he announced in the local press a retirement plan for all employees. Negotiations for a new contract were under way at the time of the announcement, and the union charged that Mr. Marsh was attempting to undermine the position of the union by granting voluntarily more than the union was asking for. Plant executives were somewhat embarrassed by inquiries as to the details of the plan, but Mr. Marsh was satisfied that he had shown interest in the welfare of the men.

In an effort to reduce expenses, the president recently employed an expense manager to work in the office of the controller. His function is to approve all requests for money, including salary increases and purchases of materials and equipment. He has been instructed to veto any requests that he thinks are not for the best interests of the company.

The president has also instituted an accident prevention program as a part of the industrial relations activity. He employed a safety engineer and instructed him to work with the industrial relations manager. When the new accident prevention manager reported for duty, Mr. Marsh told him that his work would consist of studying accident records within the company, devising improved work methods to prevent accidents, and making such changes in the plant layout or machine design as seemed necessary in the interests of safety. Such changes as he had made were introduced over the objections of plant executives, but Mr. Marsh is convinced that the accident record has been much improved.

Mr. Marsh complains that he has more work than he can accomplish within

the hours of the workday. He has been considering the possibility of reorganiz-
ing at the top. His plan would be to make the presidency a dual arrangement,
with himself managing the divisions performing the line functions and another
executive managing the divisions performing the staff functions. The two top
executives would work from the same office with adjoining desks. He feels sure
that he can promote an executive to the other top position who would co-operate
with him. In any case of disagreement, the opinion of Mr. Marsh would prevail.

Another question raised by Mr. Marsh concerned the program of executive
development. For some years the company has been employing college graduates
in chemistry as research people and also as prospective executives. As a result of
the promotion of such people, the top positions have been filled with the college
graduates and few opportunities have been available to people without such
training who seek their way up through usual channels. Some dissatisfaction with
this situation was reported by junior executives. Some of the top executives who
were graduate chemists thought that the junior executives rendered no more than
half-hearted co-operation in carrying out the company programs of production
and sales.

Required:

Criticize favorably or unfavorably the organization and management of the
company.

8. AN EXECUTIVE DEVELOPMENT PROGRAM

The president of the Thermond Company, Mr. Carl Hunter, was greatly
concerned when the treasurer of the company developed a nervous disorder and
retired because of ill health. Mr. Hunter did not believe that any other person
in the company could adequately meet the requirements of the position. He
offered the position to a management consultant who had completed several
engagements with the Thermond Company to the satisfaction of Mr. Hunter.
The consultant accepted the offer. Although he was competent in finance, he
had difficulty in getting the co-operation of his immediate subordinates and his
associates who resented the fact that an outsider had been given the important
position of treasurer. Mr. Hunter then dictated a memorandum to all major
executives which stated that each should develop a capable replacement for himself during the next six months. The memorandum also stated that the personnel
director would consult with any executive who wished assistance with the program.

When the newly appointed treasurer received the memorandum, he decided
that the new requirement did not apply to him because he himself was still
attempting to learn about his division and his duties. However, he had observed
that Mr. Coxe, the office manager, seemed not to be fully co-operative. To give
outward compliance he talked with Coxe about the possibility of his attending the
management development program of a well-known university. He then wrote a
memorandum to the president suggesting that arrangements be made for Mr.
Coxe to attend the school for six months.

The personnel director was in charge of a department of eight persons. In
view of the small number of persons, he saw no reason to be unduly concerned

about developing a replacement for himself. However, he had a talk with the chief of the interviewing section to suggest that he keep himself informed of new developments as reported in current literature and that he seek to take a more active part in the meetings of local management societies.

Mr. E. G. Alford, the plant manager, was 58 years of age, and he enjoyed good health. He saw in the memorandum a threat to his own position because he knew that he would probably not be promoted to a higher position, even if one should be available. He had had no special coaching or development program prior to his promotion to the position of plant manager, and he believed that any replacement could learn in the way he had done. Mr. Alford also observed that Mr. Hunter frequently became excited about an idea which he later forgot. He filed the memorandum with the intention of giving it further consideration when the pressure of current problems lessened.

Mr. Adams, the director of sales, had attended a management meeting at which methods of rating people had been discussed. He decided to institute a rating program which would provide for the periodical rating of all his subordinates and the review of each person's rating with that individual. Mr. Adams knew very little about methods of executive development, and his assistance was limited to the interview following the rating. This interview was discontinued after the second rating, and no further ratings were made.

Mr. Hunter sent a memorandum to each executive after six months requesting a report on the program for developing a replacement. The replies were received by Mr. Hunter's secretary and duly filed in her office. No further inquiries or reports were made.

Questions:

1. Do you see anything wrong with this program?
2. What should Mr. Hunter have done to make the program successful?

6 Problems at the Foreman Level

THE position of the foreman depends in part upon the type of organization adopted by the company. In many small businesses which provide few staff services by specialized departments, the company may be organized on the principle of the line. In such a company the foreman holds a position similar to that of the foreman in the Midvale Steel Company when Taylor began his studies about the year 1880. In the line and staff organization, the foreman retains the sole responsibility for the activities of his department but has the assistance and co-operation of departments performing staff functions. Staff services are commonly provided in the organization of large companies, and most of the discussion in this chapter relates to the position of the foreman in the line and staff organization.

The work of the foreman may be roughly classified under two principal headings: technical and human relations. His work in human relations pertains to relations with subordinates and with persons in the management. The management people with whom he works include his own supervisor and persons performing staff functions. The various aspects of the work of the foreman are closely related, and they are classified in this manner merely for convenience in discussion.

TECHNICAL RESPONSIBILITIES OF THE FOREMAN

The foreman deals directly with the work at the machine, and he must see that the work is efficiently done, that quality is maintained, and that schedules are met. He is concerned with machines, materials, work in process at the machines, and work conditions.

Responsibility for Directing the Work. The foreman usually must assign men to their tasks; for although the planning department is responsible for over-all scheduling, the foreman may schedule work in the department. If production is centrally controlled by a planning department, the foreman should see that production schedules are followed. He should see that machines and tools are properly used and that safety regulations are observed. He may be required to requisition the purchase of materials. He sees that tools are returned to the toolroom when they are no longer needed and that completed work is moved to the next workplace. He arranges for the disposition of defective or spoiled materials. In case of emergency, he takes the necessary action to protect workers and the interests of the company. In short, he is responsible for the orderly conduct of his department and for keeping down the costs of materials, labor, and expense. Because of the importance of the foreman in directing the work, he has been called "the key man in production."

Responsibility for Working Conditions. The foreman should keep informed concerning developments relating to the workplace and the conditions of work. He should make suggestions for the improvement of the layout of the workplace and the flow of work in the department. He should study the requirements of the various jobs from the point of view of lighting, heat, and other conditions. He should co-operate with the personnel department in the evaluation of jobs for purposes of wage determination, employee rating, selection and placement of workers, and other programs.

The foreman should be familiar with the qualifications of workers, and he should see that they are qualified for the work they are doing. He may determine the adjustment of the worker to the job by observing his output and his conduct from day to day.

Maintaining Quality. The foreman has a responsibility for maintaining the quality of the product because quality results from a control over manufacturing processes. A quality product is made from material of the right grade on machines properly fitted with the proper machine tools and kept in good operating condition, through maintenance. Quality also requires that employees be properly trained and willing to co-operate in turning out good work. Inspection does not necessarily mean quality control. Its value is limited to seeing that standards have been maintained.

In the work of maintaining quality, the foreman is assisted by various other persons in the management, such as the purchasing agent, the maintenance foreman, the toolroom manager, the engineer in charge of product design, the personnel manager, and the chief inspector. However, the foreman is principally responsible because he has direct supervision of the work. He is required to see that machines are kept operating and that work is kept moving according to plan.

Controlling Costs.   Responsibility for costs in the department rests with the foreman even though many elements of costs are beyond his direct control. He is subject to a budget which he is expected to meet. Unit costs of the product in the department are composed of materials, labor, and manufacturing expense. Materials cost is affected by waste and scrap which the foreman is expected to keep at a minimum through effective supervision. Labor cost is affected by the efficiency of the workers, their willingness to co-operate, absenteeism, and accidents. Manufacturing expense per unit is affected by the number of units produced, the downtime of machines, and numerous other factors. The responsibility of the foreman in the area of costs extends to a wide variety of activities.

RELATIONS WITH WORKERS

The foreman necessarily plays an important part in maintaining good relations with employees. He represents the management in his contacts with workers, and his relationships are close and continuous. He understands the attitudes and the problems of workers much better than others in the management. Effective worker co-operation cannot be achieved without his support.

Nature of Employee Relationships.   The foreman requisitions help when it is needed. Although he is no longer required to interview and select workers, the worker must meet with his approval. When a worker is sent to his department for work, the foreman sees that he is instructed as to the requirements and conditions of the job and that he is otherwise inducted. He maintains discipline during work hours. He sees that workers fill out their time tickets, and he approves payment for work done by signing the payroll sheets. He makes sure that specifications are followed and informs workers of changes in specifications. As a leader, the foreman aids in the training and development of workers.

The foreman can meet his responsibility for handling employee problems only if he has the support of persons higher up the line. He should have authority commensurate with his responsibility, and he should know just what his authority is in various situations. In certain cases, he might have authority to issue a warning or to give a reprimand. In handling minor problems, he might be given authority to act without making any report to his superior; and in other cases, he might be authorized to act but required to make a report of the circumstances. In serious cases, he might have no authority to act but would be expected to refer the matter to his superior for instructions or recommendations.

As manufacturing processes have become more mechanized, the number of operators supervised by each foreman has decreased while the value of machinery and equipment in a department has increased. If machines are fully automatic and the materials are moved from one workplace to another by materials-handling equipment, production-line workers may be entirely eliminated. In such cases, the foreman becomes a supervisor of technical operations. His human relations would remain important because of his contacts with maintenance men, engineers, and other persons in the management.

Communication with Workers. The foreman is an important link in the channel of communication to and from employees. Most of the communications between foremen and workers are oral, and the writing of numerous memorandums indicates a lack of personal contacts and of personal understanding. For a new employee, communication from the foreman begins with an explanation of departmental regulations, introduction to fellow employees, assignment to a job, and explanation of what is expected. Later communications concern assignments to new work and the discussion of specific problems or developments, such as needed changes in working conditions, investigation of accidents, and assignment to new work. The worker is expected to communicate to the foreman a report of any difficulty he may have in maintaining quality standards, meeting production schedules, or understanding instructions of work to be done. He also reports to the foreman concerning any absences. The foreman keeps his own superior informed of developments within the department.

If the foreman is properly to perform his function in communication, he must receive adequate communications from his own superior at the next level in the chain of command. Information transmitted to him might include a foreman's manual on company policies, copies of the union contract, copies of the minutes of grievance committee meetings and decisions rendered, and executive orders. Information on current developments and proposed changes may be transmitted through daily contacts, interviews, and discussion meetings. Communications may consist of information, advice, or specific instructions.

Handling Worker Complaints. A complaint is defined as a spoken or written dissatisfaction brought to the attention of a management or union representative. A grievance is a complaint which has not been properly handled by the management or possibly by the union officials. It may have been ignored or dismissed without due consideration. Complaints and grievances may concern wages, supervision, seniority rights, promotions, and general working conditions.

The foreman should investigate the facts concerning all complaints which come to him. If he finds that the complaint is justified, he may be able to correct the difficulty. He may find it necessary to inquire what the policy of the company is concerning the question at issue. If he is not informed as to company policy, he may communicate with the general foreman, who may consult the division chief; or he may have to ask for a ruling in case no policy has been established.

In some cases the employee may make the complaint to the union steward. The steward is an employee of the company who has a regular job but represents the union in dealing with the foreman. Cases referred to the steward are usually settled by a conference between the foreman and the steward. If an agreement cannot be reached, the foreman may refer the question to the general foreman. The case may be carried to the division chief and the works manager. The shop steward will also refer the question to his superior officer in the union organization, who may be the business agent or the chief steward. Above the chief steward are the executive committee and the president of the union.

The handling of worker complaints may create a situation that calls for much tact because the steward is also a worker. As a worker, he is a subordinate of the foreman in the ordinary man-boss relationship, and as a steward he is the equal of the foreman because he represents the union. The steward may have received training from the union in the handling of complaints and grievances, and he may be more familiar with some aspects of labor regulations and procedures than the foreman. In any event, the foreman is required to change his method of dealing with a subordinate when that person changes his role and becomes a spokesman for the union.

If a grievance is to be carried to the higher levels in the organization, the foreman should ask that the worker prepare and sign a written statement. This plan has several advantages. If a worker must sign a written statement, he is likely to tone down the charges and to state the facts correctly. In many cases the result is that the employee looks at the matter in a somewhat different light, and he may decide to withdraw the complaint. A second advantage is that both the foreman and his boss can see precisely the question at issue. The difference between the foreman and the worker can then be reduced to a question of fact or of principle. A third advantage is that the keeping of records by the foreman is facilitated. The next time the same issue is raised, he will know the policy of the company relating to the question. The decision may also be communicated to other foremen.

If possible, the foreman should not permit a complaint to become a grievance. The fact that a worker thinks he has a grievance is in itself undesirable. A grievance may indicate a lack of attention to the difficulties of the worker, or it may indicate an inability of the foreman to show the worker wherein his attitude is wrong. Because of his close contact with employees, the foreman has been called "the front-line personnel man."

RELATIONS WITH OTHER MANAGEMENT PERSONNEL

As a member of management, the foreman has numerous contacts with other people in the organization. His contacts extend to his immediate supervisor, and indirectly to others in the scalar chain. He also has frequent contacts with other foremen and with persons in departments performing staff functions.

Transmitting Information. Executives at the higher levels of management may keep informed of the problems and attitudes of workers through oral and written communications from the foremen and the supervisors in middle management. Reports of this kind are very important for the executives who do not have direct contact with workers and conditions on the production line. In some cases, the inadequacy of upward communication concerning workers' problems has given rise to the development of personnel departments and has encouraged the growth of unions, which provide additional channels of communication.

Communication up the line is important to both the foreman and middle management. Reports to higher levels are used to judge the efficiency of the foreman and his success in keeping the work moving on schedule. Middle management also needs to be informed in order that activities of different departments may be properly co-ordinated and that corrective action may be taken when necessary. However, the foreman wishes to control upward communications from his department in order that his record may be reported in the best light and that he may not be unfairly criticized by his supervisor.

Each foreman also communicates with foremen in other departments and with representatives of departments which perform staff functions. The staff personnel may create problems for the foreman because the staff has its own channels of communication. When a representative of a staff department comes into a line department he may send information up the line which the foreman would prefer not to have reported. For this reason, the foreman may prefer to handle his own problems without calling upon the staff. This attitude defeats the purpose of management in providing for departments to assist the foreman with certain types of problems.

In making his reports, the foreman usually would prefer not to inform his supervisors of difficulties which are due to his own mistakes. If he is having difficulty in meeting a schedule, he may not report the situation unless he thinks his superiors may learn of it from some other source. He is anxious to submit favorable reports of quantity production and unit costs. However, if the reports this month are very good, an equally good report may be expected next month. Consequently, the foreman may be as interested as the worker in seeing that current performance sets a standard that can be comfortably met in the future. A standard that is too tight will not allow for delays or mistakes.

Co-operation is made easier for the foreman if he is made to feel that he is really a part of management.[1] He should be notified in advance of changes affecting his department. He should receive proper credit for good performance in such matters as production, safety, and personnel relations. He should know company rules and regulations in order that he may know what position to take concerning problems which arise. All orders affecting his department should be transmitted through his office.

In order that foremen may be properly informed, some companies hold weekly or monthly meetings of all members of management. At such meetings, current developments relating to the company are considered, such as changes in production plans, scheduling of work, maintenance, and expansion. The production records of various departments are graphically displayed on blackboards or bulletin boards, and the reasons for failure to meet schedules are considered. Mere mention of the cause may be sufficient to correct it. Members of management, from general manager to foreman, may be permitted to present a problem in which others may be interested. Meetings of this kind serve not only to

---

[1] For an excellent discussion of the relationships of the foreman, see Burleigh B. Gardner and David G. Moore, *Human Relations in Industry* (3d ed.; Homewood, Ill.: Richard D. Irwin, Inc., 1955), chap. iv.

keep all members of management informed but also to build up the self-respect and morale of the foremen.

Relations with Staff. The staff departments with which the foreman establishes regular contacts include maintenance, standards and methods, engineering, safety, employment, inspection, planning, cost accounting, and stores. He may request the services of the maintenance department when he believes a machine needs repairs or adjustment. The standards and methods department sets the standards of performance for each task. The foreman may call its representative to re-examine any standard which he believes to be too tight or too loose. If a worker has difficulty in meeting the quotas set, or if he can meet the quota too easily, the foreman may ask that another study of the task be made. However, the foreman may not report that a standard is loose; because of his nearness to the worker, he may prefer that all standards be such that they are easily met. If the workers meet the standards, they will not complain. If they cannot meet them, they may cause trouble by making a complaint. Moreover, if the standards are loose, production may be maintained on days when things do not go just right. Loose standards may provide the slack to compensate for delays in production without the necessity for detailed reports of difficulties.

The engineering department investigates the possibilities of improvements in layout and rearrangement of equipment or in the design of the product. If a worker has difficulty in turning out a part according to specifications, or if he finds that a part does not function properly when the product is assembled, he notifies his foreman, who in turn may notify the engineering department. However, the calling of the engineering department may be interpreted as a confession of incompetency on the part of the foreman who would ordinarily be expected to instruct and assist workers in meeting specifications. Usually, the engineering department must find out for itself the weak spots in the layout, the arrangement of machines, and the design of the product. An objective of top management in its contacts with foremen is to make them more cognizant of the services rendered by staff departments and more willing to make use of them.

Although the foreman is expected to co-operate with various line and staff people in carrying out company plans and programs, he may not actively participate in the formulation of the plans and the development of programs. The reason for this neglect of the foreman usually is that he has too many other duties and that his point of view may be limited.

Furthermore, the company organization may include many foremen, and the authority for company policies and programs is necessarily centralized at the higher levels. This situation complicates the problems of the foreman and explains the name of "marginal man" which is sometimes given to him.

COMPENSATION OF FOREMEN

Foremen are usually paid a weekly or monthly salary. This method of payment has a basic appeal provided the salary is sufficiently high to provide a satisfactory differential above the pay of the people whom he supervises. A difficulty may arise if workers put in sufficient overtime to enable them to earn as much as the foreman's salary, or more. A pay raise for workers frequently requires an increase in foremen's salaries to provide a satisfactory margin of difference.

Some companies provide for incentive pay for supervisors in addition to the basic salary. Some such plans base the extra compensation upon the performance of workers in the department. The bonus may depend upon the number of workers who meet production standards or some other measure of their efficiency, attendance, labor turnover, or safety record. According to another plan, the foreman's bonus depends upon his ability to keep down controllable costs, which are those elements of expenses or cost that he authorizes or controls. Before such a plan can be effective, the authority of the foreman should be carefully defined, and the basic salary paid to him should be fair. The amount of the bonus should be large enough to build up his interest, and the details of the plan should not be too complicated.

TRAINING OF FOREMEN

In time of business expansion when new plants are being put into operation or new shifts are being added, special attention should be given to the problems of the training of supervisors. At other times, the normal rate of turnover may require special training programs for the purpose of maintaining loyalty and enthusiasm and of keeping foremen abreast of developments in company programs, technology, and other problems.

Selection for Training. Training for the position of foreman is given either at the time of promotion or at a later time when improvement in some area seems to be needed. Promotion to this position should be based upon an analysis of the duties of the position, the traits required for successful performance and the rating of possible candidates for the position. A person is not necessarily qualified for promotion merely because he is a skilled craftsman, has had long experience with the company, or has completed a course of formal education. A training program will not enable a person who lacks the essential personal traits to become a good foreman. The selection of foremen is usually made on the basis of an evaluation of employees by supervisors at different levels in the management.

Training in Management. A person has a difficult adjustment to make when he ceases to be a worker and becomes a part of management. He may be afraid of making mistakes and therefore may be hesitant to take action; or in his anxiety to prove himself worthy of his new position, he may act hastily. If he asks for assistance, he may be accused of incompetence. If he does not ask for assistance, he may be accused of overconfidence. The problems of the foreman are further increased by federal regulation of labor relations which makes the employer liable for such acts as enforcement of arbitrary rules, discrimination, or firing workers without cause.

Some training courses are designed to facilitate the entry of foremen into the ranks of management. The course for new foremen is given after promotion rather than before. If the program were given before promotion, the man would have to return to his job to wait for an opening. In the meantime, he would be subject to the jealousy and suspicion of the other workers. The man would also lack motivation because he might never be made a foreman.

Training in Company Organization. One type of training program for foremen is intended to give them an understanding of the organization of the company. It may begin with a series of meetings, lectures, and conferences with top management. Each of the executives may discuss his work in relation to the work of the foremen. The foremen may be conducted through the various offices. In conferences with the president, the sales manager, the controller, and other officers and also with the heads of such departments as employment, engineering, purchases, stores, and maintenance, the foremen are made to see that the company is an assemblage not only of machines but also of persons. The relation of the foremen to each of the various executives of the company is indicated. The purpose is to show that top management and the staff departments perform necessary services.

Because the foreman comes into close contact with the workers and may influence their attitudes and thinking concerning company activities and policies, he may require training to develop proper attitudes of his own. The training program may therefore attempt to give him a better understanding of the system of private enterprise and the place which the company seeks to occupy in the system. It would show the necessity for a profit in order that the company may expand, raise capital for new machines and equipment, assure security of salaries and wages, and provide for more jobs. The course might also show the relation of increased efficiency to wage rates and regularized employment. If the foremen and workers do not have confidence in the fairness and sincerity of the management, such a training program may easily be dismissed as propaganda.

Technical Training. In many industries, the work of foremen has become increasingly difficult because of mechanization and the application of science to the processes of production. A training program may attempt to acquaint foremen with new methods of production, new machines, control mechanisms, problems of maintenance and repair, the design of a new product, and the reading or interpretation of diagrams or drawings. Other topics that might be considered are work simplification or motion study, planning to make the most effective use of time, accident prevention, and the development of new programs to reduce scrap, improve the flow of work, or otherwise increase efficiency. The nature of the training would depend upon the needs of the persons enrolled. If the foremen are not convinced of the need for a program, they will not benefit greatly from their participation in it.

Training in Human Relations. The need for training in human relations has been increased by such developments as the growing strength of unions, the complexities of state and federal labor legislation, the higher level of education of workers generally, decreased immigration, the higher percentage of American-born workers, shifting age groups within the population, and the increased employment of women. The objectives and the content of the program in human relations would change from time to time. Topics treated might include labor laws pertaining to the problems with which the foremen must deal, methods of dealing with unions, handling worker complaints and grievances, wages and financial incentives, social security and retirement plans, disciplinary measures, and the supervision of women.

A program of leadership for foremen may be designed to develop a better understanding of worker motivation. It might be concerned with the basic desires of people, such as the desire to become a part of the enterprise, to gain the respect of one's associates, to receive fair treatment, to feel secure financially, and to be protected from bodily injury. A program of training of this kind would also show the foremen what happens if the basic needs are not met. It would include a discussion of proper use of rewards and penalties. It is intended to inform foremen as to the proper methods of supervision and to induce them to want to gain worker loyalty and co-operation.

The methods of training vary somewhat with the purposes. The program may include conferences and discussions with top management, conferences among the foremen for the discussion of their problems, and classes with a fixed program of study. A continuous program may consist of meetings for the presentation of news bulletins, policy announcements, and achievements or problems of various departments. Visual aids, such as charts, drawings, diagrams, and motion pictures or slides, have been found to be helpful. Demonstrations, such as new work methods or safety devices, are also effective.

FOREMEN'S UNIONS AND CLUBS

During World War II the unionization of foremen became a pressing problem. Top management feels that a foremen's union is inconsistent with principles of the organization and management of private enterprise. A union of foremen means that management is unionized because the foremen are a part of management.

While practice varies between industries and unions, the general rule in the mass-production industries has been that foremen and supervisors have not been permitted to become members of labor unions. In a few industries, unions have permitted foremen to become members. Such an arrangement exists in the building trades, parts of the metal trades, and the teamsters' union. A few long-established unions confine their membership to foremen. Some of the foremen's unions are affiliated with the AFL-CIO, and some are independent.

Reasons for Foremen's Unions. When foremen organize or join a union, the usual reason is that they feel that they must protect their interests against mismanagement at the top levels. In some companies, the foremen have not had sufficient contact with top management through discussion meetings and in other ways. Their authority has frequently been usurped by their own superiors, and management has permitted them to be bypassed at times by workers, union stewards, and representatives of departments performing staff functions. Such persons may communicate directly with top management and thereby cause the foreman to lose control of the channels of communication as they pertain to his department.

Another reason for foremen's dissatisfaction is the failure of some managements to provide for their needs in the way that the company provides for worker needs. Security in the foreman's position is not always provided to the extent that the union demands job security for the worker. If a foreman is returned to worker status because of a reduction in output or for any other reason, he may lose the seniority which he had prior to his elevation to the position of foreman. In many companies, no procedure has been established for the handling of the complaints of foremen. All the machinery has been directed to the settlement of worker complaints.

Legality of Unions.   In December, 1945, the National Labor Relations Board recognized a union of foremen in the automobile industry as a legal organization for bargaining purposes and directed the Packard Motor Company to bargain with the union as the exclusive representative of the foremen. The significance of this decision was not that the foremen were given the legal right to form a union, for they already had that right. The significance was that that union and its members had the rights guaranteed by the National Labor Relations Act. The effect of the decision was to prevent any interference by the management in the affairs of the foremen's union and any discrimination against the members because of their membership. The company was also compelled by law to bargain with the foremen's union, whether it wished to do so or not.

The Labor Management Relations Act of 1947 withdrew the protection of foremen's unions which had been extended to them by the decision of the National Labor Relations Board, although it did not prohibit foremen's unions. The act merely excluded supervisors from the definition of an employee. This provision conforms with the view that the foreman is a part of management and is responsible for much more than the execution of orders received from higher levels in the organization. Management believes that its effectiveness would be greatly decreased if the horizontal line separating management and men should be drawn above the foremen.

Foremen's Clubs.   After the federal legislation had clarified the legal status of foremen's unions, many companies that had bargained with such unions notified them that such negotiations would be discontinued. The reason usually given was that the company had considered the union as an experiment and that the arrangement had failed to better relations. To replace the unions, many managements have encouraged foremen to organize clubs for purposes of mutual improvement and for social activities. The clubs provide a forum for the discussion of foremen's problems. Membership is sometimes limited to the foremen of one company, and it sometimes includes foremen from various companies in the area. The clubs are federated into a national organization which assists in the development of a local program and in the forming of additional locals. These clubs have rendered a valuable service, and they have raised the prestige and the quality of work done by foremen.

JUDGING THE WORK OF FOREMEN

The management should develop some plan for judging the work of foremen and of informing them of the respects in which they succeed or fail to meet the standards of the company. Usually this information is communicated to foremen in their daily contacts with other people in the management. However, some plan of reviewing the work of foremen at predetermined intervals may also be desirable. Such a plan would require, first, that some standard of accomplishment be established, and, second, that each foreman be compared with the standard.

Desirable Qualities of a Foreman.   The qualities that the person holding the position of foreman should possess are many even though he now has the assistance of various facilitating departments. He necessarily knows a great deal about the technical aspects of the work, such as operation of machines and equipment used, the kinds of materials, the operations performed in processing the materials, and the problems of care and maintenance of machines. He should know how to gain the co-operation of workers and how to deal with them in making job assignments, in giving commendations and other rewards for good work, in administering disciplinary measures, and in handling other personnel problems. He should be able to co-operate with his superior, with his associates in the staff departments, and with other foremen. He should be able to deal tactfully and effectively with union officers. He need not have the qualities that would be expected of a plant superintendent, as Taylor said of the foreman in a pure line organization, but he should be a person of many talents.

Rating of Foremen.   In order that his superiors and also the foreman himself may know how he is measuring up to his responsibilities, some companies make a personal evaluation or rating of each foreman every six months or every year. The foreman may be assigned points on each quality that is rated on the basis of ten points for each quality. If the rating sheet makes provision for ten traits, the total possible points might be 100, and the foreman might receive a total score as a percentage of that figure.

Although the traits used in a rating sheet may be designated by a name such as loyalty, dependability, soundness of judgment, or ability to handle people, a rating sheet of this kind may be misleading to the management because the meanings of the traits are subject to various interpretations. The rating sheet may be more meaningful if a sentence is used to describe the trait. For example, a trait might be described in this way: "Consider his success in going ahead with work assigned and his ability to make methods improvements." The ratings of the trait should also be described by phrases rather than a single word. The highest rating of the trait to which reference has been made might be stated as follows: "Very resourceful; has initiative and ability; improves arrangement of materials and methods of work." A low rating might be described as "needs urging" or "seldom shows initiative." The rating sheet can be further improved if the rater is asked to cite instances to illustrate good or poor performance.

Reviewing Ratings with Foremen. The rating of a foreman is usually reviewed with him, although this procedure may not be followed. Difficulties arise when a person is not doing well and seems unable to improve. In other cases, a foreman may be satisfactory in his present work but unable to qualify for a higher position. Sometimes a foreman may feel that a rating is unfair. In still other cases, the rater may have reviewed the traits with a foreman at an earlier time and he may have no new suggestions or comments to make. Situations of this kind require understanding, sympathy, and tact on the part of the rater who discusses the ratings with the foremen. If the ratings are fairly made and the results are properly used, they should improve the morale of foremen and increase their efficiency.

QUESTIONS

1. The director of manufacturing of a large clothing company says that every person in the management in his division is interested in quantity, quality, costs, and human relations. In what respects is the foreman interested in these problems? In what respects is his authority limited with respect to each problem?

2. Distinguish between the responsibility of the foreman and that of the personnel director with regard to human relations.

3. When does a worker complaint become a grievance? How can the foreman prevent the complaint from becoming a grievance?

4. Why has the foreman sometimes regarded himself as the forgotten man of industry?

5. How has the function of the foreman as the source of information for

middle management been affected by the growth of unions? How has it been affected by the development of departments performing staff functions?

6. Why might the foreman hesitate to call upon the personnel director in handling a disciplinary problem? If he thought that a time-study standard was loose, why might he hesitate to call in the time-study man?

7. Is the method by which foremen are paid important to the management? Why?

8. What is the need of the foreman for training when he is promoted to the supervisory position?

9. Should training be given before the person is promoted to the position of foreman or after he has been promoted?

10. Should foremen be permitted by the management to form unions? Why?

11. Why might foremen desire to form a union?

12. Should a person be advanced to the position of foreman because he is the fastest worker, the most loyal to the management, or the best educated? What other traits might be important?

CASES

9. RELATION OF FOREMAN TO WORKER

When Howard Leeper was employed by the Northern Machine Works, he was assigned the task of operating a semiautomatic machine for the cutting of gears. The work consisted of fastening two blanks on a shaft, placing the shaft in position in the machine, and starting the machine. A rotating steel tap would then move into contact with the blanks and cut them in such manner as to make the blanks into gears of prescribed dimensions. When the machine finished the cut, it would stop automatically. Howard was expected to remove the shaft and the gears, insert another set of blanks, and again start the machine. He had plenty of time to prepare the next set of blanks while the machine was making the cut.

When Howard was inducted into his job, he was told by the foreman that he was expected to prepare the next set of blanks while the machine was operating. He followed his instructions the first day, but he ran out of work in the middle of the afternoon. He was told to assist another worker in moving materials for the remainder of the day.

When Howard reported for work the following day, he found at his work station about the same number of blanks as he had completed the day before. He decided to watch the processing of the blanks until the machine had completed the cut, then to remove the parts, and keep the machine stopped until he had prepared the next blanks for processing. In this way, he kept busy at the machine all day and was not required to do any other work.

After one week, the foreman observed that Howard was watching the machine in operation while he was supposed to be preparing the next set of blanks. He reminded Howard of the proper manner of doing the work, but he appeared not to be much concerned because Howard would finish the required number of gears by the end of the day. On three other occasions, he mentioned to Howard that he was expected to prepare the blanks while the machine was running, but Howard continued to do the work in his accustomed manner. The foreman did not press the matter because the work of processing the gears was kept on schedule and the work in other departments was not delayed.

After Howard had been on the job about six months, the company received several large orders for machines that would require a 25 per cent increase in the number of gears per day. The hobbing machine had the capacity to produce the gears if it was operated as the company expected it to be operated. The foreman was instructed to increase production to fill the new orders. He told Howard he was expected to increase production by keeping the hobbing machine in continuous operation. Howard stated that he needed to watch the machine to see that it was operating properly. After a heated exchange of words, the foreman told Howard to go home and see if he could return the next day with a more co-operative attitude.

The next morning Howard reported for work in company with the business agent of the union. They asked to see the personnel manager who immediately went into conference with them. They told him that the foreman had been "hounding" Howard and that the criticism resulted from a personal dislike. The business agent said that if the foreman did not cease the unfair criticism, a work stoppage would be called. After further conferences between the personnel manager and other executives, Howard was told that he would be reinstated in his job and paid for the lost time.

Question:

What mistakes were made in this case?

10. THE WORK OF FOREMEN

The plant superintendent of the Special Products Company regularly conducted conferences on plant management at which foremen were asked to discuss their problems. At these meetings, he frequently heard the complaint that the foremen did not have sufficient time for personal consultations with workers or with members of staff departments. At lunch one day, he mentioned this complaint in talking with the vice-president for production, who asked how the foremen spent their time. He replied that he had no definite information on the subject, and the foremen seemed to be rather vague in talking about what they did. The vice-president, in a personal conference with the president, mentioned the problem. After some discussion, the president authorized the vice-president to engage a consultant to study the demands upon the time of the foremen.

When the consultant arrived at the plant, he first talked with the vice-president and then with the plant superintendent. The superintendent introduced him to the foremen at a special meeting called for the purpose, and he urged them to give their co-operation. The consultant decided that the best method of studying the problem would consist of an observation throughout one day to see how one foreman actually spent his time. He selected a foreman who had frequently complained about the demands upon his time. The consultant recorded each action of the foreman on a memorandum slip of paper, and he later transcribed the information on each slip to a tabulating card. He then ran the cards through a sorting and tabulating machine to determine the total time spent at each kind of work.

The tabulating cards for the 480 minutes of a working day totalled 620. Thus, the record showed that the foreman performed 77 different tasks each hour. Most of the work done was found to pertain to clerical or routine tasks. For example, the foreman spent 48 minutes checking on the progress of work being done in the department, finding out when the work would be completed, and planning the further flow of work in the department. He spent 45 minutes getting information for time tickets for work to be done, filling out the tickets, and distributing them to the work stations. He spent 22 minutes moving the materials to the next work station or arranging to have them moved. He spent 65 minutes arranging for the proper machine tools and patterns, checking the tools and patterns, and instructing workers on machine set-up and operation. He spent 8 minutes instructing workers in the use of gages for inspecting parts and in checking the quality of the product. He spent 15 minutes finding a replacement for a worker who failed to report for work because of illness. Other duties included: investigation of injury to a worker because of a fall, 16 minutes; talking to the safety director, 8 minutes; interviewing an applicant referred by the employment manager, 10 minutes; hearing the complaint of a worker concerning his last wage payment, 8 minutes; and reporting materials spoiled and the need for a reorder, 7 minutes. He spent the rest of the time walking through the department to see how things were going, talking with the general foreman and other persons in the management, and filling out reports.

The consultant thought that the time spent on tracing the progress of the work and in making assignments for new work was least productive. He recommended that a production planner be assigned to each general foreman and that he free all the foremen from the necessity of following the progress of the work, filling out time tickets, and assigning new work to machines and workers. The production planner would also be assisted by a tool specialist and set-up man who would see that each machine was equipped with the right tools and was properly set up for each new operation before the work was started.

The consultant found that foremen were not giving sufficient time to quality control and that the number of rejects was high. He recommended that an assistant foreman be added to the staff of the general foreman. The quality control assistant would be expected to improve quality and reduce the number of rejects in any way that he could. He would instruct new employees, check the quality of materials and parts being used, see that machines were properly operated, and see that inspection was sufficiently close but not too close. These recommendations were received by the management for further study.

Question:

What should management do about the recommendations of the consultant?

11. PREPARING A MANUAL FOR FOREMEN

The plant superintendent at the Reynolds Company found that foremen frequently failed to co-operate with other foremen and with representatives of departments performing staff functions such as maintenance and production planning. For example, a foreman might ask a mechanic in his department to make minor repairs to a machine when the repairs should have been made by a maintenance worker. In other cases, one foreman might call for a maintenance man to use an oil can to apply a few drops of oil when another foreman would require each worker who operated a machine to oil it. Such differences in practices were confusing, and they frequently resulted in controversies with the union, which claimed that certain workers were denied an opportunity to perform work.

As for production planning, foremen sometimes failed to follow the schedules prepared by the production control clerk. If they had two or three work orders, they would select the order that could be completed in least time because they could make a good showing of total production for the week. However, this procedure sometimes disrupted schedules in the department where the work was next processed and also delayed deliveries to customers. Foremen who were questioned concerning failure to follow the schedules asserted that the schedule clerk was not their boss and that they were responsible only to their immediate supervisor who was the general foreman. Similar difficulties arose in the relationship of foremen to other departments performing staff functions.

Difficulties also arose concerning company policies which all foremen were expected to follow. These policies had never been written out in any one place but were embodied in executive memoranda or had been orally stated in meetings of foremen and their supervisors. Difficulties sometimes arose because supervisors regarded the policies as unrealistic. For example, a worker requested an advance of pay for the next month because of the illness of his wife, and the foreman forwarded the request to the pay office with his approval. The request was rejected because it was contrary to company policy, and the worker quit to look for a job elsewhere. The foreman knew that the worker needed money, and he did not like to lose a dependable worker in the department. Other misunderstandings had arisen because of policies concerning transfers, promotions, disciplinary measures, and other problems.

The plant superintendent discussed the problems of staff relationships and company policies with foremen and also with staff executives. It was agreed that the company should prepare a manual for foremen which would attempt to answer all of their questions. It was pointed out that the manual would be valuable as a reference book for foremen with records of service and that it would be particularly helpful to any person who might be promoted to the position of foreman.

Before work was started on a manual, the plant superintendent discussed the plan with the vice-president for production. Although the vice-president approved the idea, he saw some danger in putting company policies in writing because under changed conditions the management might not want to be held to a fixed course of action. Moreover, the organizational relationships might require revision under some unforeseen circumstances. However, he agreed to mention the matter to the president. After some discussion, the president said he thought the idea was good provided proper control was maintained over the contents of the manual and provision was made for revision.

The plant superintendent gave the personnel director the duty of preparing the manual. The personnel director decided to write the entire manual himself rather than to have each staff department write the section pertaining to its relations with the foremen. He thought that some department heads might use the manual as a medium for enhancing the prestige of their departments. Moreover, the style of writing would vary with the individual. He decided to confer at length with a representative of each department to determine the co-operation that was expected and to discuss the work of each department with the foremen to ascertain their points of view. If differences could not be reconciled, the problems were referred to the plant superintendent for his decision. The personnel director wrote the description of his department and its policies, being careful not to elaborate or to devote an undue amount of space to its work. This description was written after consultation with the plant superintendent.

Company policies were compiled from company orders, executive memoranda, reports by foremen and others, and discussion with various executives. Where policies seemed vague, the personnel director asked for an opinion from the plant superintendent. The personnel director was told by some staff executives that no policies could be stated at present because methods would soon be changed. In such cases, the personnel director wrote the parts of the manual for which data were available, and he then pressed the executives for a statement of the present relationships and methods. This procedure eventually proved successful.

After the material was in final form, it was submitted to the plant superintendent for his review and approval. Several statements of policy were referred to the vice-president and the president for clarification or elaboration. After final approval, the manual was printed in such form that it could be inserted in a loose-leaf binder. It was again discussed with foremen who were asked to study the entire manual of 175 pages. At subsequent meetings foremen were given the opportunity of asking questions on any parts that they did not understand.

Questions:

1. Was a manual desirable?
2. Was it prepared in the best way?

7 Problems at the Worker Level

THE PROBLEMS of developing teamwork within an enterprise increase in difficulty at the lower levels of the organization. The success of the company requires a proper control over the costs of material, labor, and expenses. Excessive costs may arise at the machine where the work is done. Worker co-operation is essential to the maintenance of the quality of the product and the meeting of production schedules. To gain his co-operation, management must employ good methods of communication in order that the worker may understand what is wanted and required. Management must also provide effective motivation, channels for the handling of worker complaints and grievances, and satisfactory relationships with labor unions. The solutions of these problems depend upon an understanding of the attitudes and needs of people.

The attitudes of workers are affected by all of the conditions under which they live and work. If their attitudes are favorable, they will be willing to co-operate in the accomplishment of group objectives. If morale is low and people throughout the organization do no more than is necessary to keep out of trouble, the results will be reflected in the costs, the quality, and the volume of production. A low state of morale would also be reflected in complaints, tardiness, absenteeism, lack of interest, an early wash-up, horseplay, and other such conduct. Dissatisfaction might also manifest itself in more serious actions, such as insubordination, violation of company rules, destruction or theft of company property, and quitting the job.

WHAT THE WORKER EXPECTS FROM HIS WORK

A person is well adjusted if the satisfactions which he receives from his work are at least equal to what he expects. The development of a work force in which most people are fairly well adjusted may be difficult or impossible of accomplishment because the objective of a plant or factory is production and not the accomplishment of personal satisfactions. However, something may be accomplished in this direction if attention is given to the basic wants of people at work. These basic desires are usually considered to be: (1) satisfactory compensation for work, (2) security of person and income, (3) a feeling of belonging, (4) social and organizational status, and (5) treatment as an individual. No effort is made to list these desires in the order of their importance because all of them are important. The needs of the individual are discussed in the present chapter from the point of view of the worker, although they influence the attitudes of supervisors and executives as well. The emphasis changes when people are promoted, but human nature remains essentially the same.

Satisfactory Compensation for Work. Payment for work done assumes major importance in the thinking of every person, although undue emphasis may be placed upon the wage rate. Many lists of the desires of workers have been compiled; in most such lists, pay ranks one fourth or more of the way from the top. The ranking of the desires of workers is difficult, however, particularly if based on the statements of persons questioned. If the pay is satisfactory, a person will be inclined to name other things first because they are uppermost in his mind at the time. Moreover, people are often irrational in their statements as to the reasons for their actions.

If the rate of pay is considered inadequate, the reason may be that some jobs are thought to be paid more than others in relation to the skill, experience, physical effort, working conditions, or other factors. Differentials in pay for similar kinds of work are likely to cause dissatisfaction, and it will usually be assumed that the higher rate is the proper one. The level of pay is usually less disturbing than discrimination.[1]

The payment of salaries which are considered excessive has an effect upon morale similar to the effect of wage differentials. The pay of executives may be thought to be out of proportion to the pay of employees, even after allowance has been made for differences in require-

[1] For a similar statement, see Robert Saltonstall, "What Employees Want from Their Work," *Harvard Business Review*, Vol. XXXI, No. 6 (1953), pp. 72–78.

ments of the work. The pay of various persons in the organization cannot be determined by any measure of the worth of the services rendered. The differentials result from numerous factors, including bargaining power and influence with persons higher up in the organization. The demand of labor unions that they be permitted to "look at the books" arises in part from the effort to convince workers that management has been concealing something from them.

While the management cannot expect to remove all of the dissatisfaction over rates of pay, it can do much to correct inequities and injustice by paying rates that are fair in comparison with wages paid by other companies in the area and by adjusting rates to the requirements of each job. It may also be able to provide steady work and income by reducing fluctuations in employment. Worker morale may also be improved by planning the flow of work to eliminate delays and to permit workers to earn bonuses. Annual reports, together with explanations of the items appearing on financial statements, may help to improve morale if workers can be convinced that payments to executives and stockholders are not excessive.

Security. Much dissatisfaction is due to a feeling of insecurity. The majority of executives as well as workers live in urban or suburban areas where their living expenses cannot easily be reduced during periods of unemployment. Their outlays for food, medical expenses, and rent cannot be cut sharply without undue hardship; and most persons outside the higher income groups do not have substantial reserves of cash or other savings. Provision for unemployment benefits under the Social Security Act and for severance pay by the employer has lessened but not eliminated the feeling of insecurity.

A question which has long been uppermost in the minds of workers is how long the work will last. The older person wants protection against the younger ones, and he finds a plausible reason in the argument that his experience makes him more valuable to the employer. A desire for security of employment and of wage rates is one reason for opposition to the employment of Negroes, women, and other groups. Many workers believe in a limited membership in their trades. The usual reason is that, if the trade becomes "crowded," there will not be enough work for all. The desire for security is a reason for restrictions on admission to unions and for high admission fees. Security is also a reason for placing restrictions on the kinds of work a member of the union may do.

The dropping of workers in slack times in reverse order of seniority, that is, dropping first the workers with shortest periods of service, gives the older workers some assurance of steady employment. A measure of security for other workers may be achieved by spreading the work among all employees regardless of the length of service or giving preference to persons with dependents. Frequently, the employer would prefer to base layoffs on merit in order that he might keep the most efficient workers or those who show promise of developing into executives. The union contract usually makes provision for layoffs and also for rehiring when more workers are needed. It may permit the employer to make exceptions to the usual seniority rules in the case of persons who are in the executive development program or who are considered by management to be potential executives.

Management can relieve the fears for security by informing workers of proposed changes. Uncertainty is created by rumors of changes in the design of the product, the layout of the workplace, or methods of setting standards. Such changes are often less serious than they are reported to be. A proposed change in the assembly line, for example, may create no real threat to security. A design of the new system together with an explanation posted on the bulletin board or published in the plant magazine may assure workers that their jobs are secure and perhaps that their work will be made more pleasant.

Management has many reasons for its accident prevention programs, and an important reason is their effect upon worker morale. If a person has a safe place to work, he is a better worker because he is relieved of one cause for worry. The same is true of measures that are designed to provide proper work conditions, such as the elimination of dust and dirt in the air, excessive heat, excessive humidity, and contamination by fumes. Medical and dental care and the reduction of fatigue by the installation of machines to do heavy lifting have a similar effect upon morale. Such programs are important for their effect upon both the mental attitude and the physical comfort of the worker.

In addition to the possibilities of unemployment, accident, and illness, the worker may face the prospect of old age without adequate financial support. Old-age benefits under the Social Security Act are now compulsory, with contributions by both the employer and the employee. However, the benefits are not large, and the employee faces the risk that the purchasing power of money may decline to such an extent that he cannot maintain himself on the payments. To be sure, large numbers of persons now employed will not live to advanced age and will therefore not be confronted with the situation which they may fear. The effect upon morale arises from the uncertainty. Managements have provided many plans to increase security. Financial plans include provision for employees to purchase stock in the company, the organization of credit unions, group insurance for death benefits, and group hospitalization and health plans.

A Feeling of Belonging.   Usually, the person who is employed by an enterprise would like to feel that he is recognized as a member. He would like to believe that he has a voice in decisions which affect him. Failure of management to allow worker participation in decisions on matters clearly affecting them is one reason for unionization. Union members can participate in union meetings and elections; and, indirectly through the union, they can participate in the formulation of company plans at the lower levels. Worker participation in decisions is not easy, and it can never be continuous.

The willingness of management to inform workers in advance of proposed changes gives employees a feeling that they are a part of the company. The types of information given will naturally vary with the requirements of the particular situation. Announcements may pertain to changes in policies and practices as to working conditions, hours of work, new employee services, and the activities of persons in the management as individuals. Much information cannot be publicized because it would be made available to competitors and others outside the company.

As a part of the plan of keeping workers informed, some companies make annual reports to employees. The typical report summarizes the financial results for the year in an informal and conversational manner. It tells something about the stockholders, how many there are, how many shares each owns on the average, where the stockholders live, and how much was paid to them in dividends. In a similar vein, it tells of the directors, officers, distributors of the product, and consumers. The purpose is to show the employee that he is one of a group and that all persons in the organization make certain contributions. It is intended to convey to the employee the idea that he is participating in an important project.

The proper timing of communications may greatly increase their effectiveness. A report may be made prematurely, or its release may be too long delayed. When announcements of contemplated changes are delayed, rumors may be circulated and the facts may be distorted. Erroneous impressions are not entirely corrected when the facts are later made known.

Organizational and Social Status.   Status is the position which a person holds in the formal and informal relationships of any group. It is the respect and the authority given to him. Status determines the privileges, rights, duties, and obligations of a person in relation to others in the group. Status may also place restrictions or prohibitions upon the actions of a person. For example, a supervisor would be permitted certain privileges and he would be required to perform certain duties because of his position, but he would also be expected to refrain from doing certain things that would be permissible to his subordinates. Likewise, a member of the executive group would have certain rights and privileges, and his conduct would differ in certain other respects.

Organizational status exists by reason of the position which a person holds within the company and the title that may pertain to the position. Social status is the position which the person has in his informal relationships with other people. It may be enhanced by organizational status, but a person is not required to have a high position in the company to command the respect of his associates and to be able to influence them. Some people do not aspire to gain a higher organizational status because of the increased duties and greater responsibility that would be attached to a higher position, but most people enjoy having the respect and good will of their associates.

The social groups within any plant bear many resemblances to social groupings in any other society. The most marked distinction is between the workers in the shop and those in the office.[2] Workers in the office often have a feeling that their social status is superior to that of workers in the shop. This feeling is sensed by shopworkers, who may argue against it but nevertheless recognize it. Because such a difference exists, shopworkers would usually consider a transfer to the general offices to be a promotion.

A desire for group approval may assist or defeat the purposes of management. Frederick W. Taylor found when he became foreman at the Midvale Steel Company that the informal organization of the workers was opposed to any increase in output. Since each person desired group approval, Taylor had great difficulty in securing the co-operation of the men and in getting them to accept his idea of what constituted a fair day's work. In the studies at the Hawthorne plant of the Western Electric Company, it was found that the workers had developed standards of conduct which each person was required to observe if he was to be

---

[2] For discussions of social groups within the factory, see F. J. Roethlisberger, *Management and Morale* (Cambridge, Mass.: Harvard University Press, 1941); F. J. Roethlisberger and W. J. Dickson, *Management and the Worker* (Cambridge, Mass.: Harvard University Press, 1939); Burleigh B. Gardner and David G. Moore, *Human Relations in Industry* (3d ed.; Homewood, Ill.: Richard D. Irwin, Inc., 1955); Wilbert E. Moore, *Industrial Relations and the Social Order* (New York: Macmillan Co., 1946); Robert Dubin, *Human Relations in Administration* (New York: Prentice-Hall, Inc., 1951).

accepted. According to the code a worker should not do too much work, or he would be regarded as a "rate buster." If he did too little work, he was a "chiseler." If he said anything to a superior which might get one of his associates into trouble, he was an "informer." Straw bosses who acted officiously also lost favor with the group.

The fact that most workers desire the esteem of their fellow workers can be used to strengthen the spirit of the organization. Many symbols are generally interpreted as an indication of success. Some symbols are regarded as indications of a higher level of social status and others indicate higher rank in the organization. Such symbols include exemption from the requirement of punching the time clock, payment by the week rather than by the hour, receiving pay by special messenger instead of having to stand in line, possession of a special type of pass or identification, the use of a certain washroom, the inclusion of one's name in the house telephone book, the size of the desk, possession of a name plate for display on the desk, and perhaps the location of the desk or the workplace in a favored position in relation to the door or windows. The employee may also consider as significant the manner in which he is greeted by the foreman, failure of the foreman to call him by name, a request by the foreman to assist in making a new employee acquainted in the shop, or an assignment to a job requiring special skill. Some companies have found that loyalty may be fostered by the use of badges, buttons, pennants, and other such symbols. Shields for display in the department may be awarded for good housekeeping, the best safety record, or other accomplishment. Recognition of this kind is probably significant to the worker, provided it is not relied upon as the only incentive.

Treatment as an Individual. The worker has a right to expect treatment as a human being. This statement implies not only that certain things be done but also that they be done in a way that indicates recognition of the dignity and worth of the individual. This attitude is reflected in almost everything that people in the management do in dealing with workers. It first appears when the applicant is interviewed for his prospective job. The interviewer may consider the applicant as a person who has the problem of finding work to support himself and his family, or he may treat him as a possible factor in production. When the applicant has been accepted and is to be inducted into his job, the foreman may seek to allay his doubts, quiet his fears, and make him feel at home with his fellows, or he may limit his induction procedure to a sketchy statement of what the job requires. After induction, treatment as an individual would mean that an effort is made to correct employee grievances, that a person who is having difficulties would be shown how to improve, and that he is credited with satisfactory work. When a person leaves the company, he should be treated as courteously as he was treated in his employment interview.

Individual Attitudes and Social Relationships. Some of the factors in employee attitudes seem to be individual and others appear to result from group relationships. However, none of the factors can be separated from the relation of each person to his fellow workers. Compensation for work, for example, is a relative matter, and pay is considered as fair or unfair only by comparison with the pay of other workers. Furthermore, the worker gains both self-respect and increased respect from his associates if his pay is higher than the wages of other workers. Similar considerations apply to increased security. In handling any worker problem, management deals with a member of a group rather than an isolated individual.

Differences between Workers. While all workers are motivated by the same basic desires, they differ in the emphasis they place upon them. Their attitudes are affected by a great many personal differences. For example, young men may consider the opportunity for advancement to be most important, while older men might place greater emphasis upon security. Young women may regard their employment in industry as temporary and they may therefore be most interested in working conditions and rates of pay. Later, they may become interested in the opportunity for advancement and in security, provided they have not married in the meantime. The attitude of single men will differ from that of married men. Employee attitudes are also affected by such factors as health, the number of dependents, political affiliations, religious beliefs, union membership, previous experiences with the company and with other employees, and the psychological make-up of the individual.

Handling Morale Problems. Although the factors in employee morale as discussed in the present chapter may be assumed to be important in every situation, some factors may be considered by employees to be more important than others. The first step in the development of better human relations, therefore, consists of an analysis of the existing situation from the point of view of both the individual and the group to determine the favorable and the unfavorable factors. Second, management should consider the possible corrective measures and motivating practices that may be used. The most appropriate measures would then be decided upon and put into practice. Finally, the results would be reviewed from time to time to determine the corrective measures that might be taken.

Human Aspects versus Work Aspects. The question that demands an answer from the management concerns the extent to which policies should be determined by personal relationships. The question might well be asked, "Can management be too human?" If policies are designed primarily to improve morale, the objective of production of goods and services for sale at a profit could be neglected. For example, production schedules and cost considerations might suggest that tasks be further simplified in order that each person may perform a smaller and smaller part of the total work of production. The desire of the worker for status and a sense of belonging might suggest that the tasks assigned to any one worker be enlarged. To cite another instance, the effort of management to provide workers with financial security might result in the provision of services that would ultimately make them dependent upon others for things they should provide for themselves. Management must find a middle ground that builds up morale without sacrificing the objectives of production and profit. High morale does not necessarily mean a high rate of production at low cost.

MEASURING WORKER ATTITUDES

Worker attitudes and opinions may be determined in many ways. Foremen usually know how workers feel about their jobs and about the company because they are close to the work situation. They can transmit much information up the line provided they are given the opportunity to do so. However, top management cannot be sure that the information is complete or that it correctly portrays worker opinion.

The personnel department can appraise worker attitudes in several ways. Employee attitudes affect the reputation of the company throughout the community, and this reputation can be partially evaluated through interviews with applicants for jobs. Exit or separation interviews may provide additional information, although opinions expressed by either applicants or persons leaving the employment of the company may mislead the management. Statistical data for the evaluation of worker opinion include resignations, transfers, complaints and grievances, absences, tardiness, discharges, suggestions submitted, and waste or scrap. Such data are most helpful if they are compiled by departments, jobs, age, sex, full-time or part-time workers, or other such basis.

Opinion Surveys. A questionnaire is sometimes used to obtain expressions of opinion from all employees. A survey of employee opinion by questionnaire may accomplish a great deal if it is properly conducted and the results are correctly interpreted. The greatest difficulty probably lies in the question of how to get employees to say what they think and how to obtain a fair sample of employee opinion. A requirement for success is that personnel relations should be generally satisfactory at the time of the survey. Before the questionnaire is prepared, all reasonable causes for dissatisfaction should be corrected. Otherwise, management will be swamped with criticisms when the results are tabulated.

The questions asked in making the survey usually are concerned with those things which are closest to the worker. They have to do with supervision, the attitude of the foreman, the induction and training program, the policy of promotions, service in the plant cafeteria, recreation and sanitary facilities, hours of work, time studies and standards, safety, and other conditions of work. An attempt should be made in formulating the questions to find out what the worker really thinks about the company.

The questions may be prepared by a committee which includes the foreman and one or more representatives of the personnel division. The questions should be short and easily understood. Each question should deal with only one subject. The number of questions should be large enough to cover a wide variety of problems. Space should be provided after each question to permit comments, discussion, or suggestions in addition to an answer of "yes" or "no." The questions are changed each time a questionnaire is prepared.

The employees should be prepared for the survey by a preliminary discussion of the plan at a general meeting or in some other manner. The form may be accompanied by a letter stating the purpose of the survey and giving instructions as to the method of completing and returning the form. No signatures are required, and all answers are confidential except for summaries. Guarantees should be given that no employee will find his position jeopardized by his answer.

The best method of distributing the questionnaire seems to be to send it to the home, with the request that the form be filled out and returned by a certain date. Mailing to the home probably results in more complete and more worthwhile answers than the plan of having it filled out at the plant on company time. Returns may be mailed in by the employee or dropped in a box at the entrance to the plant.

Using the Information. What is done with the return is just as important as the preliminary work of preparation and distribution. If many workers sign the returns, the results may be tabulated to show the attitude of men and women, young workers and old workers, workers in various departments, or other groupings. If the attitude of a group can be established concerning any one problem, such as the piece-rate or the bonus plan, standards set by time study, or safety conditions, the management may determine that certain conditions should be corrected. If the workers do not sign the returns but indicate their departments, such classification as is possible should be made. The results of each survey should be compared with the results of earlier surveys on comparable questions. The report of each questionnaire may be summarized and made available to workers as well as to members of the management.

Value of the Survey. The principal advantage of the employee questionnaire is that it reaches all workers and gives each one an opportunity to express an opinion. It may serve to indicate whether complaints are coming from a minority or whether workers as a whole object to certain conditions. It provides an additional channel for the communication of information to the management. Its value depends upon the manner in which the form is prepared and distributed, the sincerity of employees in responding to the request for information, and the way the results are summarized and interpreted by the management. The most that can be claimed for the questionnaire is that it provides some basic clues and primary data from which may be constructed a pattern of employee attitudes and feelings.

QUESTIONS

1. Is pay for work important to the worker merely because it provides the necessities of life? Explain.

2. Under what circumstances is compensation inadequate?

3. How can the union determine from "a look at the books" whether the workers should have a wage increase?

4. What does a worker mean when he says that the craft or trade is becoming crowded?

5. How can a worker feel a "sense of belonging" when he knows that he is not a part of management?

6. Why might a worker be skeptical of management if he is told that he should be satisfied with his wages because he is better off than a worker in China or Russia? Should management publish such information to the workers?

7. Distinguish between organizational status and social status. How can management assist workers in acquiring social status?

8. How does the attitude of a younger person differ from that of an older person? Which would place the greater emphasis upon current earnings, security in the job, and opportunity for advancement?

9. Describe the method of conducting an employee opinion survey.

10. Of what value is an employee opinion survey? What are its limitations?

11. The union sometimes claims to be the only organization that is interested in the employee as a human being and that the employer is interested in him as a source of profit. Is this a fair statement?

12. Distinguish between employee morale and *esprit de corps*. How are the two concepts related?

CASES

12. EMPLOYEE SERVICES AND MORALE

In 1925 James C. Lucy established a small canning factory to purchase spinach, beans, and other vegetables and to can the vegetables for sale to grocery stores in the territory adjacent to the plant. Later, in off seasons, Mr. Lucy used the facilities to can dried black-eye peas, red kidney beans, and similar products. The business prospered and eventually was placed on a sound financial footing.

Mr. Lucy instituted many of the employee services that were common practice during the decade of the 1920's. Once a year he gave a picnic for the employees and their families. A caterer from a nearby city provided food for all of the people. Mr. Lucy always addressed the group and explained his interest in their welfare. He gave each employee a term life insurance policy of $500 after one year of service with the company. The amount was increased $100 with each year of service until the total amounted to $1,000. Each employee was allowed a paid vacation after one year of service. Employee clubs were organized for dominoes, checkers, bingo, and bridge. A room at the plant was set aside for meetings of the clubs. Once a year one of the clubs provided an evening of entertainment for all employees and their families. Other employee services included a credit union, a plant periodical, and a plant cafeteria.

Before Mr. Lucy died in 1947, he turned the management over to his two sons, George and Raymond. George became the president and Raymond the production manager. George was a college graduate in history and Raymond had majored in mathematics. Both had worked for several years at various jobs in different departments of the company.

When the change in management was made, George announced that the policies that had successfully guided the company for so many years would be continued without change. However, he replaced the sales manager with a former classmate who had made a good record with an advertising agency. Later he dismissed the treasurer in order that he might appoint another classmate who had made a good record with an investment banking firm. Similar changes were eventually made in three other top positions.

The employees services were gradually extended to include group hospitalization, surgical benefits, coffee breaks in mid-morning and mid-afternoon, free parking facilities, the purchase of company products in case lots at a low price, and first-aid facilities. Mr. George Lucy was confident that the employees were pleased with these arrangements.

When union organizers were reported to be in the vicinity, Mr. Lucy was not disturbed. When a vote was taken by the employees on the question of unionization, however, 73 per cent of the plant employees voted for the establishment of a union as their agent for collective bargaining. At the first meeting between

Mr. Lucy and the union representatives, the union requested the reinstatement of an employee who had been discharged by a foreman after a heated argument. Mr. Lucy first learned of the discharge at this meeting. After he had heard the foreman give his reasons for the discharge, he agreed to the reinstatement. Mr. Lucy then asked the personnel manager for an explanation of the failure of the employee service activities and for the lack of control over the improper discharges of workers. He also asked for recommendations for correcting any improper company practices.

Question:

What possible explanations and recommendations might be given?

13. WORK ON A PRODUCTION LINE

At the packing plant of the Virginia Fruit Company, apples are cleaned, sorted, graded, and packed for shipment. The apples are put into wooden boxes as they are picked from the trees, and the boxes are shipped by truck to the plant. At the head of the production line, the apples are poured from the boxes onto a conveyor belt which moves them from one work station to another.

The first step in the preparation of the apples for the market consists of brushing and cleaning. The apples are moved against a row of circular brushes which rotate continuously to clean and polish the fruit. At the same time, the smallest apples drop down between the brushes and the end of the conveyor. These apples are moved by another conveyor belt to a packing station where they are dropped into boxes for movement to the cooking room where apple jelly is made.

As the larger apples are jostled by the rotating brushes, the pressure of other apples behind them causes them to pass over the brushes onto another conveyor belt which moves them to the sorting station. This conveyor belt is 24 inches wide, and above it is another belt which moves in the same direction. At the sorting station, three girls stand on each side of the belt. The girls watch the apples as they are moved along on the conveyor. The vibration and the foreward movement of the conveyor belt cause the apples to roll continuously, and girls can easily observe the entire surface of each apple by the time it has passed the last girl. The sorters pick up the apples that have blemishes, broken skins, or other defects and place them on the upper conveyor belt which transports them to another packing station for shipment to the cider mill. Each sorter is expected to use both hands in picking up apples. She looks constantly at the lower conveyor belt and places the apples on the upper conveyor without looking up.

After the apples pass the sorters, they move to another automatic grader which permits the smaller ones to drop through, and then to another which permits the next larger size to slip through to another belt. The three sizes are moved to three different packing stations where they are packed for shipment. The packers give the apples another inspection for blemishes or other defects as they place them in boxes, but most of the apples reaching the packers are of good quality.

The plant manager has found that personnel problems are most likely to arise at the sorting station where the girls remove the low quality fruit. For example, the girl at the head of the line on one side of the conveyor is Mary Brice. Mary is 23 years old. She lives at home with her parents. Her muscular co-ordination is below average, and she seems not to like to work with both hands at the same time. The other girls accuse her of being lazy and not doing her share of the work. Mary has told the supervisor that she removes as many defective apples from the belt as any other girl and that the others have a personal dislike for her.

Questions:

1. What personal traits should be used as a basis for selecting workers at the sorter station?

2. How should the problem of Mary Brice be handled?

PART III

EQUIPMENT
AND
WORKING
CONDITIONS

8 Choosing

a

Location

MANAGEMENT is required to give attention to problems of physical equipment as well as to people and their organizational relationships. Physical facilities include the building, machinery and equipment, and working conditions such as light, color, noise, and air conditioning. The building requires attention to two major problems: its location and suitability for production. Machinery and equipment raise three general problems: selection, layout or arrangement within the plant, and maintenance and repair.

PLANNING FOR PHYSICAL EQUIPMENT

The work of planning for production facilities and of keeping machinery and equipment in proper operating condition is largely the responsibility of the engineering division. The chief engineer may be a major executive reporting directly to the chief executive. If the company owns or operates several plants, the engineer would be represented at each plant by an engineer who would be the head of an engineering department under the plant superintendent. The chief engineer would advise with other executives of top management concerning the location of new plants, the purchase and installation of equipment, revisions of plant layout which might be necessitated by changes in the product line or the development of new products, and the replacement of equipment due to depreciation, obsolescence, or inadequacy. He would also advise concerning problems that arise in case a plant is closed or moved to a new location.

The engineer at each plant would be under the line control of the local plant superintendent, but he would have a functional relationship with the chief engineer at the main office. He would be responsible for seeing that physical equipment operates efficiently, is maintained in good working condition, and is overhauled or repaired when necessary. In meeting his responsibilities, he would work with operating executives including the plant superintendent and the foremen, the accident prevention manager, the personnel manager, and other persons who perform staff functions.

The Problem of Location.   If a new enterprise is being launched, the decision to organize the company may follow the development of a new idea for a product or a service to consumers. The inventor designs the product and estimates the volume he can make and sell at a profit. He selects equipment necessary for its production and plans the layout for a plant. In the execution of the plans, the finding of a suitable location is one of the first things to be done. Formerly, the plant was located in the area in which the inventor or promoter lived. This fact may indicate that the promoter found it convenient to locate near his own home. It might also indicate that he did not thoroughly survey the possibilities elsewhere. In many cases, the enterprise was originally thought of as serving a local rather than a regional or national market.

The problem of plant location is very different for a going business that already operates one or more plants. The choice of a location in such a company would depend in part upon the nature of the product to be made in the new plant in relation to products made in existing plants. For example, if the plants will all make the same kinds of products, such as glass jars and bottles or metal containers, the best location might be a place near markets not now being adequately served. If the new plant is to make parts for shipment to existing plants for assembly, other considerations would be more important.

FACTORS INFLUENCING LOCATION

The decision to establish a plant in any area is affected by a great many considerations, which vary in their importance with the industry and the individual company. In some industries the plant should be near the source of raw materials, in other industries it should be near the market for the product, and in other industries it should be located with particular reference to transportation facilities.

Nearness to Market.   Markets may be nation-wide or local. If markets are nation-wide, production may be centralized in one or several plants; or production may be decentralized in many plants near the consumers. Industries in which production may be centralized, even though distribution is national, are watches, clocks, jewelry, fountain pens, books, magazines, and radios. In these industries the product is relatively light in weight, and labor is an important percentage of the cost. Goods produced locally include cement, brick, cheap furniture, bakery products, and some metal products.

Some processing plants increase the bulk of products or make a fragile or perishable product. Such industries profit by being near the consumer. Examples are cheap furniture, bakery products, barrels, tin cans, coffins and caskets, stoves and ranges, and cheap pottery. Industries in which the fashion element is important locate near the centers where fashions originate, even though the product is sold nationally. An example is the clothing industry, which is centered around New York City. Hollywood has also become important as both a creator of fashions and a center for the manufacture of women's apparel.

Industries which produce goods in accordance with the specifications of consumers may profit by locating near the market. Examples are custom-made clothing, draperies, and tombstones. However, it may be more profitable to concentrate production in a large, centrally located plant and forward to it the specifications of the customer. This method is followed by some manufacturers of Venetian blinds and men's suits.

Nearness to Raw Materials. Nearness to the place where materials are produced is a controlling factor if the materials are perishable, bulky, or low in value and are changed by the manufacturing process to a less perishable or less bulky product. Examples of industries that make the product less perishable are fish and oyster processing, fish canning, fruit and vegetable canning, and plants for the quick freezing of food. Industries that make the product less bulky are meat packing, lumbering, and ore refining. In these industries, nearness to raw materials is the most important factor. The materials may be carried through the first manufacturing process near the source and transshipped for further processing near the consumer. Lumber and metals are examples.

For some companies, nearness to the source of raw materials means nearness to the fabricating plant which supplies parts. Although the parts may not be perishable and are easily shipped, nearness to the source of supplies reduces the time required in shipping, permits deliveries to be made by truck, and enables the purchaser to confer with the vendor when personal conferences are desirable.

Transportation Facilities and Costs. Transportation in terms of cost and time is very important. This factor is closely related to both nearness to market and nearness to raw materials. One reason for the location of steelworks at Sparrows Point (Baltimore), Gary, and Birmingham is that heavy materials can be delivered to the plant at low cost. Another consideration is that large consuming areas are near the plant. The privilege of milling in transit, extended by the railway companies, has been an important reason for the location of flour mills at Minneapolis and some other cities in the Middle West. Grain is unloaded, milled, and shipped as flour to points farther east. The freight rate charged is the through rate for flour plus a charge for setting off cars loaded with grain and picking up cars loaded with flour. To a limited extent, fabrication in transit is used in the processing of steel and lumber.

The place where material is transferred from one method of transportation to another is frequently a good place for the location of a processing plant. The point where a railroad crosses a river or connects with lake or ocean transportation is frequently a good location. Water and rail transportation offer substantial advantages for moving heavy bulky products. Transportation costs are less important in the location of factories for the manufacture of such commodities as silver, jewelry, clocks, watches, locks, and cutlery because the cost of transporting the material is a small percentage of the total cost. Moreover, freight charges do not increase in proportion to distance shipped. The railroads have built up a complicated freight-rate structure with many broad zones in which rates do not increase.

Highways and truck transportation have lessened the advantages of rail connections, and many plants are being constructed without direct access to rail lines.[1] Some companies sell most of their output to other manufacturers or to consumers within a limited area, and they may ship by means of a fleet of trucks. Their use of rail transportation may be limited to an occasional less-than-carload shipment. Some executives also believe that location on a highway has a substantial advertising value as compared with location on a rail line. Such companies may be content with a location that would permit the construction of a spur line from the railroad if future conditions would require it.

Local transportation facilities are important for securing workers and executives. The value of a suburban or small-town location is increased by the existence of adequate interurban and highway connections with nearby residential areas and with cities that afford shopping, theater, and

---

[1] The importance of transportation facilities is illustrated by the plant of the Chrysler Corporation at Fenton, Missouri, which was built in 1960. To supply the plant, 125 freight carloads and 40 trailer truckloads are required daily. (*Factory Management and Maintenance*, Vol. CXVIII, No. 5 [May 1960], p. 91.)

other attractions. Local transportation conditions, however, may change within a relatively short period of time.

Labor Conditions. The number of workers and the particular crafts or skills needed should be considered in relation to the labor available in an area. Some factories employ young people or unskilled labor, while others use highly skilled or semiskilled workers. A factory which uses low-paid labor should be located near the workers. Highly paid workers, on the other hand, can be induced to travel a greater distance. This factor affects the choice of a city or suburban location.

Labor cost is affected by the efficiency of labor, the number of unemployed workers in an area, the extent of unionization, the level of wages, the cost of living, and the housing conditions. A larger percentage of native-born labor is available in some sections of the country than in others. In some areas, manufacturers have trained a supply of local labor in the skills required in a number of industries, such as metalworking or woodworking. Apparent differences in wage rates may prove to be misleading because of differences in the efficiency of workers in certain crafts. Another significant fact is that differences in wage rates within an area may be just as great as differences between areas. Localities with low wage rates may be found in some areas where wages are thought of as being high.

Whether other industries in an area have seasonal demands for labor which coincide or dovetail with the labor requirements of the projected plant is another important question. Management will have lower labor costs if it can complement other industries in the area rather than compete with them. For example, a shirt manufacturer located three plants in northern Minnesota where the wives and daughters from the families of miners may be employed. Labor supply was an important factor in determining the location, although other factors, such as the availability of buildings for lease, were also considered.

The effect of labor supply upon plant location has been changing because of increasing mechanization and the control of production through electronic devices. As methods of production become more mechanized, less direct labor is required to produce a unit of output and fewer machine operators and assembly-line workers are required. Semiskilled and unskilled workers become less important, while a greater need will be created for highly skilled workers such as tool and die makers, maintenance men, electricians, and patternmakers. Similar developments require that management consider the number of qualified foremen in an area, or the number of persons who can be developed into good supervisors. Future foremen will be required to handle problems arising from the new equipment and new processes, and they will also be expected to comprehend budgets, material control systems, statistical and accounting reports, and other management techniques. Although a nucleus of a force of supervisors can be moved into an area, managerial problems are lessened if local personnel can be employed in whole or in part.

Power and Fuel. Fuel and power are important to factories requiring a great deal of power, but this factor is of decreasing importance. Electrical power costs have been decreasing because of the development of more economical methods of generation and transmission. The development of cheap electric power has been a significant cause of the decentralization of industry throughout the United States instead of the former centralization in relatively limited areas. The dependability of the power supply is exceedingly important for some industries, particularly those which process perishable materials. Such companies find an alternative source of power a decided advantage.

As a fuel, oil has supplanted coal in some cases, and natural gas has also increased in importance. Both oil and gas have advantages in cleanliness and labor cost. If a close control over heat is required, oil and gas have additional advantages. These differences have sometimes caused plants to be located in communities that are served by natural gas in preference to other locations, although the extension of gas transmission lines is causing this factor to decrease in importance. The factor of fuel is subject to further changes because of the mechanization of coal mines. Fuel costs may also be affected by the development of atomic power, although this development is still uncertain.

Vulnerability to Air Attack. Since the beginning of World War II, many companies have located new plants with reference to possible attack by the enemy. In making loans for the financing of new construction, the government has specified that, so far as possible, new plants should be built outside certain congested areas. Another consideration in government requirements has been a desire to avoid overtaxing the transportation facilities in certain areas and to avoid making new demands upon a limited labor supply. The increase in the range of missiles and bombing planes has caused a shift in emphasis toward the dispersal of facilities. The government has tended toward the policy of awarding contracts to companies outside certain congested areas and has at times refused contracts to companies in congested areas if new facilities would be required. The plan of dispersal seeks to reduce the extent of destruction which might result if all of the plants producing certain types of supplies were located within a restricted area. However, dispersal increases some elements of cost and would create a problem of transportation if railroad yards or bridges between the different areas should be destroyed. The only feasible solution to this problem seems to be the working out of plans for international co-operation and the avoidance of war.

Cost of Land. The cost of land is an important factor in choosing between a city location and one in a town or suburb. Suitable land is limited along some water or lake fronts, and a lack of adequate space may force the company to choose a multistory building when other considerations indicate that a single-story building would be more desirable. Many companies require space for parking facilities, adequate light and air, and protection against undesirable neighbors. Space for possible expansion should also be available, although this need is easily overlooked. In many cases, the available land is restricted to small parcels, and zoning regulations may limit plant locations to certain strips or blocks that are too small to provide for all requirements. However, a location should not be chosen merely because land or a building is for sale at what appears to be an attractive price. Location is not easily changed, and a poor location may burden a company permanently with heavy fixed charges.

Water Supply. Many industries generate large amounts of heat and use water for cooling as well as other purposes. Air-conditioning systems use large amounts of water, and a large plant can use up the surplus water supply of a community and cause a deficit. The country has an adequate supply of water, but it is not well distributed, and shortages exist in many areas. The principal reasons for the shortage are failure of local water supply systems to keep pace with the increase in population and the shifting of families from one location to another. Other reasons are the rapid industrial expansion and the vogue for air conditioning.

A related problem is the existence of impurities in the water, although this factor has decreased in importance because of improved methods of softening and purifying water in large quantities. Most states have passed laws to prevent the pollution of their streams; but the possibility of pollution by steel mills, soap factories, and other plants should not be overlooked. Chemical tests of water may not be dependable unless several tests are made at different times, for the composition of water in streams varies with flood or low-water condition and high or low tide. Some companies purify the water when it is removed from a river for use and purify it again before it is emptied back into the river.

Waste Disposal.   Ore-processing plants, steel mills, and chemical plants must dispose of large quantities of waste.   They may be prevented by state law from dumping waste into streams and by local ordinances from piling it on land within the city.   Some cities have provided public facilities for the disposal of certain kinds of waste.

Building Costs.   The costs of building construction do not vary sufficiently from one area to another to require much consideration.   Costs are affected by local building codes regulating the width of streets, the height of buildings, the building line, and various features of construction.   Such regulations are usually advantageous because they reduce the hazard of a conflagration and affect fire insurance rates.   Usually, a company is not fully protected against the losses incident to a fire even though it has adequate property insurance.

Service Industries.   Industries which serve others tend to locate near the plants which they serve.   Some companies purchase gas, repair services, repair parts, legal advice, income and accounting services, engineering services, statistical services, advertising, and management services such as might be rendered by consultants.   A new company usually purchases many services which it provides for itself after it has become established.   A newly organized company could profit by a location which is accessible to service industries.

Taxes.   Tax rates differ from one locality to another, and some states depend more upon certain kinds of taxes than do others.   For example, one state may levy high corporate and personal income taxes, while another may levy heavier property or sales taxes.   However, the heaviest taxes are now the federal income, excise, and social security taxes which must be paid regardless of location.   Moreover, most of the states are seeking new sources of taxes for roads, schools, and other such purposes, and the possibility of permanently reducing taxes through plant location is not promising.   Some tax advantage may be gained by a small-town location as compared with an urban site, but in the choice of a small-town or urban location other factors might be even more important.

Industries Which Use By-products of Others.   Steel companies in Detroit use scrap metal from automobile and other metalworking plants in the area.   Toy manufacturers use scrap metal in the manufacture of toy airplanes and automobiles.   Many articles are made as by-products of meat packing.   Gas is a by-product of coke.   The manufacturer of the main product may himself utilize the scrap in making a by-product, and in that case he must consider the question of the most profitable location of the by-product processing plant. This problem is a special phase of nearness to the source of materials.

Climate. Workers are presumed to do better work in some climates than in others. Extremely cold, hot, rainy, or dry climates are not desirable. The most important question is whether workers, foremen, and executives and their families would object to living in an area. Air conditioning within the plant may make it possible to provide good working conditions even in a location with poor climate, but complete air conditioning is expensive. However, industries which require controlled air conditions for manufacture of the product, such as humidity in textile mills, temperature in candy factories, or dust removal in fine manufacturing, cannot usually rely upon natural air conditions in any area.

Financial Aids. Some cities grant tax exemption for a number of years or donate land in return for an obligation to maintain a minimum labor payroll for a stated number of years, or civic groups may sell stock if a plant is located in the city. A corporation should look at the "gift horse" before accepting it. The aid rendered may be more than offset' by disadvantages in other respects.

Civic Values. Numerous features of community and civic life contribute to the desirability of the city or town as a place for employees to live. If the city provides many services for its residents, the worker and his family may receive benefits which are properly a part of his real wage. The benefits include public health services; public playgrounds; public schools, including night schools for adult education; museums; band concerts; sewage and garbage disposal; hospitals; police and fire protection; and charitable organizations. Facilities for paid amusement, transportation services, shopping centers of various kinds, and the character of residential districts are other community factors. As the populationtion of an area increases, many such services may later be provided by the city, by civic organizations, or by the company itself. In the meantime, difficulty may be expected in maintaining a satisfactory labor force if the services are inadequate.

The company that moves into an area with a new plant should consider not only the facilities available but also the demands that the company and its employees will make upon such community services as schools, libraries, hospitals, housing, parking, traffic control, parks, and other facilities for recreation.[2] The company may be required to assist in the development of such services either because of business necessities or because of a sense of obligation to the community. The mainte-

---

[2] For discussion and illustrations, see Wesley C. Calef and Charles Daoust, *What Will Industry Mean to My Town?* (Washington, D. C.: U.S. Government Printing Office, 1955).

nance of good employee and community relations requires attention to these problems.

CHOICE OF TOWN OR CITY

A decision that should be made early in the planning for new facilities concerns the location in a suburb, a small city or town, a large city, an industrial park, an entrance to a superhighway, or a town that is built with particular reference to the needs of one company. Each of these possible choices requires some discussion.

Suburban Location. The tendency in recent years toward suburban location has been hastened by improved transportation, particularly the private automobile and the bus, which have made it possible for workers to reach their work easily and quickly. If roads are good and lightly traveled, labor can be drawn from a radius of about thirty miles. Beyond that distance, skilled craftsmen can be induced to accept jobs only if special advantages are offered to them. Workers who live in the suburb may have more living space, while they may also enjoy some of the advantages of the city.

The lower prices of land in the suburbs make possible the one-story building, which has many economies in certain types of operations. Space may also be provided for possible future expansion, for parking facilities for automobiles and trucks, and in some cases for storage of certain types of materials in the yard. Taxes may be lower, and zoning regulations may be less stringent.

Suburban locations are subject to certain limitations. As the population increases, suburban tax rates may catch up with city rates because of the increased need for various services. Local governing authorities and service industries may offer the new enterprise less assistance in planning for streets and other facilities. For these reasons, many companies prefer a site on the fringe of populous communities but inside city limits.

Small-Town Location. When a large company decides upon the small town as a desirable place for a plant, it usually operates two or more plants in as many towns. It attempts to utilize a local labor force and to gain other advantages that may be gained by such locations.

The plan of operating several plants in different locations is called *dispersal.* Facilities are dispersed instead of being concentrated. Each plant presents its own problems of building design, location, layout, organization, machine maintenance and replacement, expansion, and the like. Traffic congestion is lessened, and the possibility of losses by fire, windstorm, and enemy attack is reduced.

The location of plants in small communites is also called *decentralization* of physical facilities. The operation of several plants may necessitate some decentralization of authority because local managers may be in the best situation to make certain kinds of decisions or to handle certain types of problems. The plan of decentralizing facilities may therefore depend upon the willingness of management to decentralize authority.

The plan of decentralization assumes several forms. In some cases, certain parts and subassemblies may be manufactured in feeder plants located a short distance away from the assembly plant. The parts can be shipped to the assembly plant by truck within a few hours or possibly by an overnight trip. Instead of requiring workers to travel considerable distances to the plant, a part of the plant is moved to the workers. For bulky products such as automobiles and electrical appliances, the assembly plants may be located at considerable distances from plants making parts or accessories. Another form of decentralization is the setting-up of a complete production line in each of the plants located in different areas. This plan is feasible for a bakery, a shoe company, a textile mill, or a fruit-canning company. With this form of decentralization, the plants may be located in distant sections of the country. Another form of decentralization provides for specialization between plants, with certain products being manufactured in each plant. Examples are food-processing companies and companies manufacturing a variety of products, such as chemicals, paints, and salad dressing.

Decentralization is designed to improve labor relations. Workers may gain many advantages in living in a small city or town. Some costs of living, such as rent and transportation, are less; the same money wages mean higher real wages; and younger members of the family may live at home while they work. In small cities, workers may own their homes and also have an opportunity to do gardening, fishing, and various odd jobs. The workers are more likely to know each other personally, and their relations with their foreman are often personal and informal. A community atmosphere is established inside as well as outside the plant. From the point of view of the company, the people in small cities and towns who apply for work are often very good workers. The high school graduate in small communities is usually inclined to stay with the company, provided that he is given an opportunity to advance. Absenteeism is also reported to be less in small towns.

The small-town location has limitations as well as advantages. Workers are not skilled in factory work and may be inefficient until they have been trained. Many people object to working in factories because it is confining indoor work. The community is often lacking in fire and police protection, which the company may be required to supply for itself. Another objection to the small-town location is that workers may depend upon the one plant for their employment, and local retail stores and service establishments may derive their support largely from workers at the plant. If the company should find it profitable to reduce employment, close the plant temporarily, or move to another location, public and employee relations would be adversely affected. For this reason, some companies prefer not to locate in a town where its plant would provide the only employment for industrial workers. The decision might depend upon the nature of the product, the degree of skill required of the workers, and the attitude of management toward its public responsibilities.

From the managerial point of view, decentralization presents a number of problems. Since local plant managers are given greater responsibility, much depends upon the ability of top management to select and develop good local managers. More attention must be devoted to problems of planning and scheduling production. Such problems are particularly difficult when parts are manufactured in local plants and assembled in another plant. Communication between plants and the central office becomes more difficult because greater reliance must be placed upon such methods as telephone, teletype, and the mails, with less opportunity for personal consultation on day-to-day problems. Officials from the central office are required to spend time and money visiting local plants and advising with local managements. Decentralization also gives rise to greater complexity in the managerial organization because such functions as personnel, engineering, cost control, and production planning must be centralized in the main office, while the functions are managed locally at each plant by persons under the line control of the plant superintendent.

Location on a Superhighway. New problems of plant location have been created by the building of throughways or express highways with limited clover-leaf entrances and exits. Some companies have found the points of entrance and egress to provide very desirable locations for branch plants. At such places, land is available for one-story buildings with adequate room for economical plant layout, storage space for materials and finished products, and loading facilities for trucks. Housing developments may provide homes for workers adjacent to the plant. Workers not desiring to live near the plant can drive to work within a short time provided they can use the throughway. Shipping time required for receiving materials and parts from vendors in other cities and for delivering the finished product to customers is reduced by shipping over the highway. Even though tolls must be paid for the use of the highway, shipping costs are reduced because of the greater speed and the elimination of stops for intersections and traffic lights. The reduced accident record on superhighways or throughways may also constitute an important advantage.

The Industrial Park. Another suburban or interurban development that has resulted from improved highway transportation is the planned industrial district and the industrial park. In both types of plant sites, the area is zoned for a certain kind of industrial establishment, and land use is limited by restrictive agreements. The industrial park has greater restrictions than the planned industrial area would impose.

To assure that plant sites are attractively landscaped and that buildings are esthetically pleasing, the industrial park prescribes minimum lot sizes, minimum land-use ratios, the nature of the landscaping, and the type of building construction. The factory would not be permitted to dump waste upon the land or to release obnoxious gases and fumes. Provision is made for the enforcement of the agreements in future years and also to modify the terms of the agreement if developments should render them obsolete. In the original plan for the industrial park, provision is made for sites of the proper size, adequate utilities, and easy access to each location by automobile, truck, or train. These sites are sold or leased to tenants for a long term of years.[3]

Although many types of business will continue to require urban or other locations, other firms will find that the industrial park has many advantages. Land will probably cost less than urban land, although development costs will absorb a part of the difference. The industrial park management may provide for sewage disposal, fire and police protection, light and power facilities, and water connections. The cost of the services would be assessed against the property owners in the park. The restrictions upon the use made of adjacent properties provide protection for each tenant against smoke, odors, noise, and vibration, and they afford some guarantee against the deterioration of the area. These arrangements are made for the tenant by the park management in advance of occupancy.

The industrial park has several disadvantages as a plant location. Provision for expansion is difficult or impossible because of the minimum acreage requirements. The cost of additional land is high because all land in the park is provided with utiltiy services and access to highway transportation. Some firms cannot agree to the restrictions upon land use, and they may be unable to develop new products or to

---

[3] R. T. Murphy, Jr., and W. L. Baldwin, "Business Moves to the Industrial Park," *Harvard Business Review*, Vol. XXXVII, No. 3 (1959), pp. 79–88.

utilize new manufacturing processes that are made necessary by technological change. Businesses most suited to the industrial park include research organizations, distributive outlets, sales offices, light manufacturing, and assembly plants.

The Company Town.   In the chocolate, mining, textile, and some other industries, corporations have found it desirable to build towns as well as plants. Such towns provide homes, stores, recreation facilities, and power and water services for the employees.

The company town has several advantages. It can be built in accordance with a plan for the entire community, including the residential areas, stores, places for recreation and amusement, and other services. The plant can be built in any location without regard to the willingness of real estate developers to provide housing facilities or the ability of employees to finance them. If the company provides the only available employment in the community, the risk involved in private construction of homes might be prohibitive. The company town can be established near the source of mineral deposits or with due regard to water supply, power, or other services. The company town also enables the company to profit by any increase in land values which may result from the growth of a city on undeveloped or partially developed land sites.

Most corporate managements seem to believe that company towns are not desirable. The company-owned town increases the capital required for the enterprise, and it requires that a larger percentage of the capital be invested in fixed assets. New problems of organization and management are created by the entrance of the company into real estate management. The development of a competent, dependable, and loyal labor force becomes more difficult when employees live constantly under the shadow of the company whether they are at work, at home, or in places of recreation. The situation is particularly objectionable if poor living conditions are provided or if the houses all follow the same pattern. The company is also placed in a disadvantageous position when labor troubles arise. If the company requires striking employees who are unable to pay their rent to vacate company houses, public opinion and employee attitudes are adversely affected. If it permits striking employees to live in the houses without paying rent and to buy at company stores on credit, it is financing the strike against itself.

DECIDING UPON A LOCATION

The decision to locate a new plant in a certain area is usually made by the top executives of the company. The president might assign to a staff assistant the work of making a study of possible sites and recommending a location. Because of the large number of factors affecting the decision, some of which might favor one location and some another, the problem is to find some way to balance the advantages and the disadvantages of possible locations and to arrive at a considered opinion. A procedure for making a study of the problem will be suggested for a company that already has one or more plants in operation.

Data Required. Before any sites are surveyed, it would usually be desirable to collect certain basic data concerning the company and its production program. To aid in the selection of the general area, the person would need to know what products are to be made in the new plant as compared with the products of plants now in operation. In this respect, several possibilities exist. The new plant might make the same products as the present plants. Examples would be a steel company, a container manufacturing company, or a shoe company. In such cases, the decision as to location might depend upon the extent to which market areas can be economically served by the present plants, whether transportation costs to some areas are preventing the realization of full sales potentials, and whether delays in deliveries are interfering with prompt and satisfactory services to customers. Data on sales in certain areas in comparison with possible sales might suggest that a branch plant can profitably be located in a certain territory. The decision might depend upon the extent of competition in the area as indicated by the location of plants of competitors.

If the new plant is to make certain parts for assembly in another plant, the new location should be chosen with reference to the location of the assembly plant. Both the parts and the final assembly might be light in weight and might require only a small plant site. In that case, the parts plant and the assembly plant might be located with primary regard for labor supply and other factors. If the parts are relatively compact while the assembly is heavy and bulky, as in the case of automobiles, the parts plants may be located near the sources of raw materials and an adequate labor market, while the assembly plant may be located in a distant part of the country where the product is to be sold.

The purpose of the new plant may be the manufacture of a product not now made in any other plant of the company, such as instant coffee or frozen vegetables in the case of a diversified food-processing company. If this is the situation, the person making the study would need to know the varieties of product which will be made at the plant. He would also need to know the size of the plant necessary for the production of a sufficient volume to meet the contemplated sales, the space necessary for storage of materials and finished product, and possible plans for future expansion. This information would be necessary to determine the size of the new site, the desirable contour of the land, and the transportation facilities required.

Another factor in the initial planning is the intention of the company to rent a building or to construct a new plant. Greater freedom of choice is permitted if the company plans to build. However, management may delay the decision to buy, rent, or build until the survey of possible sites has been completed.

On the basis of information as to the nature of the product to be made at the new plant, the present sales of the company, the nature of the competition, and other important factors that would affect the location, the person selecting the site might first select the part of the country which seems most desirable. Next he might decide upon the city or the particular area, and finally he might decide upon the exact plant site within the area. These three phases are not independent of each other because the difficulty of finding a site in a city might cause a change in the whole plan. However, this procedure indicates a possible approach to the problem.

The study of plant sites in an area may begin with correspondence or personal interviews with officials of local chambers of commerce, or the first approach may be made to the Office of Domestic Commerce of the United States Department of Commerce. Either source can supply a substantial amount of basic information concerning the available public services, labor supply, and other factors in the location. Either agency can assist in meeting public utility executives, real-estate companies specializing in industrial sites, bank executives, officials of railway and trucking companies, and other persons who can provide information. Most state governments maintain research agencies that collect information pertaining to such factors as natural resources, transportation, labor supply, and public utility services in various parts of the state.

The information collected by the person who makes the survey may include a questionnaire filled out by himself in personal conferences with various persons who are in a position to supply information. He could get additional information from road maps showing street and highway connections, maps of railway and steamship connections, aerial photographs, contour maps, and reports of personal inspection of properties. The questionnaire consists of detailed questions covering all of the points on which information is desired. The questions should be carefully prepared in advance of each interview in order that no pertinent data will be omitted. The answers to the questions concerning any one site may be obtained from several persons. If any problem exists relative to waste disposal, fumes, contamination of streams, or other menace or nuisance, the company should first plan to control them and then confer with local or state officials concerning its program.

Comparison of Different Sites. After the information has been collected, it may be summarized to show the required capital outlay for each of a few selected sites. This summary would show the costs of land, improvements to the land for grading and landscaping, building, equipment, and other facilities. These outlays are initial costs and are largely nonrecurring. Another statement may be prepared to show the estimated cost of producing a given number of units of product at each location. The statement would indicate the costs of materials, labor, fuel, power, indirect labor, propety taxes, and corporate expenses. These costs are recurring in nature.

The estimate of costs is not entirely satsifactory because unit costs vary with the volume of production. This form of statement could not be used satisfactorily by a company producing a variety of products. In many cases an estimated statement of profit and loss is preferable. This statement shows for each contemplated location the estimated sales, the estimated costs of production, and the estimated selling and administrative expenses. State and federal income taxes are computed to determine the net balance available for stockholders and for reinvestment.

Several difficulties arise in the preparation of an estimated statement of profit and loss. First, many variables cannot be accurately evaluated. Although the statements are valuable estimates, they should not be regarded as conclusive. Second, the results of operations will not be uniform from one year to another. Extra expenses will be incurred during the first year in setting up the organization and building up the labor force. These problems will be much the same in any location. Third, results even after the business has been established will vary from one year to another. This problem can be met in part by assuming varying rates of output in each location.

The computation of costs, expenses, and sales at each contemplated location has been much simplified by the development of machines which will make the computations in a very short time. Once the data are available, they can be quickly summarized and compared with similar data for other locations. Computing machines also make possible the use of more factors of costs and expenses than might otherwise be used. The final decision has become more a matter of fact and less a matter of opinion.

The Break-Even Point. The desirability of one or more proposed locations may be determined by reference to an estimated break-even point, which is the volume of production and sales of the product that would result in neither a profit nor a loss. On that volume, the company would just break even so far as its financial operations are concerned. If the break-even point is known, the company could determine whether the estimated volume would be sufficient to carry the estimated overhead expenses, and it might estimate the probable number of months or years of operation that would be necessary to build up the volume that would be required to make a satisfactory profit.

The method of computing the break-even point depends upon the variety of the product line. If the proposed plant will be used to make a single product, such as sugar or coffee, the cost of materials, labor, and variable expenses may be estimated by reference to similar cost data in other plants. If these elements of cost total 60 cents per pound or per unit and the product sells for 90 cents, the proceeds of sale of each pound or unit would cover the direct costs and pay 30 cents toward the fixed charges. If the estimated overhead expense totals $600,000, the company would be required to sell 2,000,000 units ($600,000 ÷ 0.30) to break even. If the company plans to make more than one variety of product, such as different kinds of candy, different varieties of cookies or canned fruits, an average sales price and an average cost of labor, materials, and variable expenses could be used in the computation.

The company might plan to produce a wide variety of products in the plant, such as toys, ceramics, or metal and fiber containers. In this case, unit sales and costs might lose their significance in the computation of the break-even point. Instead, the computation could be made in terms of the dollar value of the sales which would be necessary to break even. For example, if the materials, labor, and variable expenses would average 60 per cent of the sales, 40 per cent of each sales dollar would remain to cover the fixed overhead expenses. If the overhead expense is estimated at $600,000, the total sales necessary to break even would be $1,500,000 ($600,000 ÷ 0.40).

While the break-even point is a useful concept in relation to both plant location and general business management, it should not be regarded as fixed and unchangeable. As volume falls and the profit diminishes toward the break-even point, the overhead expense which is usually considered to be fixed can be reduced in various ways, such as by cutting salaries, laying off people, eliminating positions, and raising work standards. Costs and expenses are not easily classified into such categories as fixed and variable.

Limitations of a Cost Analysis. Probably the most serious difficulty in connection with estimates of costs and expenses at various locations arises from the effects of changes that may not be foreseen. The location of a large new plant in an area will in itself affect labor, housing, and other conditions. In time the development of new transportation facilities may alter the relative advantages of different locations. During the last 150 years, for example, some locations have gained and others have declined in importance with the development, first, of canals and, later, of railroads and highways. Cheaper and more rapid means of transportation have been made available. The invention of steamboats was followed by steam locomotives, automobiles and trucks, airplanes, and diesel locomotives. Industries locating in New England to take advantage of moist climate, water power, and an efficient labor supply have seen their advantages disappear with the invention of moisture-control systems of air conditioning, the building of flood-control and electric-power projects in the South and West, and the development of labor markets in other areas. Companies building or acquiring plants near the source of raw materials have later found their locations to be disadvantageous as mineral deposits and timber resources have neared exhaustion and new deposits of minerals were discovered and new timberlands were developed in other areas. Plants locating in the East to be near the market have lost their advantage in this respect as the center of population has moved westward. Such illustrations could be continued indefinitely. They indicate the necessity for supplementing any cost studies with a general economic analysis in an effort to forecast the trend.

DEVELOPING FAVORABLE PUBLIC RELATIONS

After a company has decided to locate a new plant in a community, it may take measures to assure that local residents, businessmen, and prospective employees will not be antagonistic. The company might make some member of the management responsible for the development of a favorable community attitude, and that person may formulate a plan for the dissemination of information to the public. He might supply data pertaining to the plant to the newspapers, radio and television stations, and local government officials. The public might be assured that buildings and grounds would be planned to improve the appearance of the community, that trucks would be routed to avoid traffic congestion, and that no smoke or other nuisance would be created. Plans for the dedication exercises might include local government officials and representatives of civic organizations. In various other ways, the company might seek to develop the good will of people in the community.

Within the company organization, also, attention should be given to possible anxieties on the part of executives, foremen, and workers. They will want to know what work will be transferred to the new plant, whether production will be cut back at existing plants, and who will manage and operate the new plant. Usually some people will be transferred from existing plants, and additional personnel at various levels will be recruited and trained locally. People should be given official explanations of the various problems in order that rumors may not be circulated and fears magnified.

QUESTIONS

1. The western part of the United States has been called the "great crescent" because industry has found location in that area to be desirable. One point of the crescent is in Washington and the other point is on the Gulf coast. The area includes California, New Mexico, and Arizona. What developments have encouraged industry to locate plants in that area?

2. What industries might be especially encouraged to move to the South and West?

3. What types of industries can profitably locate plants along the superhighways without regard to railway connections?

4. What types of industries require railway connections and easy access to ocean transportation?

5. Might a company find that the workers in an area are unsuited to its needs even though plenty of workers apply for employment?

6. How can the position of Detroit in automobile manufacture be explained?

7. In what type of industry is the factory located near the source of raw materials? In what type of industry may the plant be profitably located at a distance from the source of the materials?

8. A large shirt manufacturer located one plant in Georgia and two other plants in Minnesota. Could these choices of plant location have been wisely made?

9. How has the development of automatic machinery affected the problem of plant location?

10. Why might management prefer not to build a company town?

11. Explain how you would proceed if you were assigned the task of recommending a site for a new plant. Indicate the information you would need to

start the study, the information you would need as to different locations, the sources of the information, and the method of evaluating the information.

CASES

14. LOCATION OF A CARPET MILL

When a large carpet manufacturing company sought a suitable site for a new mill, it established a set of basic requirements for the new location. The first requirement was that the mill be convenient to railway transportation because both the raw materials and the finished carpets are heavy and require transportation by rail. A second requirement was that the mill be near a river into which waste could be dumped. While the company intended to treat the waste and to render it innocuous, a river seemed to provide the cheapest and easiest means of waste disposal.

Another basic requirement was an efficient and dependable labor force. The management believed that a rural community or a small town afforded the best chance for development of good workers. Previous factory experience of applicants was not considered necessary because the company would transfer the managerial force and a few skilled workers from its existing plants. Workers should be willing to accept factory jobs and should not insist upon office work.

A highway system connecting with the plant was important in order that workers might not be required to live adjacent to the plant. The company was anxious to avoid any possible charge that it was fostering a slum area.

Nearness to market was not a primary requirement, although it was considered important that the plant be located in the eastern part of the United States where there would be easy access to the large cities of the northeast. Location in this area was also important because the carpets were made of imported wool.

The local area should be fairly level to permit the construction of a plant, railway sidings, loading platforms, and parking lots. The elevation should be sufficient to assure that the building site would not be subject to overflow in time of high water.

After the basic requirements were determined, the company began its study of possible locations by scrutinizing maps. It compiled a list of all the places in the eastern half of the country where railroads crossed rivers. It found about one hundred such places. By a process of elimination, it found that only a few of the places met the other requirements. A few locations were then visited, and investigations were continued at possible plant sites. The company had no difficulty in finding one site that met all basic requirements.

Required:

Evaluate the procedure followed by the company in selecting a location for the new plant.

15. RELATIONS WITH LOCAL COMMUNITY

The Johnston Textile Products Company, located in a city of 85,000, had never permitted plant visits by people in the community. The reasons of the management were, first, the accident hazard; second, the possibility of fire; and, third, the possible effect upon production. The plant superintendent considered plant visits a nuisance because members of the management would be expected to serve as guides.

The personnel manager learned from applicants for employment and from people in the community that there was much misunderstanding of company policies and conditions within the plant. Disgruntled employees made exaggerated statements concerning working conditions and management methods. There was a general feeling that the company was trying to conceal something. Many employees felt uncertain about their jobs because of rumors that the company was on the point of bankruptcy.

In an effort to improve community relations, an outside consultant was engaged. He advised that as a part of the program an open house be organized to extend over a period of one week. During that time, people in the city and particularly the families of employees would be invited to visit the plant to see what conditions were like. The suggestion was approved by the plant superintendent and the president of the company. The personnel manager was appointed chairman of a committee to work out the details.

A number of subcommittees were appointed for publicity, ticket distribution, reception, guide selection and training, and registration and information. A ticket distribution committee was considered necessary to assure that an excessive number of visitors would not report on any one day.

The plan met with a favorable response from the community. Capacity groups were shown through the plant each day. The families of employees were especially pleased to see the machines at which a member of the family worked. The plant superintendent and the personnel manager agreed that it would now be more difficult for anyone to start a rumor in the community concerning the company. It was also expected that the employment department would have less difficulty in recruiting applicants for jobs.

Questions:

1. What costs arise from a plant visitation program?
2. What advantages might the company gain?
3. How can the management determine whether the program is worth its cost?
4. Would regular plant visits be preferred to the plan of the open house?

9 The Building as Productive Equipment

THE building should be regarded as a part of the productive equipment of the enterprise. It provides protection for machinery and materials being processed, and it also provides a place for workers to perform their assigned tasks under conditions which may be favorable or unfavorable. The main building or a separate building provides offices where members of the management can carry on the functions assigned to them. The size and plan of the building may determine whether the company will succeed, although many other factors will obviously contribute to its success.

PLANNING FOR THE BUILDING

Buildings provide services at a cost which may or may not be excessive. A building has long life and requires expenditures for heating, taxes, maintenance, and other expenses throughout its life. The depreciation charge is determined according to a schedule which is fixed at the time the building is acquired, and it continues throughout its life. Other expenses, such as heat and light, alterations, the control of the pollution of air and water, and the cost of materials handling may depend upon the way the building was planned. If the charges are excessive, the enterprise may be unable to realize a satisfactory return from its investment.

Some companies use buildings that are inefficient and unattractive. In some cases the buildings were originally designed for other purposes and are not suited for present operations because of size, number of stories, poor facilities for employees, obsolete heating and lighting systems, or other reasons. Some enterprises use poorly adapted buildings because the plants were offered for sale or lease at low prices by other companies that had been liquidated or had found the building unsuited for their purposes. If a location within a certain urban area appears desirable, a company may be required to choose between a few buildings, none of which are especially suited to its needs. If a building is available at low initial cost, it may be chosen despite certain disadvantages.

The Decision to Build. Many enterprises begin operations in rented properties. Until the owners can be sure that the product can be marketed at a price that will yield a profit, they would usually face too great a risk in immediately acquiring a building. If the future is uncertain, the company might lease a building until a market for the product has been developed. The need for space may also be reduced by purchasing parts instead of making them.

Frequently an established company finds that its plant space is inadequate and that it needs a new building or an addition to the existing plant. In this case, the management may be able to introduce operating economies that will permit an increase in output without an increase in plant space. The economies would include increased mechanization, better methods of materials handling, reduction in the downtime of machines for repair, and a reduction of idle time for other reasons. For example, a fully automatic machine may have sufficient capacity to replace four or five machines that are manually operated. Such a machine decreases the need for space, not only for machines, but also for the storage of materials and for the operator. Less aisle space may also be needed. In fact, some companies plan to build a new plant that provides only enough space to meet the present demand for the product and they expect that additional capacity will be provided by a continuing program of improvement in plant facilities.[1]

If a company has several small buildings and finds that it needs one large building to permit a better layout, to provide better employee services, and to reduce costs by improved methods of production, it may be able to modernize its plant facilities by consolidating the building space and connecting existing buildings. However, alterations and additions of this kind are costly and the cost per square foot, or cubic foot, may be almost as much as it would be in a new building. New walls,

---

[1] "Big Company V.P. Takes Aim at 1960 Costs," *Factory Management and Maintenance,* Vol. CXVII, No. 12 (1959), pp. 59, 60.

doors, and windows may be necessary. Ramps may be required in equalizing differences in floor levels. The arrangement of machines and production lines may be changed. Alterations of this kind can be made only where existing buildings are structurally sound. The advantage of such alterations is that the human resources of the company may be kept intact.[2]

Before plans are made for either modernization or the construction of a new building, the management should inquire into the sales possibilities for the products of the company, including any new products which are contemplated for the next five or ten years. Present increased demand may prove to be temporary, or competitors may be preparing to increase their output to supply the market. During periods of business prosperity, demand is often illusory because of overordering and the placing of duplicate orders by customers. The effect of a decreased demand during periods of depression or business recession should also be considered. Some authorities contend that expansion of plant facilities should not be made unless the enterprise can break even on the production and sale of 50 per cent of the normal output. Before any commitments are made, it would be well for management to know where the break-even point is, that is, at what volume of production the company neither loses nor makes money. This point will vary with changes in the selling price of the product and changes in the cost of labor, materials, and supplies; but losses due to gross miscalculations may be avoided by attention to this phase of the problem.

If the demand for the product appears permanent and if the new building can be safely financed, plant ownership will relieve the company of the fixed rental charge, which may result in a net saving. The plant is an asset of the company; and if it is paid for out of profits, the financial ratios as indicated by the figures on the balance sheet are improved, and the financial standing is bettered. The company may also have greater freedom to make alterations and improvements in a plant that it owns, and the initial construction may provide a more modern plant.

Sale-and-Lease-Back Arrangement. A manufacturer or other business may construct a building to suit its particular requirements, sell the building to a finance company, and lease it for a fixed rental for a term of years. This arrangement enables the company to use the building without having to invest its own money or to borrow money

---

[2] This method was followed by Pitney Bowes, Inc., in modernizing its facilities at Stamford, Conn. See "Six Plants Work as One," *Factory Management and Maintenance,* Vol. CXII, No. 12 (1959), pp. 44–49.

for the building. On the balance sheet, the building is not included with the assets, and the future rental payments are not included with the liabilities. The financial ratios of balance sheet items and groups of assets and liabilities are therefore not affected. The company is not required to enter into any restrictive agreements that limit its future financing. Such covenants are frequently required by investment banking institutions when bonds are issued to finance construction.

A financial institution that becomes a party to the sale-and-lease-back arrangement will usually expect to earn a higher rate of return on its investment than it would require on an issue of bonds or a mortgage. The higher rate of return is reflected in the rental charge. One reason for the higher rate is that the risk is increased by the possibility of cancellation of the lease contract in case of bankruptcy. The risk of the lessor is also increased by the difficulty of marketing the leasehold contract if the lender desires to recover his investment prior to the termination of the lease. The financial institution can also charge more because it is drawn into real estate transactions and not merely a lending operation.[3]

Some companies have found after a period of years that changed conditions have made leased properties unsuited to their requirements, and they may be unable to move to a more desirable location because they have become obligated to continue the rental payments. A property that is owned can be sold, but a leased property can be vacated only by finding a suitable tenant or by bankruptcy proceedings.

Effect of Inflation.   Since the close of World War II, the possibility of continued inflation has been a factor in the decision to rent, to build, or to modernize. During periods of inflation, a person may protect himself by owning large amounts of assets and possibly owing large amounts of debt which can be paid later in dollars of decreased purchasing power. However, a lease contract that provides for a fixed rental for the life of the asset affords a similar advantage to the lessee because the rent is paid over a period of years as inflation decreases the purchasing power of the dollars paid as rent. The lessee may use his credit line to purchase additional assets and to incur other indebtedness. Plans based upon the assumption of "creeping inflation" obviously involve risks. They could result in losses if the inflation is checked or the lessee does not experience an increase in the volume of his sales and rising prices for his products.

Tax Considerations.   The effect of ownership upon federal and state income taxes will enter into the decision to rent or own the build-

---

[3] Robert F. Vancil and Robert N. Anthony, "The Financial Community Looks at Leasing," *Harvard Business Review,* Vol. XXXVII, No. 6 (1959), pp. 113–30.

ing. The questions involved are complicated and will require detailed study in each case. However, the lease arrangement has tax advantages in some cases because the lessee can deduct the entire amount of the rent as a business expense, whereas the owner of a building can deduct depreciation, property taxes, repairs and maintenance, interest paid, and other building expenses. The determining factor would be the amount of rent in comparison with the building expenses. If the owner or lessor is an institution that can afford to invest at a low interest rate, the rental payment may be sufficiently low to make the arrangement profitable to both the lessor and the lessee.

The Building Plan. Having decided to build, management should put down on paper the plans for an ideal arrangement of the building. This plan can be made without regard to cost, contour of land, streets and highways, existing railroad facilities, or any other local conditions. If three or four good arrangements are planned, it may then be possible to choose the one that offers the greatest advantages in costs of production, maintenance costs, employee comfort, depreciation, taxes, appearance, and other features. In making such a plan, an analysis should be made of the product, the parts that go into it, and the processes required for the production. The workplaces can then be planned, with due allowance for space required for workers, machines, and materials. Plans should also be made for aisle space and for equipment used in internal transportation. Space may also be provided for storerooms, locker rooms, washrooms, cafeteria, dispatching desks, toolrooms, and shipping room. Outside the plant the area desired for yards, sidewalks, driveways, and parking facilities should be indicated. It may be necessary to modify the plan when costs are considered; but planning in this manner emphasizes the fact that the plant, like a machine, should be designed to fit production requirements.

Some companies have found that a standardized design of building is feasible for all of their buildings in different locations. The architect's plans for a building in one location can be used for a building in another location with only slight modifications for size or changes because of differences in the contour of the land. Standardized buildings have been found to be suitable for manufacturing plants as well as chain stores, hotels, garages, and chain restaurants.

TYPES OF BUILDINGS

The essential differences in types of buildings relate to the number of stories, the size of the building, and the nature of the construction. These problems are closely related, since the decision to build a single-story or a multistory building will depend in part upon the number of buildings and the nature of the construction.

Single-Story Buildings.   One-story buildings have been increasing in number for two reasons. First, improved methods of transportation have caused many new plants to locate in small cities or towns where adequate space is available and land is low in cost. Second, the one-story building is less expensive to build and, in some industries, results in substantial operating economies. Industries that use heavy machines or make a heavy product must have the manufacturing operations on one floor. Examples are foundries, forge shops, locomotive and car builders, steel mills, and press and stamping shops. Some automobile manufacturers have also found one-story buildings to be more economical than multistory structures. In initial cost the single-story building is usually considered less expensive.

The single-story building requires fewer columns throughout the central area than does the multistory structure because only the weight of the roof has to be supported. The spacing of the columns depends somewhat on the type of trusses in the roof. A wide spacing of the columns is possible, though at a cost which increases rapidly because the roof trusses must carry longer roof beams. In a multistory building the spacing of columns depends upon the floor loads and arrangement of the steel used in the structure. Wide spacing is advantageous because it affords unobstructed work areas, permits greater flexibility in the layout and arrangement of the workplaces, lowers the cost of transportation, and permits better supervision.

The advantages of the single-story building constitute one of the reasons for the trend toward small-town locations where land is available for all processing and service departments to be located on one floor. Furthermore, the single-story building in a small town can be enlarged with less cost than a multistory building in a city. For this reason, the trend toward the single-story building in many industries is affected by the developments in plant location.

Multistory Building.   Enterprises that are engaged in light manufacturing frequently find a multistory building to be more economical than a one-story plant. If both the materials and the machines used are lightweight, a multistory structure may meet all requirements. Examples include food processing, shoes, clothing, printing and publishing, drugs, chemicals, beverages, and light hardware. When the materials can be moved by gravity chutes or other gravity conveyors, the multistory building makes possible low-cost operation. Examples are bread baking, sugar refining, glass-bottle manufacturing, and soapmaking. In some industries, height of buildings is desirable for storing or processing the product, even though a floor may not be required at each level. This situation exists in plants making granulated soap and in certain food-processing plants. In a multistory building, much space on the upper floors may be used for storage. A second story may be desirable for office space in order that the offices may be isolated from the noise of the shop.

The most important saving in the multistory structure is in the cost of the plant site. In locations where land cost is high, multistory buildings are necessary. Industries that find an urban location desirable in order that they may be near markets or for other reasons will usually be located in multistory buildings.

Number of Buildings. Sometimes the plant consists of two or more buildings adjacent to each other. Separate buildings are more costly to construct and require more ground space. An added item of construction cost is the requirement for pavements between the buildings. Maintenance costs are increased, particularly the cost of heating and air conditioning; in the winter the courts between the buildings must be kept free of snow. Operating costs are increased because the flow of work from one workplace to another is interrupted and because employees must spend more time going to and from various service facilities unless duplicate facilities are provided. As the plant grows, the operations are likely to become disorganized because of the difficulties of keeping an effective, orderly arrangement of workplaces. These weaknesses may be minimized by constructing passageways between the floors above ground and by providing roofing over the ground area between the buildings. Where several buildings are constructed instead of a single building, the reason may be that different processes require different types of construction. Fire and explosion hazards may be decreased by the segregation of certain departments. Separate buildings may also be used to house the administration offices, research laboratories, and the power plant. Any auxiliary buildings should be so located that they will not impede future expansion of the main building and its operations.

Types of Construction. Regardless of whether the building has one story or several stories, it may be any one of five types of construction. These types are not always clear-cut and distinct, since they have many adaptations. The choice of a type of construction, like many other management problems, should be made by balancing various phases of cost, including original cost, maintenance, depreciation, and fire protection.

Light frame buildings are constructed of thin wooden joists and rafters with light studs inside the partition walls. The frame is sheathed with relatively thin wooden boards. Since the edges of the wood are exposed, fire could spread rapidly along the length of the boards. The fire hazard is increased in factories because of the possible saturation of the floors and walls with oil or grease. Wooden stairways increase the risk to life and property because they aid in the spread of the fire to the upper floors.

Frame buildings are little used for factory construction, although their initial cost is low. They are unsuited for permanent structures because of their rapid depreciation, the great danger of fire, and high insurance costs. Some enterprises that are definitely temporary use frame buildings because they are quickly constructed at low cost and are easily altered to meet changed conditions.

In brick or stone wall-bearing construction, the weight of the upper floors and the roof is transmitted to the walls by steel or wooden beams. The side walls are of brick with heavy pilasters or brick columns to carry most of the weight. The pilasters may project from the wall by as much as one third of their thickness. Brick construction also requires heavy center columns. Since much of the weight rests upon the walls, the size of the windows is limited. This type of construction is better than light wood-frame construction in that it is more permanent, depreciates more slowly, and is low in cost. It can be used for operations that do not require heavy floor loads.

Standard mill construction, also called slow-burning construction, is especially designed to reduce the hazard of fire. The walls are built of brick; the floors and roof are made of heavy timbers or thick planks which burn slowly and which will continue to support the weight of the building after they are partly burned. In the frame of the building, no timbers are used with any dimensions less than six inches. The roof planks are two or three inches in thickness, and the floor planks three or four inches. Timbers and planks of these dimensions will prevent the collapse of the building even though fire may have penetrated half an inch or more into the wood. With reasonably good fire protection, the flames will be extinguished before they have burned through the supports to walls, floors, and roof.

Mill construction is also designed to prevent the spread of a fire from one floor to another. No chutes in the floor are permitted. Elevator shafts and stairways are fully enclosed by walls of heavy wood or noncombustible construction. Doors that open to stairways or elevator shafts are self-closing and fireproof. In parts of the building where the fire hazard is increased by manufacturing processes, the ceilings are made of plaster or other noncombustible material such as sheet metal or asbestos. They are also equipped with automatic sprinklers. The beams and columns are chamfered in order that they may not catch fire easily or assist the spread of fire.

Mill construction has other advantages in addition to reducing the fire hazard. The building will safely support heavier floor loads than buildings of either light wood-frame or brick construction. Vibrations of machinery are not easily transmitted because of the firm and heavy construction. Alterations in the floor arrangements may be made, or openings in walls or floors for piping and power lines may be cut with relative ease.

The mill type of construction is subject to several disadvantages. The heavy timbers are costly, and the lumber is not readily available in quantity. The building is not easily lighted because of the limited window space and the large columns. Wide unobstructed areas within the building cannot be achieved, and layout of machines and equipment is inflexible. The movement of materials and work in process of manufacture is slowed by columns and the nature of the openings between floors. In fact, the competitive position of some plants and some areas is seriously affected by the use of buildings that cannot be easily adapted to take advantage of recent developments in materials handling, machinery and equipment for production, lighting, air conditioning, and methods of planning and controlling production.

In the steel-frame type of building the weight of the upper floors and the roof is carried by a series of steel columns which are braced together by horizontal girts. The walls are usually of brick or hollow tile. Corrugated sheet metal may be used for the partitions or even for the walls, but it is not entirely satisfactory because it deteriorates rapidly when exposed to dampness. Rooms with sheet metal walls are also hard to heat because of excessive radiation. An advantage of steel-frame construction is that alterations and reinforcements are easily made.

Unless the entire building is fire-resistant, steel-frame construction carries a decided fire hazard because the steel columns will soften and become weakened when heated. The buckling of the steel will cause the entire building to be wrecked. For this reason, floors should be of concrete or other fireproof material. The roofing material should also be fireproof. Since the contents of the building may burn and cause intense heat, the steel frame should be fireproofed with concrete. A steel-frame building under construction is shown in Figure 7.

In reinforced-concrete buildings the weight of the building is supported by a frame of concrete in which steel reinforcing bars are imbedded. The floors are also made of reinforced concrete, although they

Courtesy of Bethlehem Steel Co.

FIG. 7. Steel-Frame Building under Construction

may be surfaced with wood, linoleum, or other material. Columns along the outside wall and also within the building space support the floors and roof. The side walls may be of brick, stone, or hollow tile. Much of the wall may be of glass, since the walls do not carry the weight of the building. The roofs are usually of reinforced concrete, although they are surfaced with other waterproofing material.

Reinforced concrete is a favorite type of construction for multistory buildings. The cost is somewhat less than it is for steel construction; yet the building carries very little fire hazard, is cheaply insured, and depreciates slowly. Maintenance and housekeeping costs are low. The floors are rigid and free from vibration and can be constructed to carry heavy loads.

The objections to reinforced concrete are that the plan of the building is not easily changed as manufacturing processes change, and that new openings for power lines, heating and ventilating equipment, or for other purposes are not easily made. Machines cannot be readily attached to concrete unless their location is anticipated and provided for during construction by imbedding anchor bolts in the concrete. A reinforced-concrete building must be correctly proportioned to prevent deterioration due to stresses which result from expansion and contraction with changes in temperature and from uneven settlement of the foundation.

Floors. The floor should be adapted to the use to be made of it. In a steel-frame or reinforced-concrete structure, the building may be made to support any type of floor that is required. It is not necessary that the same type of floor be used in all areas or departments. Plain concrete floors may be used in toilets and dressing rooms, since this type of floor is durable and easy to clean. A concrete surface with an armored grid reinforcement is adapted to open passageways and elevator openings where the traffic is heavy. This type of floor is long wearing and affords a safe footing. Hardwood tongue-and-groove or smooth-edged flooring provides a satisfactory base for light machines and is not uncomfortable for employees. Unless the base is perfectly flat, however, the edging of the boards will break under heavy weight or in traffic. Brick floors are used in heat-treating departments. Wooden blocks, installed on end with the wear on the end of the grain, are sometimes used for the shipping room and certain other departments. If machinery is set upon wooden blocks, anchor bolts must reach through the blocks to the concrete floor to hold the machinery firmly. Asphalt tile is satisfactory for offices. Other types of floors are available for departments that have special requirements.

When additions are made to buildings or when new buildings are erected, special attention should be given to the standardization of floor levels. At the time of acquisition of such facilities, uniformity in floor levels may not seem to be important. However, the management may later consolidate the various facilities by the removal of walls and the construction of connecting rooms and hallways. In that event, the differences in floor levels might substantially increase the cost of the building changes and subsequent operating costs.

Roofs. The choice of roof depends upon such factors as cost of construction, appearance, ease of inspection and maintenance, air conditioning, and relation to materials handling. A common type for either single-story or multistory buildings is the flat roof. This type is easily inspected for leaks and is easily repaired when defects are discovered. In single-story buildings, flat roofs are sometimes used for parking, although such use requires sturdy construction of the roof and strong wall support. Easy access by means of a ramp or otherwise is also essential. Some companies are experimenting with the spraying of water on flat roofs in hot weather to lower the temperature inside the building.

The saw-tooth roof, as the name suggests, gives the appearance of the upturned teeth of a saw when viewed from the side of the building. The short side of each "tooth" consists of windows which face, preferably, to the north. The windows are usually vertical to reduce the accumulation of dirt, although they may be slanting. The principal advantage of saw-tooth roofs is that air and natural light may be admitted from the windows in the roof as well as from windows in the walls. A building with a saw-tooth roof is shown in Figure 28 on page 253.

The monitor roof has a raised central portion with windows along the sides of the monitor section similar to a railroad passenger car. The roof on either side of the monitor section may be either flat or sloping. The principal advantages of the monitor-type roof are, first, the effective use of natural light and, second, the additional overhead space which may be used for cranes or other materials-handling equipment.

The pitched roof, commonly used for residences, consists of two sloping sections. This type of roof is best adapted to a one-story or two-story building, although it is sometimes used for taller buildings. It

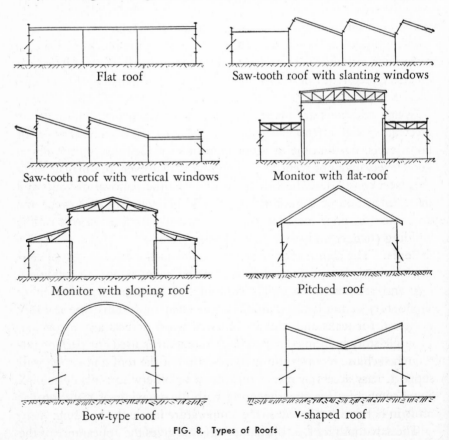

Flat roof   Saw-tooth roof with slanting windows

Saw-tooth roof with vertical windows   Monitor with flat-roof

Monitor with sloping roof   Pitched roof

Bow-type roof   V-shaped roof

FIG. 8. Types of Roofs

Courtesy of Davis & Geck, Inc.

FIG. 9. Exterior of Building Planned for Production

provides additional overhead space which assists in the movement of air if the ceiling is omitted.

The bow-type roof has increased in popularity during recent years, particularly for warehouses and temporary structures. It provides a maximum of overhead space; for this reason, the walls are sometimes not as tall as in buildings of more conventional types.

The V-shaped roof hastens the flow of rain water, as compared with the flat roof. It reduces the need for gutters and downspouts and makes icicles less likely in winter. However, it provides less overhead space and many intensify the effect of ice and snow. The lack of broad eaves to protect walls and windows from rain and to afford some protection from heat in summer may be another objection to this type of roof. The various types of roofs are illustrated in Figure 8.

A building that has been constructed with particular reference to production requirements is illustrated in Figure 9. This building, which is used for the manufacture of surgical supplies, is partly one-story and partly two-story. The roof and wall supports in the one-story section have been built to permit the addition of a second story when additional space is needed, since the roof consists of a concrete slab and all utilities are available in the space between the roof and the ceiling. While the structural lines are pleasing, the building construction is economically planned for production rather than esthetic beauty. The window space and also the interior arrangement have been planned with particular reference to the requirements of lighting and air conditioning.

ADAPTATION OF THE BUILDING PLAN

The plan for the building should be adapted to the need of employees, the manufacturing processes, and the standards of appearance and cleanliness expected by the community. The building can greatly affect employee and public relations as well as manufacturing costs.

Employee Comfort. The building should be designed to provide comfortable, healthful, and reasonably quiet working conditions for the employees. Problems of employee comfort should be considered in the initial plans; for in many respects, employee health and comfort are affected by features that are embodied in the building structure and are not easily changed after the building has been completed. For example, the building plan may make provision for air conditioning, dust and fume control, a proper use of color inside and outside the building, glare-reducing glass, glass blocks in the walls, accoustical partitions and ceilings, and roof insulation. Private offices for foremen which shut out dust and noise but permit a clear view of the work area may be incorporated in the original plan. Foremen's offices permit confidential talks with employees and also make readily available the various records needed for supervision.

Provision should also be made in the original design for such employee services as toilet and washroom facilities, showers, first-aid rooms, and possibly canteens, a cafeteria and kitchen service, meeting rooms, and an auditorium for recreation and training. Before the original plan is completed, these services should be located and the amount of space to be allotted to each should be fixed. Provision should also be made for employee traffic. Some building plans provide for enclosed walkways and passages flanking the production floor in order that employees in reporting for work may not interfere with production or be exposed to accident hazards. Space in locker rooms and at entrances may permit the incoming shift to keep off the floor until the previous shift has vacated the production area.

Built-in Safety. Safety is another problem which should be considered in the original plans. Building codes and fire regulations make specific requirements for safety. In many cases, such regulations are regarded only as the minimum requirements, and safety provisions not required by law are often incorporated in the building plan. Many features of the building entrances, stairways, elevators, materials-handling equipment, lighting, and heating affect safety. Concrete steps may be capped with a metal grill or other device to prevent slipping as well as to prevent wear. Rail supports should be provided for stairways inside and outside the building. The stairway should be wide enough for a double line of travel but not wide enough for three persons unless there is an intermediate handrail. The angle at which the steps rise to the next floor, the width of the tread, the height of the rise, and the uniformity of both the tread and the rise are important features. A door should not be placed to open immediately upon the stairs. Doors that lead to stairways should be self-closing and protected with wired glass. The lighting facilities and also the location of the electric switches are important in safety. Overhead cranes that are located in such a position that heavy materials are lifted over the heads of workers create an accident hazard. The dangers resulting from crossing highways, railroad tracks, and production lines are frequently eliminated by underground passageways leading from entrances or locker rooms to the main floor. After the building has been completed such features as these cannot be changed except at substantial cost.

Another important feature of safety is fire prevention or fire control. A single fire can wipe out the profits of years of successful operation not only because of the property damage but also because of the loss of profits resulting from the interference with production. Fire insurance rates vary with the extent of the hazard. Buildings cannot be made entirely fireproof because of the hazards incident to the processes, including the use of paints, grease and oil, and solvents. A fire that gets out of control may cause the building to collapse because steel beams may buckle with heat and pressure from the weight of the roof and the superstructure. Important features of the building plan for the reduction of the fire hazard are automatic sprinklers, sufficient hydrants to permit two streams of water to be played on any part of the building, the provision of two sources of water supply, roof decks of noncombustible material with the joints sealed to prevent any combustible waterproofing substances from dripping into the building in case of fire, ventilators to exhaust heat and smoke, and provision of portable fire extinguishers and ladders in sufficient numbers at convenient locations. While a building is being constructed, especial attention should be given to fire protection because of the possible accumulation of trash and the exposure of steel beams. Roadways should be kept clear, and trash should not be allowed to accumulate.

Provision for Expansion. The need for increased capacity in the future should be considered in locating the plant, planning the building, and arranging the layout. Such provision is most easily made in a small-town or suburban location where additional land may be acquired at prices that are not prohibitive. Building plans may provide for temporary walls, prepunctured steel beams, large service distribution lines, and proper location of services. The amount of anticipated expansion will affect the plans. The expected expansion may be anywhere from 10 to 50 per cent.

Closely related to expansion is the problem of flexibility to permit new production methods because of changes in product design, the development of new products, the installation of new machines, and new materials-handling equipment. Flexibility in production may be increased by high ceilings, few columns, wide bays, and strong floors. Flexibility in the arrangement of production facilities is also achieved by the arrangement of connections for light and power and the provision of extra connections for use when the layout is changed. The plumbing facilities may be constructed to facilitate changing the location and arrangement of the service areas.

The need for flexibility has been emphasized by such developments as new types of conveyors, lift trucks and pallets, fully automatic machines, and automation. The amount of storage space both in the usual storage areas and along the production line may be increased to prevent interruptions to production because of labor troubles in the plants of vendors and interruptions to transportation services for various causes.

Courtesy of Truscon Steel Co.

FIG 10. Steel Roof Supports and Wide Unobstructed Floor Space

The development of new alloys and the increased use of metal in building construction have permitted significant changes in building designs in respect to wide spans and type of roof. Figure 10 shows the interior of a building that provides wide spans for workplaces which have been made possible by steel supports for the roof.

The additional plant capacity provided through plant expansion is often found to be less costly than the same capacity provided by a new plant. The lower cost of plant expansion may arise in part from the more effective use of plant services available at the old plant. For example, an expansion of the manufacturing department may be made with little or no expansion of the raw materials storeroom, employee service facilities, receiving and shipping platforms, railroad trackage, service roads, water mains, and other services. To be more explicit, a steel company increased its capacity by erecting another blast furnace with no expansion of coke ovens, rolling mills, fabricating departments, or plant services. However, other considerations may sometimes require the construction of a new plant in a different location.

External Appearance. At little extra cost, the exterior of the building may be made pleasing and attractive. At least it need not be ugly and objectionable. It should not be decorative or ornamental, and no attempt need be made to conceal the fact that it is a factory building. Good design is achievel by proportion, balance, and strong, flowing lines. Landscaping is important, for no building makes a good presentation in an ugly environment or in crowded quarters. This fact is an added advantage of a suburban location, the industrial park, or a location on a superhighway, although in urban industrial districts many manufacturing concerns could do much to improve the appearance of the city by giving proper attention to the building and grounds.

Building appearance is an important factor in employee morale. People like good environment. Whether or not employees consciously analyze the causes of their attitudes, they respond to those acts of their employer that indicate that he is interested in their comfort and welfare. Appearance is an important factor in the development of good community relations.

Maintenance Program. Maintenance problems are considered in the original building plan since maintenance costs can be reduced by proper attention to floors, walls, type of construction, ceiling heights, and the location of the maintenance department. After the building is put into service, management should seek to protect its investment by keeping the property in a good state of repair. Preventive maintenance is designed to discover the need for repairs before extensive damage has been done. Some features of the building require more frequent attention than others, but the program should be organized on a five- to ten-year basis. Attention should be given to floors where damage may be caused by moisture, oil, or heavy traffic loads. Cracked masonry joints in the walls should be repaired by replacing the mortar. Walls that permit water to penetrate should be calked, and cracked putty around the glass should be replaced. If glass in windows is broken, the cause should be found and corrected if possible. Broken windows may indicate a settling of the building or excessive loads on the floor above the window. It may also indicate the need of wire guards inside or outside the building. The maintenance program should include roof inspection and repairs, painting, window washing, and ordinary housekeeping. It should preserve both the operating efficiency and the good appearance of the plant.

Renovation of Building and Equipment. Some companies find, after a period of years, that their building and equipment are not adequate to meet changing conditions. The need for renovating plant and equipment could arise because of one or more limitations. Ceiling heights might be too low for certain types of materials-handling equipment. Floors or walls might not carry the weight of machines and materials required by changes in technology or products. Aisles might be too narrow for the manuevering of trucks or trackless trains. Columns might interfere with the movement of materials and equipment. Building construction may make good lighting or air-conditioning costly. Plant construction may not permit efficient layout or adequate capacity. Employee facilities may not be sufficient in view of changed personnel policy. External appearance may be objectionable. An accumulation of these limitations may require action by the management.

The obsolesence of the building might be reflected in increasing costs of the product, higher maintenance expenses, increased downtime of machines, delayed deliveries, and the loss of business. If a company operates a second plant in another city, the difference between the operating expenses at the two plants may be revealed in the monthly cost figures. The company might continue to operate the old plant even though it is not as efficient as a new plant would be, but it should at least give careful attention to the alternatives.

When a company finds that it cannot compete effectively with its present plant, it may follow any one of four alternatives. First, it might close the plant. In this case it would sell all the equipment and dispose of land and buildings in order that production may be concentrated at other existing plants. Second, it might build and equip another plant in the same area, possibly in a suburb or in a nearby city. Third, it might keep the old plant and its equipment for certain specialty products and build an additional plant to house new equipment with special requirements. Finally, the company might modernize the old plant and its equipment to reduce operating costs and provide facilities for new products. The choice of alternatives will depend upon the cost of the change-over, the plans for future expansion, the availability of capital, and the economies to be achieved.

The decision to abandon, renovate, or build would be made by the president and the board of directors, with the advice of the major executives. The plant superintendent might make a study of the problem with the aid of a committee whose membership includes the factory manager, the chief accountant, the manager of industrial and public relations, and the purchasing agent. Possible plant sites would be studied, data as to cost of machinery and building would be compiled, and the costs of renovation would be estimated. If a modernization program is decided upon, the co-operation of general foremen and foremen would be expected. The changes should be planned with a minimum of interference to production and delayed deliveries to customers.

QUESTIONS

1. Under what conditions might a company rent a building instead of owning its plant?

2. Explain the advantages of the sale-and-lease-back arrangement. What are the disadvantages?

3. If the management decides that the next 30 years will be a period of "creeping inflation," would it prefer to own its building or to sell and lease back?

4. Show the relation of type of building required to plant location and the layout of the plant. Why cannot one problem be settled without reference to the other?

5. Name some industries that could use the multistory building to advantage.

6. Name some industries that would require a single-story building.

7. What are the advantages of the steel-frame construction for single-story buildings? For multistory buildings?

8. Illustrate methods of built-in safety.

9. Why are precautions against fire important in the steel-frame building?

10. Why is the external appearance of a factory building important to the company?

CASES

16. HAZARDS IN A FIRE-RESISTANT BUILDING

The transmission plant of General Motors Corporation at Livonia, Michigan, had been designed with a view to the elimination of fire hazards. No wood was used in the walls, roofs, or roof supports, but the construction throughout was of steel. The only wood in the building was the wood-block construction of the floor. The roof structure was sufficiently strong to carry much more than the usual load of roof coverings, snow, and ice, and the building would withstand any wind pressure that could reasonably be anticipated. The materials and parts used in making transmissions were noncombustible. Automatic sprinklers had been installed on one side of the building for the entire length of the structure and also in other areas that might be reasonably regarded as danger spots. Fire extinguishers and water hydrants were also placed in various places throughout the plant. However, a fire got beyond control and caused the entire building to collapse within thirty minutes from the start of the fire. The plant became a complete ruin half an hour later. Three employees lost their lives in the fire. Property damage was estimated at more than $700,000,000, including the loss of production.

The plant covered an area of 34.5 acres. It had no fire walls or curtains to provide roof support or permit the localization of the fire. Only 20 per cent of the total area was protected by automatic sprinklers. The steel roof deck did not provide sufficient insulation to prevent the heating of the asphalt in the roof or the dripping of combustible material from the roof into the area below, after the steel beams in the roof structure had buckled. The fire hose and fire extinguishers were found to be inadequate not only because water and chemicals could not be sprayed upon the flame in sufficiently large quantities but also because the danger of collapse made fire fighting too hazardous after the fire was started.

On the day of the fire, a welding crew of four men was working on the overhead roof structure near the center of the building. A tarpaulin of combustible material was hung between the welders and the working area below. The crew members were employees of an outside contractor. As the crew moved along, the men were supposed to move the tarpaulin. They apparently failed to move it, although the evidence on this point is uncertain. Of the four men in the crew, two did the welding, one attended the safety ladders, and the other man watched with a fire extinguisher in his hands.

Beneath the welders was a conveyor for the housings of the transmissions. The housings were dipped in a tank of rustproofing material, and a drip pan was installed beneath the conveyor to catch the drippings from the rustproofing compound and carry them back to the tank. The wood blocks in the floor were soaked with the compound and with oil. The compound had a flash point of 100 degrees Fahrenheit.

About 3:45 P.M. the fire watcher called that the compound in the drip pan was on fire. Two fire extinguishers containing carbon dioxide were immediately turned upon the fire. Within a few minutes, ten hand extinguishers were brought into use. However, the extinguishers could not be directed at the base of the fire because the drip pan was eleven feet above the floor. Employees turned a small water hose upon the fire. According to one report, the water served to spread the burning liquid to other areas.

Within a few minutes, the drip pan became warped and twisted. The flaming contents were spilled upon the wood-block floor which immediately burst into flames. At the same time, oily deposits on the steel roof supports ignited. The roof deck buckled under the weight of the roof. The asphalt roofing material began to drip through the cracks in the roof. When the asphalt caught fire, flaming substances were quickly scattered. Intense heat was dispersed throughout the building. The coverings of the electric cables burned off, and the power system failed. Presently, roof and walls began to collapse. When firemen from nearby towns arrived, they were unable to get into the building or to reach the fire with their hoses. They turned their attention to saving the adjacent buildings.

Questions:

1. Why can no building be made fireproof?

2. What precautions should be taken in a building of this kind to reduce the fire hazard?

17. RELATION OF BUILDING DESIGN, MATERIALS HANDLING, AND PLANT LOCATION

The National Container Corporation is one of the largest manufacturers of metal and fiber containers in the United States. Its products are used for packaging fruits, vegetables, coffee, meats, fish, olive oil, motor oil, milk, and numerous other products. The company has usually sought to locate its plants near the markets because the product is bulky and relatively expensive to ship. The usual method of shipment of tin cans is as follows: From the can-making machines, cans go by overhead conveyor to the shipping department and to the freight car in which the cans are shipped. Cans are stacked in tiers across the car, with the open ends of the cans toward the middle of the car. No shipping containers are used, but the sides of the car are lined with a fiber covering to prevent damage. A worker stands inside the car and lifts the cans from the conveyor by means of a forklike wooden tool which permits him to lift ten cans from the conveyor at a time.

At the canning plant the cans are not placed in a storeroom but are sent directly from the freight car to the production lines. Cans are picked up in the car and placed on a conveyor by means of a forklike tool similar to that used in loading the cans. Because of the economy in loading and unloading cans, freight cars are used for shipment even for short distances.

Since the business of the National Container Corporation is expanding, the management is contemplating the building of a new factory in California. The president has been approached by the executives of a soup company with the suggestion that the company locate its new plant on land adjacent to the soup plant in a small town in southern California. This arrangement would enable the cans to be sent directly from the can lines to the canning plant without the necessity of shipment by freight car. In this way, transportation costs would be reduced; and delays due to car shortages or failure of the railroad company to place or move cars would be eliminated. The saving in costs would be shared by the two companies.

The president of the container company inquired concerning the regularity of demand for cans by the soup company and was told that demand was more constant than the demand for cans by most packing companies because some varieties of soup can be made during off-seasons. The attorney for the container company advises that long-term contracts with the soup company for containers would probably be illegal under the antitrust laws and that new contracts would have to be negotiated each year. There is also some question as to the legality of the arrangement under the Robinson-Patman Act, which prohibits discrimination between customers. While the United States Supreme Court has not passed upon the legality of pricing by a plant that is located adjacent to the plant of a customer, a federal court held in 1949 that the American Can Company was discriminating between its customers in granting lower prices to a customer who received his cans from the plant of the can company by means of a conveyor. In that case the court said:

"The defendant may in good faith construct its factories in certain localities and thereby incidentally create a locational advantage to those customers situated nearby. In such a case, defendant may sell f.o.b. the factory, provided it is the normal source of supply, and the nearer customers will receive their cans at a smaller delivered price than those less favorably situated. This, however, is not discriminating for the difference is justified in delivery costs. When, however, additional facilities, the runway here, are furnished so that those near the factory receive their cans at a price lower than that normally incident to locational advantage, a discrimination does exist, and the seller, defendant here, must either furnish proportionally equal facilities to all customers purchasing that commodity, discontinue the furnishing of such facilities, or, in this case, discontinue the granting of a discount based upon the existence of the facilities." (*Russellville Canning Co.* v. *American Can Co.,* 87 Fed., Supp. 484, 498.)

The container company cannot provide the same service for all of its customers because it has 3,000 customers and only 58 plants.

The labor supply in the town in which the soup company is located appears to be fully employed, but the container company employs a relatively small number of unskilled workers since can making is largely mechanized. Most of the machines are fully automatic. The company would be required to move a substantial part of the management group from its present plants to the new location.

Materials would be available at plants of steel mills in the San Francisco Bay area. Although tin plate has at times been in short supply, both the steel manufacturers and the government have favored food container manufacturers in making allotments of material.

Land is available for the proposed location at prices that are low in comparison with land in industrial areas adjacent to large cities.

Questions:

1. What additional information would be required before a decision is made as to plant location?

2. What would be the advantage of the proposed location?

3. What would be the disadvantages?

4. How is building design affected by location and methods of handling materials?

10 Machinery
and
Equipment

THE problem of the selection of machinery and equipment first arises when a new enterprise is to be established. The plans for a new business usually begin with machinery and equipment because the amount and types of equipment determine the need for the building to house and protect it. After the operations have been started, problems of machine selection arise from time to time as expansion programs are planned, layouts are changed, and old equipment is found to be inefficient because of depreciation or obsolescence.

Basically, machines and equipment consist of two types—machines for fabricating or fashioning materials and machinery and equipment for moving or storing materials.

EQUIPMENT FOR PRODUCTION

A machine is a device to transmit or modify a force or motion and to direct it for the purpose of performing work. It consists of three parts: (1) a rigid frame or base, (2) moving parts which transmit the force, and (3) one or more tools for performing work. The purpose of the frame is to hold the other parts in proper alignment. The moving parts which transmit force include belts, pulleys, gears, clutches, and shafting. The tools may be grinding wheels, rollers, needles, hammers, screw drivers, knives, brushes, or shaping devices.

A machine may perform three types of operations. The first operation is that of moving or transporting the material. The machine may move the material or container to the proper position for fabrication. After the operation has been completed, the machine may eject the material or move it to a storage place, bin, or conveyor. The second operation is holding. The material may be held in position and the tool moved to it, or the work may be advanced to the tool, or both the work and the tool may be moved. The third operation is fabrication. In the canning of fruit, for example, fabrication includes grading for size, cutting in half, removing core or seed, peeling, bleaching or coloring, placing in containers, and cooking. In metalworking industries, operations consist of rolling, cutting or shearing, punching, forming, drilling, finishing, welding, assembling, polishing, and painting.

From the point of view of the amount of attention required of the worker, machinery and equipment can be grouped into four classes: manually operated, semiautomatic, fully automatic, and automation.

Manually Operated Machines. Manually operated machinery requires constant attention because the worker is required to place the material in position for fabrication, and he may also be required to start the machine. With some types of operations, he may also stop the machine to remove the finished part. He may be required to guide the tool; and with some machines, such as power saws, he may guide the material as the operation is performed. If the machine completes the fabrication without any worker attention other than placing the part in position and starting the machine, continuous attention may still be required because the cycle of work is very short. The power for the operation of a manually operated machine may be supplied by any source, such as electricity, gasoline, or steam, or manual effort. Examples of manually operated machines are typesetting machines, welding machines, gasoline and electric trucks, and earth-moving equipment. In the office, manually operated machines include typewriters, adding and computing machines, bookkeeping machines, and some types of duplicating equipment.

The most important fact concerning manually operated machines from the managerial point of view is that a worker is required for each machine. When the worker leaves the machine, production at that machine stops. Production is disrupted also by absenteeism, tardiness, and strikes. If the worker quits or is discharged, a replacement by transfer or the hiring of a new worker is necessary. Adjustment of output to seasonal variations in demand is not easily accomplished because an increase in production may require the hiring and training of workers. The quality of work done on manually operated equipment depends upon the skill of the worker, but the quality may be better. Custom-made clothing, for example, is usually made on manually operated equipment.

Semiautomatic Machines. Machines which are semiautomatic operate through a cycle of production without attention. A semiautomatic machine requires attention only in loading, starting, and unloading it for each successive cycle. The machine may deposit the processed material in a pile which may be removed at the convenience of the worker. A common example is the machine for slicing meat, although some slicing machines are manually operated. Small bakeries may be equipped with a similar machine for slicing bread.

Another example is the hobbing machine, which is used for cutting gears. A hob is a grooved or fluted hardened steel tap which is firmly fastened to a shaft. The outer surface consists of a fluted steel worm or a series of teeth which will cut grooves of the proper dimensions. When the worker prepares to cut gears on the machine, he fastens one or more blanks on a shaft, places them in the machine, and starts it. The rotating hob approaches the blanks and begins the cut, moving across the piece until it finishes the cut, when it automatically stops. While the machine is making the cut, the worker prepares the next blanks for the machine.

Semiautomatic machines are more expensive than manually operated equipment, but the unit cost of the product may be less if the machines can be operated continuously. Investment in semiautomatic machines is profitable provided, first, that the volume of production is sufficiently large to keep them operating at a high percentage of capacity and, second, that the machines are adaptable to changes in product design or to the manufacture of new products.

From the point of view of management, the significance of semiautomatic machines is that one worker can attend to a battery of machines. While one machine is processing the material, the worker may fill the hopper of another, remove the processed material, or start another machine. The number of machines that one operator can supervise cannot always be determined precisely, and the question of the number of machines per worker is frequently the cause of difficulty with labor unions. Increasing the number of machines that one worker can operate efficiently without stress or strain to him has been given the significant name of "stretch out."

The number of machines one worker can attend will depend upon the time required to adjust the machine and get it started again, the time required to walk from one machine to the next, the time necessary for the machine to process the material, the need of the worker for rest periods, and the regularity of the operating time. If the worker is required to keep too many machines in operation, more than one machine may be down at the same time, and an excessive amount of machine time may be lost. If the worker has too few machines to keep going, he will spend time waiting for the machine to process the part and his time is not used productively. The problem of management in each case is to determine the optimum number.[1]

To illustrate the problem, assume that the time required to set up the work and start the machine is two minutes and the operating time is five minutes. If one minute is required to get a new piece ready before the machine stops, the worker would be idle four minutes while the machine is running. The machine would run for five minutes and be stopped for one minute. If the worker is assigned a second machine, he would be kept busy for four minutes and he would be idle two minutes for each run of the two machines. He might be able to keep a third machine in operation if he takes no rest periods, does not have to walk far from one machine to another or from the materials storage place to a machine, if the running time of each machine is always the same, and if he has no interruptions. The assignment of three machines would probably mean some lost time for the machines. Management would therefore be required to balance the cost of idle time of the worker when he has two machines against the cost of idle time of the machines if he is assigned three machines. Other factors would be the fatigue and nervous strain of the worker, the effect upon worker morale, the traditions of the plant, and the attitude of the union. The difficulty of keeping all machines in operation when one worker is required to operate two or more machines is called multiple machine interference.

Fully Automatic Machines. This type of machine operates continuously through successive cycles. Fully automatic machines do not stop when they have finished with one cycle of operations or one batch of material but continue with the processing of other units. Material is introduced continuously by the machine, and extra parts are available when required at any phase of the operation. In some machines the material, such as paper or cloth, is introduced as continuous stock. Examples are the paper used by a machine for wrapping bread and wire used in making nails. In other machines the materials are placed in a magazine, from which they are automatically fed into the ma-

---

[1] For a discussion of methods of determining the proper number, see D. H. Denholm, "How Many Machines per Operator?" *Factory Management and Maintenance*, Vol. CXII, No. 7 (1954), pp. 107–9.

chine. The magazine may be refilled while the machine is in operation. Examples are automatic stokers, coffee grinders, and flour mills. The material may be fed into the machinery by a conveyor system. For example, in a bakery, the mixture for doughnuts may be poured into a magazine, from which it is drawn and shaped and dropped into hot fat for cooking. The machine turns the doughnut at the proper time and lifts it onto a conveyor, which moves it along as it cools and finally drops it into a machine for coating with powdered sugar. No attention is required of the worker during any of these operations.

When several fully automatic machines are organized into a production line and connected with conveyors which automatically transport the material from one place to another, the factory resembles a single huge machine with highly complicated and fully integrated parts. Worker attention may be limited to supervision, inspection, and possibly a few manual operations at certain stages. This condition is approached by many factories that refine crude oil, ore, or sugar; process milk or cereals; or can fruits and vegetables.

Fully automatic machines require fewer workers than do semiautomatic machines. In busy seasons, production can be increased without a large increase in the number of employees. However, automatic machines are more expensive to purchase and install and can be justified only when the output is large and designs of the product are fairly stable. If standards of product are exacting, fully automatic machines are not always satisfactory because of the frequent attention required by cutting tools or because of variations in quality. For example, in the manufacture of corrugated paper cartons, the sheets may be automatically fed into the machine for stapling; or in another type of machine the worker may place the material in position and start the machine by pressing a pedal with his foot. Quality may be more uniform when the manually operated machine is used because the worker can place the sides in proper position. However, an unskilled or careless worker may produce a lower quality product with the manually operated machine.

When one machine performs more than one operation, or when several machines perform a synchronized series of operations, a delay at one machine or one part of a machine means a delay all along the line. For example, where one machine prints, cuts, folds, staples, and wraps a magazine and prints the mailing address on the wrapper, the stoppage of one part of the machine means the stoppage of all other parts. The difficulty can be minimized but not eliminated by the operation of the conveyor in such manner that a few parts are banked while awaiting fabrication. In a rolling mill, for example, the slack between operations is taken care of by a pit into which the sheet may be permitted to dip. When one machine fills cartons with a product or fills bottles with a liquid and the next machine closes the carton or caps the bottle, a reserve supply of cartons or bottles may be provided by a loop in the conveyor between the two machines. However, arrangements of this kind may provide merely for slight differences in the rate of fabrication or other operation at different stages. They do not eliminate the difficulties of long delay due to machine breakdown.

Automation. With increasing mechanization and the development of electrical controls for manufacturing operations, a production line may be set up which not only moves the materials from one fully automatic machine to another for further processing but also provides for automatic correction of any maladjustment of a machine at any point in the processing. This advanced concept, which is known as *automation,* includes the five following elements:

1. The material is automatically moved from one workplace to another. It may be moved by conveyor belts, chains, slats, or other method. The movement may provide a continuous or intermittent flow of materials.

2. The material is automatically fed into the machine at the next workplace by transfer from the conveyor, or the material may be delivered from storage racks, hoppers, or reels of stock. The method of delivery depends upon the machine which is to perform the work, the physical characteristics of the material, and the optimum rate of production.

3. The processing of the materials is performed by machines according to an established sequence and time schedule. The machine operations include the usual manufacturing work, such as drilling, pressing, assembling, riveting, or bolting.

4. The materials are automatically discharged from the machine when the processing is completed. They are removed by conveyor, gravity chute, pneumatic ejector, or other device. The discharge of materials by the machine is the least difficult phase of automation.

5. The machine inspects the product or the conditions under which the work is done, and it corrects itself if any correction becomes necessary. The principle of self-correction is known as the *feedback.*

The feedback embodies the principle that control is related to performance rather than planned operations.[2] In the automatic factory, for example, a machine might be set for a processing time of three minutes; and if the inspection of a part indicates that the time is insufficient, the operator is required to reset or to adjust the machine to

---

[2] John Diebold, "Automation—the New Technology," *Harvard Business Review,* Vol. XXXI, No. 6 (1953), pp. 63, 64.

A change occurs in the product, process, or machine regarding:	The change is converted into an electric signal by:	The electric signal is amplified or regulated by:	The signal actuates a device, such as:	The device adjusts the plant operation by:
Thickness Temperature Pressure Color Rate of flow Viscosity Other quality	Crystals Photocells Resistors Strain gages Other device	Electron tubes or Transistor	Relays Motors Transformers Solenoids	Opening valves Closing valves Shifting gates in chutes Moving conveyors Operating machines Stopping machines Cutting off flow of materials Making other change

FIG. 11. Automatic Control of Plant Operations

correct the difficulty. In the automated plant if the machine time is insufficient, the machine can automatically allow more time through the principle of the feedback or the electronic control. Likewise, the governor on a steam engine will automatically adjust the flow of the work load rather than permit the machine to remain at the prearranged setting. If the materials are to be processed at a certain temperature with a given air pressure and with a given amount of humidity in the air, the machine corrects itself in case a variance should develop. Feedback devices may be tied together to form a complete system of machines that process the materials and are self-correcting. Parts are automatically gaged or inspected after each operation, and the machine is automatically corrected when the parts begin to drift from quality limits. All assembly, finishing, and packaging operations are integrated into one system. The method of electronic controls in automation is illustrated in Figure 11.[3]

A section of an automated plant is illustrated in Figure 12. This pic-

Courtesy of Ford Motor Co.

FIG. 12. Automated Engine Plant

[3] Adapted from Norman Weissman, "What You Need to Know about Electronic Controls," *Factory Management and Maintenance*, Vol. CXI, No. 9 (1953), pp. 118–27. Used by permission.

ture, which shows a part of the engine plant of the Ford Motor Company at Cleveland, was taken while the department was in full production. It illustrates how a series of fully automatic machines may produce without worker attention. In the department shown, 115 separate machining operations are performed on the engine block as it moves through the 19 stations. The air vent tubes in the center of the work area remove particles of metallic dust and contribute to the cleanliness of the workplace and the quality of the product.

Many kinds of production cannot be automated, but where automation is possible the results are far reaching. Plant location is affected less by labor requirements and more by such factors as nearness to sources of raw materials, service industries, markets, and power. Plants need long clear spans to simplify the installation of equipment and the free flow of materials. Less square feet of floor space is required because the machines can be placed closer together and the space requirements for machine operators and personnel services are reduced. Plant organization is affected because the number of workers performing manual operations is reduced. More workers in the skilled classifications are required. For example, industry needs more tool and die makers, patternmakers, cost estimators, and engineers. Automation therefore results in technological unemployment in some areas and shortages of workers in other categories. Labor problems are changed because of the smaller number of machine operators or production-line workers. Since machines do not practice slowdowns, go on strike, or require rest periods and coffee breaks, the character of supervision is also affected.

Automation changes the break-even point because of the greater overhead expenses for depreciation, taxes, insurance, interest on investment, and maintenance. An increased amount of salary expense becomes fixed because of the need for maintenance employees, technical assistants, and machinists. Employees in these classifications cannot safely be laid off with each decrease in the volume of production. However, automation decreases payments for annual wages to employees, supplementary unemployment benefits, and other indirect payments. Ultimately the effect of automation, like other improvements in efficiency, will be a higher standard of living, a greater amount of leisure time, and less manual effort on the part of the people employed.

General-Purpose Machines. From the point of view of the variety of uses, machines are classified as general-purpose and special-purpose. A machine is designated as general-purpose if it can be used to perform more than one type of work. This statement does not mean that the machine will perform all types of operations, for all machines have relatively small adaptability. An example of a machine that is used for many purposes is the lathe. This machine holds and rotates a piece of wood, metal, or other material to which a cutting tool is presented. The earliest form of lathe was the potter's wheel which was used in ancient times in the making of vases, bowls, and other pieces of pottery. It was a crude table which was rotated and on which a lump of clay was molded into symmetrical form by the hands of the worker. An improved type of potter's wheel is still used in making many types of pottery. One type of lathe is shown in Figure 13. In this picture, the worker is

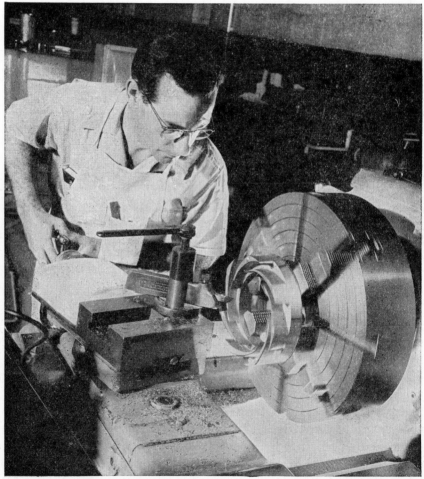

Courtesy of Westinghouse Electric Corp.

FIG. 13. Lathe Used for Machining the Contour of a Part

machining the top contour or face of the diffuser for a centrifugal pump.

In a manually operated lathe the cutting or shaping tool is held or clamped against a rest. In a semiautomatic lathe the tool is held in a slide which automatically moves across the part to make the desired cut. A number of cutting tools may be fixed in a turret or monitor which is pivoted in such a manner that any one or more of the tools may be presented to the work. The lathe is adapted to a wide variety of operations by a change in the cutting tools.

Another widely used general-purpose machine is the milling machine. This machine is equipped with fluted, sharp-edged rotary cutter surfaces for shaping and dressing metal. The hobbing machine which was mentioned earlier is an example of the milling machine. It may be adapted to various types of work by changing and adjusting the cutter. The milling machine is one of the most flexible machines found in industry, since it can be used for smoothing wood or metal surfaces as well as for cutting milled edges and grooves. Other general-purpose metalworking machines are drilling and planing machines.

Some machines that have relatively little adaptability can be used for more than one type of operation. For example, the machine that is used for slicing bread can easily be adapted to different thicknesses of the slice and different lengths of loaf. A machine for shearing a sheet of metal for making a can is adaptable to different sizes of the sheet and different sizes of strips. A machine for making glass bottles and jars can be used for many shapes and sizes by changing the molds. The changing of machine tools and fixtures for a new type of operation is called setting up the machine, and the worker who makes the change is called a set-up man. The costs incident to such a change include the wages of the set-up man, the downtime of the machine, and the delay in production.

General-purpose equipment affords many advantages. Plants that are equipped with general-purpose machines can produce a variety of products by a variety of operations. In fact, a company whose products are not standardized must use machines and machine tools of a wide range of usefulness, size, and type. A second advantage of general-purpose equipment is that a change in design of the product or the addition of a new product does not necessitate new equipment or a new layout, although such a change may require changes in tools or attachments. The cost of general-purpose machines is relatively low because the machines are standardized and machinery manufacturers can produce them for stock. The total investment in machinery and equipment is at a minimum because the machinery is adaptable to various types of work and can more easily be used to capacity. Repair costs are kept low because parts are standardized and some kinds of parts can be used in two or more machines. Repairmen become familiar with mechanical difficulties that arise and with methods of making repairs. Workers and foremen become familiar with the operation of the machines. The objection to general-purpose machines is that they are relatively slow and may not produce the parts in the desired quality.

Special-Purpose Equipment.   This type of equipment cannot be used for any work other than that for which it was designed. For example, a machine might be especially designed to peel pears, cut peaches in half, remove grapes from the stems, or test a tin can for leaks. Such a machine would ordinarily not be profitable to buy if a change of product might require that it be scrapped. Much special equipment has been used by manufacturers in the mass-production industries. The installation of special-purpose equipment depends upon such factors as initial cost, maintenance required, efficiency of operation, obsolescence, possible changes in the design of the product, the volume of output, and the amount of special work the plant is expected to produce. Machines of special design may be fully automatic and capable of producing a large quantity of work within a short time.

The initial cost of special-purpose machines is high because each machine is especially designed and manufactured. Maintenance expenses are also high because many of the parts are not standard. However, the unit costs of parts made or processed on such machines may be low because the output per hour is high, downtime is less, and quality is more uniform. Because each type of machine has certain advantages, a plant may be equipped with some machines of each kind.

Some plants use general-purpose machines for special purposes by means of especially designed fixtures or machine tools. The machine is used continuously on the same operation until a run is completed or perhaps until the design of the product is changed. This arrangement permits the company to realize some of the economies of special-purpose machines while minimizing the costs of changes in plant layout and in product design.

Factors in the Selection of Equipment.   In addition to the amount of supervision or worker attention required by a machine and the operations which it is designed to perform, other features are important in selecting equipment. One factor is the permissible variances in the dimensions of parts. A machine will process a part to certain dimensions, but the parts will not be exactly the same. The standards for the product permit some variations from the prescribed dimensions which are called "tolerances." If the parts as processed by a machine vary from the standard dimensions by more than the tolerances, further machining is necessary to remove the excess material, or the parts must be scrapped. One factor in the selection of machinery, therefore, is the required exactness in the processing of the material.

Another consideration is the maintenance necessary to keep the machine in good operating condition. Maintenance includes lubrication and the replacement or adjustment of moving parts. The ease or difficulty in adjusting or lubricating the machine is sometimes important. Many machines are equipped with self-contained lubricating units which keep them properly lubricated while they are in operation. This device reduces maintenance expenses, lengthens the life of the machine, and decreases the amount of downtime.

Repair costs are also affected by the cost of parts and their availability. If a new gear to replace a broken one can be obtained only from the manufacturer, the purchaser of the machine may be required to keep an abnormally large supply of repair parts or run the risk of delay as a result of machine breakdown.

The output of a machine should be compared with the cost of electric power, gasoline, or other fuel required to operate it. A familiar example is the cost of gasoline for an automobile in relation to the number of miles traveled. The output per hour or day of a machine is also important. This figure may be compared with the miles per hour for an automobile.

The machine may materially affect conditions for persons who work with it or near it. In some cases, the machine may cause an excessive amount of noise and vibration, which will affect both employee and community relations. A machine may give off an excessive amount of heat, which will complicate the problems of air conditioning. Some machines or processes emit fumes and gases that are objectionable or even injurious. Machine design will also affect lighting conditions, although color can be changed by repainting.

In the selection of machines, attention should be given to safety features, although all machine manufacturers now attempt to design their products to meet rigid safety requirements. Safety features embodied in machine design usually include mechanical devices to feed the material to the cutting tool and to eject the finished parts. Control devices may require the worker to use both hands to operate such machines as cutting and trimming machines in a bookbindery or a machine for pressing suits or ironing shirts in a laundry. Guards on circle saws may be designed to make it impossible for workers to get into the danger zone. Some machines are equipped with a device to push the hand of the worker out of the way of the tool as it advances toward the work. Numerous types of covers, fencing, barricades, and other enclosures protect workers from falling into moving parts. As a further precaution, moving parts may be located away from rather than adjacent to aisles and passageways. Belts and cranes may move overhead, where the danger of contact is eliminated. Automatic control levers, buttons, switches, and safety control devices should be located at a point on the machine where they are readily accessible to the worker at all times, in order that he may stop the machine in an emergency. The accident hazard is also reduced by having the machine do the heavy work. This arrangement allows the worker greater freedom of movement.

EQUIPMENT FOR HANDLING MATERIALS

Among the newer phases of industrial management are the development and widespread use of specialized equipment for the handling of materials. In the days of Frederick W. Taylor, much of the handling of materials was done by hand methods. Men with shovels loaded and unloaded cars of coal and gravel. Before World War I, improved methods were developed for the movement of various kinds of materials both inside and outside the plant; but in many cases the new methods were not immediately installed. Because interest was centered in the development of efficient machinery for processing, inefficient methods continued to be used for the transportation of the material. Since 1920 and particularly since World War II, the adoption of improved materials-handling methods has been more rapid.

Costs Resulting from Poor Methods. An obvious cost of poor materials-handling methods is the wages paid to laborers. In factories that fabricate lightweight materials, such as clothing, radios, watches, or telephones, internal transportation is less costly than it is for a cement mill or a meat-packing plant; and in some departments, the materials may be merely pushed along the bench from one worker to another, or a worker may leave his workplace to get a batch from another machine. However, this method may result in damage to parts if the materials are not carefully moved. In plants that move heavy, bulky material, the wages paid to workers employed in moving materials have sometimes constituted as much as 80 per cent of the total labor cost. This factor is a significant part of the cost of manufacture.

Poor materials-handling methods are also costly because they increase the cost of plant space. When materials are handled by man power, wide aisles should be provided for trucking. Material must be stored at the workplace until it can be moved. In the storeroom, material cannot easily be stacked to the ceiling unless special equipment is used to lift it and to place it back on the floor when it is needed. Space is not properly utilized, with the result that the plant operates below its maximum capacity. The congestion of material between departments and around the workplaces may create a false appearance of activity. Improved materials-handling equipment causes the parts to be moved along rapidly to the assembly line, the storeroom, or the shipping room.

In estimating the possible savings from the installation of equipment for handling materials, the plant engineer would make a careful survey of present methods in comparison with the proposed methods. This survey might be made with or without the assistance of equipment manufacturers. The report of the survey would show the number of men engaged in moving materials, the time spent, and the labor cost. It would also include an estimate of the time lost by workers in each department waiting for materials and the wages paid for idle time. The costs of interruptions to production and the annoyance to foremen and workers due to delays should also be estimated, even though the costs cannot be accurately determined. In some companies that handle heavy materials like cement or make a bulky product like tin cans, the planned production from week to week may vary considerably unless efficient methods of handling materials can be used. The cost of storage space adjacent to the workplace and the loss of overhead space that cannot be utilized without the better methods of materials handling should be estimated. Estimates should also be made of accident costs, premiums on compensation insurance, and losses on spoiled work due to the poor methods. A survey of this kind is designed to determine whether any changes should be made and what type of equipment should be installed.

Principles of Materials Handling. Although the principles that will guide management in planning for materials handling will vary with the materials and the methods of production, attention may be directed to certain objectives. Safety assumes special significance because workers may be injured by improperly lifting heavy packages or by having materials dropped on feet or hands. Gravity conveyors or chutes are economical when they can be used. Movement of materials in a straight line constitutes another objective.

The unit-load principle suggests that the more pieces or pounds moved in a single handling operation, the lower will be the cost per unit and the shorter the time required. However, the size of the unit load may be limited by weight, bulk of the unit, the width of aisles and doors, and capacity of the floors for carrying heavy loads. The size of the unit load may be increased by the use of skids or pallets which are moved by lift trucks.

Other principles of materials handling apply to the equipment. Mechanical equipment for lifting and moving materials has decided advantages in the handling of heavy materials or large numbers of units. The economies of materials handling should permit the management to recover the cost of equipment within a relatively short time. The economies in the use of equipment are affected by the speed at which a truck or other unit moves, the ratio of the weight of the equipment to the weight of the load that is carried, and such equipment details as automatic couplings, nonfriction bearings, and rubber tires. The nature of the materials handled may require that the equipment be capable of a variety of uses.

Factors in the Selection of Equipment. Some plants may effect greater savings from materials-handling equipment than others. One difference results from the weight of the materials because some heavy materials require cranes or trucks while lighter materials may be moved by conveyor or by the workers. Hot materials require special types of equipment. If the number of units is great, such as loaves of bread or tin cans, a conveyor would usually be economical. The value of each unit constitutes another consideration. Differences also arise

Courtesy of American Can Co.

FIG. 14. Movement of Tin Cans to Freight Car by Conveyor

because of the need for a continuous and uniform rate of movement for certain kinds of materials. Other factors are the distance to be moved, the possible damage to materials in handling, and the flexibility required. Flexibility may be provided by the linking together of a number of units as shown in Figure 14.

Types of Materials-Handling Equipment. It is not possible to describe, or even to enumerate, all of the various types of equipment that are available. Hoisting machinery includes various types of cranes, derricks, cableways, bucket conveyors, power shovels, and dredges. The

Courtesy of Westinghouse Electric Corp.

FIG. 15. Powered Conveyors and Gravity Chute

railway and motor-truck systems outside the plant are an important part of the equipment for handling materials. Elevators for moving materials from one floor to another may be automatic or may be operated by an attendant. Materials may be moved from an upper to a lower floor by gravity chutes. To delay the descent, the chutes may be circular or spiral. The friction of the material against the outer wall of the chute slows its movement and prevents damage when it spills out at the end of the chute. Powered conveyors and a gravity chute are shown in Figure 15.

Overhead Conveyors. One type of overhead conveyor is a crane which moves on a runway. It may move the length of the shop. Overhead chain conveyors may be used to carry parts of any type from one workplace to another. The carrousel conveyor is an endless chain which moves from the storeroom to the assembly line and back again to the storeroom. It is often used to keep the assembly line continuously supplied with parts. The conveyor may be directed upward in some areas

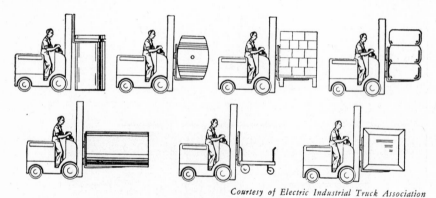

Courtesy of Electric Industrial Truck Association

FIG. 16. Some Uses of Lift Trucks for Materials Handling

and may be dipped downward where the parts are needed. Such an overhead conveyor has also been used to store parts until they are required. A part on the conveyor line is always within reach of the worker, but it need not be removed from the line until it is needed.

Trucks. Trucks may be used to pull one or more trailer loads. Some trucks are equipped with cranes for lifting heavy parts; others are equipped with forks which may be inserted beneath skids loaded with materials and which may thus lift the entire load without rearrangement. Trucks may also be equipped with devices to lift newsprint, oil drums, reels, sheet steel, concrete or steel pipe, and other materials. Some uses of lift trucks are illustrated in Figure 16.

In many plants, materials-handling methods have been revolutionized by the use of pallets and lift trucks. The pallet is a platform or two-faced skid. It has a flat base that rests on the floor. Above the base are short legs or runners which support a second platform of the same dimensions as the one which rests on the floor. Material may be piled on the pallet with the cartons interlaced to prevent them from falling off when moved. When the loaded pallet is to be moved, the fork of a fork-lift truck is inserted between the two faces of the pallet, and the whole load is lifted off the floor; pallet and material are then moved to the new location. The truck can set the pallet on the floor or lift it to any desired height within a considerable range. Since the pallet has a flat base, one load of material can be piled upon another without damage to the material. With a fork-lift truck the top load of a tier of palletized material can be easily removed, or the entire stock of material can be rearranged if necessary. The pallet system makes

Courtesy of Safeway Stores

FIG. 17. Use of Lift Truck for Storing Materials on Pallets

Note manner of interlacing cartons to prevent falling. Driver is protected by grillwork above his head. Inventory taking would be facilitated if the same numbers of cartons were placed on each pallet. More even piling would reduce the danger of damage to cartons and contents.

possible a more effective use of storage areas and the utilization of overhead space. It reduces the possibility of damage to materials and injury to persons. It promotes cleanliness and orderliness in the storeroom. It saves handling time by eliminating the need for dunnage boards to spread the weight of a stack of material. The pallet and lift-truck method is illustrated in Figure 17.

Many special types of pallets have been designed and developed. Some are made of sheet metal; and others called *boxed pallets* have boxed-in sides and a top to prevent materials from falling while they are being moved. Some boxed pallets have double-faced tops as well as double-faced bottoms. A fork-lift truck has been devised which will invert the pallet and place the opposite side up. This device is especially adapted to up-ending condensed milk which must be turned about every thirty days to prevent spoiling. Special boxed pallets have been designed to store odd-shaped materials.

When the pallet system was first developed, it was used largely for intraplant transportation. The pallets were considered to be too expensive for interplant movement of materials unless the pallets could be returned. Later, many companies began the practice of packing finished merchandise on expendable pallets for shipment to customers. The pallets are made of cheap grades of wood or fiber and need not be returned. Each shipment of this kind constitutes a relatively large quantity. The amount stacked on one pallet should be planned in relation to the usual quantities purchased by customers and the width of the freight car or truck in which the shipment is made. When pallet loads of materials are stored in a warehouse or storeroom, the pallets may be placed at an oblique angle to the aisle to reduce the labor costs of storing and issuing. If a pallet is placed at right angles to the aisle, it must be removed in the same way. A pallet that is placed at an angle is part of the way out of the row when the truck begins to move it and the possibility of damaging the materials is reduced. A small amount of additional space is needed when pallets are placed at an angle, but the difference is not substantial.

Another type of truck for storing and moving materials is shown in Figure18. Although this type of truck may be used in the handling of materials of various sizes and shapes, the illustration shows a special use for it. The metal tubing may be placed on the truck during an operation, moved into a storeroom or stored at the workplace until it is required at the next workplace, and then placed in position for use at that station. The materials in the illustration shown are heavy, and large numbers of them are used. However, the movement of the

Republic Steel Photo

FIG. 18. Hand Truck Used for Storing and Moving Materials

materials from one workplace to another is not continuous, and convenient storage at each workplace is desirable.

Responsibility for Improving Materials Handling. Some companies regard the problems of materials handling as so important that
they have created a special position to devote continuous study to it.
Such an executive is called superintendent of materials handling, ma-
terials-control supervisor, or engineer for plant layout. A more common arrangement, however, makes this work one of the duties of the
industrial engineer or the plant engineer. Executives in both of these
positions perform staff duties. Suggestions for improvement in materials handling may also be made by the plant superintendent or the
foreman. If the company has a suggestions system, additional suggestions may be made by employees. The money for improvements in materials handling would be provided by a capital budget, which requires the approval of the president and the board of directors. Some

companies that recognize the need for more efficient methods of materials handling are unable to make the needed improvements because the building is multistory, has floors that will not support heavier loads, columns that would interfere with conveyor equipment, obsolete elevators, or other serious limitations.

THE REPLACEMENT OF EQUIPMENT

Equipment must ultimately be scrapped because of obsolescence or decreased operating efficiency. Obsolescence means that the equipment ceases to be economical in operation because more efficient machines or processes have been developed to perform the same or similar work. Decreased operating efficiency is reflected in lower output per hour, a larger amount of time when the machine is out of use for overhauling or repairs, and the increased cost of labor and parts for repairs. Ultimately, machinery will have to be junked regardless of the regularity and the thoroughness of the repairs and maintenance.

The decision to replace a machine depends upon a number of factors which must be balanced one against another, such as the probable volume of production requiring the use of the machine, possible alternative uses of the machine, the number of years the present machine might be kept in use with proper maintenance, and the possibility of the development of more efficient machines in the future, which would make the new machine obsolete. If certain assumptions are made for the factors involved, definite computations can be made by estimating operating cost per year or per unit of product with a new machine in comparison with the machine now in operation.[4]

The total amount of money that may be expended for machine replacement in any one year may be determined in one of two ways. One method provides for the expenditure of an amount of money equal to the annual depreciation charge for machinery and equipment. This amount may be expended each year, and the figure may not be exceeded. The second method provides for the replacement of a machine and the purchase of a new one at any time when savings in cost can be expected by doing so. This plan places no limit on the total amount, and it does not provide any fixed sum. In this case, machine replacement may be planned through a plant and equipment budget.

Continuous Replacement. The funds provided each year by profits or other income may be retained in the business by an amount equal

[4] Philip A. Scheuble, Jr., "How to Figure Equipment Replacement," *Harvard Business Review*, Vol. XXXIII, No. 5 (1955), pp. 81–94.

to the annual depreciation charge, and this amount may be used for replacement of equipment.[5] For example, if the equipment is estimated to have an average life of ten years, the annual depreciation charge would be 10 per cent. When an entry is made in the accounts charging depreciation of machinery, the effect is not only to decrease the profits by the amount of the entry but also to retain cash in the business by the same amount, provided that the business is not operating at a loss. The entry for the depreciation charge does not bring cash into the business, but it does reduce the amount available for dividends or required for the payment of income taxes. In the absence of a definite policy of machine replacements, the amount of cash retained in the business may be used for any purpose, such as the payment of liabilities or an increase in current assets. By action of the management, the funds withheld may be used to replace any equipment that has become so inefficient that it should no longer be kept in operation.

Continuous replacement requires the co-operation of the plant superintendent, the foremen, and the plant engineer. Equipment that is known to be inefficient is listed by the shop superintendent and is then investigated by the management. Comparison is made with new equipment available, and replacements are made where the operating economies appear to be most promising. The total amount spent for new equipment in one year is limited by the amount of the funds provided by the depreciation charge.

The advantage of the plan of continuous replacement is that it usually results in the scrapping of machines at the end of their useful life. No attempt is made to keep machines in operation indefinitely after their useful life is passed. It is also argued that any other plan causes the funds provided by the depreciation charge to be invested elsewhere, even though the purchase of equipment would be more profitable. Continuous replacement also equips the shop with machines that embody the latest principles of machine design and construction.

Effect of Rising Prices. A new machine may cost more than the one replaced because the price level has increased since the original machine was purchased and because designs have been improved. The depreciation charge may therefore not provide sufficient funds for replacement and the total investment in machinery and equipment must be increased if the efficiency of the plant equipment is to be kept up. The usual provision for investment in equipment consists of a capital

[5] Lewis H. Kimmel, *Depreciation Policy and Postwar Expansion* (Washington, D.C.: Brookings Institution, 1946), p. 9.

budget and of additional funds by the reinvestment of a part of the profits, by borrowing, or by the sale of additional capital stock.

Another possibility is the charging of depreciation as a percentage of replacement cost. This plan has the effect of increasing the cost of goods manufactured. The higher cost of the product may decrease the net profit, or it may result in higher selling prices for the product provided market conditions will permit. However, the effect of higher cost upon selling prices is uncertain because the selling prices are affected by many factors other than cost.

The Treasury Department will not permit depreciation to be computed on replacement cost for tax purposes. This requirement presents no difficulties, however, because depreciation can be recomputed on cost for income tax purposes. If a company is subject to the requirements of the Securities and Exchange Commission, its financial statements issued for the information of investors are required to show a figure for depreciation based on original cost.

Estimating Savings from Replacement. A second policy in the replacement of machines provides for their purchase only when the savings will pay for their cost within a few years. A new machine may operate more efficiently because of savings in labor, power, repairs, supplies, and space costs and because of greater output. However, the new machine may result in higher costs in some respects, such as depreciation, taxes and insurance. To determine whether the purchase of a new machine to replace an old one is profitable, the total cost of operating each machine may be computed and the difference in costs determined.

The method of estimating the savings from the installation of a new machine raises many theoretical questions. Formulas have been developed by different companies for estimating the savings from scrapping an old machine to buy a new one, and some of them are quite complicated. To illustrate the difficulty, assume that a company has a semiautomatic machine which it acquired five years ago at a cost of $30,000. Its capacity is 28,000 units per year. An automatic machine is now available at a cost of $40,000, but its capacity is said to be 40,-000 units per year. The new machine will have lower costs for labor, maintenance and repairs, and power; but it will require greater costs for floor space, taxes, and insurance.

The costs of operation with the new machine in comparison with the old one should be figured on the present value of the two machines. The difference between the original cost of the old machine and its present value should have been charged to cost of the product or to

expense during the years when it was in use. If it has not been depreciated properly on the books to reduce book value to trade-in value,
the difference is regarded as a sunk cost, which cannot be recovered
either by scrapping it or by continuing to use it.

The comparison of the total cost per year and the cost per unit of
product with the old machine and also with the new one is shown in
Table 1. In this computation, the old machine is assumed to have a scrap

TABLE 1

COMPARISON OF COST OF OLD MACHINE AND NEW MACHINE

	Old Machine (5 Years Old)	New Machine
First cost...........................	$30,000	$40,000
Annual operating costs:		
Labor	$5,000	$1,000
Maintenance and repairs	300	200
Power	1,800	1,500
Depreciation	600	4,000
Interest, 5 per cent	150	2,000
Floor-space cost	400	600
Taxes and insurance	2,000	4,000
Total cost per year	$10,250	$13,300
Number of units produced	28,000	40,000
Cost per unit	$0.3661	$0.3325

value or trade-in value of $3,000, and depreciation is computed at 20
per cent of that amount since the remaining life is five years. Interest is
figured at 5 per cent. This table shows the costs for the first year only
The cost will vary slightly in later years as a result of the decreasing
investment in the machine. Offsetting this decrease in unit or annual
costs might be an anticipated increase in maintenance and repairs as
the machine nears the end of its useful life.

This computation indicates a slightly lower cost per unit with the
new machine. However, a decision to purchase it should not be made
until some other factors have been considered. The new machine has a
capacity of 40,000 units, whereas the old machine has a capacity of
only 28,000. If the old machine is adequate to take care of existing demand, the purchase of the new machine might result only in unused
capacity. On the other hand, if the old machine is inadequate, the new
machine might lower costs on other machines by permitting them to
operate at nearer capacity. A further consideration is whether changes
in the design of the product are contemplated. A change in design

might make the new machine obsolete before its cost could be recovered in production. These uncertainties suggest that formulas cannot be used as infallible guides to policy in such matters but that the final decision will depend upon the judgment of management.

Lease or Buy. Much machinery and equipment can be purchased or it can be leased for a period of years. Some companies make no lease contracts, while others find them advantageous in certain cases. Lease arrangements may be feasible if management wishes to modernize a department or a process without tying up its capital for the life of the equipment or without assuming long-term obligations for loans or mortgages. In some cases, equipment may be needed for only a short time, and a rental arrangement may permit the manufacturer to use a machine for the limited period of time. If the manufacturer of the machine contemplates technological improvements, the lease arrangement reduces the risks due to obsolescence. A plant manager may resort to the lease arrangement if the president and the board of directors decline to include in the budget the money for plant expansion but are willing to permit a temporary increase in current expenses for rental payments.

The lease arrangements may prove to be a costly way to obtain equipment because the lessor must charge a sufficiently high rental to enable it to recover the cost of the equipment during its useful life, pay its own financing and operating costs, and provide a net profit. The rental charge may also be high enough to cover the risk of obsolescence. For this reason, many companies prefer to buy machines rather than to lease them.

The lease arrangement may have a tax advantage. The entire rental payment is deductible for tax purposes, unless the contract includes certain provisions that make it in fact a purchase, such as an option to buy and the application of the rental payments toward the purchase price. Under the present tax provisions which permit the cost of the equipment to be depreciated rapidly, the lease arrangement does not necessarily result in lower taxes. The tax advantages require careful study in each case.

Most of the calculations described in this chapter assume that the dollar has a stable purchasing power. The conclusion might be different if the possibility of inflation is taken into consideration. During periods of inflation, the ownership of assets that increase in value becomes an advantage, and the owing of debts on which payments of interest and principal are made in dollars of decreasing purchasing power also give the debtor the advantage. To make the payments, however, the owner of the machine would be required to produce and sell manufactured goods at prices which reflect the decreased value of the dollar. The prospect of continuing or "creeping inflation" would usually be a factor in the decision to replace or keep a machine.

Responsibility for Selection of Equipment. Because the ability of the company to produce at a low cost and to maintain its competitive position depends in part upon the selection of equipment, the decision to buy or to replace is usually made only after consultation with many persons. Although the purchase or replacement of machines is principally an engineering problem, it also concerns the treasurer and the budget committee. The purchasing agent may know much about market conditions as they affect the cost of new or used machines. Other persons who might be consulted about a new machine include the methods and time-study engineer, the accident prevention manager, the manager of product design, and the production planning engineer.

LABOR AND MACHINE PRODUCTION

When the introduction of a new machine results in net economies in production costs, the usual reason is that labor costs are decreased. To the worker, the increased use of machinery may mean temporary unemployment. Older workers may suffer a permanent reduction in pay, rank, and social status, since the machine may reduce the amount of skill required by the worker. A person who is over fifty years of age may not easily find another job. He may become permanently unemployed, or he may be required to work for much lower wages. In some cases, a worker may be compelled to move to a new community to find employment, and he may be able to effect such a transfer only at considerable cost to himself and his family.

The cost of unemployment caused by new machines may be borne in several ways. The worker who is thrown out of work may be required to find a new job for himself and to live as best he can until he does so. In this manner the cost is placed upon the worker and his family. Another possibility would be for the worker and his family to seek gratuities from local charitable organizations. In this way, the cost is shifted to the people who live in the neighborhood of the plant. The federal government might provide public works or make-work projects to support workers who would otherwise be unemployed. This plan shifts the cost to taxpayers. In various ways, the cost might be borne by the employers individually or as a group. Each employer might keep a displaced worker on the payroll until he finds work elsewhere. If all employers follow such a plan, they may be able to raise prices and to shift a part of the cost to the consumers of the product. The employers might jointly bear the cost through unemployment insurance as provided by social security legislation. The government may bear a part of the cost through its payment of the expenses of the administration of the plan. The incidence of the cost in this case is uncertain. The cost may eventually be shared by consumers as a result of higher prices, by workers as a result of lower wages, by stockholders as a result of decreased profits, or by the general public through taxes or contributions to social agencies.

The introduction of machinery is frequently regulated by contract between the company and the union. The contract may provide that the company will confer with union officers when a reduction in the work force is contemplated because of mechanization and that it will attempt to arrive at an equitable solution before any employee is dismissed. The company may agree to render notice to the union and to any affected employee six months in advance of the proposed changes. The company may also agree that when a job is eliminated by mechanization, it will attempt to give the displaced employee an opportunity to learn new skills and to prepare himself for another job. To eliminate any possibility of discrimination, the company may agree that necessary dismissals will be made in the reverse order of seniority. When the work force is later increased, any employee who was previously dismissed may be given preference provided that he is qualified to perform the work of the new job. Severance pay, in addition to payments specified by law, may be required by the contract. Because provisions of this kind may be interpreted differently in individual cases, the contract frequently provides for the arbitration of disputes. Both parties agree in advance to abide by the decision of the arbitrator.

QUESTIONS

1. Compare the personnel problems with manually operated machines with personnel problems in a fully automated plant.

2. How are employees affected when a plant becomes fully automated?

3. What is the attitude of workers and unions toward the question of increasing the number of semiautomatic machines supervised by one worker?

4. Distinguish the fully automatic machine and automation.

5. How are costs affected by increased mechanization?

6. Were workers happier when each person made a complete product with

hand tools than workers in a present-day plant with its mechanization of production and the division of the work into numerous tasks requiring a relatively small amount of skill?

7. How does automation affect the organization of a plant? How does it affect overhead expenses and labor costs?

8. Does automation increase or decrease the need for employee training? Compare with a plant that uses manually operated machines.

9. How do special-purpose machines affect overhead expense and labor cost? Compare with general-purpose machines.

10. It has been said that moving materials does not increase their value. Moving them adds only to the cost. Show the application of this statement to the selection of materials-handling equipment.

11. What economies may be achieved by the use of the pallet system in: (a) loading freight cars, (b) unloading, (c) stacking materials in the storeroom, and (d) issuing materials from the storeroom?

12. What difficulties arise in estimating the savings from machine replacement?

CASES

18. NUMBER OF MACHINES SUPERVISED BY ONE WORKER

One of the principal products of the United Bag and Paper Company was a heavy paper bag that was used for cement, sugar, plaster, insulating materials, and other heavy bulk products. The bags were imprinted with a label, the name of the manufacturer, and certain other descriptive material according to the specifications of the customer. When the machine had been set up for a run, the bags were stacked in a hopper or magazine, the machine was started, and the run was continued until the run was complete. While the machine was running, the worker could refill the hopper when necessary, attend to other machines, or do other work.

By practice or custom, each experienced worker was expected to keep five machines in operation. Since the company had nineteen such machines, three workers were assigned five machines each, and the least experienced worker was given four machines. Workers were paid on an hourly wage plus a bonus of 25 cents per day for each machine tended. The plant superintendent questioned whether five was the most economical number; and he asked Mr. Carmichael, the time-study man, to study the operation and to make a report of his recommendation. Mr. Carmichael, with the assistance of the foreman and a co-operative worker, first studied the amount of necessary downtime between operations. The downtime was used for changing setups from the old run to the new one, adjusting and oiling the machine, and making minor repairs when they were needed. The time required for filling the hoppers was not included in the downtime because the operator could do this work at any time while the machine was running. The time for filling hoppers was separately estimated at 1.1 per cent of worker time for each machine. Mr. Carmichael found that each machine was out of production 6.3 per cent of the total shift time.

In the next step of the study, Mr. Carmichael determined the additional down-time that was caused by the number of machines operated by one worker. Because the operator was required to walk from one machine to another, some of his time was spent unproductively; and downtime might be increased if the worker had too many machines to keep going. The time spent in walking was estimated to be 0.2 per cent for each machine tended, or 1.0 per cent for five machines. Another factor in downtime was multiple machine interference, which means that two or more machines might be out of production at the same time. The loss of time due to this factor was difficult to estimate because the percentage increases with the number of machines. This problem was solved by means of a formula which was developed by an assistant in the time-study department. By means of the formula, Mr. Carmichael estimated the loss of time due to multiple machine interference for varying numbers of machines from four to seventeen for each operator. He found that four machines per worker resulted in too much idle time for the worker and seventeen resulted in too much loss of time for machines. The optimum number was somewhere in between these extremes.

The next step was to estimate the total operation time of the worker who might tend various numbers of machines. For example, the study showed that when the worker tended five machines he was busy about 35 per cent of the time in getting the machines back into production, walking back and forth between the machines, filling hoppers, and getting materials. With proper allowance for fatigue, personal needs, and delays, the time was increased to 39 per cent. On the basis of this information, Mr. Carmichael estimated that the maximum number of machines that a worker could tend was twelve. If he were assigned thirteen machines, his time requirement would be over 100 per cent. He would be unable to keep all of the machines in operation, and downtime would necessarily result. He would be unable to keep thirteen machines in operation even if the factor of multiple machine interference were disregarded.

The proper number of machines for one worker to tend was finally fixed at ten. To permit more effective planning of production, to make possible the neces-ary overhauls of machines, and to provide for some increase in production, Mr. Carmichael recommended that one more machine of this type be purchased. If each worker were assigned ten machines, worker dissatisfaction might be lessened. If one worker were to be assigned nine machines, and an attempt were made later to increase the number to ten, opposition would likely be encountered. The two workers displaced by the new arrangement could be transferred to some other de-partment, possibly to maintenance. The saving in wages would more than offset the increase in costs resulting from the purchase of the new machine.

Another problem considered by Mr. Carmichael was the possibility of treating the entire group of machines as a single operation to be supervised by the two workers. Each worker would be expected to service any machine that happened to be out of production. This plan might reduce downtime because in some cases one worker might have two or three machines out of production, while the other worker might have no machines that required his attention. However, Mr. Car-michael decided against this arrangement because of its possible effect upon in-dividual initiative and responsibility. He thought it was better to make each worker responsible for a smaller number of machines and to evaluate his perform-ance by his ability to get a machine back into production in a short time. He recognized also that the final decision concerning work assignments would be made by the foreman and the operating executives.

Required:

Evaluate the methods and the recommendation of Mr. Carmichael.

19. STAFF ASSISTANT FOR MATERIALS HANDLING

The chief engineer of the Northeastern Electric Company, Mr. White, attended a round-table discussion conducted by a national society for the discussion of materials handling. At the conference each person was asked to make a survey of methods of making a product of his company and to record the number of production operations in comparison with other operations, such as receiving, moving, counting, inspecting, storing, removing from storage, and other handling. Mr. White made such a survey for one product assembly and found that the assembly was made of five parts in 37 operations. The parts were handled a total of 208 times and were placed in temporary storage 98 times. Mr. White was very much surprised and disturbed at the results of his survey, and he learned that the other members of the conference were equally surprised at the large number of times that parts were handled and moved in their companies.

After his return from the conference, Mr. White discussed the question of materials handling with the president, who was also much concerned. After further discussion, the president authorized Mr. White to create the position of staff assistant for materials handling for the purpose of making a thorough study of the handling methods and of making recommendations for improvements. The assistant would select the operations and activities to be improved. He would work with the plant superintendent and the foremen to find situations where methods could be improved, study the possibilities in each case, rank the changes needed in the order of priority, and estimate the capital outlays required in making the changes. He would establish and maintain favorable relations with all departments which were concerned with the problem, such as purchasing, traffic, plant engineering, inspection, and production planning and control. He would keep abreast of developments in new methods and equipment outside the company and seek to keep the methods of the company at the most economical level.

An experienced engineer who was familiar with the products of the company and who seemed to possess tact, ingenuity, imagination, and much energy was selected for the new position. He first made some further surveys of conditions within the company. He compiled figures for the number of man-hours spent in manufacturing operations in comparison with the number of hours spent in handling, storing, and inspecting. He found that 26 per cent of the man-hours were spent in moving and handling and that the average part was handled 100 times. He also made studies of the time spent in processing materials as a percentage of the total time the materials were in the plant. For one part, the total time was 230 hours and the time spent in processing it was 16 hours. These results were considered typical of the general experience.

The results were submitted to Mr. White, and the problem was discussed with operating executives and various staff personnel. The proposed solutions included pallets and lift trucks, gravity and powered conveyors to transport the materials to the proper position for use by operators, the elimination of temporary storage wherever feasible, and the establishment of new control points for inspection. The design of the product was restudied to determine whether automatic machines might be substituted for manually operated machines. The cost of the machines required was estimated through conferences with the manufacturers of lift trucks, conveyors, and machines. The savings in each case were estimated by the assembly of data on man-hours, space costs, power, taxes, interest, and depreciation. Plans were made for the installation of the most profitable machines, and other improvements were placed on a priority basis.

To allay worker fears and suspicions, foremen were kept informed of developments, and they were asked to discuss the situation in their departments. Since man-hours would be reduced, some jobs would be eliminated. However, the growth of the company and the increased volume of production and sales would make possible the continued employment of all workers through transfer or promotion.

Required:

Evaluate the procedure and methods of the company.

11 Layout
of the
Plant

LAYOUT is a problem that confronts the manager in any type of business activity. In any enterprise the management must decide what departments or workplaces are necessary or desirable, fix their location in relation to each other, determine the proper amount of space to be assigned to each, plan the boundaries of aisles and passageways for transportation and communication, and provide for the location of facilities for clerical work and the personal needs of workers. These problems constitute the work of layout.

PHYSICAL REQUIREMENTS

Certain objectives are sought in plant layout. First, the materials should be moved short distances and doubling back should be avoided if possible. In some industries, the product may move progressively from one workplace to another. In some cases, however, a machine may be placed out of line because of excessive vibration, fire or explosion hazards, or other special requirements.

The method of transferring materials between workplaces should fit the type of material to be moved. As a general rule, manual handling of materials should be at a minimum, and the distance of moving should be as short as possible. These principles are based upon the idea that the moving of materials adds only to the cost; it adds nothing to their value by changing their form. Although the continuous movement of materials between operations would decrease the value of the inventory of work in process and thereby reduce costs, it may be desirable to arrange for small banks of materials at each workplace in order to avoid delays.

The capacities of various departments should be balanced. The ideal arrangement would provide that when one department is working at capacity, all others would be working at capacity. Balance is not always possible because the capacities of workplaces vary and because some machines must be provided for stand-by equipment in emergencies. Capacity utilization can seldom be achieved because some machines are occasionally out of production for repairs, change-over, or adjustment. In most industries, daily, seasonal, yearly, and cyclical variations in pro-

Courtesy of Monarch Machine Tool Co.

FIG. 19. Workplace with Store of Materials

A store of parts at various workplaces reduces lost time due to machine breakdown and other causes.

duction cannot be entirely eliminated. Interruptions are caused by labor turnover and transfers and the necessity for training new workers.

Equipment should make efficient use of the plant space, including overhead space. It should make supervision easy. It should reduce accident hazards incident to the movement of materials, provide for sufficient aisle space, and make provision for the safe storing of materials where storage is necessary. Figure 19 shows a workplace designed with special reference to the varied requirements of materials and equipment. Materials are stored in shelves and in circular rotary bins divided into compartments. The storage space allows for adequate supplies of materials for one week's work.

Layout by Processes. In a factory organized by processes, all of the machines performing the same or similar operations are grouped together to constitute a department. Since most companies make more than one product, the operations would never be precisely the same for any two products; but several operations might be performed on similar machines. A plant that makes a variety of products on the same machines would usually be organized by processes. If a company contracts with customers to make the product according to their specifications, its plant would usually be laid out by processes. Such a plant is sometimes called a job shop, and the production is said to be diversified. Organization by processes is sometimes referred to as organization by functions.

The plan of layout by processes may be illustrated by the arrangement of machines used to manufacture a circle saw for cutting wood. The operations to make a saw might include the following steps:

Withdraw materials from stock room and send to first manufacturing department.
Cut to size.
Punch center hole.
Punch teeth.
Round and clean teeth.

Heat and shape.
Harden and temper.
Polish.
Block and etch.
Sharpen and set.
Ship to customer.

If the company made only circular saws, the departments could be arranged with eleven departments, placed in the order in which the work is done. However, the factory might make such other products as hacksaws, knives, printers' steel rules, hand saws, and crosscut saws. The manufacture of each of these products would require some, but not all, of the operations required for circular saws. The total number of departments might therefore be from fifteen to twenty. In addition, a number of service departments would be necessary, such as purchasing, storage, engineering, manufacturing standards, accounting, general offices, and employee services.

The layout of a candy factory by processes is illustrated in Figure 20. The processes include mixing, cooking, processing after cooking such as rolling and cutting, hand dipping for chocolates and bonbons, machine dipping, piece wrapping (for some pieces), and boxing. Separate departments are provided for nut sorting and processing, taffy wrapping, and the making of nut clusters. Each batch of candy would be separately planned and routed through the appropriate departments.

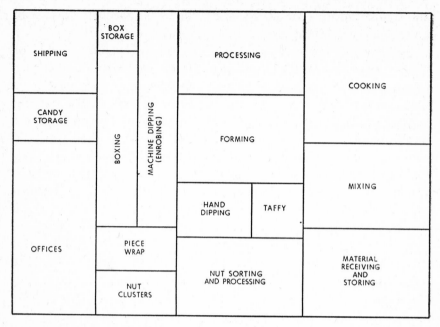

FIG. 20. Layout of Candy Factory by Processes

A layout by processes would not be feasible in all types of operations; but in industries that are suited to this arrangement, several advantages would be realized. Workers and supervisors become specialists in one type of work. The total investment in machines may be smaller because some machines can be used in the manufacture of more than one type of product. It is easy to keep a group of similar machines in operation if each machine can be shifted from the production of one product to another. Adjustments can more readily be made for variations in the output of any one product, for the dropping of a product from the product line, or for the adding of a new product.

Even in industries that can use a layout by processes, the arrangement may have several disadvantages. Usually the product will be moved longer distances. Internal transportation increases the cost and adds to the noise and confusion within a department. The cost is especially large if the materials are bulky or heavy. Damage to materials is likely to be increased, particularly if the goods are fragile. Transportation by a conveyor system of moving belts or other mechanical means is difficult because of the degree of flexibility required. In this type of layout the product does not follow a fixed course from one department to another. The product moves more slowly because of the distances to be transported. The inventory of work in process of manufacture is increased because of delays incident to transportation. A large inventory of finished goods must also be maintained because the dates for completion of work are not always dependable. Transfers from one department to another frequently require inspection, counting, weighing, and other paper work, which increases the cost. Much time is spent in each department in the verification of incoming and outgoing batches of work in process.

Layout by Products. In a factory that is laid out by products, a production line is established for each type of product. Each line is organized in a manner that may be compared with the organization of a sepa-

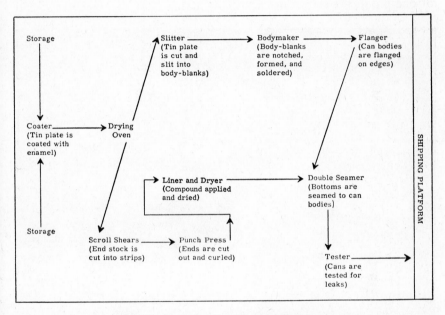

FIG. 21. Production Line for Metal Containers

rate plant. All operations for the manufacture of one product are under the control of a division chief or general foreman. Each production line may make more than one size or style of product, but the various products are fashioned on the same machines by adjusting the machine or by using different machine tools. To provide balance for each line, more than one worker or one machine might be used in one operation.

A layout by products is desirable if the number of products is not too great and the processes differ materially. For example, a soap company might make bar soap, granulated soap, shaving cream, and wave set in the same plant. A container company might make metal cans, milk cartons, and cylindrical boxes in the same factory. Since the processes differ, a separate line would be required for each product. A production line for metal containers is shown in Figure 21.

Some plants produce a single line of products in a limited number of varieties, and in such a plant a layout by products may be desirable. For instance, a plant may make only frozen orange juice concentrate or refined sugar. Assembly lines for products made of many parts, such as automobiles, electric refrigerators, or computing machines, are laid out by products even though several varieties of the product must be made on the one line. Automobiles are made on a single production line even though the product may be made in more than one color, body design, and combination of accessories. A layout designed for the manufacture of one product is shown in Figure 22.

Courtesy of Victory Adding Machine Co.

FIG. 22. Production Line for Assembly of Adding Machines

The layout by products obviates the disadvantages of the layout by processes. Usually the distances for the movement of the product are shorter. For this reason, the risk of damage to materials is reduced. A conveyor system is more likely to be feasible. Processing time is reduced. Paper work is lessened because the number of transfers from one department to another is decreased. Fewer inspections may be required, and interdepartmental friction may be minimized.

In some industries, a layout by products would have distinct disadvantages. Foremen are required to have a familiarity with dissimilar processes, although they may become more familiar with the processes necessary to the manufacture of the one product. They can no longer specialize by operations, although they may specialize in one or a few products. With a layout by products, the investment in machinery and equipment may be increased because balance is difficult. In other words, machines of varying capacity cannot be kept equally busy. Idle capacity means lost overhead as well as idle time for workers. Special requirements of any machine or workplace for air conditioning, noise control, or light can be met only at increased cost. The line is less flexible. If a product is discontinued, it may be necessary to remove the entire line. If a product is added, a new production line may be necessary, unless the new product is sufficiently like a former product to permit production on the same line.

Since each method of layout has its advantages as well as its disadvantages, many plants utilize both methods. A large printing plant, for example, might have most of its departments arranged by processes, such as estimating, typesetting, engraving, proofreading, electrotyping, printing, and binding. In a line of printing that has a large and stable volume of work, machines and workers may be organized in a department to handle that work. The plant of a manufacturer of a machine or an appliance may be laid out by processes in that part of the building where parts and accessories are made, and it may be laid out by products on an assembly line basis in another part of the building.

Work Centers. A variation of the plan of layout by products is an arrangement that has been designated as the work center.[1] This arrangement makes special provision for the production of items that account for relatively small percentages of the total production. If such items are produced on the regular production and assembly lines, machine shutdown and adjustments for the change-overs are necessary with consequent delay and confusion. To reduce the frequency of such delays, production of the item might be continued on the main production line until the quantity on hand is sufficient to meet the sales requirements for a year. While this method reduces the manufacturing costs, it increases other costs that result from a slow turnover of inventory. The solution to this problem is the layout by work centers where an item needed in small quantities can be produced on a continuing basis. A few workers are assigned to each work center to work solely on the production of the one item. The work cycle of each person at a work center is longer than it is on the regular production line. Some advantages and possibly some disadvantages result from this arrangement, but an important advantage

---

[1] "Work Centers Put These Workers into Business," *Factory Management and Maintenance*, Vol. CXIII, No. 7 (1955), pp. 124–25.

is decreased monotony of the work. Where the plan of the work center is adopted, the rest of the plant might be laid out by either processes or products.

Changing the Basis of the Layout. In a small plant that makes a variety of products, a layout by processes may be necessary because the volume of one product is not large enough to employ the capacity of the machines that would be required for a separate production line. As the volume of production increases, new machines may be purchased and installed, additional service facilities may be added, additions may be made to the building, or a larger building may be acquired. If the volume of production of any one product is increased sufficiently, the management may find that a change to a layout by products is feasible for one or more products. For example, a plant that formerly made both toilet soap and laundry soap on the same machines may find that separate machines and equipment for each product would reduce costs. A plant that formerly made a variety of glass jars on each line might be able to establish a separate line for some sizes or types of jar. Other illustrations could be found in a candy factory, a bakery, or a paper box factory.

The most important consideration in the change of the layout would probably be the extent to which machine capacity could be utilized. In a plant that is laid out by processes, machines are idle a part of the time because of the necessity for changing machine tools or resetting the machine. Machine time is also lost because of a lack of balance between machine capacity and immediate needs. Production may not be accurately scheduled for the various machines. Man-hours are spent transferring work in process from one workplace to another and in moving materials into the proper place for each operation.

When the change is made to a layout by processes, machine utilization may be increased provided the volume of production is sufficient to keep the machines fully occupied. However, in such a layout, machine utilization may vary from 0 to 100 per cent. Some idle machine time may result from the differences in machine capacity. For example, a production line might require one machine of a kind, six machines of another kind, and four machines of still another type. Since fractions of a machine cannot be installed, some idle time is unavoidable.[2] The engineer must determine the most effective arrangement in each case. The extent of machine utilization and the cost per unit will be changed as the demand for the product and the rate of output increase or decrease.

[2] Donald D. Deming, "When to Shift to Straight-Line Production," *Harvard Business Review*, Vol. XXXVII, No. 6 (1959), pp. 62–68.

A company may find that a building that has been used for many years has become obsolete because of the need for a revision of layout resulting from developments in machine design and materials handling. To support the greater weight of new machines, special foundations may be necessary. The floors may not be able to carry the weight of new and more economical types of materials-handling equipment. If doorways are too small to permit the transportation of a new machine into the plant, the company may be required to choose between the purchase of smaller and less economical machines and the temporary removal of a wall. The company may continue to use a building that does not permit an economical layout because moving expenses would be excessive.

Relation of Layout to Other Problems. The layout should be planned after a study has been made of the requirements of the individual plant. A layout plan cannot be adopted by one plant merely because another has found it to be feasible and economical. The number of stories in the building will determine the type of materials-handling equipment which can be used. Gravity chutes from one floor to another may be possible. The height of the ceiling affects the plans for overhead cranes, the use of lift trucks, and the installation of offices or employee facilities on the mezzanine floors. Other features of the building that should be considered are possible floor loads, the types of floor covering, the presence of a basement for dead storage, the relation of the building to railway sidings and highways, the location of entrances and exits, the number and spacing of columns, and the total amount of space available in relation to the facilities to be housed. As previously explained, the building should not be leased or constructed without reference to possible layouts.

The layout may be designed for the manufacture of a few products or a large number. If only a few products are manufactured, layout by processes may be preferred. The number and nature of the products also affect the types of materials-handling equipment, which in turn affect the layout. For example, lift trucks require wide aisles, particularly for turning, and pallets may require storage space at the workplace. Maximum floor loads should also be considered because the floors may not support a lift truck and a load of heavy materials. If conveyors are used, the workplaces may be grouped about the conveyor. When materials and parts are pushed by hand or carried from one workplace to another, workplaces may be close together, and aisles need not be so wide. Overhead conveyors may reduce the need for wide aisles since materials may be lifted above the floor level for moving. Similar considerations apply to other methods of handling materials.

Layout is affected by the nature of the manufacturing processes. In continuous-process industries the material is carried through a series of operations. In intermittent-process industries, several parts are fabricated and then assembled. The first assemblies, called "subassemblies," may be combined with other subassemblies for the final assembly of the finished product.

Continuous-process industries are classified as analytical and synthetic. Analytical processes separate and refine the raw material to make two or more finished products. Examples are meat packing, gas and coke, flour milling, oil refining, lumbering, and branches of the chemical industries. The layout of such a plant may spread out like a fan from the point where the raw material is started in process. Each rib of the fan represents the progressive processing of a material which has been separated from the original material.

Synthetic industries combine and process two or more raw materials to make a finished product. Examples are rayon, paper, cement, bread, medicines, and soft drinks. A plant that makes a product by a series of synthetic processes may be laid out like a fan with the ribs converging upon a main line, where the final product emerges. However, the separate materials may be combined early in the process, as in bread making, and one combined material may then be processed at a series of workplaces arranged progressively.

A plant that makes a product by the assembly of a number of parts, subassemblies, and accessories may also be laid out like a fan. The product may move along a conveyor in the center and the parts and subassemblies may be moved up to the main line by means of feeder conveyors. The automobile is assembled in this manner. If the product is light in weight, however, the parts may be made in any part of the plant and moved to the assembly line on hand trucks or other conveyors. Examples are shoes, men's suits, and adding machines.

The type of material used also affects the layout. The material may be heavy or light in weight, fluid or solid, wet or dry, bulky or small, hot or cold, fragile or sturdy. If the material is heavy or bulky, it may be easier to take the machine to the work instead of taking the work to the machine. Examples may be found in various branches of the construction industry and also in the manufacture of locomotives, streetcars, and electrical installations. The problem of what to move is illustrated by the early experience in the automobile industry. The initial plan was to assemble a complete car in one place by bringing all parts to that place. The second step was for workers to specialize in a limited number of operations and to move from one car to another to perform their operations. The third plan was for the workmen to remain in one area but to push the chassis along from one workplace to another. The next development was to put wooden spacers between the chassis and to push the entire line by means of a power drive at the beginning of the line. The industry finally developed the plan of a continuously moving line for the complete assembly.

If the management anticipates a change in product design next year, it might not want to incur the expense of changing the layout to lower the cost of making the product as now designed. The decision would be made by balancing the following factors: the volume of production anticipated during the year before product design is changed, the cost of revising the layout, the operating losses incident to the interruption of production while the change is being made, and the possible change in product design which might be made later. If the revision of the layout can be made during vacation periods or over week ends, the operating losses can be reduced. Any changes in layout should be co-ordinated with the work of the production scheduling department and the product design department to minimize the costs of revision.

Production Planning. The work of planning for production and scheduling the work will vary with the layout. If an assembly plant is laid out by products, the planning is simplified because the materials and parts are moved to the beginning of the line and the schedules are released to the first workplace. Other parts are delivered to the line as the units in production are moved along by conveyors or other method of handling. If the plant is laid out by processes, more detailed methods of planning and control are necessary. The work for each machine must be planned and scheduled. Reports of the progress of the work are necessary, and corrective measures may be necessary when work falls behind schedule.

MAKING THE LAYOUT

Planning the layout is usually a part of the work of the plant engineer. In some companies, the layout comes under periodical review because of changes in product design, the addition of new products to the line, the expansion of facilities to meet increased demand, the purchase of new machinery, and other such developments. In other companies, the layout is revised less frequently.

Information Required. When any person is asked to plan a layout, his first consideration pertains to the products to be made, the quantities planned for immediate production, and possible expansion. Each product is analyzed from the manufacturing standpoint to determine the parts, subassemblies, and accessories of which it is made. The engineer would also know which materials and parts will be manufactured and which will be purchased. Machines or production lines will be provided for the parts to be manufactured.

If the product is made by the manufacture of parts and their later assembly, the engineer would make provision for the processing of each part and for assembly. If the part is made by carrying a material through a series of processes, such as bread, concentrated orange juice, or soap, a different type of layout would be planned.

The Process Chart. In planning for any product, the engineer would write out the series of operations or processes necessary to production. In an assembly industry, he would list separately the steps necessary to make each part and a separate list of the operations necessary to assembly. In a process industry, he would prepare a statement of the processes through which the material is passed. A diagram or chart that indicates all of the steps necessary to the manufacture of a part of a product is called a "flow process chart," or merely a process chart. Frank B. Gilbreth, who originated the process chart, classified all activities in production into five types and assigned a symbol to each type. The activities and the symbols used to designate them are as follows:

SYMBOL	ACTIVITY	DESCRIPTION
◯	Operation	Any work on the material, such as drill holes, cut threads, or assemble parts.
○	Transportation	Move by truck, conveyors, elevator, or manpower.
▽	Temporary Storage	Place the material in a position to be moved, inspected, or processed.
▽	Permanent Storage	Place the material or part in the storeroom. When material is permanently stored, it can be withdrawn only by requisition.
☐	Inspection	Examine or test for workmanship or quality.

A part of a process chart prepared for the flow of material in a factory is shown in Figure 23. The chart shows the number of feet the material is to be moved from one workplace to another.

PROCESS CHART

Operation___Extruded Cots – Cot Finishing___

Subject___Analysis of Flow of Extruded Cots___

DIST. IN FEET	TIME IN MINS.	CHART SYMBOLS	PROCESS DESCRIPTION
		▽	Rod Storage – 3rd Floor – Bldg. No. 8
6		O	To Carton 5 Rods per Move
		▽	On Flow along Side Racks in Carton 150 per Carton
116		O	To Cot Cutoff
6		O	To Bench
		▽	On Bench
		◯	Cut to Length 36 per Rod
		▽	Under Table in Shaker 1,200 to 1,500 per Shaker
6		O	To Storage in Aisle
		▽	In Aisle
20		O	To Finishing Machine – Change Hopper
		◯	Finish O.D.
		▽	At Finishing Machine
40		O	To Beveling Machine

Courtesy of Armstrong Cork Co.

FIG. 23. Process Chart Showing Steps in Manufacture of a Product

After the process chart has been prepared, it should be determined whether any changes can be made that will shorten the time required for manufacturing or otherwise lower the cost. Special attention should be directed to transportation and storage, since these activities do not add to the value of the product. Value is added by manufacturing operations, and other activities should be incidental. In some cases the manufacturing operations can be improved. The following questions should be asked at each step:

Is the operation necessary to production?

Can one operation be combined with another? A finishing operation might be completed while the material is being moved. Inspection might be made while an operation is being performed, or inspection and packing for shipment may be combined.

Can the procedure be simplified by changing the sequence of the operations?

Can an operation be simplified? Simplifying an operation might mean, for example, rearranging the workplace to improve lighting, to eliminate lifting or carrying, or to reduce the hand or arm motions that are made in doing work.

Planning for Equipment. The next step is to determine what machines will be necessary. Since the output of different machines will vary, it will be necessary to determine how many machines of each type will be required to produce the product in the volume called for by the production budget. The number of machines necessary would be determined as follows:

1. Multiply the number of units of finished product to be manufactured in any period of four weeks by the number of parts of a kind in each product.
2. Multiply the number of plant hours in four weeks by a use factor, say 80 per cent, which is the percentage of time a machine may be in actual production, to determine the estimated number of hours the machine will operate.
3. Multiply the number of hours by the output per hour to compute the output for the period of four weeks.
4. Divide the required production for four weeks by the output for one machine for that same period to determine the number of machines required. If the result in each such computation is approximately a round number with no fractional machines required, the layout can be balanced.

Several other factors may be considered in determining the number of machines required. Allowance may be made for parts that do not pass inspection and must be reworked or scrapped. The use factor may be improved by a reduction of the time for setting up the machine and for maintenance work. The available hours of work may be increased by overtime during busy seasons. If a machine is manually operated or is semiautomatic, the output may be increased by better training or motivation of the worker. Where the line is unbalanced because of varying capacities of machines, provision may be made for extra machines of certain types. However, if the machines are expensive, a minimum number of machines may be provided and the additional production requirements at peak seasons may be met by overtime or extra shifts.

After the number of machines of each type has been determined, the space required for each machine is computed. Space may be needed for materials waiting to be processed and for parts waiting to be moved. Additional space may be required for repairs and for the worker. In locating machines or other workplaces, it might be best to start with the shipping room and work backward to the raw materials storeroom. In a continuous-process industry, it would be equally advantageous to begin with the raw materials storeroom and arrange the workplaces in order from that point forward. If a conveyor system is installed, the machines and workplaces would be grouped about the conveyor.

Special Requirements of Machines. Some machines may require location in isolated areas or in parts of the building that can be air conditioned. For example, noisy equipment such as speed hammers may be located in enclosed areas to reduce the noise in areas where many workers are employed. Some machines may require an exhaust to the outside of the building. Examples are grinders, sanders, and saws. Exhausts may be required for equipment that gives off harmful fumes, such as painting and plating equipment. Special ventilation may be necessary for large equipment that generates an excessive amount of heat. Shock machinery such as drop hammers should not be located near machine shop equipment where close tolerances are required in the production of parts. Instrument rooms and paint shops should be air conditioned to control temperatures and to eliminate dust. These special requirements of some machines and equipment may indicate a location where the processing cannot continue in a regular sequence, and some doubling back of materials may be necessary.

Service Departments. The next step is to locate the service departments. Such departments include tool cribs, storerooms, fire equipment, inspection areas, drinking fountains, telephones, soft drink dispensing units, offices for foremen and staff personnel, reading room, toilets, washrooms and lockers, cafeteria, recreation hall, the dispensary and first-aid room, and other nonmanufacturing departments. These departments would be located near the workers and preferably where the light is not suitable for other work. Frequently, some of them may be located in a mezzanine floor which would be reached by an open stairway. The power plant is usually in a separate building. The amount of space to be allotted to all service departments is usually estimated to be about one third of that of all manufacturing departments. If too much space is devoted to them, excess capacity is created which is seldom or never used. If the facilities are inadequate, workers are required to spend too much time waiting; or they lose time because of crowding. If the facilities are either too large or too small, the layout is lacking in balance.

Review of Space Allocation. By the time the plan for the layout is completed, the engineer may find that space is not available for some workplaces or service facilities. He then reviews the allocation of space to find places where savings may be made. Space for some work areas or service departments may be reduced. More careful planning of the flow of work may reduce the amount of work in process and the space required for it. The storeroom space for the materials inventory may be reduced by careful planning of purchases for stock. Work standards may be reconsidered to determine whether the output of each workplace and each machine has been correctly stated. Materials that will not be damaged by weather may be stored in the yard with a saving of plant space. The flow process chart may be reviewed to determine whether any step can be eliminated or some work may be assigned to other companies under contract. A mezzanine floor may be added if ceiling heights and floor loads permit. The plan for a mezzanine requires attention to safety regulations and fire hazards. If all available space is utilized, room for expansion may be lacking and management may begin to plan for an addition to the plant.

Choosing the Best Layout. Usually the best layout is a compromise because no one arrangement will combine all of the advantages of the different methods. For this reason, the layout engineer may have some difficulty in deciding among the various alternatives. If information is available, he might figure the cost of operation or the unit cost of the product by different methods of layout. The cost data would include installation costs, the costs of tools, handling equipment, and fixtures, labor and material costs, and miscellaneous expenses such as floor space, power, and insurance. Another way of comparing different layouts consists of a listing of the advantages and disadvantages of each proposed arrangement. Usually this method brings to light sufficient considerations to make possible a decision. A third method consists of a listing of the important factors, such as materials-handling cost or floor space required, and then assigning to each possible arrangement a ranking number for each factor. For example, one arrangement might rank first in regard to material handling, second on amount of floor space required, and third on worker satisfaction. When this method is used, the final decision is reached by considering the ranking of each method on the total number of factors. As a further refinement, the various factors could be assigned weights, and each method of layout could be given point values on the basis of the weights. However, the final decision will depend upon the judgment of the layout engineer rather than the mechanics of any procedure.[3]

Completing the Plan. After a plan has been adopted, a diagram of the proposed layout is prepared. Usually it shows various details, such as elevator shafts, stair wells, doors, windows, and other features. The machines are drawn to scale. The purpose of this procedure is to make sure that all persons who check the layout visualize the pro-

---

[3]"How to Evaluate Alternative Layouts," *Factory Management and Maintenance,* Vol. CXIII, No. 2 (1955), pp. 126-29.

posed arrangement in the same manner. Unless such a diagram is made, some workplace may be overlooked in the original plan and the moving and rearranging of equipment may be necessary.

Models of the proposed layout are often prepared. A model of the plant itself is first prepared on a scale which is carefully followed. In the usual scale, one-quarter inch equals one foot. If the building is multistory, the model is so constructed that the upper floors can be removed without disturbing the arrangement of the lower floors. In some

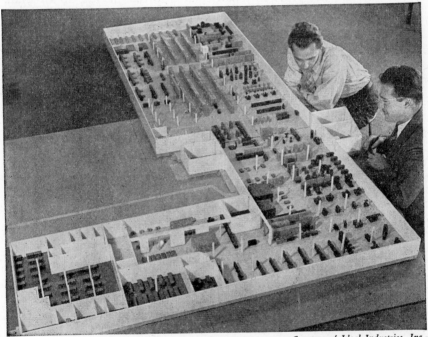

Courtesy of Ideal Industries, Inc.

FIG. 24. A Three-Dimensional Model of Plant Layout

cases the models may be cutouts in two dimensions. Such models are called "templates." Three-dimensional models are usually preferred. A completed model of building and machines is very similar to a completely furnished doll house. Persons who are not accustomed to the reading of diagrams can easily understand the layout by an inspection of a model of the factory and its equipment. A model of this kind is shown in Figure 24.

Frequently, numerous refinements are introduced into the preparation of the models. Plastic floor sections may be prepared with one-inch squares etched into the floors. The scale on which the plan has been drawn is apparent from the etching without the necessity for making measurements. The etched lines will also show in a photograph of the model. Another refinement is the use of colors. Machine tools may be salmon color; stationary equipment, green; conveyors, yellow; and storage bins, red.

All persons who will be concerned with the new plant or who may offer constructive criticisms should be invited to inspect the layout as planned. The group would include foremen and shop supervisors, time-study men, the safety director, maintenance foremen, and any engineers who had not previously participated in the making of the plan. As previously explained, the production scheduling and the product design departments should be kept informed and also invited to make suggestions. Changes are easily made at this stage, and suggestions should be encouraged.

The next step is to make drawings and photographs of the new plan. The layout has now been perfected, and authorization to make the installations should be sought.

The new layout cannot be installed until top management has been convinced that it is practical and economical, that the change will not interfere seriously with filling current sales orders, and that the required capital outlay is not excessive. In presenting the plan to top management, therefore, the executives who are responsible for the designing should include data covering the following features:

> The time required to make the new installations.
> The cost of the change.
> The time required for processing the product under the present and the new plan.
> The value of the inventories of work in process and finished goods under the present and the new plan.
> The monthly operating cost, including labor, depreciation, taxes, insurance, and all other expenses under the present and the proposed layout.
> The cost per unit of product under the present and proposed layout.
> The time required for the savings to equal the cost of the new installations.

A favorable attitude of foremen and workers should be developed. Foremen should be encouraged to study and criticize the plan while it is still in the formative stage, and any practical suggestions should be incorporated into the final layout. Their suggestions will probably result in operating economies, and their attitude toward the project is likely to be favorable if they have had a part in it. The foremen's attitude may also determine whether worker opinion is favorable or unfavorable.

The worker should be informed of the proposed changes by the management. He should not be permitted to get this information through the rumor factory or the grapevine. As soon as rumors begin to spread, the worker fears the worst. As economy is the purpose of the change, each worker may think that his job is one of those to be dispensed with or that his job is to be simplified and that his pay may be reduced. Fear and suspicion should be dispelled by a free discussion of the proposed change and its effects. The worker may receive his information from the foreman, through the public-address system, through bulletin board announcements, and in other ways.

QUESTIONS

1. Contrast methods of layout in a synthetic industry such as bread making with an analytic industry such as meat packing.

2. How is layout affected by the type of building construction?

3. How is a layout affected by the type of materials-handling equipment?

4. Contrast the problem of layout for a plant that makes the parts for final assembly with layout in a plant that does only the assembly.

5. A company that has made a variety of products in limited quantities finds that the volume of production of one product has increased to the point where a separate production line might be feasible. What factors would be considered in making a decision to set up a separate production line?

5. How do organizational problems change when the layout is changed from the process method to the product method?

6. Are worker attitudes affected by the method of plant layout? Are lines of promotion any different in different types of layout?

7. Mention products that might be assembled by the use of a conveyor. Mention products that might be assembled by being pushed along on a bench or by being carried from one workplace to another. Consider washing machines, dresses, adding machines, and telephone instruments.

8. When a conveyor is used in an assembly line, how does management determine the proper speed at which it should be run?

9. An ideal arrangement would mean that the product always moves forward and never doubles back to the same workplace. Would this principle ever be violated in practice?

10. Is layout strictly an engineering or mechanical problem, or are human relations problems also involved? Explain.

11. Would you expect to find that the work at various workplaces along an assembly line always makes the same demands upon the workers? What problems are created by a lack of balance at the various workplaces?

12. What information is necessary to the making of a good layout?

CASES

20. PROCESS CHART FOR CONCENTRATED ORANGE JUICE

The manufacture of concentrated frozen orange juice that retains the natural flavor and vitamin content was developed as a result of the perfection of a vacuum process. In a vacuum, orange juice boils at a temperature of about 55 degrees Fahrenheit. At this temperature, the natural taste and vitamin content are not affected. When the customer adds water to the frozen concentrate, he can make a healthful orange drink that tastes much like the fresh juice.

At the plant where the frozen concentrate is made, truckloads of fresh fruit are received from the groves and unloaded into bins on the receiving platform. The fruit is first transported on a moving belt conveyor to a grader which sorts the oranges as to size. Oranges of a specified uniform size are diverted into separate wooden containers where they are crated and shipped as fresh fruit. The small or irregular shaped oranges are used to make the frozen juice concentrate.

The oranges are passed through a washing machine and then transported to the cutter which halves them. Next the juice is extracted, and the rinds and seeds are ejected into a bin. The rinds are sent through a separate process and made into marmalade. The juice is passed through a filter which removes the pulp. The pulp is chilled, some juice is added to it, and the mixture is later added to the concentrated juice to make the final product.

After the juice has been filtered, it is pumped to the machine which passes it through a vacuum to reduce the moisture content. Next the concentrated juice is mixed with the pulp, the mixture is placed in cans, and the cans are sealed. The cans of juice are then passed through a freezer where the concentrate is quickly frozen. The cans are then placed in paper shipping cartons, the cartons are sealed, and the boxes of canned juice are placed in cold storage until they are shipped. All of these operations, except for some handling of the boxes, are performed by equipment that is automatically controlled.

Required:

Prepare a process chart, indicating all of the steps. Use the form and symbols as illustrated on page 225.

21. PROCESS CHART FOR BOXMAKING

The American Box Company makes boxes of corrugated paper that are used for shipping fruit jars and other glass containers. All boxes are made according to the specifications of the customer. In most cases the name and trademark of the customer are printed on the outside of the box by a special process. The boxes are made of three materials: brown paper, glue, and staples.

The plant is laid out by processes as follows: receiving and storage, papermaking and cutting, lithographing and printing, automatic stapling, hand stapling, divider assembly, and final assembly. The paper is received in large rolls at one corner of the building where it is stored until required in production. As the rolls of paper are very heavy, they are lifted, stored, and removed from storage by overhead crane. When an order is to be run, the paper is moved from the storeroom to the papermaking machine and placed in position for processing. Three rolls of paper are used in making the corrugated paper. The inner strip of paper is crimped or fashioned in a wavelike effect, and the three pieces of paper are then glued. The machine also shears the strips of corrugated paper into the proper lengths to make any box. The cutting knife of the machine is set at the beginning of any operation to cut the paper into the lengths desired. The machine piles the pieces of corrugated paper onto a truck or dolly.

Since the jars and bottles which are to be packed inside the box are fragile, each box is equipped with cross strips called "dividers." The paper for the dividers is made on the same machine as that used for making the boxes. The machine is set in such a way that the corrugated paper is cut into strips of proper size, and each strip is slotted with cuts of the proper size and depth.

From the papermaking machine, the paper for boxes is moved to the lithographing and printing machine, which has been set to imprint the name and trademark of the customer on each box. The sheets of paper for boxes are fed into the manually operated machine, which will process them as rapidly as the worker can handle them. The sheets are ejected by the machine and piled on a hand truck.

The next operation consists of forming and stapling the box. The company has two types of machines for this operation. Some machines are fully automatic and some are manually operated. The manually operated machines are used for small boxes which require greater precision in the work.

The corrugated strips of which the dividers are made are assembled by a special-purpose machine which was designed for this one operation. The machine has two magazines or hoppers, one for each size of strip of paper. The machine picks up the strips, fits them together, and drops the assemblies on a hand truck.

The boxes and dividers are now ready for final assembly. They are moved to the final assembly department while they are still piled on the hand trucks. Workers put the dividers inside the box in a manual operation and then place the boxes on a conveyor belt. Bottles and jars are made in the plant in the adjacent building. Some conveyors bring the boxes to workers, and other conveyors bring the jars and bottles to them. After the glass containers are placed inside the boxes, the assembly is shipped by truck to the customer, which may be a fruit or vegetable processing company.

Required:

Prepare a process chart for the operations. Use the form and the symbols as shown on page 225.

22. PLANT LAYOUT IN NEW LOCATION

In 1923 the Arabian Coffee Company established a plant in Los Angeles. In 1958 the company decided to move to the East San Francisco Bay area, and a site was selected at San Leandro. This location was chosen because of the facilities for ocean shipping at the nearby port of Oakland, the highway and railway facilities, the availability of an undeveloped plant site, the central location in the market area, and the availability of housing facilities.

At the Los Angeles plant the company had four production lines for coffee.

Because of the emphasis upon freshness as a quality of good coffee, the company was unable to build up an inventory to supply customers during the period when machines and equipment were down for moving. It was therefore decided to move one line at a time and to keep three lines continuously in production. With some overtime the company would be able to keep customers supplied and thus retain the market.

As the building in San Leandro neared completion, the chief engineer drew up a time schedule for moving. The location of each machine in the new building was planned, and the exact position was marked on the floor. Each machine was numbered, and the corresponding number was used to identify the location in the new building. As soon as one line was set up and placed in production, the next line was moved according to schedule.

Employees and members of the management at Los Angeles were given the opportunity of moving and retaining their positions. The company agreed to pay each employee $300 to meet moving expenses, and it also agreed to pay the additional living costs while the employee was finding a place to live. Wherever possible, the company granted leave with pay for two days to those employees who wished to visit San Leandro prior to moving to look for a place to live. Sixty-five per cent of the employees accepted the offer to move with the plant. The high percentage was due in large part to the fact that the production lines were largely automatic and that most of the people held specialized positions at good salaries.

Each employee was told when his line would be moved. As soon as a line was taken out of production, employees on that line who were not making the change were shifted to other lines; and enough employees from other lines who wanted to move were transferred to the new plant to fill the positions. With new recruits at San Leandro, three lines were kept fully manned. To prevent premature quitting of employees not making the change, a bonus was paid each person for continuing work as long as his services were required.

Questions:

1. What costs are involved in moving a plant?
2. Under what circumstances is a company justified in making such a change?
3. What steps did the company take to reduce the costs?

12 Maintenance of Machinery and Equipment

WHEN machinery and equipment are selected, purchased, and installed, the management problems are not ended. Maintenance is important in its effect upon the life of the equipment, upon the amount of downtime, and upon the quality of the service a machine may render. Increasing mechanization and the use of fully automatic machines mean that maintenance problems require greater attention. In many companies, maintenance does not receive the emphasis that it should.

ORGANIZATION FOR MAINTENANCE WORK

The organization of the maintenance department will vary with the size of the company, the degree to which operations are mechanized, the attitude of the management, and certain other factors. Each operating department may attend to its own maintenance problems, or a centralized maintenance department may handle all major maintenance work throughout the plant, leaving to each operating department only minor repairs and lubrication work.[1] A centralized maintenance department is usually considered better for a large company, and this type of organization will be assumed in the discussion which follows.

The Maintenance Department. The work of maintenance is a part of the manufacturing division, which may be headed by a vice-

---

[1] Harold E. Bliss, "How to Find and Control Your Maintenance Costs," *Factory Management and Maintenance*, Vol. CXI, No. 3 (1953), pp. 113, 119.

president in charge of manufacturing. Next below him is the plant engineer, to whom the maintenance foreman reports. The maintenance foreman might be assisted by a dispatcher or maintenance clerk and perhaps by a stock and crib attendant who would be in charge of the storeroom for repair parts and would requisition the purchase of additional parts when needed. The chief or leadman for each group of craftsmen, such as carpenters, electricians, and millwrights, would report directly to the maintenance foreman. In a smaller company, some of the units would be consolidated in some manner, depending upon the nature of the company and the amount of maintenance work. In a still smaller plant, the craft foreman would report directly to the plant engineer, and the engineer himself might attend to the work

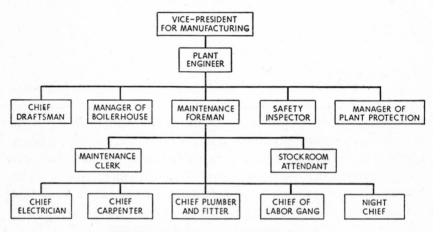

FIG. 25. Organization for Maintenance Work

of planning and dispatching. The total number of employees engaged in maintenance work averages about 8 to 10 per cent of the workers employed in production. A possible method of organization for maintenance is illustrated in Figure 25.

The maintenance department may be made responsible for repairs to both buildings and machinery and equipment, or it may be responsible for the maintenance of only machinery and equipment. Such maintenance would include routine inspection, repairs found by inspection to be necessary, regular overhauls of machinery and equipment, and emergency repairs necessitated by breakdown or accident. Some plants employ outside service companies to do a part of their maintenance shopwork. The contract with the service company usually provides for peak loads, and the routine maintenance work is done by the company itself.[2] Other companies use outside contractors only for special types of work, such as window cleaning, roof repairs, elevator work, overhaul of air-conditioning equipment, and major repairs to buildings.

Most of the maintenance work must be done at the machine or in that part of the building in need of repair. The worker takes the tools and the materials and goes to the place where the work is to be done. In some cases, however, a unit of the machine may be removed and taken to the shop for repairs, and sometimes the entire machine may be taken to the shop. The tools used may be the usual hand tools of the craft, but more often the tools are motor driven. Power tools will perform such work as cutting, drilling, riveting, welding, sanding, finishing, spray painting, and lubricating. Power tools are economical not only because they reduce labor cost but also because machines are repaired and returned to production more quickly.

Relation to Operating Departments. In some companies, the maintenance department, which functions as a service department for operations, lacks the prestige that is associated with manufacturing departments. Its members may be assigned a less desirable location in the building than members of the operating departments. Maintenance workers may be required to use equipment that is no longer considered adequate for production work. The maintenance foreman may have difficulty in getting appropriations that he considers necessary. Clerical services and operating facilities may be inadequate as compared with the facilities of the operating departments. Although maintenance employees may frequently be required to work overtime and on week ends, the credit for increased production and low cost may be given largely to line personnel. The situation requires special effort on the part of the plant engineer and top executives in order that the efficiency of the maintenance department may be kept at a high level.

The position of the maintenance department in the organization may also require special attention to the morale of the maintenance employees. Frequently, this problem is neglected because the plant engineer who heads the department is essentially a technical expert rather than a supervisor or administrator. He should stress the importance of maintenance work and see that employees are provided with adequate tools and facilities. To increase worker interest, he may keep maintenance men informed of the work accomplished and also

---

[2] "Contract Maintenance," *Factory Management and Maintenance*, Vol. CXVII, No. 7 (1959), pp. 171-214.

of the projects that are planned in order that they may not be afraid of running out of work. He may solicit their ideas concerning needed repairs, maintenance methods, and operating procedures. The morale of any group may be improved when they can have a voice in the way their work is to be done.

Hours and wages of maintenance workers create special problems. Overtime is difficult to avoid, and the manner in which it is assigned to different workers may seem to constitute a discrimination. Although piece rates and bonus plans may be developed for maintenance work, production workers usually have a better opportunity to increase their earnings by increasing their production. Craftsmen in maintenance work usually are paid less per hour than similar craftsmen employed by building contractors. The comparison of the wages of the two groups may create particularly difficult problems when outside contractors are engaged in special projects at the plant. Although the differences in wages may be explained by regularity of employment, better working conditions, and indirect financial benefits, the wage differential sometimes causes worker dissatisfaction.

Other problems may arise within the department as a result of inadequate supervision. Maintenance foremen may need special training in human relations and methods of supervision since their earlier training and experience have been largely of a technical nature. The supervision of maintenance work is especially difficult because the work must be done at any place in the plant and possibly at some distance from the foreman's desk. Foremen should not be permitted to become involved in paper work but should spend most of their time supervising maintenance work.

PLANNING FOR MAINTENANCE

The planning and scheduling of any kind of work permit orderly and efficient procedure. Although excessive paper work should be avoided, the scheduling of maintenance work should make possible adequate preparation for personnel, parts, tools, and materials. General planning permits workers to make detailed plans of their own work and to develop a feeling of orderliness. Maintenance men should have some assurance that they can complete any task they start without being shifted back and forth from one place to another. In planning for maintenance, management can give priority to such work as may be necessary to keep the downtime of equipment at a minimum. Each craft can more easily be assigned to the type of work for which it is best fitted.

Problems of Scheduling. Although most companies plan and schedule lubrication, inspection, and major maintenance work, many of them do not attempt to schedule a large part of the work. Many maintenance executives believe that work cannot be planned in advance with any assurance that the work can be completed on schedule. The difficulty is that breakdowns and accidents interfere with any attempt at orderly planning. When such interferences occur, the scheduling of work in advance is found to be wasted effort. However, planning for inspection and overhauls should reduce the number of breakdowns and emergency repairs. A maintenance plan that can anticipate 80 per cent or more of the work for one day ahead is usually better than no plan at all. When any such plan is made, it should provide for small tasks as well as large. The small tasks may be neglected indefinitely if this procedure is not followed. Sometimes a number of tasks may be grouped together and scheduled as a single larger task.

Determining the Work Load. Each assignment of maintenance work requires a written authorization by the proper authority. In large companies, the authorization for repairs to machinery and equipment may originate with the plant engineer, the plant superintendent, the foreman of the department needing the repairs, or some other executive, depending upon the company organization. The order for major repairs or maintenance work on buildings may originate with the plant engineer, the vice-president for manufacturing, the plant superintendent, or other executive. In many cases, the approval of more than one executive is required. If the work is urgent, a request may be made by telephone to the person who issues work orders. A request for work indicates the nature of the work to be done, the tools and materials required and their cost, and the estimated labor cost. Central control may be established by means of work orders, to which numbers are assigned. No maintenance work can be assigned to maintenance workers until a regular work order has been properly authorized, numbered in proper sequence, and scheduled by the dispatcher.

Preventive maintenance schedules are prepared on the basis of machines to be inspected or serviced. The first step in the preparation of such a schedule is the listing of all plant assets. Each machine is described on a separate card and is given a number. The type of service required by each machine and the nature of the inspection are indicated. Servicing and inspection schedules are then established, and the work is planned to distribute the work load by weeks and by days of the week. To prepare such a schedule, the engineer should know the approximate time that will be required for each work assignment. This information is best obtained by time study.

The work load should be arranged on some kind of priority system. The work orders may be ranked on a basis similar to the following:

Repairs that are necessary because of breakdowns.
Repairs whose need was determined by inspection.
Repairs for the correction of accident hazards.
Repairs for the prevention of damage to materials or breakage of machinery.
Routine requests from operating executives.
Alterations or rearrangements of machinery and equipment.

The ranking is only the beginning of the scheduling, as the date when each work assignment is to be started and completed should be indicated.

Any one of several methods may be used to indicate work planned. According to one simple method, a separate order for each assignment is prepared and placed on a spring clip bulletin board. Three spaces on the board are provided for each group of craftsmen. Under the first clip are the work orders for the assignments on which the men are presently engaged. Under the second clip are the next orders planned, and under the third clip are work orders for completed assignments. When an assignment is completed, the order is removed from the first clip and placed under the third clip. The work order on top under the second clip is removed and advanced to the first clip. Several variations in the method of using the board may be followed, but all of them are based upon the same principle.

Following the Progress of the Work. The craftsman who does the servicing of the repair work indicates on the work order the nature of the repairs made or other work done. If an inspection indicates the need for additional work, this fact is stated on the completed work order. The maintenance foreman would inspect the completed work orders each day and send them to the plant engineer. The cost accounting department would also be notified of work completed in order that it may compute the cost. The plant engineer is notified of the cost, and he enters this information on his copy of the work order. The file of completed work orders is used in conferences with the maintenance foreman concerning the work of the department. The record also serves as a basis for estimating the costs on work that may be contemplated.

More complicated methods may be used where a large volume of maintenance work is scheduled and dispatched. Some companies plan major repairs for a year in advance. Their estimates would indicate planned starting and completion dates and the number of men to be used on each project. The schedules are prepared in a conference of foremen and executives of the manufacturing departments who take into consideration the desired sequence of the work, anticipated weather conditions, and the availability of men and materials. The plans are graphically portrayed by means of a Gantt chart, on which the horizontal scale shows the weeks or months of the year. Each project is represented by a horizontal line, the length of which indicates the estimated time for the work. Such a chart is illustrated in Figure 26.

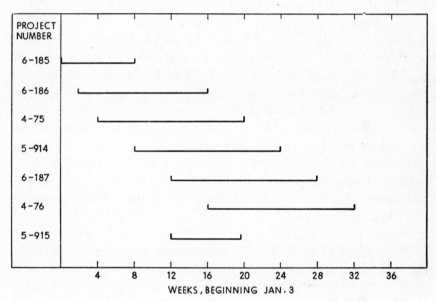

FIG. 26. Gantt Chart Showing Planned Major Projects

Completed work may be shown in a similar manner but with a heavier line on the same chart. Some companies use a bulletin board of the pegboard type to portray such information. This pegboard is the same as that used in any production planning, as explained in Chapter 34.

A record of the maintenance work done on each machine may be kept in the office of the plant engineer or the maintenance foreman, depending upon the organization of the company. This record would indicate the date when the work was done, the nature of the work, and the cost. This information would be useful in scheduling future maintenance, estimating costs, and planning for machine replacements.

Management of Maintenance Stores. The control of the inventory of parts and supplies used in maintenance is necessary to assure that parts will be available when they are needed to minimize downtime, to reduce losses of repair parts due to negligence or pilfering, and to make possible an accurate determination of maintenance costs.

Most plants now have a separate stockroom for maintenance materials and supplies. They keep records of parts on hand. A stockroom attendant under the direction of the maintenance foreman is responsible for inventory management.

The control of the inventory of maintenance materials begins with the purchase of a new machine. When the machine is ordered, the manufacturer may be asked for a complete list of the spare parts that will be necessary for its continuous operation. This list should be checked against the inventory of similar parts. Any parts not on hand may be ordered at that time. When any machine is retired, it should be stripped of all parts that might be useful in the repair of other machines. The parts are indexed and placed in the storeroom. At that time, also, any parts for the unit retired which cannot be used on other equipment may be removed from the storeroom and scrapped.

Some parts that are readily available from local supply houses may not be kept in stock but may be purchased when needed. If the time required to obtain such parts is short, the company may keep an inventory of only the parts that will be needed in an emergency. The maintenance foreman should regularly review the inventory to make sure that all such parts are in stock but that the inventory is not excessive.

The method of operating the maintenance storeroom is similar to the methods used in storerooms generally. The room should be closed to all persons except the regularly authorized attendant. The person in charge should be accurate in keeping records, and he should also have sufficient mechanical ability to measure and issue parts and supplies and to recondition standard parts. Purchase requisitions should be checked in the receiving room. Incoming materials should be counted or weighed for quantity and inspected for quality. Records should be kept of quantities issued, and amounts on hand should be regularly compared with book inventories. The stockroom attendant performs various services for the manufacturing departments, such as cutting bar or hollow stock to the lengths needed, splicing belts, and repairing valves and other parts.

CONTROL OF MAINTENANCE PERFORMANCE

Periodically the maintenance foreman, the plant engineer, and the top executives will want to know whether the maintenance costs are reasonable and whether the maintenance work is being well done. A comparison of the maintenance costs of one plant with similar costs throughout the industry or in other plants is not likely to be helpful. One reason such comparisons do not provide reliable standards is that more maintenance is required in plants moving heavy materials and using large units of equipment. The type of operation also affects the need for maintenance. Other factors are the age and condition of plant and equipment, the degree of mechanization, the number of work shifts per day or week, and the amount of overtime in case the plant operates only one shift.

Standards of Performance. The standards for maintenance management may be designed to show the extent to which work has been successfully planned, the distribution of the maintenance work load, the nature and amount of the maintenance expenses, and the relation of maintenance work to the productivity of the plant. While various standards may be established, the success of the management in planning for maintenance may be measured by the man-hours spent on emergency work as a percentage of the total man-hours of the department. Planning efficiency may also be measured by the overtime hours for a month or other period as a percentage of total man-hours for the same period.

Maintenance management may also be judged by the distribution of the current work load. The current "backlog" of work may be stated in terms of the number of weeks of work planned ahead. If the work as planned will require several weeks for completion, some essential work may be neglected or postponed for too long a period of time. Another comparison might show the percentage of total man-hours for the month which have been spent in planned preventive maintenance and the percentage spent in each other class of repair and maintenance work.

In the area of monetary cost, data may be compiled to show the maintenance expense as a percentage of the investment in buildings, machinery, and equipment. Maintenance expense may also be shown as a percentage of the total cost of the product. Maintenance expenses may be classified to show the percentage of the total that has been expended for routine maintenance work, inspection, repairs of defects disclosed by inspection, emergency repairs caused by breakdowns, and other possible types of maintenance work.

The efficiency of the maintenance staff may be measured by several kinds of data. One such standard is the number of persons in the maintenance department as a percentage of the total man power engaged in production. Another standard is the percentage of operating time lost in downtime for maintenance reasons. The number of units of product for each dollar spent in maintenance work may also be used as a standard. In each case, the performance for the current year may be compared with the performance for the preceding year or some earlier year which may be used as a base period.

Management Reports. The information pertaining to maintenance costs should be made available to management if it is to be useful. One desirable report might show the maintenance costs by departments and machines. Management is sometimes surprised to learn that excessive costs are incurred in connection with certain machines that were rated highly when they were purchased. Another report might be a weekly summary of maintenance costs showing the costs by crafts and indicating for each craft the actual labor hours, the standard or estimated hours, the overtime, and the excess of the actual labor cost over the standard. Another section of the weekly report might show the cost of repairs in each department. A job progress report might be made monthly to indicate the work orders completed during the month, the orders in progress, and the orders planned but not yet started. A space opposite each listing would be used for pertinent comments as to each project. One purpose of such a report would be to attract attention to any work that might otherwise be postponed from month to month.

Information as to the costs of maintenance may also be used as a guide to the purchase of new machinery. Maintenance costs are increased when manufacturers use special parts that are not readily available. They may also design the machine in such fashion that lubrication is difficult and worn parts are not easily replaced. For this reason, the maintenance manager should be consulted before a new machine is purchased. The user of a machine may render a service to the machine manufacturer by reporting features of machine design that increase maintenance costs.

An analysis of the causes of machine breakdowns may disclose inadequacies in the program for the regular inspection or maintenance of machines and equipment. For example, the maintenance crew may fail to inspect or lubricate certain parts, or the preventive maintenance program may be inadequate in other respects.

The maintenance department should strive to render effective and efficient service to the operating departments in order that manufacturing operations may be conducted at low cost and repair work may be kept on schedule. The objectives of all production departments are low cost, quality in accordance with predetermined standards, quantity production, good personnel relations, and customer service.

QUESTIONS

1. How can the maintenance foreman plan for maintenance work when he is expected to take care of breakdowns of machines and other such emergencies?

2. Why might a worker prefer to be assigned to a manufacturing department instead of maintenance? What might be the advantages of doing maintenance work?

3. How can the management determine whether its maintenance work is well done at low cost?

4. Under what circumstances might a company contract with outside concerns for its major repair work? Give examples of contracts that might profitably be let to outside companies.

5. Can management establish standards of performance for maintenance work when many kinds of repair work are done?

6. What types of maintenance work can best be done by the worker at the machine or under supervision of the foreman?

7. Why might a craftsman such as a painter or mechanic receive more pay when he works for an outside contractor than when he works for a manufacturing concern?

8. How is the problem of maintenance affected by the development of fully automatic machines and by automation?

9. Maintenance is usually a staff function because the maintenance department renders a service to the manufacturing departments. How does this fact increase the problems of the foreman of the maintenance department?

10. Can the maintenance department advantageously use an incentive method of wage payment?

CASES

23. REPORTING DAMAGE TO EQUIPMENT

At the Winchester plant of the Allied Machine Company, the foreman of maintenance informed the plant engineer that he thought much of the damage to machinery and equipment could be avoided if proper care were exercised by operators of machines and drivers of trucks, automobiles, and lift trucks. Although workers could not be charged with carelessness, many of them did not take sufficient precautions. For example, a driver of a lift truck that was loaded with pallets stacked with cartons attempted to pass a box that had been left in the truck lane a few minutes earlier. One of the cartons on the truck was pushed against a switch box that controlled a turret lathe, and the box was torn off the wall. The damage could have been avoided if the driver had stopped the truck and removed the box, or if he had waited until the stock handler had time to move it. In another instance in the yard, a truck driver failed to devote full attention to his driving and ran into the rear of the truck in front of him. Damage to machines on the production line frequently could be attributed to inadequate training of the operator, indifference, congestion due to an accumulation of materials, and poor housekeeping. Damage was also caused by failure of the operator to report that a machine was in need of repair.

The maintenance foreman believed that damage could be reduced if workers were made to realize the cost of making repairs and the nature and extent of their own responsibility. Upon his recommendation, the plant engineer, after consultation with other executives in the operating departments, authorized a system for the reporting and investigation of all incidents requiring repair work. According to the plan, a worker who is involved in any such incident is required to fill out and sign a written report describing the incident and the extent of the damage. The maintenance department then estimates the cost of repairs and the probable downtime of the machine and enters the information in the appropriate spaces on the same form.

Each incident reported is investigated by a committee of four persons, composed of the assistant works manager, the assistant personnel manager, the foreman of the department where the incident occurred, and the general foreman. As soon as the incident is reported, the chairman of the investigating committee calls the other three members by telephone and the committee convenes immediately. The committee makes a report describing the nature and extent of the damage, the cause of the incident, and its recommendation for preventing a recurrence. The committee has no power to act; it merely recommends. A copy of the report is filed by each member, and one copy is placed in the personnel file of the employee.

The company has found that employees dislike the preparation of reports of incidents in which they are involved and the filing of a report in their personnel records. However, under the system the reporting is necessary because the maintenance department will not make the necessary repairs until the report has been submitted. Incidents causing damage have been decreased to such an extent that maintenance employees now average 7 per cent of the work force as compared with 10 per cent before the present system was adopted. The assistant works manager believes that the discussion of costs, safety practices, downtime, and other such problems while the case is being investigated has had a wholesome effect upon worker attitudes.

Questions:

1. What are the advantages of the new plan?
2. What objections may be made to it?

24. FOREMEN KEEP MACHINES IN REPAIR

Mr. Walter C. Clark, president of the Central Manufacturing Corporation, had reason to believe that costs throughout the various divisions of the company were too high, but he was unable to determine the causes or to take the proper corrective action. The problem of costs had been discussed at meetings of the policy committees without bringing to light what Mr. Clark thought were the basic causes. The president therefore decided that a management consultant should be engaged to make a study of the organization and the policies and practices of the various divisions and to recommend corrective action.

The reason Mr. Clark decided to call upon an outside consultant was that an outsider could talk freely with executives, foremen, and workers and they could talk freely with him. Anything that might be said by any person would be considered as confidential. No person would be quoted, and the information given would not be used in a manner that would enable others to identify him. Both Mr. Clark and the consultant assured everyone that confidences would not be betrayed.

When the consultant talked with the maintenance foreman, he learned that some foremen failed to report that machines were in need of repair or overhaul and that they continued to operate machines until serious trouble developed. When repairs became necessary, a foreman might have a worker in the department do the work instead of calling upon the maintenance department. In such cases, the repairs were not properly made and trouble again developed after a few weeks. The foreman did not report the trouble to his supervisor; or if he did report it to the general foreman, the information was not passed further up the management chain of command. The cost clerk, who recorded the labor cost of the repairs, entered the charge in a miscellaneous expense account and rendered no report. The maintenance foreman could not cite any specific instances of these practices, but he was sure that they occurred and that they lowered the efficiency of the plant and increased costs.

As the consultant talked with the foremen in the manufacturing departments, he eventually led them into a discussion of mechanical efficiency and maintenance practices. Most of them admitted that the maintenance foreman had correctly described the situation. One foreman made the following comment:

"My department is given an efficiency rating at the end of each month. I don't know just how they figure it, but I do know that I have a production quota and that if I do not meet it, my rating goes down. If it drops below 90, my boss calls me into his office for an explanation. Once it dropped to 83 and all the top brass was around looking over the department and ordering me to make changes. I have to keep the machines going even if they do not operate as smoothly as they should. After the end of the month when I have met the quota and held up the efficiency of the department, I can put a man onto a machine when he has a little free time. I have some good mechanics in the department and they can repair a machine in less time than a maintenance worker could do it. Our men know these machines and they know what to do. I have a machine over there now that is making a lot of noise but it is still going and I think it will hold up until I get the quota for this month out of the way. As long as they assign me a quota and figure my efficiency, I am going to try to beat the game.

"Another thing is that I can have one of my men make the repairs for less money than maintenance would charge. They limit me to a budget, and I have to keep my expenses down. When I call maintenance, the accounting office charges the cost of repairs against my budget. I don't know how they figure the cost, but I think they must add a lot for overhead or something. I operate the only practical way I can under the circumstances."

Question:

What should the consultant recommend as a solution to the problem of maintenance?

25. A TRANSFER PROBLEM

At the Fiske Company, transfers could be arranged by any worker in any department in the plant through the offices of the personnel department. Notices of vacancies were posted on the plant bulletin board, and any worker could apply for transfer. If several qualified workers applied for the same position, the worker with the greatest seniority was given the preference. The foreman of the department where the worker was currently employed was always consulted, but he usually considered it unwise to attempt to keep a worker if a better position was available elsewhere. Likewise, the foreman of the department in which the vacancy existed was consulted; but since the union stressed seniority rights in the filling of vacancies, the foreman usually accepted the qualified worker who had the greatest seniority.

When Sam Jones sought employment at the Fiske Company as a machinist, he was placed in the maintenance department. This type of work was acceptable to Jones because he liked repair work. However, he soon discovered that work in the maintenance department was disagreeable in several respects. Major overhaul work was regularly scheduled for Saturday and Sunday. The hourly rate for such work was the same as the weekday rate unless the total hours for the week exceeded forty. Moreover, Jones was frequently asked to work extra hours at night because of emergencies caused by breakdowns. While he received extra pay for such work, he disliked it because his wife could never plan social activities with any assurance that Sam would be at home.

Maintenance work was frustrating to Sam because he could not always complete a task the way he would like to. He frequently was required to leave a task half finished to answer a call for help in an emergency. At some times, however, maintenance men seemed to loiter around because no breakdowns occurred. A further objection to maintenance work was that the position did not carry the same prestige as a machinist job in production. Operating employees were regarded as more important because they made goods for sale, whereas maintenance workers merely facilitated production or served the line.

When a vacancy in a machinist's position in a production department was posted on the bulletin board, Jones decided to apply. When the foreman of the maintenance department heard of the application, he filed a protest with the personnel department because of his inability to keep good workers in the department. He contended that transfers should not be posted on the bulletin board. He insisted that he was required to contend with a constant stream of workers into and out of the department.

Required:

1. Criticize favorably or unfavorably the practices of the Fiske Company.
2. Explain what action should be taken in the case of Sam Jones.

13 Working
Conditions: Light
and Color

GOOD working conditions include adequate lighting, proper use of color in the work areas, air conditioning, elimination of unnecessary noise, possible use of music and other broadcasts, and control of monotony and fatigue. Working conditions depend partly upon the physical equipment, such as buildings, machinery and equipment, and methods of work.

LIGHT

Reference was made in Chapter 1 to the Hawthorne experiments in lighting and other working conditions. Although these experiments indicated that the effect of changes in physical environment can be overemphasized, they should not be interpreted to mean that such changes are unimportant. They suggested that changes in lighting can affect output by changing employee attitudes. They indicated that when one event precedes another, the first is not necessarily the cause of the second, unless the causal relationship is interpreted to include worker attitudes.

Advantages of Good Illumination. Much information has been collected to show that good illumination soon pays for its cost. Although the results of experiments in lighting should not always be accepted without reservations, the installation of a good lighting system has been shown to have several advantages. Production may be increased with good light because the worker perceives tools, materials, and machine controls more readily and can perform his tasks more quickly. In certain types of work, quality of product may be improved because the worker makes fewer mistakes when he can clearly see the work. Examples are matching pieces of cloth to make a garment, making buttonholes or performing sewing operations, painting by spray or brush, grinding, or polishing. An automobile manufacturer found that a better lighting system enabled workers to detect more readily slight changes in shades of paint. In tobacco processing, better light aided in the grading of tobacco. In metalworking operations, micrometer scales were read more quickly and more accurately. Increased light has been found to be accompanied by less spoilage in the manufacture of such products as electrical equipment, automatic machine tools, and other work made to close specifications.

Lighting conditions are closely related to other conditions of work. Floor space may be more effectively utilized because machines and workplaces can be located in space which could not otherwise be used. Good lighting also encourages better housekeeping. Poorly lighted areas and passageways afford convenient places to throw trash and to store excess material which should be returned to the storeroom or thrown into the scrap collection. Dirt is often permitted to accumulate in poorly lighted areas, while well-lighted areas are more likely to be kept clean. Accident hazards are decreased by better illumination because good light increases perception, lessens fatigue, and permits quicker nervous and muscular responses.

Lighting affects employee mental attitudes and also physical condition. Consciously or unconsciously, employees react to better working conditions and respond by increased co-operation. Poor lighting eventually leads to eyestrain, which in turn causes defective vision, headaches, and nervousness. Workers who suffer from eyestrain feel the need for more rest and relaxation. They may seek relief by taking unauthorized rest periods, by using extra motions to delay the flow of work, or by taking days off.

Phases of Illumination.   The provision of adequate lighting requires attention to two problems: the effective use of natural light and the installation of a good artificial lighting system. For day shifts, natural lighting may be used as much as 90 per cent of the time. The exact percentage varies with the type of buildings and equipment, the location of workplaces within the buildings, and the location of the plant in relation to other buildings. Natural light is not entirely satisfactory because the intensity is not uniform. Both the intensity and the angle at which the light is received will vary with the hour of the day, the weather conditions, and the season of the year. With either natural or artificial light, seeing is affected by the intensity of the light, the size of the objects observed, contrasts in light or color, the length of time allowed for seeing, and the time during which a person is engaged in seeing tasks. All of these factors are subject to a measure of control. The factor that is most easily controlled is intensity or brightness.

Essentials of Good Lighting. An important quality of light is the absence of glare from the direct source of light or a reflecting surface. Glare is defined as excessive brightness within the field of vision. Reflected glare is caused by glossy paper, polished metal parts, or polished wood or glass surfaces. Glare causes eyestrain and fatigue because the eyes attempt to adjust themselves to varying and changing conditions, and a flickering light will exaggerate the effect. Glare is corrected by using a less intensive source of light, by diffusing light at the fixture, and by changing the position of the source of light.

The color of light is an important quality when the work requires color discrimination or the matching of colors. The selection of lighting equipment for a workplace where this kind of work is done is a technical problem which requires the services of an expert. If color discrimination is not important to the work, the color of light is a matter of personal preference. Most persons prefer a color that is similar to daylight. Women workers may object to a color of light that detracts from their personal appearance. Some colors of lights when combined with the colors within the room result in a cold or displeasing effect. When this situation is found, it may be necessary to experiment with different colors of lights to find a pleasing combination.

The Intensity of Light. The standard for measuring the intensity of light is the foot-candle, which is the amount of light produced by one standard candle at a distance of one foot. The proper intensity depends upon the nature of the materials, the equipment, the background of work, the care and attention demanded of the worker, and the vision of the worker. Usually older workers need more light than young persons if they are to see as clearly and distinctly. After the age of 45, a decrease in visibility often becomes pronounced. However, a general guide for required intensities in foot-candles is as follows:

Rough work, such as loading, packing, washrooms, cafeteria, conference rooms, and reception rooms: 10 foot-candles.

Casual seeing tasks, such as classrooms, filing, casual desk work, and foundry work: 20 foot-candles.

Critical seeing tasks, such as bookkeeping, stenographic work, sewing, type-setting, general fabrication, and general assembly: 50 foot-candles.

Detailed seeing tasks, such as drafting, fine assembly, inspection, and proof-reading: 100 foot-candles.

Specialized applications, such as color inspection, extra-fine assembly, and fine inspection: 200 to 500 foot-candles.[1]

Light intensity is measured by the light falling on the workplace and is not entirely a characteristic of the light source. Intensity is affected by the distance of the sources of light, the type of reflector or lamp fixture, the arrangement and distribution of the light sources through-out the rooms, and the reflecting surfaces. The effect of the spacing of light fixtures upon the intensity is illustrated in Figure 27.

Courtesy of Westinghouse Electric Corp.

FIG. 27. Spacing of Light Fixtures

Light intensity is measured by a light meter. Inadequate intensity may be manifested by employees taking work to a window on dark days to see or to inspect it, by employees squinting as they work, by a gloomy and cheerless appearance of the shop or office, and by a spotty appearance caused by dark areas. Inadequate lighting may also

[1] See Harris Reinhardt and William Allphin, "Planned Lighting," *Factory Management and Maintenance*, Vol. CX, No. 5 (1952), pp. 113–23.

manifest itself in a high accident rate and other results of a poor lighting system.

Effect of Building Construction. The most important feature of the building in its relation to natural lighting is the type of construction, that is, light wood-frame, brick wall-bearing, mill or slow-burning, reinforced-concrete, or steel construction. Possible window space is less in the first three types because the walls must be strong enough to carry the weight of the upper floors and the roof, whereas in the other two types the frame carries the weight, thus leaving the walls free for window space. In single-story buildings, window space can be 30 per cent of floor space, which is adequate, though no maximum percent-

Courtesy of Jones and Lamson Machine Co.

FIG. 28. A Building with Saw-Tooth Roof

Note ventilators in roof and side wall.

age can be prescribed. Since light fails in intensity as it passes toward the center of the building, provision is usually made for lighting single-story buildings from above. A saw-tooth roof with the glassed side toward the north provides good lighting without glare. This type of structure is especially desirable in such industries as textile manufacturing and printing, where direct sunlight is objectionable. A building with saw-tooth roof is shown in Figure 28.

The color of walls is another factor in light reflection. Walls may be painted white; but gray, cream, and off-white colors are frequently used. The type of floor is another factor. Concrete floors aid in the diffusion of light, particularly in work that is done on the underside of a machine or bulky product.

Glass blocks in wall construction contribute to the effective use of natural light because they permit a small amount of light to penetrate into the building without causing glare. They also permit a small amount of artificial light to penetrate to the outside area adjacent to the building. This feature may assist in plant protection and in accident prevention at night. They cause a minimum of glare and aid in the diffusion of light both inside and outside the building.

Although glass blocks are more costly than brick, they have increased in popularity for several reasons. They permit the installation of greater window areas because they will carry a part of the weight of the wall

Courtesy of Pittsburgh Plate Glass Co.

FIG. 29. A Building Constructed with Glass Blocks

above them and because no window sash is used. They are frequently used in monitors as well as in side walls. The dead-air space in the blocks gives them an insulating value and helps in the control of temperature and humidity. They prevent the entry of dust and dirt, protect precision machinery, and reduce distracting sounds which may enter through an open window. The blocks are easily cleaned. Rows of glass blocks lend themselves to sweeping, flowing lines which are architecturally pleasing. Figure 29 shows a type of building construction in which glass blocks are used.

Cleanliness of Walls and Windows. Vertical windows may lose from 50 to 60 per cent of their efficiency through six months' accumulation of dirt and grime on the inside and outside. The exact amount of loss depends on the conditions in the city where the plant is located as well as on the air conditioning within the plant. Vertical sashes are partly cleaned by wind and rain, but windows on a slope accumulate dirt very rapidly. The glass in monitors or saw-tooth roofs should therefore be vertical. The difficulty of keeping the glass clean is a serious objection to skylights.

Methods of Lighting.   Three methods of lighting are used in industrial and commercial establishments: general lighting, localized general lighting, and local lighting. The general lighting system provides for light which is diffused at a substantially uniform level throughout the room. Reflectors are spaced symmetrically and in uniform rows throughout the lighted area.

Localized general lighting distributes the light according to the varying requirements for illumination at the machines or workplaces. If machines or materials-handling equipment cast shadows or interfere with the diffusion of light in some areas, extra fixtures may be required to provide the necessary illumination. In the localized general lighting system, the fixtures are not arranged in a straight line or in a formal pattern. Some fixtures are out of line, and some may be nearer the work floor than others. Local lighting directs the light toward the point of the tool or the individual workplace. Local lighting should not be used alone because it causes a sharp contrast between the lighted area and the rest of the room. Local lighting without supplementary general lighting would cause eyestrain and fatigue.

The Source of the Light.   Light may be received directly from the source, or it may be reflected. Four types of source are possible: direct, indirect, semidirect, and semi-indirect. Direct lighting is supplied by a fixture which directs all the light to the workplace. In an overhead fixture, for example, the reflector is above the light, thus preventing any of the light from reaching the ceiling, except that which is reflected from lower areas. The danger of glare from direct lighting is very great, unless the fixtures are located well above the line of vision.

In indirect lighting the reflector is placed between the source of the light and the workplace, thus directing the light toward the ceiling or the wall from which it is reflected and diffused throughout the room. This type of fixture eliminates much of the danger of sharp contrasts. The difficulty is that this arrangement may not provide sufficient intensity. The reflecting surface should be painted a cream, white, or other light color to prevent the absorption of an excessive amount of the light, and the surface should be kept reasonably clean. Indirect lighting systems have limited application, unless they are supplemented by some other system. The cost of operation is increased by the fact that a part of the light is lost by absorption.

In semidirect lighting, some of the light proceeds from the source toward the work area and some is directed toward the ceiling which reflects it. A glass fixture may be placed over the light globe and the light rays may penetrate the fixture in all directions. In semidirect systems, from 10 to 40 per cent of the light is distributed upward, and the remainder is distributed downward.

In semi-indirect lighting, some of the light may proceed downward through a fixture, while some of it is directed toward the ceiling. The fixture in semi-indirect lighting is partly metal and partly glass. The metal part of the fixture provides the indirect light. In semi-indirect lighting, from 10 to 40 per cent of the light is distributed downward, and the remainder is distributed upward.

Types of Lamps. Incandescent lamps are the most familiar type of light bulb. No special equipment is required for their use. The principal precaution in the purchase of incandescent lamps is to obtain them in the right size and wattage for the equipment in which they are to be used. If the lamp is too large, it may extend beyond the reflector and cause glare. If it is too small, a large percentage of the light may be trapped within the reflector, with a resulting loss of efficiency.

The mercury vapor lamp consists of a long tube in which mercury is vaporized, similar to the familiar fluorescent lamp. When first introduced, it achieved great popularity; but it was partly supplanted by other forms of lighting because it was deficient in red rays and did not make possible accurate color discrimination. This deficiency has been corrected, at least in part, and mercury vapor lamps have increased in popularity, particularly for outside lighting and for inside applications where high mounting heights are necessary.

The operation of fluorescent lamps requires the use of auxiliary equipment to regulate the electric current and to make possible the operation of the lamps at low voltage. Lamps vary in length from 6 inches to 60 inches. The color of the light produced by fluorescent lamps is determined by the color of powders inside the tube. The colors commonly used are white and shades of off-white resembling the color of daylight.

Various types of reflectors are available for fluorescent lighting, and the reflectors may be arranged and installed in various positions. In some cases, the reflectors are recessed in the ceiling. This arrangement is particularly desirable in offices because the reflectors do not collect dust, and the general appearance is pleasing. Light is more generally diffused because of the greater distance from the fixture to the floor, but a greater intensity at the light source may be necessary. However, installation at the ceiling height may be impossible because of the nature of the ceiling construction and the interference of pipes and other service connections. In such cases, the fixtures may be suspended by chain or other type of hanger. The reflectors may be solid, or they may contain apertures to permit the circulation of air for cooling and also the lighting of the surface of the ceiling.

Maintenance of a Lighting System. A system that is efficient at the time it is installed will gradually become inefficient because dirt collects on the reflectors, lamps, ceilings, and walls, and the light output of the lamps decreases. Maintenance is likely to be neglected unless a regular maintenance schedule is established. The need for maintenance should be tested by a light meter. If the illumination is no more than 75 per cent of the required standard, the equipment should be cleaned and perhaps the bulbs replaced.

In the replacing of lamp bulbs, a practice known as group relamping may make possible substantial savings. Under this plan, all of the lamps in an office, shop, or other area are replaced at the same time after a predetermined period of use. At the time of replacement, only a few of the lamps will have burned out but many of them will be giving less light than new lamps. The principal advantages of this plan are lower labor cost and proper maintenance of the efficiency of the lighting system.

USE OF COLOR

Workplaces were formerly dull, uninteresting, and lacking in color. The first change occurred when machines were painted gray instead of black and the walls were painted cream. Recently, color has been used in the workplace, with machinery painted medium green and other parts of the workplace painted yellow, orange, red, or blue. The use of color is promoted not only by manufacturers of paint but also by consultants in management. The object in using color at the workplace is to induce clear, three-dimensional seeing instead of the dull, flat effect produced by use of one or two dull, dark colors. Better color schemes have three definite purposes: they provide (1) better visibility because of contrast, (2) color conditions that are not too harsh for continuous comfortable seeing, and (3) color conditions that are pleasant and easy to live with.

Some Effects of Color.   The color scheme should be planned in relation to the lighting system. Some colors reflect light, and others absorb
light. White reflects the most light. Light gray and yellow also reflect
a substantial amount. Black reflects the least, but the reflection from
dark blue or red is also small. The amount of reflection is affected by
the height of the ceiling, the size and shape of the working area, and
the direction of the exposure to sunlight.[2]

The colors that are used overhead should be a neutral gray or
perhaps white to reflect the light. A darker hue in the ceiling is objectionable because it would attract the eye to overhead pipes and girders,
which are unsightly. The colors within the field of vision should not
offer severe contrasts. If some of the colors used at the workplace reflect
light while others quench it, the effect is similar to glare and causes
eyestrain and physical discomfort. The color of the walls and machinery should be planned to avoid such contrasts. The color of materials used should be considered in choosing the colors of machinery
and walls. For ease in distinguishing the details of the work, the color
of the machine should complement the color of the material rather
than blend with it.

Blue tends to attract the eye and a background of blue behind the
work will aid the worker in concentrating his attention upon the task.
Medium green is a favorite color for machinery, and slowly moving
parts of machinery are often painted buff. Bins, racks, and shelving
are painted a neutral color because they are unimportant and should
not attract attention.

Color has a desirable effect upon the attitudes of employees and the
satisfactions which they derive from their work, provided that colors
are not used to excess and the scheme is carefully planned. Although
persons differ greatly in their color preferences, some effects of color
upon individuals are almost universal. Some colors, such as the shades
of blue and violet, are cold and tend to have a subdued or even depressing effect. Other colors, such as the shades of red and orange, are
relatively exciting in their effect, while yellow has a cheerful influence.
Greens are usually regarded as tranquil. While these influences are
weak in comparison with such forces as hunger or pain, their effects
should not be disregarded.

A motley array of color may give the effect of clutter and confusion.
For example, if machines are installed in a variety of colors as they
are received from the manufacturer, some of which are bright and
some subdued, and if alongside the new machines are old ones in dirty

---

[2] For example, see *Color in Industry,* published by U.S. Gutta Percha Paint Company;
and *Color Dynamics,* published by Pittsburgh Plate Glass Company.

gray or black, the effect is certain to be disturbing. A consistent and well-planned color scheme has been found to improve worker attitudes, to encourage better housekeeping, and to result in better care of machines. When a color plan has been tried in one department, workers in other departments frequently ask that the plan be extended to their surroundings.

Increasing attention is being given to the use of color in offices, and more than one color is frequently used in the same room. For example, if the natural light is excessive, the wall opposite the windows may be painted in a color that will absorb light rather than reflect it. It is desirable that the wall in front of the desks be soft in color to relieve the strain upon eyes raised from paper work. The color should be so planned that the wall in the line of vision of an interviewer will have a restful rather than a glaring effect. On the other hand, the window wall may be painted a color that will reflect light since the wall on the window side is usually the darkest in the room and contrasts sharply with the windows. Likewise, the wall behind the desks may be painted a color that reflects light rather than absorbs it. If the ceiling is marred by pipes, ducts, or beams, the color of the ceiling may be planned to reduce the glare that might be caused by shadows. These suggestions are not intended as a comprehensive discussion of the planning of color but are given to indicate some of the factors that should be considered.

An excessive use of color will cause fatigue because the eyes become tired of a continuous display. Some colors cause discomfort much sooner than others. Visual efficiency is decreased if a large mass of color is constantly within the field of vision, though the loss of efficiency varies with distance. Bluish green causes the greatest loss of efficiency, while yellow is least fatiguing. The color scheme should be planned to reduce fatigue and to prevent light absorption, color contrasts, and distracting effects. The planning of color schemes is a problem which requires the services of a specialist. Advice on the use of color may be obtained from representatives of paint manufacturers or from management consultants.

Color for Safety.   Any planning for color in relation to worker comfort and efficiency should also make provision for standard safety colors as recommended by the American Standards Association. In this color code, vivid red is prescribed for fire protection equipment and apparatus, danger signals, and stop signs. Vivid orange is recommended for designating dangerous parts of machines that may cut, crush, or shock. Orange is also used to emphasize such hazards as open enclosure doors or exposed and unguarded moving equipment. Vivid yellow stripes are recommended for designating caution against hazards which may cause stumbling, falling, or tripping. Brilliant green is recommended for designating safety and first-aid equipment. Strong blue is used to indicate the need for warning against moving equipment that is being repaired or worked on. Vivid reddish purple is used to designate radiation hazards, such as X ray. Black and white in certain combinations designate traffic and housekeeping markings. Although the colors used in the safety code are vivid or brilliant, they do not necessarily dominate the field of vision because they do not always emphasize objects that are of large size.[3]

QUESTIONS

1. It has been said that in the Hawthorne experiments management spent thousands of dollars to learn that workers are human. Is this a fair statement?

2. Can good lighting be justified on other grounds than an expected increase in production?

3. Why was the control group ineffective in measuring the exact effects of better lighting in the Hawthorne experiments?

4. Because of the possibility of glare from natural light and the loss of heat through the windows in the wintertime, some companies have constructed buildings without windows. Can such buildings be desirable if workers seriously object? Why might workers object to solid walls without windows?

5. A company installed a new lighting system; and during the next six months, output increased, rejects decreased, and absenteeism was' less. What conclusion may properly be drawn from the results?

6. Explain how the following are related to the effective use of natural light: plant location, height of building, type of roof, and painting of walls inside the plant.

7. Explain the relation of the following to the use of color: amount of light required at the workplace, color of the materials, temperature of the workplace, and accident hazards.

8. Explain the relation of the following to the control of glare: glass top for a desk, type of material, location of the workplace and windows, nearness of adjacent buildings.

9. Compare colors for painting the walls of the workplace with color of walls in the cafeteria or restroom.

CASES

26. MAINTENANCE OF LIGHTING SYSTEM

A company installed a new lighting system in an office to provide illumination of 400 foot-candles, which was the amount of light recommended by the Illumi-

---

[3] The color code was announced in February, 1954. *Factory Management and Maintenance*, Vol. CXII, No. 3 (1954), p. 113.

nating Engineering Society for the type of work done in the office. Eighteen months later, a representative of an electrical manufacturer who happened to call checked the illumination with a light meter and found that the illumination was only 330 foot-candles. This amount was considered inadequate, but the decrease in illumination had not been noticed by the office manager because it had occurred gradually. An inspection for the causes disclosed that the reflecting surfaces of walls and ceilings had become darkened by dust and smoke. Dirt and the bodies of insects had accumulated on the light fixtures. The glass in many of the light bulbs was found to be darkened. After the walls had been repainted, the fixtures cleaned and darkened light bulbs replaced, the efficiency of the lighting system was restored to normal.

Questions:

1. If the decrease in light had not been noticed, would the efficiency of the office force have been affected?

2. What should be done to prevent a recurrence of the deterioration of the lighting system?

27. USE OF COLOR IN THE PLANT

A manufacturer of storage batteries employs about one thousand workers, of whom 75 per cent are women. The company has painted each machine a different color in order to please the workers. Colors used are various shades of red, orange, and green. The machines have also been rearranged to permit each worker to have a clear view of all machines in the department in which she works. Protruding parts of machines and piping which constitute accident hazards have been painted different colors according to the generally accepted color code used in the industry. The walls have also been painted in a variety of colors. Lower walls are pastel green, upper walls are yellow, and roof girders are a lighter yellow.

After six months of experience with the color scheme, the management reports that production has increased 20 per cent. Visits to the plant dispensary for treatment of headaches and nausea have decreased substantially.

Questions:

1. Can the company safely conclude that the color scheme is the cause of the increased production and decreased illnesses?

2. Is any significance to be given to the fact that 75 per cent of the employees are women?

14 Working Conditions: Air, Noise, Music, Monotony

IN addition to light and color at the workplace, the provision of good working conditions requires attention to air conditioning, the elimination or reduction of noise in some cases, and various other aspects of the work. If the work is demanding of physical or nervous energy, rest periods may be desirable. If the work is necessarily monotonous, the broadcasting of music may be desirable or other measures may be taken by the management. These phases of working conditions will be considered in the present chapter.

AIR CONDITIONING

The most common phase of air conditioning is control of temperature, which may require either the cooling or the warming of the air. However, the conditioning of the air for purposes of providing good working conditions includes also the control of humidity, which might require that moisture be added to the air or removed from it. Other aspects of air conditioning include smoke and dust removal and the removal of air that is overheated or that contains injurious gases or fumes.

Temperature. An ideal condition would exist if, irrespective of the weather, workers were not distracted by the temperature of the air and the quality of their production were not impaired because they felt too hot or too cold. Room temperatures should not be so low as to require the wearing of sweaters or other garments which hamper the freedom of movement; and they should not be so high as to create a feeling of oppressiveness.

The ideal temperature for all persons seldom prevails. People differ as to their desires and possibly as to their needs, although each person has a comfort zone. Differences may be due to the amount of clothing worn, health, age, sex, and possibly race. People who are engaged in different kinds of work require different temperatures. Persons doing clerical work require a higher temperature than those engaged in more active work.

Air may be warmed by steam radiators, hot air, or steampipes along the walls. In a small room, radiators should be placed under windows because they can warm the air as it enters the room. The principal disadvantage of this position is that the space next to the windows becomes unavailable as a workplace. In a large room, small unit heaters are often placed overhead. Such heaters are equipped with fans to provide for the circulation of air.

Radiant heating is a system of heating the wall and floor surfaces instead of heating the air. Coils for steam or hot water are placed in the walls, floors, and ceilings. Advocates of this system contend that, since the radiant heat passes through the air without disturbing it mechanically, alternate strata of warm and cold air are eliminated. No dependence is placed upon the circulation of air to warm it. The result is that air temperatures are almost uniform and remain at about the average temperatures of the walls and floors. Consequently, the temperature can be kept five to ten degrees lower than in rooms heated in the conventional manner. The system cannot be changed after the building has been constructed, but it has flexibility because the heating units are built in panels or units which are separately controlled. Partitions between rooms can be changed, and the units in parts of the building not requiring large amounts of heat can be separately controlled.

An interesting application of the principle of radiant heating is its use for melting snow on outside loading areas in winter. Pipes are enclosed in the concrete when it is poured. The pipes, which are filled with an antifreeze solution, are connected with the heating system. When snow begins to fall, the system is turned on and the snow is melted as it falls on the warm concrete. After the snowfall has ceased, the system is turned off and is not used again until the next snowfall. The pipes are not drained in summer and do not require refilling in winter. The same system has been used to clear runways and walkways of ice and snow.

Temperature control includes cooling the air during warm weather as well as heating it in winter. The usual system for cooling air operates by forcing it to pass over coils which contain a substance at low temperature. The principle is essentially the same as that embodied in the construction of automatic refrigerators and ice-making plants. A compressor places pressure upon a refrigerant, such as ammonia or carbon dioxide. When the pressure is released by the operation of valves, the refrigerant vaporizes inside the lines within the refrigerating unit, cools rapidly, and absorbs heat from its surroundings. The refrigerant is again placed under pressure, and the cycle is repeated. In indirect systems the refrigerant cools a liquid which in turn cools the air. In direct systems the refrigerant cools the air. The cooling system is installed as a complete unit as it comes from the factory.

The control of the temperature by an air-conditioning system affects not only workers and the amount of their production but also materials and equipment. Such products as pharmaceuticals, meats, and chocolate require cool temperatures. A manufacturer of hosiery found that his maintenance costs were reduced 80 per cent after air-conditioning equipment was installed. The reason was that the knitting machines, which are 57 feet long with 0.002 inch clearance, expanded and contracted with variations in temperature, and the expansion caused jamming. With controlled temperatures, the machines required only occasional adjustment.

Humidity.   The amount of moisture in the air is closely related to temperature. Humidity is stated as a percentage of the capacity of the air to hold moisture. When air has all the moisture it can carry, the humidity is 100 per cent. When air cools, its capacity to hold moisture is decreased; and it may drop a part of the moisture as rain, dew, frost, or other precipitation. When air is brought inside the house and heated, its capacity to hold moisture increases. Consequently, air that was comfortable before being warmed becomes dry and uncomfortable after it has been heated. Moisture should therefore be added. A relative humidity of from 60 to 70 per cent is usually considered comfortable if the temperature is no more than 70 degrees.

In some industries the amount of moisture in the air will affect the quality of the product. In the processing of cotton cloth, for example, the air must carry a substantial amount of moisture to prevent the breaking of threads. Air that carries too much moisture, however, will cause a swelling of the thread and may result in an uneven piece of cloth. The moisture content of the air is also important in the manufacture of paper, gelatine, and some other products.

Moisture is removed by passing the air over a cool surface. Since cool air will carry less moisture than warm air, the air will drop some of its moisture when it has been sufficiently cooled. The principle is the same as that which causes moisture or frost to be deposited on walls or windows in the winter or dew on the grass in summer. In another type of system, very cold water is sprayed into the air from which moisture is to be removed. If the temperature of the cold water is below the dew point of the air, the air is compelled to drop a part of its moisture. It may be necessary to reheat the air after the moisture has been removed. Other types of systems operate on the same principle.

Moisture may be added to air by sprays, by steam jets, and in other ways. The amount of water to be added is automatically controlled by a humidiostat, which regulates the opening and closing of valves or vents. This instrument makes use of a substance which responds to humidity, such as human hair, certain types of wood, or paper.

Smoke and Dirt Removal. The problem of purification of the air by the removal of smoke, dust, gases, and objectionable odors presents two aspects. One phase of the problem pertains to the purification of air within the plant for the protection of workers, materials, machinery and equipment, and the building itself. The other phase relates to the protection of people and property outside the plant against the effects of smoke, dirt, and gases that may be released unless proper precautions are taken. In many cities, the protection of the people against what has come to be called "smog" or "smaze" has become a difficult problem requiring the co-operation of public authorities, apartment and home-owners, and the managements of private enterprise. However, the fault should not be attributed entirely to business establishments since private automobiles and trucks are responsible for much of the air pollution.[1]

Each manufacturing plant may have some departments that cause dust. Organic particles are generated in the processing of rugs, flour, cotton, and woolen products. Inorganic particles are disseminated in the processing of metals, stone, and certain chemicals such as arsenic and mercury. All of these substances may be injurious to health if exposure is continued for long periods of time.

Cleanliness of the air is sometimes necessary to the making of a quality product. Painting and enameling can be done only in rooms that are free of dust. Examples of products to which such finishes are applied are refrigerators, washing machines, and automobile bodies. A company making spray-painted instrument panels reduced its rejects by two thirds by air conditioning the finishing room. Dust from a tennis court in an areaway adjacent to a machine shop has been known to double the cost of maintenance of machine tools.

In the filtering of air, the early air-conditioning systems used a

[1] George A. Boehm, "The Noisome Problem of Car Fumes," *Fortune*, Vol. LXI, No. 1 (1960), pp. 112 ff.

piece of coarse cloth as the filter material. The particles of dirt adhered to the cloth as the air passed through it. The cloth proved to be an inefficient material, however, since it was not easily cleaned and offered resistance to the movement of the air. Filters now are made of spun glass, vegetable fiber, or some type of metal fiber such as steel wool. When the filters are dirty, they may be discarded, cleaned, or renewed by replacing one or more of the layers. Washable filters are cleaned by dipping them in a bath of specially prepared liquid. The fluid washes

Courtesy of Owens-Corning Fiberglas Corp.

FIG. 30. Installation of Air Filters in a Flat Bank

the filter and coats it with a substance which causes dust particles to adhere to it when it is put back into use. In some systems the filter is automatically cleaned and replaced. An instrument which is actuated by the resistance of the filters to the flow of air causes the filters to be dipped into a bath when air resistance has increased to a certain point. The filters are automatically returned to the proper position. Some air-conditioning systems provide for washing the air to remove dust, dirt, allergy-producing pollens, and disease germs. Figure 30 shows how filters may be installed in a flat bank.

Air-conditioning systems may be local or central. In local systems a separate control and air-conditioning unit is provided for each room or other area. This system permits conditions to be varied according to the requirements of different departments. In central control systems, one unit regulates conditions throughout the whole building. Some systems control all phases of air conditioning; others are designed to control only one feature, such as heating, humidifying, or dust removal.

The protection of the community against air pollution by manufacturing processes does not permit of an easy solution. The management may not even realize that the plant is responsible for air pollution since fumes and smoke from many plants, the traffic on streets and highways, apartments, and other sources are intermingled. The extent of the pollution by any one plant varies with the kinds of dirt emitted, the height at which the fumes are released, the temperature of the discharge, the distance of the plant from residences or other buildings, the topography of the land, the climate, and the weather. Usually a plant does not produce enough smoke or other pollution to mark it as the offender. Each plant merely contributes to the objectionable conditions.[2]

Various methods are used to remove or counteract objectionable gases. Gaseous substances may be absorbed by water sprays that contain a chemical to improve collection. Several types of filters are available for removing dust, ash, or metal substances. The type of filter depends upon the size of the particles, the temperature, and the possible corrosive effect of the gases. Some dust collectors whirl the air or gases and cause particles to be thrown out by centrifugal force. Many technical societies and industry committees are prepared to supply information as to methods that are effective in any given situation[3]. Each case requires special study.

Movement of Air. The movement of air is related to both temperature and humidity, for it is associated with the control of body temperature. If air is kept moving, the temperature and humidity may be increased somewhat without causing discomfort. Experiments have shown that people cannot endure high temperatures unless the air is kept in motion. However, if the air is cool and relative humidity is high, the circulation of the air may have undesirable effects upon the health of workers.

---

[2] "Garbage in the Sky," *Fortune*, Vol. LI, No. 4 (1955), pp. 142 ff.

[3] See L. L. Falk, "Air Pollution—a Big Problem Today," *Factory Management and Maintenance*, Vol. CXII, No. 8 (1955), pp. 98–104. This article gives a list of agencies that can render technical advice on air pollution.

In many cases, no especial attention to the movement of air is required because sufficent movement is caused by differences in temperatures or pressures or by the movement of trucks and other equipment. Fans to move the air are sometimes used when heat is generated by manufacturing operations or heated materials require slow cooling. Figure 31 shows six uses of propeller fans for removing warm air or

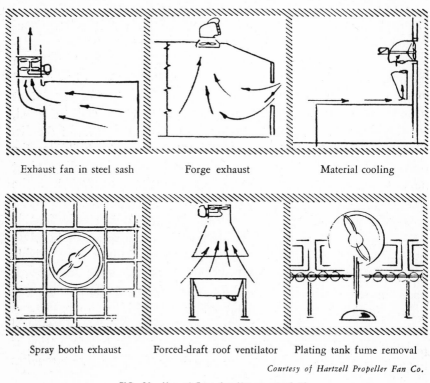

Exhaust fan in steel sash   Forge exhaust   Material cooling

Spray booth exhaust   Forced-draft roof ventilator   Plating tank fume removal

Courtesy of Hartzell Propeller Fan Co.

FIG. 31. Use of Fans for Movement of Air

air that has become contaminated by spray painting or fumes from tanks of chemicals. These illustrations do not require extended explanation.

Some protection against overheating in exposed locations may be provided by placing a shield of heat-reflective material between the source of heat and workers or equipment that would otherwise be exposed. The shielding materials, which are made of aluminum, coated steel, or nickel, reflect a major portion of the heat and absorb very little of it. To be effective, the shields should intercept all straight-line paths between the source of the heat and the persons, equipment, or materials requiring protection, and they should not have physical contact with the source of the heat. Since the heat that is reflected back to the source will increase the temperature in that area, provision should be made for removal of the overheated air.

Relation to Building Construction. For satisfactory air conditioning, certain features should be incorporated in building construction. Unless the building is well constructed, air-conditioning costs will be excessive. Roof decks, as well as walls, may be insulated to prevent loss of heat in winter and to offer protection from outside temperatures in summer. Double window sash is necessary in cold climates.

Windowless factories are designed for complete control of both lighting and air conditioning. The windowless factory is the opposite extreme of the daylight factory. It eliminates all reliance upon natural light with its varying intensities and affords a complete control of lighting conditions through proper artificial lighting. Since no window space is provided, all air is forced into areas inside the building through the air-conditioning system. Although some air may be admitted from the outside, the air within the building is continuously rewashed and reutilized. Heating costs are reduced because no heated air is lost around the window sash, and little is lost through radiation. Windowless buildings have been proved to be entirely practical. Their use depends upon their first cost, the psychological effect upon the workers, and the nature of the manufacturing processes.

NOISE

Formerly, machine designers were inclined to build machines with primary regard for their operating efficiency and with little consideration to quietness of operation. For a number of reasons, however, management has been compelled to study ways of eliminating, reducing, or isolating objectionable sounds. In some states, the courts have held that under workmen's compensation laws, a worker is entitled to payment for a partial loss of hearing that has been caused by exposure to noise. The worker is not required to prove that the damage to his hearing was caused by a single work accident or that he lost any wages as a result of his impairment of hearing. Partial damage resulting from a noisy environment may afford sufficient legal basis for an award. Since many persons suffer some impairment of hearing as they grow older, the employer may be compelled to pay many doubtful claims if he permits the work environment to become too noisy.[4]

---

[4] See Albert E. Bachmann, "Quiet Please," *Harvard Business Review*, Vol. XXXIII, No. 3 (1955), pp. 68–74.

Nature of Noise. Properties of noise that can be measured are frequency and pressure of intensity.[5] In industrial operations, noises are either steady or fluctuating. Steady noises are classified as wide band (low pitch) or narrow band (high pitch). Wide-band noises may be produced by a ventilating fan, an air conditioner, or a conveyor. Narrow-band noises might be produced by a saw, a lathe, or possibly the movement of air at high speed through a narrow opening. Fluctuating noises may result from a single impact or a series of impacts. Single-impact noise may be caused by a hammer or a punch press, while repeated-impact noise may be caused by a riveting gun or a pneumatic drill. The intensity of steady noise is easily measured by means of a noise meter. Fluctuating noise is more difficult to measure and may require special types of measuring devices. If the noise intensity as stated in decibels is less than 85, the hearing is not likely to be impaired. Examples of low intensities are the rustle of leaves, 20; office work, 50; average conversation, 60; and the average factory, 75. A punch press measures 110 and a rock drill 130.[6]

Effect of Noise. The relation of noise to worker efficiency is not easily determined. Tests have shown in some cases that the installation of acoustical materials in walls and ceiling has been followed by increased production, improvement in quality, a reduction in absences, and a decrease in labor turnover. However, these improvements may have resulted from a more favorable attitude and a feeling that the workers have been given special attention. Certainly noise interferes with production if it is so loud as to prevent easy communication or if it creates an accident hazard by interfering with the worker's ability to hear warning signals or to recognize changes in the operation of machinery.

The improvement that follows noise control is explained on biological grounds. Noise is most objectionable if it is loud and intermittent. However, continuous noise has undesirable effects upon the body functions and particularly upon the nervous system. It is believed to interfere with the regular rhythm of the heart, to increase the pulse rate, to cause transient changes in the blood pressure, and to disturb the proper functioning of the digestive system. In an effort to absorb the strain of the noise the nervous system uses energy in setting up inhibitions, and the muscles become tense. The result is nervous and physical exhaustion.

Continuous low noises may not be harmful, and many authorities

---

[5] A good discussion of the problem of noise may be found in "Industrial Noise," *Factory Management and Maintenance*, Vol. CXI, No. 12 (1953), pp. 113–36.

[6] *Ibid.*, p. 118.

contend that workers may become adjusted to these noises within a few days. Upon first exposure to noisy conditions, oxygen consumption and muscular activity increase. But after a few days, nervous excitement decreases; and the reactions gradually return to the level maintained during quiet conditions. The worker ceases to be distracted by noise when he accepts it as a background. He may even do better work if the noise is no more than a general hum of low intensity. However, if the sound is meaningful, as it would be in a radio program, or if it is loud or intermittent, it adversely affects work.

Another reason for attention to noise control is the matter of community relations. Persons living near the plant may be disturbed by noises inside the plant or on loading platforms. The objections are intensified by noises during the night hours, partly because people expect quiet at that time and partly because traffic and other noises during the day tend to make factory noise less noticeable.

Control of Noise. Noise may be reduced, isolated, or absorbed. It may be reduced by lubrication and oiling of machinery and by adjustment to eliminate vibration. The foundations of machinery may be built to absorb noises instead of transmitting them. In some cases the departments which are responsible for the noise may be segregated by moving or enclosing them. The most effective step for the absorption of noise is to cover the underside of the roof or ceiling with perforated material. The walls are made to absorb sound by using an inner layer of porous masonry material or by lining them with a material which has sound-absorbent qualities.

MUSIC AND BROADCASTING SYSTEMS

Workers have long been known to sing at their work and to work in harmony with the rhythm. One of the first companies to provide music for workers was Westinghouse Electric Corporation. The company is said to have discovered by accident, while testing radios, that the workers appreciated music on the job. A public address system was then installed to provide sound broadcasting for all work areas.

The effect of music at the workplace cannot be easily determined. Some studies have indicated that music may reduce absenteeism, tardiness, and labor turnover. However, the effect upon these aspects of employee behavior in many cases is negligible. With office workers and perhaps factory workers also, background music has been found to cause substantial increases in productivity and significant decreases in the number of errors.[7]

---

[7] "More on Music," *Factory Management and Maintenance*, Vol. CXVI, No. 6 (1958), p. 117.

Although some companies broadcast music continuously throughout the day, many observers believe that music should be played only intermittently and should be planned principally to break monotony. If it is played continuously, workers may tire of it; and it may have a deleterious effect. Lively tunes may be played for a few minutes in the morning to aid the workers in falling into the tempo of the work. After an interval of music the broadcasts may be resumed in the middle of the morning to break the monotony. When familiar tunes are played, workers may whistle the tune or sing. It seems best to play music which the workers readily recognize and which has a sustained melody. The volume should be constant. Outlets should be provided at each area and perhaps at each workplace, and they should be so constructed that the workers cannot regulate the volume.

Some companies purchase the flow of music from outside service companies, and others provide their own music from a library of records or from borrowed records. Workers may be permitted to suggest some of the records, and selections not requested should also be played to prevent the music from becoming monotonous. The program will depend in part upon the weather and the age and sex of the workers. The broadcasting of music also depends upon the size of the plant, the noise, and the monotony of the work. However, noise does not preclude the broadcasting of music, since the broadcasts are on a different pitch.

The broadcasting system may be used to bring the management closer to the workers. It gives the management an opportunity to build up group solidarity and to show an appreciation of the accomplishments of foremen and workers. Broadcasts may relate human interest stories, departmental safety or production records, years of service of older employees, birthdays and wedding anniversaries, births, and other personal events. The system may be used to announce athletic events, plant parties, rehearsals, and band concerts. Some companies use it to make announcements at any time of day when they have something important to tell the workers. Others make announcements only at fixed times, such as the beginning of the workday, at lunch, or during rest periods.

MONOTONY

Much has been said concerning monotony in industrial occupations. A well-known feature of modern industry is the subdivision of tasks into small repetitive operations. Some observers believe that the simplification of tasks has proceeded so far that the effect of monotony upon the work has offset a large part of the gains to society from mechanization and increased production.

Nature of Monotonous Tasks.   In some kinds of work, the series of motions required to perform a task is short, and the same work cycle is continuously repeated. The tendency in industry is to subdivide the tasks and to limit the worker to the performance of only one work cycle, or a very few types of cycles. The worker repeats day after day a series of motions which may require only a few minutes and possibly no more than a minute to complete. In many cases the cycle may be quickly learned and may require little initiative, skill, or imagination.

In the fabricating departments of any plant, much automatic equipment has been so highly developed that the worker has only to see that the machine is kept supplied with material and is in proper operating condition. In operating semiautomatic machines, the worker merely inserts the materials and removes the finished work. Other semiautomatic machines require the worker to see that the device which holds the material is properly cleared at the end of each work cycle, that the next piece is properly seated and locked in position, and that cutting tools are working properly. This work requires attention, care, and a feeling of responsibility on the part of the worker; but it does not require a wide range of skill. Although much of the work is classed as semiskilled, it is monotonous.

In mass-production industries, the product moves past the worker in a continuous line and he merely puts on a part, paints, polishes, inspects, corrects defects, or performs some other such operation. The work is machine paced, and the worker adapts his pace to the flow of work. Examples may be found in such industries as automobiles, metal containers, glass bottles, and certain operations for the filling of containers with sugar or soap. Work of this kind is characterized by repetitiveness, a minute subdivision of the work cycle, a minimum requirement of skill, and a requirement of surface mental attention as contrasted with mental attention in depth. Jobs on a production line are much more likely to be monotonous and tiresome than work at manually operated machines where the worker can set his own pace, subject to a measure of control through work standards and incentive wage rates.

When the production process is fully automated, the worker may become a machine tender or monitor. He is required to watch the operation and to remain alert, but he needs to take action only infrequently. The nature of the work may permit job enlargement through the assignment of a variety of operations to one worker. This arrangement may give the worker an added feeling of importance because he is assigned the responsibility for the continuous operation of a complex and expensive machine. Many workers may feel that the work of starting and stopping machines or watching for warning lights does not provide continuous interest and challenge.

Worker Attitudes toward Monotony. Workers differ considerably in their attitudes toward monotonous tasks. Some prefer a variety of motions and soon tire of work that is repetitive. Young men who are anxious to advance in their positions dislike repetitive tasks because they soon learn the routine and they do not regard the work as a promising means of advancement. Some men would prefer to have jobs that do not make heavy mental demands upon them. If a young woman regards her employment as temporary, she may prefer a routine task because she soon learns to do the work. She is not required to put much effort into it. If the woman regards her employment as permanent, her attitude may be the same as that of the ambitious young man. Insofar as possible, a worker should be placed in work that he prefers and that is suited to his mentality.

Some workers may prefer a repetitive task because the demands of the work from one day to another are uniform. Frustrating and irritating delays are eliminated by the certainty of the assembly line. Furthermore, the worker on a line is a part of a group whose workplaces are close together, and he may be able to talk with his associates as he works.

Since the work makes few demands upon the mental capacities of the worker, he can think about other things. By offering rewards for constructive suggestions, management may encourage the worker to think about ways of improving the methods of work, eliminating waste motions, or bettering the layout. However, the number of workers that are motivated to make suggestions is not large. In some cases, the worker may think about the pleasant aspects of his work, or he may allow his mind to dwell upon his personal problems at home or at work.[8] He may develop an attitude that causes him to become maladjusted or dissatisfied. This attitude may be improved by proper association with other workers in what has come to be called "informal organization." Monotony is a factor in such management programs as plant athletics, entertainment, and musical broadcasts.

---

[8] Charles R. Walker and Robert H. Guest, *The Man on the Assembly Line* (Cambridge, Mass.: Harvard University Press, 1952), p. 12. Also Arthur N. Turner, "Management and the Assembly Line," *Harvard Business Review,* Vol. XXXIII, No. 5 (1955), pp. 40–48.

Reducing the Effect of Monotony. One way to lessen the effect of monotony is to supply the work in batches rather than in a continuous stream. When the worker has finished a batch of material, he has a feeling of accomplishment—he can see how much work he has done. Production is increased, possibly because his interest is stimulated as he nears the end of a batch. When work is supplied in a continuous and endless line, a feeling of helplessness may be created.

The worker may assume a more wholesome attitude if he is shown the relation of his work to the entire production process. The service rendered by the product to the consumer should also be demonstrated. An explanation of the usefulness of the product to consumers and the relation of each task to the total manufacturing operations may be made a part of the induction procedure.

Another possibility is to break the monotony by rest pauses and the development of an interest in social and recreational activities. Shifting workers to other jobs is also a possibility, although this measure has limited application. Some companies permit certain workers to shift to three or four positions each day. For example, workers who inspect and pack glass jars for shipping may be shifted to work stations that enable them to handle several sizes and shapes of jars. In other cases a plan of rotation at longer intervals may be followed. In any such plan, however, productivity may be lowered because a period of adjustment is required when a shift is made. Labor unions use the monotony of work as an argument for a shorter work day or work week in order that a worker may develop an interest in outside activities.

Some companies have found that the best solution to the problem of monotony is to increase the length of the work cycle, although the trend has long been in the opposite direction. The work cycle might be lengthened, for example, by allowing the worker to set up the machine for new operations, to adjust the machine, and to inspect the work subject to a random inspection by a professional inspector. Another possibility is the establishment of work centers where a few workers may perform all of the operations necessary to the manufacture of the product. Such changes may result in a loss of efficiency, although the loss may be compensated by other advantages. The problem has no universal solution but requires study in different situations.

In many industries, monotonous work has been reduced by the development of fully automatic machines or automation to perform certain types of operations. A machine can be perfected to do almost any type of repetitive operation provided that the work is done in sufficient volume to justify the cost. Monotonous repetitive tasks offer the greatest opportunity for savings through mechanization.

FATIGUE

Fatigue is the effect of physical activity upon the mind and body of an individual which is reflected in a decreased capacity for work. It is closely related to the creation of certain chemical products in the body as the by-products of muscular and mental activity. The principal chemical wastes are carbon dioxide and acids. Some are known only as fatigue poisons or toxins. The effects of fatigue, however, are not confined to the muscles but reach the various parts of the nervous system.

Nature of Fatigue. Fatigue is both mental and physical. It is partly the result of muscular activity, and it is also affected by mental attitude. Some experiments indicate that attitude is the dominant factor. If the worker likes his supervisor and trusts him, he may be relieved of anxiety and nervous tension. The result is that he can do a greater amount of work before he begins to notice a feeling of fatigue. A worker who is anxious about his job and who is afraid of his boss will use up more nervous energy than the one who is properly adjusted.

The effects of fatigue are reflected in many aspects of the work situation. The experiments of Taylor, Gilbreth, and others indicate that fatigue is a cause of decreased hourly and daily output. It also increases turnover because workers hope to find less tiring work in a new job. Absenteeism will be increased because workers who feel that their jobs require too much physical or mental effort will find excuses for staying away from work. Spoilage is increased because tired workers are inefficient or indifferent. Fatigue is a factor in accident rates because tired workers are slower to react to danger. Slowness of reaction may be either physical or mental.

Fatigue is affected by all the conditions of work, including the operation of laborsaving machinery and particularly materials-handling equipment. Such work conditions as lighting, air conditioning, the use of color, noise, music and other broadcasts, and monotony of work have a bearing upon the problem. Still other factors are the nervous demands of the job, such as uncertainties and irregularities in the flow of work and interruptions due to breakdowns of machinery, poor quality of materials, accidents, and other causes.

Reducing Fatigue. One way to reduce fatigue is to design machinery for the purpose of reducing the physical and mental demands upon the worker. The machine may be made to do the lifting and the moving of materials as well as the processing. Comfort for the operator may be increased by providing toe room for a worker who must stand and leg room for one who must sit and by placing controls in the places that are easy to reach. The design of the seat and the location of controls in cranes, airplanes, and automobiles will affect both fatigue and the safety of operation. A study of machine design suggests that machines have too often been planned for engineering efficiency and that comfort and safety features have sometimes been neglected. These problems are being given more careful study.

QUESTIONS

1. Why is slight movement of the air desirable? Why is strong movement objectionable?

2. Why do some people consider that fresh air is desirable? Is freshness a necessary quality of good air?

3. Explain the advantages of radiant heating. Does this method have any disadvantages?

4. Under certain conditions, moisture collects on walls and windows because of differences in temperature. Why is such condensation objectionable?

5. Should employee attitudes and comfort be considered in planning a building, or is the building plan strictly an engineering problem?

6. Should musical broadcasts be planned for the purpose of relieving the monotony of the work, or are they intended to help the worker to work according to the rhythm of the music?

7. How do undesirable working conditions contribute to the spread of the common cold?

8. What industries require controlled working conditions for the production of a quality product?

9. How does the simplification of tasks help to increase production? How may it cause decreased production?

10. What can management do to minimize the effects of monotony?

11. Should the management arrange for the continuous broadcast of music to please some workers when others object to the broadcasts?

CASES

28. AIR CONDITIONING IN A CANDY FACTORY

The Acme Candy Company at Oakland, California, had difficulty in controlling the quality of chocolate candy. In warm temperatures, such as usually required for the comfort of workers, the candy did not become firm as quickly as was desired for purposes of packing and shipping. Often, the room became very warm because of the heat from the cooking operations. A very cold temperature was undesirable because the candy would take on a light color in a cold room.

The departments of the plant for making candy included mixing, cooking, cooling and cutting or shaping, forming and wrapping (for taffy), nut sorting and processing, and dipping (for chocolates and bonbons). No temperature problem arose in most of the departments because the facilities for heating the building were adequate, and the climate was sufficiently cool in summer. No equipment for cooling the air in the plant had ever been considered necessary.

The plant manager proposed that the difficulty in controlling the quality of chocolate be met by segregating the chocolate processing department in a corner of the building and air conditioning only that part of the building. Workers in the chocolate department would be expected to wear somewhat warmer clothing than would be needed by workers in other departments, although a temperature of 68 degrees was believed to be proper. After the chocolates were dipped or formed, they would be placed on trays and loaded on an enclosed conveyor. The conveyor would move the candy from the processing department to the packaging room, where it would be placed in boxes for storage or shipment. The enclosed conveyor could be air conditioned at relatively low cost.

Question:

What are the advantages of the air-conditioning plan as outlined by the plant superintendent?

29. ENLARGING THE JOB

William Enrico was one of sixteen welders in the jet engine department of the plant of the Dallas Engine Company. His job was classified as that of a manual arc welder, and workers at other welding jobs in the department were given the titles of automatic welding machine operators or inert-gas metal arc welders. The production planning department scheduled the flow of work and assigned the operations to each worker according to his specialty and the type of welding required for production.

Although Enrico was satisfied with his pay, he found the work to be particularly trying and at times frustrating. On some occasions, work would accumulate at his work station, and he would be pressed to meet the schedules established by the production planning department. At other times, he had no work to do, although other welders might be busy. Enrico also found the work to be monotonous and to lack the challenge to his ingenuity that he enjoyed. Because of the degree of specialization among the welders, all of his work assignments were similar. He finally spoke to the foreman concerning the possibility of transferring to some other type of work. The foreman did not approve this proposal because he did not like to lose a good welder. The personnel manager objected to it because several months of training and experience were required to develop a skilled craftsman in this work. After discussion of the problem with the other welders, the foreman recommended that the job be enlarged and that any welder be permitted to do any kind of welding that the production order required. This change in work assignments was made, and the job titles of the welders were changed to the title of mechanic.

The new setup required that some additional tools and equipment be provided for each welder, but the number of welders was reduced from sixteen to thirteen. This reduction was made possible by the better balance of work loads. The number of moves necessary for the handling of any production order was reduced by about 15 per cent because any one welder could now do more than one operation on an order. Production planning was simplified because work no longer needed to be assigned to individual welders. The work was merely scheduled for the department, and individual work assignments were made by the foreman.

The greatest advantage of the change was found to be the greater employee satisfaction. Enrico told the foreman that he was especially pleased with the new job title, which gave him increased prestige both inside and outside the plant. The quality of the welding work noticeably improved. Although most of the work formerly done had been acceptable, it had lacked the appearance that an interested craftsman could impart to a weld. The plant manager was so pleased with the improvement that he authorized the plant engineer and the personnel manager to investigate the possibility of enlarging the work of other jobs.

Required:

Explain the advantages and the disadvantages of a high degree of specialization in production work.

PART IV
THE
PRODUCT

15 Product Research

IN preceding chapters, our discussion was concerned with two of the major groups of problems pertaining to the management of industrial enterprises. These problems relate to the organization of the enterprise and the provision of physical facilities. Other problems pertain to the product to be made and sold. In the development of any new product, the first step consists of research and experimentation in product development. Next, the product is designed with reference to such structural features as lines, color, general appearance, materials to be used, and serviceability. Then the specifications of the parts and other exact features of materials, parts, and the completed product are fixed. In some cases, a further period of experimentation with manufacturing methods and possibly some trial tests of the market with limited amounts of the product may be required before full-scale manufacturing is started. Standards for the quality of the product are also established. Quality is incorporated into the product by design, construction, quality materials, and craftsmanship. To assure that the standards are maintained, the materials, parts, and subassemblies are inspected at various stages in the process of manufacture, and the finished product is inspected and perhaps tested by a trial run. The product is then shipped to the customer and installed and serviced if necessary. The steps might be summarized as follows:

Basic research.
Applied research.
Development of design, setting of standards.
Revision of plant layout.
Purchasing of materials and parts, inspection upon receipt.

Manufacture of the product, inspection at certain control points.
Final inspection and testing.
Shipment to the customer.
Installation and service.

Some of the steps in product development have been discussed in preceding chapters. The steps remaining for consideration are product research, product design, and inspection.

NATURE OF INDUSTRIAL RESEARCH

The significance of research arises from the fact that industry is characterized by rapid change in both products and methods of manufacturing. Change is the result of the discovery of new applications of scientific principles and business methods. Improvements in methods and devices have continued since man first discovered fire, the needle, the loom, the wheel, the lathe, and the use of writing to convey ideas. What is new in modern industry is the rate at which improvements are made and new products introduced. The tempo of industry is so rapid that most large enterprises find it necessary to make constant improvements in products and methods of production.

Types of Research. Research activities may be classified on the basis of the purpose or objective. From this point of view, research is classified as basic or pure, applied, and developmental. Basic research consists of investigation for the discovery of scientific principles. Much basic research is done in the fields of biochemistry, bacteriology, physics, and inorganic chemistry. Its purpose may be the discovery of the properties of organic and inorganic matter and the nature of sound, light, electricity, or other forces, without regard to possible applications of the principles. Manufacturing establishments formerly looked to the universities, various endowed institutions, and the government for research in the basic sciences. However, as corporate manufacturing enterprises have increased in size, they have made significant contributions to scientific knowledge through their own investigations.

Applied research is investigation and experimentation in the use of scientific principles to develop a new product, improve a product, or improve the container. Improvement of a product may be achieved by developing a cheaper or more economical method of manufacture, by improving the appearance or the operating efficiency of the product, or by developing new materials to be used in manufacturing, such as magnesium, aluminum or steel alloys, plastics, synthetic rubber, and rustless steel. Most industrial research is applied research.

Developmental research is investigation or experimentation for the purpose of lowering the cost of producing or marketing the product. Developmental research is usually conducted by the line or the operating departments rather than by a research department. This type of research begins after applied research has been completed. It is conducted continuously for the purpose of eliminating minor troubles in production and defects which become apparent as the product is used by consumers. Much development research is the result of complaints received from distributors or customers. Market and consumer surveys are often conducted for the purpose of obtaining consumer and distributor comments on the product and suggestions for improvement.

The question that must be decided by any corporate management is the amount of research that it will do in each of the three areas. The object of the research program depends upon the industry, the size of the company, and the attitude of the management. In some industries, such as rubber, the objective seems to be principally to improve the product in order that the company may maintain its competitive position. In other industries, such as food, more of the research appropriation is expended on the development of new products. As might be expected, large companies conduct more elaborate programs than small enterprises. Because of the relationship to sales and profits, corporations tend to emphasize applied and developmental research and to spend only a small part of their appropriations on pure research.[1]

Who Conducts Research. Many of our most notable inventions resulted from the work of individuals. Well-known inventors are Eli Whitney, Robert Fulton, S. F. B. Morse, Alexander Graham Bell, Henry Ford, Harvey Firestone, and the Wright brothers. The radio was the product of many minds, although Guglielmo Marconi is usually credited with the invention of wireless telegraphy. Thomas A. Edison produced a total of 1,097 patentable inventions, including the phonograph, the motion-picture camera, a telephone transmitter, and the incandescent electric light. The principal disadvantages of research by individuals are, first, the limited amount of time and money which most persons can devote to research and, second, the duplication of effort because of the lack of co-ordination in the research of many persons working individually.

Industrial and commercial enterprises now conduct much of the most significant research. In 1920, about 300 corporations in this country

---

[1] For discussion of the amount that a company should spend in research and the percentage that should be allocated to each type of research, see Francis Bello, "Industrial Research," *Fortune,* Vol. LIII, No. 1 (1956), pp. 96 ff.

employed 9,300 persons in research. By 1930, the number of corporations with research laboratories had increased to 1,625, with a personnel of 34,200. Corporate research work increased markedly during World War II. From 1945 to 1960, the number of scientists and engineers engaged in industrial research increased fourfold. The expenditure for such research in 1960 is estimated to be approximately $10 billion.[2] The greatest amount of industrial research is conducted in the mass-production industries, such as petroleum, rubber, chemicals, automobiles, telephone, and electrical appliances. Corporate research has the advantage of strong financial support for projects that afford the promise of profitable commercial development. The continuous life of the corporation enables it to take a long-range point of view. Moreover, in corporate research the work of specialists in various fields may be correlated or integrated. A possible limitation of corporate research is duplication of effort by companies in the same industry or in related industries.

Some corporations maintain their own laboratories for projects of limited scope which can be completed within a period of a few weeks or months, and they contract with private research organizations for research requiring longer periods of time. The work may be done at less cost by a private research organization because the facilities and the staff are already available. The private organization may also spread the overhead costs of equipment and personnel over a number of different contracts.[3]

The logical place for basic research is the university or college laboratory, and much research of this nature is conducted at educational institutions by instructors, fellows, and other graduate students. However, an increasing amount of applied research is being conducted in universities and colleges because of the income received from such work. Some of the research is financed by grants from the government, trade associations, and corporations. Much research is conducted by universities in co-operation with the federal government and private corporations.

Some research is financed co-operatively by members of a trade or industry through trade associations. The research activities of trade associations assume many forms. Some associations co-operate with com-

---

[2] C. Wilson Randle, "Problems of R and D Management," *Harvard Business Review,* Vol. XXXVII, No. 1 (1959), p. 128.

[3] Gerald Morrell, "What Makes Research Sterile?" *Harvard Business Review,* Vol. XXXVI, No. 6 (1958), pp. 149 ff.

mercial laboratories, universities, privately endowed institutions, or government agencies for carrying on research projects. Other associations serve only as clearinghouses through which the members exchange the results of their investigations, and still others maintain laboratories for research and report the results of their experiments to the members. Industries in which trade associations have conducted research include baking, dry milk, gas (for cooking and heating), steel, asphalt, car wheels, meat packing, food canning, bituminous coal, textiles, fertilizer, paint and varnish, and cement.

Trade association research has the advantage of low cost to the industry as compared with separate research programs for the various companies. Centralized research programs are not more generally conducted because each company wishes to outdistance its competitors by developing a product that is superior or unique. Co-operative research is beneficial to the industry, but it benefits all companies rather than the individual company.

Probably the best known of the technical research organizations is the National Research Council, which was established in 1916 by the National Academy of Sciences and a number of technical societies. Its membership is composed of representatives from government agencies and scientific and technical societies. Financial support is received as grants from the Carnegie Foundation, the Rockefeller Foundation, and other private organizations. The function of the National Research Council is to assist in co-ordinating and publicizing scientific work in the United States rather than to manage research projects directly. This function is important because it tends to reduce simultaneous research on the same project by various agencies or individuals. Technical and professional societies for research include the American Dental Association, the American Pharmaceutical Association, the American Society of Mechanical Engineers, the American Association of Testing Materials, and the United States Institute for Textile Research.

DEVELOPMENT AND CONTROL OF RESEARCH PROGRAMS

Each company should decide for itself certain aspects of its research program. One such question pertains to the relation of any new project to other projects, and the relation of any new product developed through the research program to the existing product line. The management should also determine whether research will be organized as a major division or as a department within the manufacturing division.

Other important questions pertain to the relation of research to other divisions of the company and the organization of the research activity itself.

Co-ordination of Research Programs. Usually no difficulty is encountered in the co-ordination of pure, applied, and developmental research programs provided the company limits the work to one field, such as electronics, chemicals, or cake mixes. Although some of the personnel may specialize in one type of research, the entire program can be conducted in one laboratory under the supervision of one research director. Problems of co-ordination are minimized if the products developed by the research staff can be manufactured with existing facilities without a revision of plant layout. Further economies are achieved if the new products can be sold by the existing sales organization through the usual sales outlets. A company with a varied product line may be able to make and sell at a profit many new products that a company with a more limited product line would find unprofitable.

In some cases, research programs may lead to new products that are manufactured by similar production facilities but are advertised through different media and sold to different groups of consumers through different channels of distribution. For example, a well-known paint company developed two slightly different types of quick-drying paint. One was sold to manufacturers of automobiles and home appliances, and the other was intended for homeowners or amateur painters. Sometimes a unified research program requires that the company branch out into new lines of production and sales if it is to utilize the discoveries made in its laboratories. In this manner, a manufacturer of paints and varnish was drawn first into the production of salad dressing and related products and subsequently into the manufacture of certain medicinal preparations. The new product lines resulted from the efforts of the research staff to find ways of utilizing scrap and waste that formerly was discarded.

In some cases, the relationship between various research and other activities is remote. For example, a manufacturer of cereals and cake mixes launched a line of electric irons and other home appliances. The two product lines, one in cereals and the other in appliances, differed in research methods, manufacturing processes, production facilities, and channels of distribution and sale. The principal relationship between the lines arose from the fact that the same group of consumers purchased the products and could be reached through the same advertising media. The company hoped that the name and reputation of the one line of products would help to sell the second. This relationship was found to be too limited, and the line of home appliances was abandoned after a trial period. The situation is shown graphically in Figure 32.

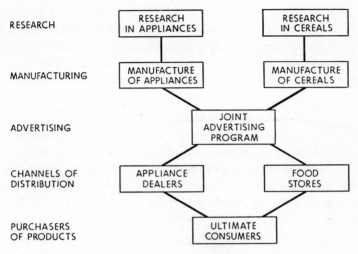

FIG. 32. Relation of Product Lines of Appliances and Cereals

Location of Research Laboratory. Opinions differ concerning the most desirable location of the research laboratory. Most businesses consider that the laboratory should be located near the factory in order that the laboratory personnel may be informed of production requirements and problems. The objection to such a location is that the research staff may be called upon to study the day-to-day problems of the factory which the executives of the line organization or the plant engineers should handle for themselves. This practice would prevent continuity in the research program which is necessary to success and might reduce the position of the research specialist to that of a "glorified repairman." However, some contact between the research division and the plant is usually considered desirable in order that the research staff may understand the problems of production. For this reason, some companies locate the research laboratory close enough to permit occasional visits to the plant but far enough away to discourage frequent calls upon personnel by plant executives.

Research a Staff Function. Many problems of organizational relationships should be clarified before production is begun. Contracts should be made with vendors for the manufacture of the raw materials and parts in the necessary and the required quantities. If the product is sold to other manufacturing companies, advertising and sales promotion programs should be directed toward this market to induce them to use the new product. For example, a container manufacturing company may be required to organize a sales campaign to persuade other companies to package their products in a new fiber or metal container. In some instances new packaging machinery may be required. The sales program may extend beyond the manufacturer who uses the container in order to reach the ultimate consumer. The container manufacturer might attempt to convince ultimate consumers that vitamins are not destroyed in the canning process or that beer in metal containers is as palatable as the same product sold in bottles. In some cases, milk commissions must be persuaded to permit the sale of milk in fiber cartons if the product is to have a wide market. In the handling of such problems arising in connection with the production and sale of the new product, the co-operation of the sales, manufacturing, and engineering divisions is necessary.

Organization for Research. Although the persons engaged in research are scientists who are expected to create ideas, they require some organizations to co-ordinate group effort and to prevent waste. The principles of organization and management that have been proved to be successful in other lines of endeavor can be adapted to the organization of the research department. However, the application of the principles of organization is proper only to the extent that they increase rather than suppress productive efforts.

The research department usually has a director, one or more assistants to the director, project supervisors, and research personnel. The success of the department depends upon the individual research specialist, who must largely manage his own work. Each productive unit of the organization, or each scientist, has unique characteristics because of differences in personality, education, and experience. Research workers dislike forms, rules, and office routines. They may accept such controls, but they do not necessarily co-operate to make them effective unless they are convinced of the need for procedures and other restraints.

Proper supervision for research personnel requires training for supervisors both within and without the company. The supervisor is usually a technician who has been promoted because he was believed to possess the qualities required for supervisory work. However, such a person usually requires some additional training in budgetary control, organization, human relations, and other phases of management. In some companies, training for supervisors of research personnel tends to be neglected.[4]

---

[4] C. Wilson Randle, *op. cit.,* p. 134.

Communication assumes increased importance because the director needs to keep himself informed concerning the research projects throughout the department. He should observe the usual channels of communication, although he may sometimes establish direct contacts with individual scientists. The supervisor or group leader would advise with the director on all problems pertaining to his section and would transmit to scientists working with him all communications pertaining to budgets, project assignments, salaries, purchases of equipment, and other detailed problems.

Horizontal communication is also important because problems are rarely solved by one person acting alone. The exchange of information between individuals and groups is necessary to collective industrial research. In any lateral communication, the supervisor of the project should be kept informed of decisions reached. All unresolved problems affecting research personnel would be referred to the supervisor for his opinion.

Communication between the research division and other divisions is also desirable, although the establishment of such channels of communication involves many difficulties. Communication between research and sales might enable research personnel to learn of the difficulties of salesmen in selling a product or service personnel in installing and servicing it. Such information would enable the research division to develop better products in the future. Communication between research and manufacturing might disclose that excess manufacturing cost is caused by certain features in the design of a product. Similar advantages would be gained by communication with the advertising, market research, purchasing, engineering, and other divisions. In many companies these channels of communication are inadequately developed.[5]

The persons who work on the research projects perform the operating activity or the line function of the research department. The line needs the services of various persons who perform the staff or facilitating work. Such services may include a library of technical books, magazines, and other materials under the direction of a librarian. The library would also keep complete records of all research projects undertaken and either completed or abandoned. A model shop may be established to make models of products being developed by the research personnel. Editorial work and photography may be separately organized under the supervision of technicians. Other special services include drafting of charts and drawings, storage and care of instruments, and the preparation of specifications against which new products are tested. Services

---

[5] John A. Howard, "Co-ordinated Product Development," *Harvard Business Review,* Vol. XXXVII, No. 1 (1959), pp. 33 ff.

of this kind are provided in order to save the time of engineers, chemists, and other scientists who are engaged in research.

Planning the Research Program. The idea for a new research project or a new product may originate with the research department. Ideas for research may also be suggested by persons in the sales division or elsewhere in the company. Occasionally, the idea may come from someone outside the company, including customers, or from scientists in government or universities. After preliminary discussion, a search of the literature may be made to determine whether anyone else has made a study of the field. The files of the company would also be consulted to learn whether the idea has been previously considered. If the idea has been proposed earlier and then rejected, the reasons for the rejection should be carefully reviewed. New developments since the idea was considered at an earlier time would be investigated to determine whether the chances for success have increased.

If the probabilities for the development for a new product seem to be favorable, it would still be necessary to inquire whether a profitable market for the product can be developed. Market possibilities might be investigated by the market research department. Promising ideas then go through the stages of laboratory research, product formulation, survey of the technical and market possibilities of the product as developed, and the formulation of a recommendation for abandonment or further development.

Before a new product is introduced on a national scale, it may be produced in a small factory or workshop known as a "pilot plant." In such a factory, equipment for the manufacture of the product in limited quantities is provided and the product is sold to consumers in a small area. Production difficulties are corrected; the product itself may be improved; and consumer acceptance is studied. If production on a large scale appears feasible, manufacturing and distribution may be expanded to cover the national market. If large-scale production is not feasible, further research may be made, or the project may be abandoned. In this manner, serious errors may be avoided.

An extension of the plan of the pilot plant is found in the semiworks, in which a production line is set up and placed in operation. The purpose of the semiworks is to discover defects in manufacturing methods and procedures before the risks incident to production on a large scale are incurred. When the new plant is built, both product and manufacturing processes have been sufficiently improved to afford a promise of success.

When to terminate the research on a project and begin the production and sale of the product is a difficult problem. Usually the research personnel are scientists who are inclined to be perfectionists. They may wish to continue experimentation and improvement in order that they may be certain that the product will render good service; and they may overlook the factors of cost, selling price, and profit. To continue research for too long a time may permit competitors to enter the market and gain an advantage that will be difficult to overcome. However, to discontinue the research too soon and to attempt to make and sell a product that is unsatisfactory to customers may cause heavy losses.

Organizing for Production of the Product. The success of the product may depend upon careful planning for the initial production. Quantities and schedules of production should be planned as a basis for the purchase commitments. New equipment may be required; but before it is bought, the management should estimate the probable time required for a recovery of its cost. A revision of plant layout may be necessary, and such changes should be made in a manner that will not disrupt the schedules and costs of existing products. The pattern of production for the old products should be adjusted to provide for the production of the new one. Some shifts in personnel may be necessary. Costs should be kept at a minimum with due regard for quality of the product and safety of personnel. Cost reductions may be effected by possible redesign of the product to reduce the number of parts or simplify manufacturing operations, by a reduction in the size of the product or its parts, provided its performance would not be affected, by the substitution of standard parts for parts especially made, and perhaps by other changes. Some of these changes would require the approval and co-operation of persons outside the research division.

Budget Control of Research. A careful control of research expense through a budget is necessary because of the uncertain nature of the work and the time required to perfect a project. Some of the programs may require several years for completion. Some companies estimate that the research program must be ten to fifteen years ahead of the product. To avoid excessive and wasteful outlays for research, management should plan all projects and should control the total amount of money spent in the work.

The total amount to be spent in research is usually stated as a percentage of sales. This method has the advantage of placing a definite limit on the amount spent for research and of permitting an increase in the expenditure as the company increases in size. Some companies use a percentage of the average sales for the preceding five years. This method of computation eliminates large year-to-year variations and permits the research director to plan a program with the assurance that it can be carried to completion. The research budget may also be planned each year to provide specifically for the cost of certain programs, with an allowance for any new programs that might be initiated during the year. The estimates may also indicate the amounts to be spent for various types of research work. For example, General Motors Corporation divides its research program into three parts, as follows:

Service to the various divisions of the company.
The making of models or samples, from which products are to be designed.
Research in pure science, such as the properties of paraffin, fuels, and lubricants, or the causes of knock in an engine.

In a large company, research activities may be conducted in more than one place or laboratory. When this situation exists, the total research allowance is apportioned to each location and also to the various projects. A part of the appropriation may be allocated to product testing and improvement.

The estimates are next reviewed by top management. The most common practice is a review by the president of the company, by a committee of which the president is a member, or by the general manager. However, the estimates may be submitted to a vice-president, the chief engineer, the research director, or the production manager. The budget may be approved as submitted, or a revision may be required. Before the budget is finally approved, top management should be assured that the total amount is not excessive, that the projects recommended give a reasonable promise of success, and that the results of successful research can be profitably used by the company. A new product developed through research should be related in some way to the existing line of products. The addition of the new product might be justified because it can be sold in the same market through the same channels of distribution as present products, because it can be manufactured with the same equipment, because it provides a use for waste or scrap, or because it offers some other definite advantage in production or marketing.

Periodical reports of cost and accomplishment for each project should be submitted to the budget committee, and all major projects should be reviewed at least semiannually. If the success of a program becomes questionable, the work should be suspended until the difficulties can be appraised or until a decision for abandonment or continuance can be made. In some companies, unsuccessful projects are continued because the research scientist or perhaps some executive has a special interest in them. Money can be wasted in research because the possibilities of a project are not easily determined in advance and results are not easily evaluated. Each project and the entire program should contribute to the objectives of the business.[6]

When a project is abandoned, a complete record should be made for future reference, in order that the work will not be duplicated later. This record would indicate the original objectives, the methods pursued, the results (which might be negative or positive), the amount of money spent, and the reasons for abandonment.

Patenting of a Product or a Design. A successful project may pass through the following six stages:

Discovery of a scientific principle.
Application of the principle to a practical problem.
Perfection of an invention.
Granting of a patent by the government.
Manufacture and sale of the product on a small scale in a pilot plant.
Manufacture and sale of the product on a mass-production basis.

A patent is granted for seventeen years. Protection begins when the application is filed, and the time limit of seventeen years begins when the patent is issued. The patent does not confer the right to manufacture and sell the product or to use a process, since under the law each person already has such a right. What it does confer is the right to exclude others from the use of the processes or from the manufacture of the product protected by the patent. Such protection is socially desirable because it affords the motive for extensive and intensive research which characterizes modern production. Industrial research results in continuous improvement in the products of industry. The benefits are in time extended to labor and consumers as well as to management.

QUESTIONS

1. How can the need for more and more research be explained? Will industry ever reach the point where more research is unprofitable?

2. In what industries is the greatest amount of research being done? Mention industries where the amount of research is relatively small.

3. Are the attitudes of research personnel toward controls different from the attitudes of persons in the manufacturing divisions?

---

[6] See James B. Quinn, "How to Evaluate Research Output," *Harvard Business Review,* Vol. XXXVIII, No. 2 (1960), pp. 69-80.

4. How does budgetary control of research differ from control over such activities as manufacturing and selling?

5. What qualities are required of the person who supervises the work of research in a company in the chemical industries? Does the best chemist make the best manager?

6. Scientists usually want recognition by their professional associates for their contributions to the subject. How can such recognition be gained by the scientist who works for an industrial corporation?

7. Does the company face the risk of working too long on a research project? Might it terminate the program too early? How can such risks be minimized?

8. What is the significance of the fact that research is a staff function?

9. Why might the research worker neglect the possibilities of profit from the research program? Why might overemphasis upon profit be undesirable?

10. What advantages does the large company have over the small one in conducting a research program? Should this difference constitute a reason why the government should favor the growth of corporations as measured by dollar value of assets or extent of the product line?

CASES

30. DEVELOPMENT OF A NEW SOAP

The Chicago Packing Company, one of the large meat-packing companies, had developed and marketed a number of brands of soap without substantial success until it perfected and marketed a new soap which it called Real. Previous attempts to market a soap met with only moderate success because of some decided defect in comparison with well-known brands. One of its soaps had a yellowish color, tended to become soft when wet, and had a questionable odor. As the company had large amounts of waste which could be used in making soap, it was particularly anxious to develop a successful product.

The management recognized that in order to compete with other soaps which were well established, the soap would have to have some quality not claimed by other brands. After considerable discussion among management people, a manager in the sales division suggested that a soap that was also a deodorant would be a revolutionary idea for such a product. The deodorant would destroy the objectionable feature of perspiration before it started and would produce a lasting pleasant effect. This suggestion was passed along to the research chemists, who soon began experimenting with possible ingredients. They discovered that a certain chemical would destroy the bacteria responsible for the objectionable odors. After further research, they produced a soap that had the qualities desired by the management.

The marketing of the soap raised a number of important questions. Retail food stores were antagonistic to a new soap because of price cutting, combination sales, coupons, and other special deals which caused them considerable inconvenience. The company therefore decided to begin the marketing of Real in drug and department stores. To induce such distributors to handle the new product, the manufacturer fixed a resale price and required that the soap be sold at that price in accordance with price maintenance or "fair trade" laws of the various states. The price was higher than the prices charged for other soaps because the dealer was guaranteed a substantial markup. This method of selling limited the sales but permitted the company to test the market.

The advertising of a product designed to prevent undesirable effects of perspiration presented a difficult problem because such advertising tended to associate the product with unpleasant ideas. The company developed the theme that "Even nice people perspire and nice people use Real." This approach did not provide a wide market because it seemed to indicate that the new soap was intended for a limited group of people. Eventually the company had to appeal to the mass market and to direct its advertising to all kinds of people.

The fixed-price policy with no price cutting by the chains limited sales in several ways. Although the price provided a liberal markup and encouraged dealer sales promotion, the product was not competitively priced. As many customers purchase their toilet soap along with their groceries, the failure of grocery stores to carry the soap seriously limited the number of retail sales outlets. This policy therefore had to be changed to permit sales at competitive prices and to offer inducements to chain stores to sell the soap.

Originally the company had produced only the large size bar of soap. To reach the larger market, a smaller size was put into production to be sold at prices comparable to the prices charged for other popular brands. With the changes in advertising appeal, the abandonment of a fixed retail price, and the introduction of the smaller size bar of soap, the company was able to get a substantial share of the market within three years after the soap was first introduced.[7]

Question:

What were the phases of research and sales methods that were peculiar to this product?

31. DEVELOPMENT OF A NEW DESIGN FOR THE PACKAGE

A large cigarette manufacturer had for many years used the same design and color of package for its product. The cigarettes had originally been sold in a small cedar box, and the package had been evolved to resemble the color and appearance of the box. Surveys indicated that customers were developing a preference for other brands, though the company could not be sure whether they objected to the package or the product itself. To answer this question, the market research department prepared packages of its own and competing brands which were wrapped in plain white paper without any identification except a serial number. These packages were distributed to smokers, who were asked to indicate their preferences. From the reports on this research project, the company concluded that the package rather than the product required redesigning.

A consulting firm which specialized in packaging and also the staff of a manufacturer of packages were engaged to recommend a new package design. The research personnel at once agreed that the drab brown package should be replaced

---

[7] Some of the facts for this case were drawn from Spencer Klaw, "How Armour Cleaned Up with Dial," *Fortune*, Vol. LI, No. 5 (1955), pp. 129 ff.

by a new and colorful package. Color was considered important because the manufacturer advertised extensively on television, and color television was already in process of development. About 3,000 package designs were developed for consideration by a small group of package experts. The number of designs was first reduced to 40 and later to 10. The final selection was made from this smaller number.

The package finally selected was a combination of red, gold, and white. The package experts said that red suggests warmth and also attracts the attention of the customer. Gold was believed to suggest quality, and white was said to suggest purity. Tests of the new package in retail stores alongside other brands indicated that the colors were prominent and easily seen. The package had greater attractiveness when it was on the periphery of vision or even on the back of the retailer's shelf. The label was easily legible and could be seen at a greater distance than the labels on the previous package or on the packages of competitor brands.

In the development of the package, tests were made to determine why customers in self-service stores had selected certain brands of soap, cereals, cigarettes, and other packaged products. To assure that the customer was free to select any brand, customers were given lists of products being tested as they entered the store and they were told to select any brand as a gift. As the customers left the stores, they were asked to state the reasons for their selections. Similar tests were made in other types of stores. These studies indicated that the package and the arrangement of the lettering greatly affected customer choices. Although the company waited until the package had stood the tests of final production and sale, the management was convinced that any package should be changed occasionally to give new sales appeal.

Questions:

    1. Did the company use a proper approach to the problem of design?

    2. Why is package design particularly important for this type of product?

16 Design
of the
Product

PRODUCT design follows the development of an idea through basic and applied research. Design also depends upon market research which seeks to appraise the probable demand for the product at a price which will permit the company to make a profit. However, the design of a new product does not necessarily depend upon scientific or engineering research because a design may incorporate principles of form or structure that are generally known. The product may reflect a change in market conditions or the ingenuity of the designer.

Design is closely related to both the engineering and the sales function. It pertains to engineering because it determines the kinds and qualities of the materials that are to be used in production, the parts and accessories that are to be purchased or manufactured, and the nature of the manufacturing methods and costs. The product should be designed with reference to the manufacturing processes, the machines necessary to production, the methods of materials handling, plant layout, and labor costs in production. In some cases, a high production cost may be possible, while in other cases the product should be designed to keep the costs and the selling prices low.

The sales division is concerned with product design because the manufacturer attempts to hold or increase his share of the market, or to develop new markets. Sometimes the advertising division may attempt to convince customers that the products of the company are more desirable than the products of competitors. The sales division also seeks to anticipate the changes in design that competitors may introduce and to persuade the management to incorporate needed changes in its products. The sales division may seek to exploit market potentials for existing designs in order to make a volume of sales that will permit as full a utilization of plant capacity as possible.[1]

INFLUENCES UPON DESIGN

In planning for design, the product engineer should take into consideration the service expected of the product, the weight, appearance, shipping costs, manufacturing cost, consumer preferences, and nature of the competition. Each of these factors requires brief discussion.

Service Expected. Some products will be used in places where they can be repaired easily, while other products will be used under conditions that make repairs difficult or costly. A product that will be used in a factory will probably be subject to more regular inspection and maintenance than a product that will be used in a home. The size and shape of a refrigerator depends upon whether it is to be used in a private residence or an institution. An automobile should be designed with reference to its use in heavy traffic and on certain types of roads.

Some products must be more sturdily constructed because they will receive rough wear. Automobile tires have been improved as automobile speeds have been increased. Railroad rails have been redesigned to carry heavier loads at higher speeds. Textbooks are more sturdily constructed than novels because they receive longer and rougher usage. A tin can that is to be used for beer and which must withstand high pressure during pasteurization must be more sturdy in construction than a can that will be subjected to a lower pressure.

Some products are intended to "last for a lifetime," while others last for a short time. If the manufacturer were to be perfectly frank, he might label certain products as "built for a day." Articles that are intended for limited use range from plated silverware and costume jewelry to souvenirs for tourists, paper-soled shoes, and cheap millinery. Lifetime products would include sterling silver, mahogany furniture, and oriental rugs.

Some products are used under circumstances that require quick visual observation and interpretation. Examples are dials on telephone equipment, switchboards, automobile license plates, clocks, and electric signs. Airplane pilots, in reporting on accidents and near accidents, have reported that errors in reading instruments were due to confusing

---

[1] See Edward Wisnewsky, "Manufacturing in Jeopardy," *Harvard Business Review,* Vol. XXXVII, No. 6 (1959), pp. 131–39.

one instrument with another, confusing the two hands of an instrument, misinterpreting the direction in which the hands moved, reading the wrong instrument, and poor legibility of figures on the dial. This information has been used to improve the design not only of airplane instrument dials but also of dials on equipment used in factory production.

Weight of the Product.   In many industries, manufacturers have been giving increased attention to the factor of weight. For some products, the advantage of lighter weight is largely a matter of convenience to the customer. Examples are baby carriages, lawn mowers, ladders, and storm windows. A reduction in the weight of some products will result in lower operating costs to the customer. Examples are airplanes, railroad cars, and automobiles. In other cases, lighter weight affords an advantage in use. For example, the weight of the uniform of a football player has been cut approximately in half through the use of foam rubber for padding and the substitution of synthetic fabrics for the heavier textiles formerly used.

Appearance.   The lines of a dressing table, a lamp, a refrigerator, or a bottle containing hand lotion may be a large factor in the acceptance of the product. The first radios to make their appearance were not readily accepted because they did not look attractive in the living room. Even the lines of a streetcar or a railroad passenger car are important.

Color is important in relation to appearance. Margarine manufacturers know that people prefer a yellow color for their product. The color of composition shingles for roofing should be considered in relation to the color of the bricks and the trim of the house, just as the color of linoleum in the kitchen is selected in relation to the furnishings. In fact, in the selection of linoleum, color is far more important than the pattern. Although the customer can be persuaded to switch from one pattern to another if the color is right, she usually will not change her color scheme. Color is important in clothing, upholstery, plastic kitchen gadgets, paints, rugs, chinaware, and numerous other articles. In mass markets, color trends change slowly. In high-style merchandise, changes are sometimes rapid.

Shipping Costs.   Much equipment can be shipped before assembly if it is designed with this purpose in mind. An automobile company which ships trucks overseas reduced the required shipping space from 878 cubic feet to 389 cubic feet by revising the truck design and by shipping in three small crates instead of two larger ones. Other products which are designed in a manner that permits economical shipment and quick assembly include porch awnings, porch furniture, overhead garage doors, doll carriages, and tricycles. The increased use of pallets in the movement of material has directed attention to the size and shape of cartons in which materials are shipped. The carton should be of a convenient size for interlaced stacking on a standard-sized pallet.

Cost to Manufacture. The cost to manufacture is obviously important in design, if the product is to be sold at a profit. A product which is of a quality sufficiently good for one purpose may be entirely unsatisfactory for another use. For example, no finish is perfectly smooth— one finish is only less rough than another. A surface that looks smooth may serve satisfactorily for the outside metal case of a vacuum cleaner but not for the roller bearings. For the bearings, the surface irregularities that are permitted are measured in millionths of an inch. Cost is also affected by the kind of material used, such as the use of fiber instead of glass for a milk container. Other features of the design which affect costs include such details as the following:

Number of accessories or special features, such as mudguards, horns, and reflectors on a bicycle.

Parts made as one piece instead of several parts which would require additional assembly cost.

The use of commercially standard parts and materials instead of specially manufactured parts. The decision to buy or to make such parts depends upon the quantity to be used, the accuracy of dimensions required, and the reliability of the outside source of supply.

The simplicity of design of parts which will permit them to be stamped or pressed into shape instead of being cut and machined with cutting and grinding tools. This feature of design depends upon the use which is to be made of the product.

The choice of bolts, rivets, screws, or welding to make assemblies.

Consumer Ideas. Consumer desires as to quality, style, color, and cost should be considered by the designer, for consumer ideas may be very different from those of the manufacturer. Henry Ford popularized a low-priced automobile which was cheap in construction and available only in black. As consumer ideas changed, he was forced to make expensive changes in design and to provide a variety of colors. The change was in part the result of increased consumer purchasing power and of a change in consumer ideas. More recently an automobile manufacturer decided that what customers needed was a short car that could be maneuvered easily in traffic and parked in a small space and also a tall car that permitted the driver and passengers to wear hats without difficulty. Since at that time the preference was for long low cars, the manufacturer learned at great cost that consumers could not be induced to buy a car that did not suit their tastes even though a short, tall car might have some advantages. Later, all automobile manufacturers were required to recognize the shift in consumer preferences to the small, compact car.

In buying many products, consumers will give particular attention to the noise factor. Quietness is a particularly important attribute of household appliances, home air conditioners, and outboard motors. In industrial plants, also, manufacturers who buy machines have been giving greater attention to the elimination of noise in production machinery.

Various groups of consumers differ in their ideas concerning the features that are desirable in design. Some will prefer a quality product, and some will prefer a low-priced product. Some will prefer a product of long-wearing qualities, and others will be willing to cast the product aside within a short time in order that they may buy something new. Consumers will differ in their preferences regarding style, materials, size, color, and other features. Their preferences are affected by age, race, sex, religious affiliation, geographical location, education, and family size. Moreover, the preferences change from time to time because of such developments as the movement of people from rural areas to the city and from city to the suburbs, changes in age groups, changes in the general level of educational achievement, and increased wages or salaries.

Because consumers differ in their preferences for a product, the manufacturer should not attempt to sell the product to people generally. Instead, the management should decide upon the groups who are expected to constitute the market. It should then develop the product design to satisfy the ideas and preferences of its anticipated customers, and it should direct its sales promotion activities toward them. The recognition of different groups of consumers in planning product design and marketing strategy is known as *market segmentation.*

Many products are sold to other manufacturers for assembly in a product to be sold to ultimate consumers. Such products may be made according to specifications supplied by the manufacturer, while other parts or accessories are made according to standard specifications for sale to any manufacturer. Products sold to other manufacturers include motors, cables, fuses, batteries, plate glass, upholstery, sheet metal, wire, ball bearings, hinges, gaskets, chains, belting, pipe fittings and metal or fiber containers.

The design engineer may find it impossible to include all desirable features in one product because he may be required to sacrifice one feature to achieve another. For example, an automobile may be designed for style and beauty regardless of cost, difficulty of parking and handling in traffic, and the extent of damage to fenders and grillwork in case of collision. Design may also disregard the possibility that some materials may become scarce.

Nature of the Competition. In planning the design of the product, the manufacturer takes into consideration the trends in the design of competitive products and the features that are stressed in competitive advertising. While the manufacturer recognizes trends in design, he attempts to develop features that make his product more serviceable, cheaper, or otherwise more satisfactory to consumers. For example, a manufacturer of electric refrigerators cannot neglect the development of roll-out shelves and doors with storage space. If he introduces such features, he would attempt to convince consumers that his shelves and his doors are in some respect better than the shelves and doors in the refrigerators of other manufacturers. Some manufacturers emphasize one feature in an effort to draw attention to one respect in which their designs are superior. Others emphasize several features in the hope that one or more of them will appeal to prospective customers.[2] Each manufacturer must select the strategy which he thinks is most effective.

Functional Design. When the idea for a new product is accepted, the product design department first attempts to develop a rough model of the proposed product that will render the required service to the consumer, or that functions as it should. The plan starts with a sketch which indicates the parts in their correct dimensions and the method of their assembly. The sketch assures that the parts will fit together as planned. A model of the product is then made. This preliminary work is called *functional design*. In planning for a complicated product such as an automobile or a refrigerator, functional design represents the work of many people.

Manufacturing Design. Before the design is accepted, it must be examined to determine whether manufacturing costs can be reduced without affecting the service the product is expected to render. For example, parts may be made in one piece instead of two, and parts may be assembled with screws or bolts instead of rivets, or a different kind of welding can be used. Cheaper materials may be used for some parts. After any such changes have been made, a new model may be made and tested to make sure that the usefulness of the product has not been affected by manufacturing design.

---

[2] John B. Stewart, "Functional Features in Product Strategy," *Harvard Business Review,* Vol. XXXVII, No. 2 (1959), pp. 65–78.

The Lag in Product Design. Although competitive pressures may require frequent revisions of product design in many industries, existing knowledge of technology may not be fully utilized in design development. One reason for the lag of design is that management may not possess complete knowledge of scientific advances and the improvements which technology makes possible. In some cases, management may believe that consumers are not ready to accept a complete revision of design and that changes must therefore be introduced gradually. Rapid changes also increase production costs. To keep costs at a minimum, design may be frozen until several changes are to be made.

Differences in the points of view within the management group may also cause a lag of design. The plant manager may emphasize simplicity of design in order to relieve the pressure upon the manufacturing organization. The engineer may prefer a product that will operate efficiently in the hands of the consumer. The sales director may wish to incorporate features that will make the product distinctive regardless of cost. The preferences of executives may be impossible of achievement in their entirety.

Design of Container. For many products, package design assumes considerable importance. If the product is placed in a container during manufacturing, ease of filling and closing or sealing the package should be considered. Examples are fruit and fruit juice, salt, soap powder, and chemicals. The container also serves to protect the product during shipment. The size of the container should be planned in relation to the usual consumer purchase, which may be a pound, a quart, a dozen, or multiples of such quantities. Unit cost may affect the usual quantity purchased or sold. If the product is sold to a mail-order house or retail store which in turn sells to consumers, the quantity purchased by the ultimate consumer at any one time would influence the size of the package.

Ease of loading and unloading trucks or freight cars should be considered in planning the design of the package. In some cases, for example, the size of the pallet and the method of stacking cartons on the pallet should be considered. The weight and shape of the package should be planned in relation to the type of materials-handling equipment to be used, which might be a hand truck, lift truck, crane, or powered conveyor. Attention to the width of the freight car or truck and the number of rows of cartons in a car or truck might result in a saving of shipping space.

Other considerations would influence package design if the product is to be displayed on the shelf of the retailer. The features would be color, shape, strength, ease of stacking, size, and display of contents for inspection by the purchaser. If the product is sold to the consumer in the original package, additional factors would be the ease of opening, removing the contents, and resealing the package. Possible uses of the container after the product has been used would be important for some products.

In planning the design of the package, both function and cost should be considered. If the product is packed in a metal container, for example, a cube-shaped can might use the least metal while a cylindrical-shaped can might make a greater appeal to the consumer. A box-shaped container might fit snugly into a truck while a cylindrical-shaped package might result in least waste from spilling. Package design depends upon a number of such considerations.

DEVELOPMENT OF DESIGN

In the development of the design of a product, specifications for parts and materials are established and the order in which the parts are to be assembled is determined. Such features as manner of operation of the product, styling, and appearance are agreed upon. The first problem in design development pertains to the specifications and standards.

Specifications. By specification is meant the standard of quality for a part or for the finished product. Standards of quality may be set for dimensions, tensile strength (as in wire or cable), the outline or contour of a part, smoothness of surface, chemical composition, color, and internal structure. These specifications should be established as a part of the work of design. They determine the nature of the manufacturing process, and they are enforced through inspection.

For a product made in quantity from a number of parts, specifications are necessary in order that the parts may be made interchangeable. If the product is made in small quantities, specifications are not so important because the parts may be machined to fit when the product is assembled. When the product is made in large quantities, however, the separate fitting of each part is not feasible because of the expense and the interruption of the flow of production that would be entailed. Parts may be manufactured and placed in the storeroom prior to assembly, but this arrangement is possible only in case specifications are established.

Permissible Variations. The specification indicates a basic or standard size from which variations are measured. However, a machine or a worker cannot make a part with precisely the dimensions indicated by the standard. The amount of permissible variation has been steadily reduced over the years of the machine age. In 1776, Bolton, a partner of James Watt, wrote as follows of the accuracy of the work: "Mr. Wilkinson has bored us several cylinders almost without error; that of fifty inches diameter, which we put at Tipton, does not err the thickness of an old shilling in any part."[3]

A variation as great as that referred to by Bolton would now be regarded as very crude. In present-day equipment, the allowance for some moving parts may be no more than 0.00001 inch, although for other parts it may be as much as 0.01 inch. The amount of permissible variation depends upon the use to be made of the product and the functioning of the part. Very small variances would be permitted in parts for jet engines and missiles. Somewhat greater variances might be permitted in parts for vacuum cleaners or air conditioners. Even greater variances would be permitted in the parts for a metal awning or a doll carriage.

The variation permitted in the manufacture of the part or the finished product is called an allowance. The extreme permissible dimensions are called limits. The largest permissible size is the maximum limit. This size leaves the most metal or wood on the part. The smallest permissible size is the minimum limit. This size limits the amount of wood or metal that may be removed. The limits and sizes are established in relation to the parts that are to be joined. The allowances are established with reference to the tightest possible fit, if the largest internal member is matched with the smallest external member. Tolerance is the allowable variation in size. It is the difference between the minimum and maximum limits.

The cost of any machining or fabricating work depends largely upon the tolerance. To remove metal or wood from a part is relatively easy. The difficulty and the cost arise from the necessity for determining the proper place to stop. Close tolerances increase the cost of machine adjustment, machine repair, inspection, and rejects. Much of the cost of manufacture is due to the establishment of small tolerances, some of which could be made larger without impairing the efficiency of the product. Variations from the basic sizes are due to such causes as improper location of the work in the machine because of the lack of training or care on the part of the operator or because of chips or dirt in the machine, shifting of the work after it is placed in the machine, inaccuracy of devices for holding the work, inaccuracy of the machine

[3] Charles F. Kettering and Allen Orth, *American Battle for Abundance* (Detroit: General Motors Corp., Undated), p. 27.

due to the stress of revolving or cutting parts, and inaccuracy of cutting or finishing tools as to size or shape.

Development of Standards. Standards are established by one manufacturer for his own products or by all of the manufacturers of an industry for certain products that are made and sold by all of them. When standards are established for the industry, each manufacturer agrees to make and sell only products which conform to the prescribed standards. The same agreement may provide for the reduction in the number of designs manufactured by the elimination of unprofitable and unneeded items. The agreement upon standards is called standardization, and the agreement for the elimination of some designs is called simplification. Because of the antitrust laws, the agreements are made under the supervision of the National Bureau of Standards.

Standards pertaining to the product are of two kinds: industrial standards and commercial standards. Industrial standards prescribe the dimensions, composition, sizes, colors, grades, and other characteristics of the product. For example, an industrial standard may specify the exact properties of wire, lumber, wheat, or cloth. The standard may prescribe the chemical composition, the moisture content, the percentage of foreign substances, the smoothness, or the tensile strength of a material or a product. The standard may also prescribe the method of testing or inspecting the product. Industrial standards may be established by the individual company, a trade association, or an engineering society.

A standard of commerce, which is sometimes called a "consumer standard," is designed to protect the purchaser or ultimate consumer as well as the manufacturer. It is a measure of the quality, performance, dimensional characteristics, or other properties of a product destined for use by consumers. It covers terminology, grades, sizes, and use characteristics of manufactured products. The agreement for establishing a standard may include methods of listing, rating, and labeling in order that a product made in conformity with the standard may be readily recognized by distributors and consumers.

The need for commercial standards arises in part from competitive practices and the difficulty of the consumer in evaluating a product which he finds offered for sale on the market. For example, formerly the mark "gold filled" on an article indicated merely a process of manufacture without any significance as to the quantity of gold applied. The weight ratio varied from 1 part gold alloy to 10 parts of base metal to 1 part alloy to 500 parts of base metal. The cheapest quality was an extremely thin coating. The standard now requires that the label for a gold-filled product indicate both the ratio of the weight of the gold alloy to the weight of the base metal and the karat fineness of the gold. The minimum weight ratio is 1 to 20.

A second need for commercial standards arises from the difficulty which the average consumer has in determining the performance which may be expected from the product. For example, when a consumer purchases a clinical thermometer, he may be unable to test it to determine whether it registers properly. The commercial standard assures reliable and standard performance. The requirements of the commercial standard include the following:

Construction, in which quality of glass, appearance, marking, range, and details of graduation are specified.

Character of the pigment, in which a test is required to determine the resistance of the pigment to removal by disinfecting solutions.

Test for entrapped gas.

Hard shaker test.

Retreat test, to determine whether the constriction in the bore is properly made.

Accuracy, in which the maximum allowable errors in registration are specified.

Ageing for four months to guard against changes in the constriction.

A certificate to accompany each thermometer to guarantee compliance with the requirements.

A third need for standards arises from the use of specifications in ordering merchandise or parts. A purchasing agent who specifies that materials are to be of "good workmanship" or "best commercial quality" is using a very vague standard. He should not purchase by stating that goods ordered are to "be like the merchandise I bought last time." The most satisfactory way of ordering is to indicate the standard as prescribed by the industry or trade. Fuel oil, for example, is bought and sold in specified grades according to distillation, viscosity, carbon residue, flash point, pour point, maximum water, sediment, and ash. The purchaser need only specify the grade required to be assured of getting the proper quality. Similarly, the grades of rope are based upon the kind of fiber, the diameter, the weight per foot, the oil content, and the breaking strength.

Standards of volume and of measurement are also used by purchasers. Such standards include gallon, quart, pound, and yard. The canners have standardized tin cans in forty-one sizes. The sizes commonly used for canned foods, such as No. 1, No. 2, No. 2½, are generally known and easily recognized. A housewife may order canned food by can size with complete assurance as to the size of the cans that will be delivered.

A fourth need for standards arises from the desirability of making certain parts interchangeable. A standard of this kind which was reached many years ago is the standard distance between wheel flanges of railway cars. The observance of this standard is necessary for the transfer of railway rolling stock from one line to another. Transferability of cars also requires the standardization of couplings, bumpers, air brakes, brake connections, clearances, and other features. A standard of great convenience to consumers is the base and socket of the incandescent electric lamp or bulb. All electrical manufacturers have adopted the standard which was first fixed by Thomas A. Edison. The standard indicates a diameter of the lamp of 1.031 to 1.037 inches and a thread depth of 0.033 of an inch. Although some lamp sockets and bulbs are larger or smaller than the usual size, the purchaser of a bulb is not required to try the lamp in the base to determine whether it will fit. Until threads on pipe connections were standardized, firefighting equipment frequently could not be used in neighboring cities because the water hose could not be connected to fireplugs. Another lack of standards which has plagued motorists has been the height of bumpers. A standard bumper height for automobiles, station wagons, and light trucks has been recommended by the Society of Automotive Engineers and approved by the automobile industry. Automobile manufacturers feel the need for a standard size of license plates, which are made in 66 sizes in the United States and Canada. The lack of uniformity in size has prevented the treatment of the license plate as an integral part of the body design and has required the continued use of external brackets, which invite theft. In other lines of product the existence and observance of standards is a great convenience to the consumer who wishes to replace a part, such as a slat in a Venetian blind, an electric fuse, or a switch.

Limits of Standardization. Standardization has definite limits which are established by the needs of consumer industries and individuals. However, the needs of consumers are recognized and protected in the setting of the standards. If needs of consumers are found to be inadequately provided for, a revision of the standard may be adopted. Style features in some lines of manufacture may preclude standardization. However, the standard as promulgated may permit variations in certain specified respects. For example, the standard for china plumbing fixtures provides for lavatories attached to the wall or unattached. It specifies that the prescribed dimensions do not indicate designs. Four basic colors, in addition to white, are regarded as standard —green, blue, ivory, and peach-brown; but each manufacturer may determine the tint in accordance with his individual production problems.

Standards should be regarded as temporary and dynamic rather than permanent or static. Unless provision is made for a revision of the standard, experimentation and improvement in the product may be hindered to the detriment of the industry and the public. For this reason the standard should be regarded as a means whereby the "members of an industry may be permitted to go forward together." It should not be regarded as a means of stabilizing an industry.

Standards are accepted by manufacturers and distributors because they meet recognized needs. The observance of a standard by the producer is desirable, provided that the needs of consumers are adequately safeguarded. Distributors and consumers find in a standard an assurance of quality and performance.

Design a Staff Function. In a large enterprise, design is a specialized and technical engineering service performed by a staff department. Product design in some organizations is a major activity, and the person in charge reports directly to the president or general manager. The reason for the emphasis placed upon design is that the success of the company may depend upon the appeal made to consumers by the product in comparison with the products of competitors. The appeal is based upon price, quality, color, service, and other features previously mentioned. Moreover, the work of product design is continuous because of technology and style trends.

In most manufacturing enterprises, product design is a department of the manufacturing division. In such an organization the design engineer reports to the director of manufacture. In any event, product design is an important engineering activity, and it should never be thought of as the routine construction of drawings. The design engineer should have a knowledge of both the mechanical and the artistic phases of the problem. He should be familiar with the methods of manufacturing and of selling, and he should keep informed of the progress of technology in his own and related lines of production and with developments in consumer markets. In some companies, the work of product design is a responsibility of the sales division. The relationship to sales is especially close when style changes are important. This situation exists, for example, in the manufacture of dresses, millinery, and other articles of clothing. The sales division can best evaluate market tendencies and develop new designs to take advantage of market trends.

The fact that design is a staff function means that the design engineer is not in a position to make changes in the product or to direct the production of a new model. Decisions of this kind are made after recommendations by the design engineer and approval by the line officers, possibly by the president and the heads of major divisions. The decision to change the design can be made after estimates have been made by the sales division as to the probable reception of the product by customers. The cost of manufacturing the product should be estimated by the cost accounting department in co-operation with the methods department. It may be necessary also to revise plant lay-out. The purchasing department may be consulted as to the availability of materials. If the manufacture of one product is to be discontinued when a new one is introduced, important considerations would be the unfilled orders of customers for the old product, the supply of the old product in the storeroom, the necessity of supplying customers with re-pair parts, and the time required to make the changeover to the new product. These problems indicate the reason that a change in the design of the product should be authorized by top management.

In small establishments the design of the product is frequently the work of the line organization. The enterprise may not be large enough to support a separate staff department, and the proprietor or manager may originate changes in design with the aid of his managers or de-partment heads. In custom-made merchandise the product may be made according to blueprints and specifications prescribed by the customer.

Importance of Timing. In the development of new designs and new styles, the timing of the decision to discontinue research and de-velopment, to begin production, and to place the new product on the market is extremely important. If the research is continued for too long a time, competitors may announce a similar product first and thereby gain a decided advantage in advertising and distribution. If the decision is made prematurely, a poorly designed product may be placed upon the market with unfortunate results for the reputation of the manufacturer as well as for the sale of the product. The adver-tising and promotion of the sale of the product should also be planned in relation to the time of delivery to dealers or other dis-tributors.

If the sale of the product is related to a seasonal demand, the im-portance of timing is increased. Examples are articles for beach wear for summer use, sleds and toys for sale in the fall and winter, books for use as texts with the opening of the school year, or articles of cloth-ing. The slow development of designs in such cases may cause the manufacturer to miss the market. Poor timing may be caused by the necessity for consulting various persons. In a large organization with several horizontal levels of management, a proposed change in design may require not only the approval of several departments but also that changes be authorized by higher levels in the organization. The approval of a policy committee may be necessary. The relative ease of obtaining approval in a small organization partially explains the persistence of small enterprises in many branches of manufacturing where style changes are important.

ELIMINATION OF UNPROFITABLE DESIGNS

A manufacturer may find that the product line has become overextended through the development of an excessive number of unrelated products or the addition of too many sizes, colors, styles, or other variations. This situation may arise because research has enabled the company to develop new designs or because a study of market conditions has indicated a latent demand for new varieties. If unprofitable items are not dropped when new designs are added, the product line may become overextended.

Pressure for New Designs. One reason for the expansion of the product line is that management wishes to reduce market risks through diversification or to increase the volume of sales to reduce the overhead expense per dollar of sales. New products may be added as the result of industrial reasearch or the creative ideas of persons in the management. The research division may have found a way to utilize waste and scrap, or it may have discovered new manufacturing methods, new kinds of raw materials, or new applications of scientific knowledge. Expansion through the development and design of new products may be planned to provide financial stability through the seasonal dovetailing of demand. The expansion may enable the company to reach markets in new territorial areas or to gain any one of many other advantages in production, sales, finance, or general management.

In most companies, the management attempts to prevent an unprofitable expansion of the product line. The addition of a new product or a new variety may require the approval of a policy committee or an executive committee whose members include the major executives. Members of the committee will inquire into the effect of a proposed new design upon such problems as purchasing, storage, inventory control, the planning of production, the requirements for new manufacturing facilities or a revision of plant layout, and other operating problems. The profitability of the new product will be questioned from the point of view of the size of the market, the probable duration of the demand, the difficulties of developing the market, the product programs of competitors, the probable cost to manufacture, and the effect upon the sale of other products. However, such expansion may eventually increase the product line to such an extent that a planned program of curtailment becomes necessary.

Another type of expansion of the product line consists of the addition of new varieties of an established product. No product research is necessary for this type of expansion, as the product is merely manufactured in more colors, sizes, body styles, finishes, or other variation. This expansion can continue indefinitely in such products as shirts, bottles, shoes, hats, paints, and linoleum. Once the additional varieties have been added, pressure for their continuance is exerted from many quarters inside and outside the company.

The multiplicity of designs has resulted largely from difficulties encountered by the sales division in marketing and from recommendations for new designs by that division. During seasons or years when sales are difficult to make and buyers' markets prevail, the salesmen endeavor to give the buyer what he wants or what he thinks he needs, even though he requests a product that is not included in the regular line. The sales division also may recommend additions to the regular line of products in order that it may offer the customer something different from products offered by competitors.

Effects of Overexpansion of the Product Line. The production of an excessive number of varieties increases manufacturing costs and the expenses of sales and distribution. The inventory of raw materials and supplies is increased when the product is made from materials of different qualities or with a varying assortment of accessories. The more frequent changes in machine setup and adjustment increase the labor cost and cause losses of machine time. The work of planning for production is made more complicated. The manufacturer is required to maintain a larger inventory of finished goods because reserve supplies of each item may be necessary. He is more likely to have broken lots or incomplete assortments, and his losses on close-outs at the end of a season are increased. Deliveries to customers may be slowed because the inventories of large numbers of varieties are not easily controlled. For the same reason the chance of error in shipment is increased.

Diversity of product also creates problems for jobbers, wholesalers, and retailers. If each distributor attempts to carry a complete and diversified line, his inventories are unduly increased, the rate of inventory turnover is lessened, more storage space is required, and sales effort is less effective because it is spread over more lines. A distributor who does not carry a complete line may lose sales in all lines because many customers will buy where a greater assortment is offered.

The question of who pays the costs of diversity is not easily answered. A large part of the cost may be borne by the manufacturer because he may be unable to increase his selling price to cover his costs. If the costs are due to a multiplicity of varieties that characterize the entire industry, and if the costs are incurred by manufacturers generally, selling prices may be increased to cover all or almost all of the increased cost. The same considerations would apply to wholesalers and retailers. Aside from the matter of selling prices, the consumer may be inconvenienced because of his inability to obtain prompt repair service or quick deliveries of repair parts.

Elimination of Unprofitable Items. The plan to discontinue the production and sale of certain varieties, which is called simplification of the product line, may be effected by any one company acting on its own initiative. However, the plan will be more successful if all of the companies in an industry formulate a general program to which all of them agree. If any one company undertakes to eliminate the slow-selling varieties it may find that it loses sales on other products as well. A retailer or a wholesaler is not likely to purchase the product in its popular sizes, grades, or colors from one manufacturer and the unusual varieties from another. Consequently, competition may compel a manufacturer to make and sell a wide variety of products unless the simplification movement is broad enough to include most of the industry.

The program of simplification is frequently organized by a trade association whose membership includes most of the firms of the industry. The suggestion for such a program may come from a consumer or from a manufacturer. If the officers of the association believe that simplification would be desirable, they may appoint a committee to assemble the information which is to be used in the formulation of the program. The committee compiles a list of the sizes, colors, types, and grades of the product and the volume of production and sales of each variety. It makes a study of the service rendered to consumers by each variety. Items of small production may be found to be essential because of special applications. For example, a circle saw of a definite size might be of great value to sawmills working with logs of a certain kind, although the number of saws they require might be very small. This study includes also probable future trends in respect to the needs of consumers. The committee recommends to the industry the items that it believes can be eliminated to the advantage of manufacturers, distributors, and consumers. A general conference of interested parties is then called to discuss the recommendation. A simplified-practice recommendation may be adopted. This recommendation lists the sizes or types which appear adequate to meet all normal demands. A standing committee is appointed by the trade association to confer with members and to encourage general acceptance of the simplified-practice recommendation. Each manufacturer is asked to accept the report and to make only the types of product recommended by the committee. Proposals for amendment of the recommendation may be made to the trade association for consideration at any time. Revisions may be necessary because of technological developments, competition within the industry, or developments in other industries. When the original recommendation is amended, the number of types of product to be manufactured may be increased or decreased.

Government participation in the program of simplification is usually required because the antitrust laws prohibit combinations in restraint of trade. A reduction of the varieties of a product which is effected by manufacturers who act solely on their own initiative, might be regarded by the Department of Justice and the courts as the first step toward forming an agreement for price fixing or other restraint. Therefore, the co-operation of the Commodity Standards Division of the National Bureau of Standards is usually sought by the trade association in the formulation of any simplification program.

QUESTIONS

1. Should a manufacturer attempt to establish the trend in design or should he follow style trends established by other manufacturers? Explain the risks that might be incurred by either plan.

2. To what extent are trends in design established by the manufacturer and to what extent are they established by consumer acceptance? Illustrate by reference to a specific product, such as dresses or automobiles.

3. The copying of designs, which is called "design piracy," destroys the value of a design for the dress manufacturer and requires him to bring out a succession of new designs. Since his sales to customers depend upon the constant obsolescence of existing designs, why should the manufacturer object to the practice?

4. What social costs are involved in the changing of the designs of automobiles each year? What are the social gains?

5. With what products is light weight an important quality?

6. How can a manufacturer determine in advance of production and sale whether consumers will like his product well enough to buy it at a price that will permit him to make a profit?

7. A container manufacturer designs a can for beer. What problems might he have in gaining acceptance?

8. Why might the people in the company more readily agree to the addition of a new design to the product line than they would agree to the dropping of a design or a product?

9. Show the importance of the standardization of parts to mass production, the assembly-line method of production, the cost of the product, and the human relations problems within the company.

10. Why are unprofitable colors, sizes, and styles of product sometimes added to the line of products?

11. Why is the discontinuance of an unprofitable variety of product sometimes difficult? Discuss with reference to consumers, the sales organization, and the manufacturing division.

12. Show the relation of container design to manufacturing cost, shipping costs, the problems of the retailer, and consumer acceptance.

CASES

32. PROPOSED REVISION OF PACKAGE DESIGN

The Dixie Cereal Company makes and sells a limited line of breakfast cereals. Its principal products are rolled oats, including a variety that can be cooked in five minutes, and hominy grits. The products are packed in cylindrical-type containers which follow a design that was adopted about forty years ago. Each package carries a picture of a southern gentleman, which is printed in colors of blue, gray, and white. This package has been made familiar to a whole generation of shoppers and customers through advertising, store displays, and its use in home kitchens. The sales of the company have been consistently good, but volume has not increased in proportion to the population or the sales of other companies in the cereal industry.

The company has been approached by a consulting firm which specializes in product design and packaging. The firm has urged the management to redesign its package, and it has offered its services in developing a new package. The representative of the firm has pointed out that many packaged cereals are being sold on the basis of premium offers, which utilize the design of the package in making the appeal. These premium offers assume a variety of forms. Some offers of the cutout variety carry the premium as part of the package. The customer can cut out a log hut, a doll house, a space ship, or some other toy from the cardboard composing the package. Another variety provides a premium which is mailed to the customer in return for a coupon cut from the package, though in some cases a small cash payment is required. Other cereal companies enclose a premium inside the package, and some supply the dealer with the premiums which are distributed to customers in return for the coupon. In each case, the package is designed to carry the appeal and to inform the customer of the premium offer.

The representative of the consulting firm uses the argument that frequent revisions of product design are necessary in order to convey the impression that the company is keeping abreast of current developments. He argues that advertising is ineffective unless it can stress a new feature of the product. A well-known example is a cosmetics manufacturer who frequently changes the name of his lipstick or face cream, devises a new color or odor for the product, and changes the theme of the advertising. The change in the product is actually very small, but it affords an opportunity for more effective newspaper, radio, and television advertising. The representative contends that a basic principle of product design is continuous revision and new sales appeal.

The company has also been approached by a manufacturer of paper containers who would like to develop a new design. The container company has a staff of artists, designers, and market specialists who are experienced in the development of new cases, cartons, boxes, wrappings, and labels. The container company has been particularly successful in designing containers which hold six bottles or cans of the beverage. These containers are assembled by folding operations which require no glue. They have resulted in a substantial increase in the sales of soft drinks.

The Dixie Cereal Company hesitates to discard its traditional package design. It believes that no real purpose would be served by the change and that the company would lose the good will associated with the present design. Moreover, the management believes that a cereal should be sold on the basis of the quality of the product rather than a premium.

Questions:

1. What would the company gain by a revision?
2. How would its advertising program be affected?
3. If it introduces a premium offer, what form should the offer take?

33. STANDARDIZATION OF PRODUCT

The Carlson Bottle Company, with a large plant in Pittsburgh, makes an assortment of glass bottles. Several other companies in Pittsburgh make bottles, but the Carlson Bottle Company does about 20 per cent of the business in the area. The bottles are sold to chemical companies, beverage manufacturers, and canning and preserving concerns. Practically all of the bottles produced are made to the order of the customer.

The process of manufacturing bottles is relatively simple. Raw materials include silica, soda ash, and lime. The ingredients are measured and mixed and then heated in tank furnaces which hold from 100 to 1,000 tons. The mixture is melted and refined, and it then flows into a cooler section of the furnace which is separated from the first section by a floating fire-clay partition. The mixture is then fed through an opening, and a sufficient amount to make a bottle is measured and sheared. The molten material drops into a mold which has been especially made according to the specifications of the customer. Three molding operations and an annealing treatment to remove possible strains in the glass complete the manufacture of the bottle. All of these operations are fully automatic. From one furnace, sufficient material can be fed to keep as many as five sets of molds fully occupied at one time.

The company has no difficulty in making bottles of different shapes, provided they require the same amount of materials of the same color. Orders from different customers are classified by size, and the molds required for making bottles of the same size and color are set up in the molding department at the same time. Since the same amount of mixture is extruded from the furnace each time, no additional cost is incurred in making bottles of different shapes except the cost of making the molds and changing molds in the machine.

In recent years the users of bottles have begun to order special colors of glass as well as special shapes and sizes in order that their product may be readily identified by customers at retail stores. The use of different colors and shades has presented a difficult problem to the Carlson Bottle Company and has substantially increased the costs of manufacturing. The molding operation could not be used to run orders for several customers unless the bottles were of the same color and could be made of the same mixture. The making of bottles of different colors meant frequent changes in the mix in the tank furnaces. Bottles of especially colored glass could not be sold at a profit at the usual prices.

The company has been considering the possibility of installing a series of small tank furnaces. However, the initial cost would be large; and operating costs would also be larger than the cost of operating the large furnaces. Another possibility is that of obtaining orders from customers far enough in advance to permit the grouping of a number of orders by size and color. An effort might be made to induce customers to accept one of a limited number of special shades and colors. If the customer would not accept a standard shade, he would be charged a higher price.

Questions:

1. Should the company attempt to supply any color of bottle in any size and shape?

2. Should higher prices be charged for special colors and sizes?

3. Should the company approach its competitors in an effort to obtain agreement on a program of standard sizes, shapes, and colors?

34. PROPOSED STANDARDIZATION OF DESIGN

Agnes Mann was an excellent seamstress. She was approached from time to time by some of her acquaintances with the request that she alter dresses which they had purchased at local clothing stores. The alterations included shortening or lengthening dresses and skirts, letting out or taking up hems, putting on a different type of button, and changing the fit about the neck and shoulders. Agnes made a charge for her work, and she was soon able to build up a good business.

Some of the women who were often unable to buy a dress of proper fit in the stores suggested to Agnes that she might make the dress to fit without the necessity for alterations. The making of a complete dress would result in a better fit and eliminate the necessity for ripping seams, trimming the cloth, and remaking the dress. Eventually Agnes extended her activity to dressmaking as well as fitting and altering garments purchased at local stores. The principal customers were the women who had difficulty finding a properly fitting garment because of their unusually large or small measurements. Customers also included some very tall and some very short, stout women.

At first, Agnes' customers would purchase the dress materials and a pattern at a local store. The pattern was helpful, although Agnes might be required to cut the cloth differently from the pattern. In time Agnes began to buy dress materials for sale to customers who wanted her to make garments for them. This arrangement was helpful to the customers because many of them could not select materials that were becoming to their size or height, and some bought a cloth that was unsuited to the kind of dresses they wanted. Other materials in time were bought for use in making dresses. For example, Agnes stocked buttons, thread, seam binding, zippers, and snaps. Additional sewing machines were purchased, three helpers eventually were hired, and the business was moved to a new building.

Agnes thought that she should now begin to make dresses in advance of orders from her customers. She could make garments during the slack periods before a season began, and with slight alterations she could fit the dress to the customer. She could purchase an electric cutter that would enable her assistant to cut the materials for ten or even twenty dresses at a time. Agnes would continue to cater to women who had difficulty finding dresses of the proper fit, style, pattern of cloth, and color at the usual stores which catered to the women of average build and taste. Agnes was sure that she knew her customers well enough to serve in this manner.

Questions:

1. What would be the advantages of the proposed plan of making dresses in anticipation of demands from customers?

2. What difficulties might be encountered?

17 Inspection
of the
Product

IN preceding chapters, the development of the product has been traced through the phases of basic and applied research, product design, and the establishment of standards for materials and products. The next step is the manufacture of the product in the operating departments which utilize the physical facilities of production. Quality depends largely upon the materials used in production, the plant facilities and processes, and the skill of workers and supervisors. The work is inspected at various stages in production to compare the quality with predetermined standards.

Although all persons in the manufacturing division should be concerned with quality, inspection is usually a separate function which is assigned to a separate department. In order that inspectors may be free to require the observance of quality standards, they should not be placed under the jurisdiction of foremen or general foremen. They cannot serve as a check on the operating departments unless they are free of their control. The chief inspector, who supervises the work of inspection, should report to the plant engineer or the plant superintendent or, in some cases, to the chief executive.

The place of quality control in the organization will depend upon the nature of the product and the emphasis that management wishes to place upon quality. In a company that manufactures medicines or drugs, for example, the quality control function might be assigned to a major division with a vice-president in charge. This function would be of less importance in a paper company or a lumber mill. Although quality should not be neglected in any company, the quality control function might be assigned to a department in the manufacturing division.

PURPOSES OF INSPECTION

Inspection plays an important role in the manufacture of a quality product. The purpose of inspection is to see that the standards for materials, parts, and the finished product are maintained. The inspection of materials is necessary to prevent payment for defective materials. Unless they are inspected, defects might not become known until sometime after materials or parts have been issued for use. Production schedules would be delayed, and excessive labor costs might be incurred by payment for work on defective materials. At various stages in production, work in process may require inspection to prevent the expenditure of additional labor on work that does not meet the required standards.

Inspection is necessary to the manufacture of a product with interchangeable parts. A worker on the assembly line should not be expected to try a number of parts to find one that will fit, and he should not be expected to machine a part. Although the parts need not be exactly alike, they should be of the same dimensions within the limits established by standards and tolerances.

The maintenance of standards is designed to assure that the product will meet customer approval in such respects as satisfactory mechanical performance, the finish of enamel or paint, cleanliness of fabrics, and other details. Public safety also requires inspection of such parts as electrical appliances, cables, cranes, and automobiles.

One objective of inspection may be the prevention of excessive costs in labor or materials on products of a quality in excess of the required standards. For example, a worker may continue to wax furniture or to polish chromium or jewelry even after the work has been satisfactorily completed. Tin may be wasted by giving sheets a heavier coating than the specifications require. In the manufacture of metal containers, sheets that are suitable for fruit cans might be used for making antifreeze or oil cans at unnecessarily high cost. In fruit canning, excessive cost would be incurred by the use of large-size unblemished fruit as materials for fruit cocktail.

Another purpose of inspection is to permit the correction of defects. Metal parts that are too large after processing may be refinished to size, although parts that are too small may be no more than scrap. Imperfect finishes may be corrected by polishing or by sanding and refinishing. Uneven threads in a shirt may be removed and replaced by reweaving. Packages of granulated soap or sugar that contain too much or too little of the product may be brought up to standard by removing or adding the necessary quantity. Errors made by a typesetter are corrected after they have been discovered by a reading of the proof.

Inspection may be designed to rate or grade the product. The imperfect articles may be marked as such and sold to the trade or perhaps to employees at a lower price. Examples are shirts, shoes, linoleum, bedspreads, towels, and ceramics. Materials classed as seconds may be used in making a lower grade product. Examples are small fruits used in making cocktail or the bruised portions of animals used in making fertilizer or soap. Irregularly shaped or dented bars of soap, broken lumps of sugar, and improperly shaped glass jars may be remelted and recast. Dented cans of fruit are sometimes sold locally at reduced prices. The shaving cream from dented tubes may be used to reclaim certain ingredients such as glycerine. Printed forms in which holes have been improperly cut or in which the printing is out of line are only waste paper.

Another purpose of inspection is to provide information concerning the efficiency of persons in the management or in the work force. For example, inspection may indicate that the most suitable material is not being purchased, that the employment procedure is not resulting in the selection of the best workers, that a training program is needed, that the wage system does not adequately reward good workmanship, or that defective or spoiled work is not being properly reworked. If the number of rejected pieces is large, management may find that the tolerances are too close, that supervision should be improved, or that machine tools are not being properly repaired or maintained.

Inspection should provide information to show the amount of good and poor work done by each worker. An employee who has done poor work may require more training or additional supervision. He may be transferred to another job, or he may be dismissed. If workers are given a bonus for quality, or if they are paid a piece rate, inspection may be necessary to determine the number of good pieces produced. The inspection report should indicate the number of parts inspected, the number accepted, and the number rejected. Defects should be traced to the worker, the vendor, or the machine.

WHEN TO INSPECT

The time of inspection varies in part with the nature of materials or products. Purchased materials and parts are usually inspected when they are received. In some cases, materials or products are inspected in the plant of the vendor during or after completion of the manufacturing processes. A shirt manufacturer, for example, sometimes contracts with textile mills for the manufacture of special fabrics of a specified weave or pattern. To assure that the materials will be of the desired quality, the shirt manufacturer may place an inspector in the plant of the textile mill. A fruit-packing company that contracts to buy the fruit from an orchard may inspect the fruit before it is picked. A milk-processing company may protect itself as to the quality of milk by inspecting the barns and the cattle of the farmer.

Work in process usually cannot be inspected by professional inspectors at every step in production. Usually the management establishes certain control points where errors may be detected before serious losses have been incurred. How many control points should be established and which points should be selected will depend upon the nature of the product and the manufacturing processes. Parts may be inspected before they are moved to a very expensive operation where an additional cost increment will be added to a part that might later be scrapped. Another common control point is the last operation in one department when parts are ready to be moved to the next department. If a later operation might conceal defects in a part or a component, the items should be inspected before the work is done. Examples of such operations are painting, plating, and enclosure in a case or box. The payment of a bonus for quality would also be a factor in the frequency of the inspection and the establishment of control points.

The product is usually inspected when it is finished. A motor is tested and broken in on a test stand. A washing machine, an electric iron, or an electric fan is connected with power lines at the completion of the assembly operations and its performance checked. Electric fuses and lamps are inspected by trying them in electrical connections. Tin cans and other containers are tested to assure that none have holes. The final inspection frequently serves as a check on the inspectors at earlier stages of production.

WHO INSPECTS

On the basis of who does the inspection, the work is usually classified as professional inspection, voluntary or worker inspection, automatic inspection, and machine inspection. Usually these methods are combined, and one company may employ all of them.

Professional Inspection. Inspection is said to be professional in nature if it is conducted by a member of the inspection department who is designated as a professional inspector. The inspection department performs a staff function, which is a service to the operating departments. Since inspection is also a check on the work of the operating personnel, the head of the inspection department should not be responsible to the foreman or the division chief but may report to either the director of manufacturing or the general manager. However, he reports to the general manager only in industries where quality of the product is considered of primary importance.

Worker Inspection. Voluntary or worker inspection, as the name suggests, is inspection by the worker himself. In many types of mechanical work the operator may be supplied with a simple gage which he can use to inspect his work as it comes from the machine. A common type of gage is a "go-and-no-go" gage, which is used to test the size of a piece or the threads of a bolt or pipe. This gage consists of a piece of metal with two openings of different sizes. The openings indicate the outside limits of the piece. If the part can be inserted in both openings of the gage, it is too small. If it cannot be inserted in either opening, it is too large. The part must be of such size that it can be inserted in one opening but not in the other. The worker may use such a gage to inspect the first parts produced after the machine has been started. If the first parts do not pass inspection, he adjusts the machine and tries again. After the parts appear to be standard, the machine may be operated continuously, with occasional testing. If parts are found to be nearing the limit of tolerance, the machine should be adjusted before the limit is reached, to prevent the necessity for rejecting defective parts. In other words, the worker should always aim at the "bull's-eye," which is the mid-point of the limits set by the standard.

Worker inspection is also used where visual methods of inspection are employed. For example, a worker who is engaged in the polishing of jewelry or in assembly work should inspect his own work visually before passing the product to the next operation. He may also inspect the work done at preceding workplaces in the line, as in the manufacture of clothing or the assembly of an instrument. Any worker who discovers a defect should report it before other operations are performed. The advantage of worker inspection is that defects are discovered at an early stage and at less cost than would result from professional inspection. The limitation is that defective materials or parts may be passed by the worker because of indifference, carelessness, or inability to distinguish defects.

Worker inspection is sometimes combined with the packing of the product for shipment to the customer. For example, workers at the end of the production line for glass bottles may inspect each bottle for air bubbles or other defects before putting it into a shipping carton. Workers who pack apples for shipment are expected to discard any fruit observed to contain bruises or blemishes. Bags of sugar are inspected to see that they are properly sealed. In all of these cases, the product has already been inspected at several work stations and receives a final inspection before shipment.

Automatic Inspection. Inspection is said to be automatic if one part is fitted to another in the assembly of a product and if only standard parts can be made to fit. Defective parts are automatically rejected by the worker on the line. Ordinarily, this method cannot be used satisfactorily because the progress of the work requires that all defective or nonstandard parts be rejected before they reach the line.

Machine Inspection. When parts are inspected by a machine, the work of inspection is usually regarded as part of the work of professional inspection. However, some machines have been perfected to the extent that machine inspection may be regarded as a separate type of inspection. For example, in an automobile factory, each car passes over a steel plate in the floor as it nears the end of the production line. If the wheels are not properly aligned, the steel plate moves to one side and makes an electric contact that rings a bell. A can manufacturing company uses a machine to inspect tin cans for leaks. The machine automatically rejects any defective can and passes the good cans to a conveyor belt that carries them to the shipping room or the loading platform. Machines are commonly used to inspect for weight certain packaged products such as sugar or soap. Packages that are over- or underweight are automatically set aside. Inspection devices have also been developed to provide a continuous check on the thickness of steel sheets or a coating of enamel. A similar device will automatically measure the dimensions of parts that are machined on a lathe and reject parts that are not within the prescribed limits.

HOW MUCH TO INSPECT

The question of how much to inspect presents two problems to the management. The first problem pertains to the percentage of the materials, parts, or products to be inspected, and the second problem concerns the method of determining the proper amount to inspect and of judging the entire lot on the basis of the results of the inspection of the sample.

Partial or Complete Inspection. When work is done by manual labor rather than by machine, it is usually necessary to inspect every piece. An example is the work of a typesetter who sets type for a book or of a typist who writes letters. The fact that a part of the work is correctly done cannot be accepted as evidence that no mistakes have been made in other parts of the work. However, the decision depends in part upon the importance of the task and upon the need for careful workmanship. The auditing of accounting records is one type of inspection; but auditors do not usually consider that the verification of every entry is necessary, unless the sample selected for verification is found to have a number of errors. Inspection is usually regarded as adding nothing to the value of the product. No more inspection should be done than is necessary to accomplish the purposes.

When work is done on a semiautomatic or an automatic machine, it is usually necessary to inspect only a part of the work. The worker may adjust the machine and inspect the first few parts by the use of a gage or other simple inspection device. As the parts are processed by the machine, the operator may put them in numbered trays or boxes in order that the professional inspector may know which parts were produced first. The inspector would later check some of the parts in the first tray, some from the middle tray, and some from the last tray. If these parts meet the standard, he can be assured that the machine was properly set for the first part and that it continued to operate in proper adjustment. If defective parts are found, it may be necessary to inspect the entire lot. The judging of an entire lot by the inspection of less than 100 per cent of the number of units is called "sampling" or "partial inspection." The increased use of machines for inspection has decreased the cost and has made complete or 100 per cent inspection feasible in many cases where partial inspection was formerly employed. Complete inspection by a machine is cheap after the machine has been made.

Use of Statistical Methods in Inspection. In the inspection of many commodities, 100 per cent inspection is not feasible because the cost of complete inspection would be excessive. In other cases, complete inspection is impossible because the units inspected are destroyed or made unusable by inspection. For example, when cans of food are opened for inspection in a packing plant, the fruit is usually given to employees. In a glass factory the bottles and jars that are tested in a laboratory are sometimes subjected to increasing weight until they break. Some containers are cut from top to bottom to permit a measurement of the thickness of the glass, and others are broken in the making of tests for stresses and strains. Other products that may be destroyed in the course of tests are electric fuses, cartridge caps, coal tested for heat units, and wire tested for tensile strength. In such cases, statistical methods and sampling techniques are employed to answer such questions as the following:

How large a sample should be inspected?

How should the items in the sample chosen for inspection be selected from the lot?

When the number of defective items in the sample has been determined, how can the number of defective items in the entire lot be estimated?

What is the possible or probable percentage of error in the estimate of the total number of defective items?

What percentage of defective items in the sample is sufficient to justify the rejection of the entire lot?

How can the number of defective items in various samples or lots be charted or tabulated from one week or month to the next in order that unfavorable trends may be detected and the causes corrected?

Statistical inspection is based upon the fact that the measurement of the quality of a manufactured product is always subject to chance variability. In every specific method of production, some stable "pattern of chance causes" exists; and within the stable pattern there is variability. The variability may extend beyond the usual pattern. Any variation outside the stable pattern is due to causes which may be found and corrected. The problem in statistical inspection is to determine the assignable causes of quality variation as distinguished from the chance variability.[1]

A few simple illustrations may be cited to indicate what is meant by "chance variability." An occasional blemish in a piece of cloth may be due to a broken thread or a knot tied to start a new spool of thread. An off-color bottle or jar might be due to an accidental dropping of a foreign substance in the mix or failure to clean the hopper thoroughly. A hole bored in wood or metal at an irregular angle might be due to the failure of the worker to brush away all shavings before seating the material. In such cases a few defects would not be significant. But if the charting of the variations shows an increase in the number of defective parts, the cause may be attributed to some basic defect which requires correction.

If parts are produced at a machine, some variations in the dimensions may be expected. If the planned thickness of a part is 1.0 inch, for

---

[1] For discussion of statistical methods of inspection, see Theodore H. Brown, "Quality Control," *Harvard Business Review*, Vol. XXIX, No. 6 (1951), pp. 69–80.

example, a variation of 0.002 may be permissible, and the parts may therefore pass inspection within the range of 1.002 to 0.998 inch. If the output of the machine follows the usual pattern of the probability curve, part sizes can be charted by means of a frequency bar chart or a frequency histogram which would take the shape of the usual bell curve. In this curve, however, the values would be clustered about the value of 1.0 inch, with perhaps a few parts falling outside the acceptable range.

Sample parts produced at the machine may be inspected at regular intervals of time, and the results of the inspections may be entered on a simple line chart for better interpretation of results. As long as the machine is producing normally or in control, the average dimension of the parts should measure 1.0 inch, and variations would fall largely within the area 1.002 to 0.998 inch. If the machine should fail to perform properly because the tool becomes worn or other difficulty develops, the average dimension might increase to 1.002 inch, and the dimensions might vary from 1.000 to 1.004 inch. The operation would now be described as out of process. The machine should be stopped and the cause of the variation corrected.

When a chart is prepared to show the dimensions of parts, the average of all parts inspected is charted rather than the dimensions of each item. Either the arithmetic mean or the median dimension of the parts may be shown. The chart would also show the extent of the deviations from the average. Average deviation may be used, but standard deviation provides a better statistical measure. The standard deviation is not computed for each sample, but it is quickly determined by reference to tables prepared by the use of computing machines. The extent of the deviations from the average may be as significant as the trend of the average dimensions. (For an illustration of statistical inspection, see Case No. 37.)

WHERE TO INSPECT

The inspection may be made on the production floor or in the laboratory. Inspection on the floor is usually easier if the product is bulky or heavy, if inspection is visual, or if special equipment is not necessary. Floor inspection is usually better if the work can be effectively done in the shop because defects are more quickly found and corrected. Losses resulting from the continued production of defective parts are less likely. Laboratory inspection is necessary if special machines or equipment are required.

In most companies, both floor inspection and laboratory inspection are used. To illustrate, in a fruit-packing plant, floor inspection is used for peaches to assure that all seeds and peelings have been removed, to see that the cut is uniform and proper, and to assure uniformity in size and appearance. Laboratory inspection is used for samples of the canned fruit, which are inspected for vacuum space, amount of head space, gross and net weight, sugar content, color and quality of the fruit, and number of pieces to the can. In a soap factory, floor inspection is used to control color and shape of bars and to assure clearness of brand name and cleanliness of wrappings. Laboratory inspection is used for chemical analysis and tests of moisture content. Both incoming materials and soap products are given tests of this kind.

KIND OF TEST IN INSPECTION

The nature of the test in inspection depends upon the materials, parts, or finished product. Some of the common tests are designed to assure that the standards as established in the design of the product are maintained. They include tests for accuracy of dimensions, contour or profile of parts, strength of material, smoothness of surface, chemical composition, color, and internal flaws.

Accuracy of Dimensions. Mass-production industries with interchangeable parts are dependent upon scientific measurement, which has made steady progress since the beginning of the nineteenth century. The accuracy of dimensions is measured by instruments that are controlled by the operator through the sense of touch rather than the sense of vision. One of the oldest and best-known measuring devices is the caliper, which was invented in 1631 by Pierre Vernier. The caliper consists of two fingers which are usually curved or bent. The distance between the fingers is controlled by turning a screw or worm wheel similiar to the method of moving the jaw of an ordinary monkey wrench. One complete turn of the worm wheel moves the points of the calipers a distance equal to the width of one thread on the wheel. This distance is subject to accurate measurement. One-half turn or any other fraction of a turn moves the points a corresponding fraction of the width of a thread. The caliper thus permits measurements to very small fractions of an inch. Some calipers are so constructed that the fingers grasp or measure the outside dimensions of a part, and others are so designed that the fingers can be inserted inside a part to measure inside dimensions.

An adaptation of the caliper is the micrometer. This instrument is defined as "a caliper gage with micrometer screw attached, used for very exact measurement." The micrometer is usually adapted for the measurement of outside dimensions, but it may also be made to measure inside dimensions. A micrometer used to measure either inside or outside dimensions is shown in Figure 33. The instrument is

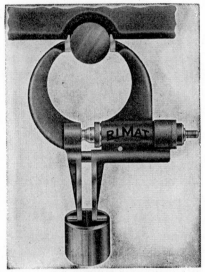

Courtesy of Richards Machine Tool Co.

FIG. 33. Micrometer for Measuring Inside or Outside Dimensions

Courtesy of Federal Products Corp.

FIG. 34. Gage for Inspecting Outside Dimensions

equipped with a dial which records the distance between the movable spindle and the anvil or frame. This instrument will measure dimensions to 0.0001 of an inch. A gage which provides a specific reading or definite measurement is called an indicating or a measurement gage. A gage of this type is illustrated in Figure 34.

The manufacture of missiles and rockets has required increased accuracy of gages, micrometers, and other devices for inspecting dimensions. In these products, a very small variation in the dimensions of a part may mean the difference between success and failure of a project. With perhaps 100,000 parts in a missile, a small variation in a few parts will greatly multiply the difficulties.[2] Similar considerations apply to the accuracy of parts in an automobile, which is expected to operate at high speed for hours at a time.

[2] E. W. Ziegler and R. S. Rice, "Inspection Today," *Factory Management and Maintenance,* Vol. CXVI, No. 10 (1958), pp. 96–101.

A gage may indicate only that a measurable characteristic is within certain limits. This type of gage is called a limit or fixed gage. An example is the "go-and-no-go" gage previously mentioned. Another limit gage is the plug and ring gage, which consists of two parts: a ring with threads on the inside and a plug with threads on the outside. Holes are tested with the plug gage. Special gages, which are equipped with dials similiar to the one shown in Figure 34, are made to measure length, width, squareness, thickness, and shape of threads; the location of holes bored in a plate; and the uniformity of the diameter of a material, such as a wire. Especially designed gages are also used to test the accuracy of the shape of a hole as well as its size. The hole that engages a shafting, a piston, or an axle must be free of mechanical defects to prevent undue vibration, weakness, wear, and unsatisfactory performance. A hole may be tapered, crooked, irregular, or bellmouthed. A gage inserted inside the hole will register such irregularities.

Because gages are valuable, a close control is usually established over their storage, issue, and return to stock. Because they are delicate and subject to wear, records of the inspection and repair of gages are also kept. The accuracy of gages is checked regularly, and the checks may be made daily or weekly. The checking is done by comparison of the measurement as determined by the gage with the measurement by a master gage. Inspection of gages is done under controlled temperatures and atmospheric pressure.

Profile Inspection. If a part is irregular in shape, the prescribing of a series of dimensions may be difficult or impossible. The standard for parts of irregular shapes and a variety of dimensions may prescribe the profile or contour of the entire part and certain of the limiting or over-all dimensions. Examples of such parts are gears, wheels, razor blades, and steel rails. Inspection for profile or contour may be made with the use of a rigid metal form which has been made to fit the part or the product according to specifications.

A very useful machine for measuring or comparing the contour of small objects is the optical comparator, which operates on a principle known as "optical projection." By means of a series of mirrors or reflecting devices, the machine magnifies the profile of the object being inspected and throws a clear reflection of the contour upon a glass screen, which resembles the screen of a television set. A master chart, which is drawn in accordance with a prescribed standard, may be placed upon the screen for comparison with the part. The number of times the profile of a part may be magnified depends upon its size. Very small parts may be magnified to sixty or more times their size. In this way, defects that are undetected by ordinary visual inspection show up very clearly. Another use of the comparator is to check the wear of gages and other inspecting equipment for scratches and gradual wear. The comparator is also used to inspect ball bearings, electric-shaver parts, knife blades, golf balls, threads of lamp bulbs,

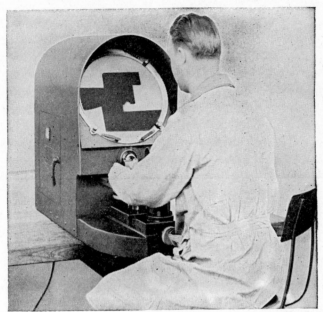

Courtesy of Jones and Lamson Machine Co.

FIG. 35. Comparator for Inspection of Profile of Parts

beads, saw teeth, and other parts. Figure 35 shows an inspector using such a machine to inspect the profile of a part.

Strength of Material. Incoming materials and finished products are frequently tested for strength. For example, steel companies make tests of the strength of sheet steel, bulletproof jackets, and wire. Cable companies test insulated wire for tensile strength and the amount of friction required to remove the insulation. Glass companies subject bottles to tests of internal pressure and weight. Tin can manufacturers test tin cans to determine the number of pounds of pressure the can will withstand. This test is made by the use of a machine that puts an increasing amount of pressure upon the can until it bursts. Since the can usually bursts at the seams, this test applies to the seams rather

FIG. 36. Device for Testing Tin Cans

This machine subjects the inside of a can to pressures far beyond the pressure in actual use.

than the material. The machine used to test tin cans is shown in Figure 36.

Smoothness of Surface. The smoothness of the surface is a relative matter. In many products a surface which appears smooth to the eye is satisfactory. Examples are bricks, linoleum, the base of a stove, or the top of a kitchen table. Visual inspection of smoothness may therefore be sufficient. A more accurate method is to use a machine for testing smoothness or roughness. One type of machine gages the surface roughness by measuring the resistance to the passage of compressed air between the surface being inspected and a smooth steel plate which is placed upon a product.

Chemical Composition. In a great variety of the products of industry, standards have been established for chemical composition and the permissible percentage of impurities. The standards are made by the manufacturer of the materials and also by the purchaser. Examples of materials for which chemical standards are important are glass, fertilizers, dyestuffs, sugar, soap, alloys, and paints. Tests for chemical composition usually require laboratory or central inspection.

Color. In the mixing of colors for dyeing textiles or making paint, the problem is to make each new batch like the standard. In the automobile industry the method has been to mix colors according to formula and to take frequent samples for inspection during the mixing process. The sample is compared with the master panel by an expert color matcher. Machines are also made to compare colors mechanically by measuring the light rays reflected from a painted surface. This device is faster and more accurate than visual inspection. Other machines are available to sort a product, such as cigars, according to color.

Inspection for Internal Faults. A method of testing metals and other materials for flaws, such as cracks, breaks, shrinkage areas, and porous conditions, by means of supersonic vibrations has been applied in the inspection of steel, aluminum, magnesium, brass, glass, and plastics. The device has been especially valuable in the discovery of hidden defects in crankshafts, railroad car axles, cylinder blocks, and other large metal parts. The machine transforms an electrical vibration into a different type of vibration which is called a "high-freqency" or "supersonic" vibration. This change is effected by means of a quartz crystal. The supersonic vibrations are transmitted into the material being tested. The vibrations from the material are directed back to the machine where they are fed into an amplifier and are reflected upon a small glass screen. A flaw or internal defect in the material shows as a break in the line of vibration on the screen. The machine indicates not only the existence of a flaw but also its extent and its depth. This information is of much value in making repairs.

Wood which is imported from areas where fighting has occurred frequently contains metal from shrapnel or rifle bullets. The metal in the wood will seriously damage machine tools if an attempt is made to process the piece. Wood from trees that once served as fence posts may also contain metal. The presence of metal in a piece of wood may be detected with a sounding device which is built on the principle of the mine detector used by the military services. An X-ray machine is sometimes used to detect internal flaws in small parts. A picture is taken of 100 or more parts and the defective units are identified by their location or position in the picture. This type of test has the advantage of detecting internal flaws without destroying the material or the product. Its use has been increased by new applications of science to industrial techniques.

MANAGEMENT OF INSPECTION

The work of inspection is important because it affects relations with vendors and customers and also because it affects the efficient and smooth operation of production. An early discovery of defects and correction of the process may prevent serious losses. The passing of defective work by inspectors or a failure to inspect may result in financial losses as well as unfavorable customer relations.

The first requirement in the management of inspection is that the inspector should be instructed as to quality standards, which include acceptable quality levels for both measurable and nonmeasurable defects. Inspectors should be trained in methods of inspection and types of reports to be prepared and filed. Persons should be selected for this work on the basis of their ability to make the tests. For example, an inspector might be required to have manual dexterity, arithmetical accuracy, good vision, or ability to distinguish colors. He may need tact and firmness in dealing with foremen and other persons. He needs a certain amount of technical skill in using measuring instruments and judgment in selecting samples. Management should establish methods of evaluating inspectors for accuracy, display of tact, and other traits.

The responsibility for quality should be established, and each person should know what is expected of him. The persons who are concerned with quality include the engineers who design the product and establish specifications, the purchasing agent, foremen, and workers, in addition to the inspectors. A foreman may make the decision that a machine is properly set to begin operations. If an inspector finds that some of the work is below standard, the foreman or his superior would decide whether to continue or to stop the operation. If the work is defective, the responsibility rests with workers and foremen rather than inspectors. The inspector performs a staff function, and he should not assume line authority by directing workers or issuing orders. Unless management properly determines standards and organizes the work of inspection, important questions concerning quality and costs will be made at a low level in the organization.

QUESTIONS

1. Distinguish between inspection and quality control.

2. Why is worker inspection desirable? Under what circumstances is it feasible?

3. Should a worker be paid only for the parts that pass inspection when he is paid by the piece?

4. Under what circumstances might the purchaser advantageously inspect parts or products in the plant of the vendor when the products are being manufactured according to customer specifications?

5. If a product is consumed or destroyed by inspection, how can the buyer determine the proper number to inspect?

6. What types of tests would a fruit-packing company use in inspecting cans of peaches? At what point or stage of production would the inspecting be done?

7. What defects might the inspector look for in inspecting a shirt?

8. Explain desirable qualities in a book other than the subject matter.

9. Why is the establishment of close tolerances sometimes undesirable from the point of view of the manufacturer? Illustrate by reference to specific products.

10. What is meant by control points? What determines the number and the places where they are set up? Does the concept of control points have application outside inspection? Illustrate.

CASES

35. A PROGRAM FOR QUALITY IMPROVEMENT

The president of the Acme Shirt Company, Mr. Foote, received a complaint letter from a customer, which he referred to Mr. Myers, the plant superintendent. The letter read as follows:

"I have just returned from a day at the office where I wore one of your shirts. My neck has been rubbed almost to the point of bleeding by the saw-like teeth which protrude along the circumference of the collar. How can you picture in your advertisements a man enjoying the comfort of one of your shirts when the collar is so rough it takes the skin off the wearer's neck?"

Mr. Myers sent the customer two new shirts for each one he had bought and asked for a return of the defective shirts together with the box in which they had been shipped. The shirts were found to contain rough edges as the customer had stated, and by means of the markings on the shirts and the box the defects were traced to the operator who was responsible. The cause was found to be a needle with a blunted point which pulled out a thread in the cloth each time a stitch was made. When the shirt was starched, the points did resemble the teeth of a saw.

Mr. Myers decided to investigate the whole question of quality. He learned that inspection was done by the sampling method and that many defective shirts were being shipped to customers. When a batch of shirts was found to be defective, some could be reworked to correct such defects as buttons out of line, broken buttons, and pockets improperly placed. Shirts that could not be reworked were sold to employees at a company store at reduced prices. The company labels were always removed from such shirts before they were sold.

The cost of defective work was so great that Mr. Myers decided to initiate a program to improve quality. Some of the causes of defects could be attributed to management, and Mr. Myers first attempted to eliminate these causes by consulting with the purchasing agent, the manager of the receiving room, the foreman of the maintenance department, the manager of the cutting room, and the foremen. The personnel director was requested to review the methods of inducting and training new employees and the instructions issued to all workers in connection with each assignment of work. Each worker should know what he was supposed to do, how he was supposed to do the work, and the quality standards that he should maintain. Indoctrination should also cause workers to understand that they were in a position to maintain quality and the reputation of the company for manufacturing and selling a quality product.

A quality-improvement campaign was inaugurated and the co-operation of foremen and all other persons in the management was requested. The program was initiated at a general meeting of workers and foremen. Workers were asked to submit suggestions for eliminating defects, and several suggestions were submitted in the regular suggestions system. The usable suggestions were rewarded at premium rates. A plant quality committee was organized with members appointed from the manufacturing, engineering, accounting, personnel, sales, and inspection departments. The committee met regularly for thirty minutes each week to present suggestions and to approve plans for improving quality. The committee formulated a program for convincing workers of the importance of maintaining quality standards. Methods used included posters, newspaper announcements, and books of matches with quality slogans imprinted on the cover. Letters from dealers and customers relating to quality were posted on bulletin boards and printed in the plant newspaper.

Mr. Myers was convinced that the management personnel and the workers should be informed concerning the success of the program. The number of defects of each kind per 1,000 shirts was compiled each week and the figures were supplied to the union, published in the company paper, and sent to foremen and others by letter from the plant superintendent. A weighted index was also computed with point values assigned to each kind of defect. This index, which summarized the entire performance, was also publicized. The figures were reviewed with foremen at their regular weekly meetings.

The formal quality campaign was brought to a close after three months with another general meeting where the results were reviewed. The workers and foremen of the various departments were commended for their co-operation. Prizes for slogans, suggestions, and outstanding performance were awarded.

To prevent a lapse of interest and a return to the earlier poor performance, the company continued to compile and publish to both foremen and workers the figures for defects of each kind and the index of quality. However, the figures were based upon sample inspection because complete inspection was regarded as both costly and unnecessary.

Required:

Criticize favorably or unfavorably the campaign for quality improvement.

36. MAINTENANCE OF QUALITY STANDARDS

The main office of the National Glass Works, Inc., is in New York. Reporting directly to the president of the company is a vice-president in charge of research and quality control. His function is to develop standards of quality and to see that the standards are consistently maintained.

One of the plants is at Oakland, California. At the Oakland plant, glass containers are made and sold to local canning companies, beverage manufacturers, and other manufacturers. The plant is under the general supervision of a plant manager. The chief inspector, who reports to the plant manager, is responsible for the maintenance of quality standards as established at the New York office. The company has a laboratory at the Oakland plant where central inspection is given by the sampling method. A few jars or bottles of each kind are taken from the production line for laboratory testing under the direction of a laboratory manager who is responsible to the chief inspector. A number of tests are made to assure that quality standards as established by the New York office and as specified in the sales contract with the customer are maintained. The bottle capacity is measured by filling the bottle with water and measuring the amount. Contour of the bottle is inspected by fitting a form or pattern around it. To measure its strength, the bottle is placed in a machine which applies an increasing amount of pressure upon it. The machine records the amount of weight which the bottle will carry without breaking. Another testing machine is used to apply an increasing amount of internal pressure within the bottle and to measure the amount required to break it. In another test, a bottle is cut from top to bottom, and the thickness of the glass at each point is measured. The bottle is examined for internal pulls and strains within the glass. This test is made by placing the bottle in a viewing device which is equipped with special lenses. If the glass has no strains, the light rays reflected through it appear uniform in color. If it does have pulls or strains, the rays will indicate streaks of a bluish or purple color. Other tests may be made by visual inspection or by special testing devices.

If any bottles are found to be defective, the lot from which the samples were taken can be determined by means of numbers which were imprinted upon the bottom of the bottle when it was formed in the mold. Corrective action to be taken depends on the nature and the seriousness of the defect. In some cases, a larger sample might be inspected or 100 per cent inspection might be necessary. A rejected lot would be broken, remelted, and recast.

On the production floor, workers regularly make certain tests for quality. In the molding department, workers visually inspect containers as they come from the molds to detect any obvious defects. This inspection is by the sampling method. As the containers move to the packing and shipping department after an annealing process, they are inspected for outside shape and contour by a machine which automatically rejects any container not of the right shape. This inspection is 100 per cent.

All containers move past a floor inspector toward the packing station. The inspector uses visual inspection for color and possible blemishes in the glass. This worker is under the line control of the foreman of the packing department but observes instructions from the chief inspector as to quality standards. As workers remove containers from the conveyor for packing in a corrugated shipping box, they inspect the bottom of each one for color, air bubbles, and other defects that might be detected by visual inspection.

Required:

1. Draw up an organization chart to show organization for quality control.
2. Explain the relation of the quality control function to manufacturing.

37. STATISTICAL INSPECTION

A manufacturer of wire products received an order from the United States Navy for 10,000,000 compression springs for a fuse of a certain type. The dimensions were carefully detailed in the purchase contract with tolerances that were fairly close. Knowing that the specifications would not be easily met, the design department checked the machines to be used in production. It saw no reason for believing that any difficulties would be encountered.

The production of the springs required inspection of incoming materials and work of precision in coiling, heat treating, grinding, and inspecting. Before production was started on any of the springs, all of the wire for the entire lot was gaged. The usual minor variations in the wire were discovered, though the differences were not great enough to justify the rejection of any of the wire. The wire was then ranked by size. According to the production plan, the largest wire would be used first and the smallest would be used last. This arrangement was followed in order that minor adjustments in the machines might be made as the work proceeded, and all adjustments would be made in the same direction.

As soon as the coiling operation was started, samples were carefully inspected. Chance variations were noted. When the dimensions of the springs in the lot were charted, they showed the usual bell-shaped curve with most of the springs having the exact dimensions specified. Although some of the springs were larger and some smaller than the specifications, all were within the allowable limits. This procedure was continued regularly with samples taken frequently throughout the day. As the results of each sample were charted, they were compared with the distribution as shown in similar charts for earlier samples.

No significant variations in the samples were discovered until the third day when a sharp increase was noted in the number of units at one end of the curve on the chart. Estimates indicated that about 22 per cent of the coils were rejected and could be used only for scrap. A check of the tools and tool settings failed to reveal any cause of the trouble, but the inspector and the foreman knew that some difficulty had developed.

In an effort to determine the cause of the trouble, a 100 per cent inspection was started. Complete inspection revealed that every third spring was defective. This information suggested that a feed roll was defective, since the rolls made a complete revolution for each three springs produced. The machine was stopped immediately, and the rolls were inspected. The shaft of one of the rolls was found to be slightly out of line. When this difficulty was corrected, production was resumed. Samples of the product then coming from the machine were inspected, and the results were charted. The samples were found to follow the usual bell-shaped curve within the allowable limits. The management estimated that the early discovery of the difficulty had resulted in a direct saving of $30,200 as compared with what the costs would have been if no inspection had been made until the completion of the order.

Question:

What principles of quality control are illustrated by this incident?

PART V

PRODUCTION
STANDARDS

18 Methods Improvement

THE establishment of a standard of production by which to measure the accomplishment of a worker, a group of workers, or a department is an important part of the work of the industrial engineer. Unless management has such a standard, it has no way of determining whether output is average, below average, or exceptional. Past performance is unreliable as a standard because it may result in the comparison of current performance with a poor, average, or excellent rate of output. Standards are used not only for determining the pay or other reward of the worker but also for handling many management problems, such as estimating costs, determining completion dates for work planned, establishing a balance in plant layout, and handling worker complaints and grievances.

Two techniques are used in the establishment of standards of production: methods improvement, or motion study, and time study. Methods improvement includes an analysis of the movements of the hands, arms, feet, and body of the worker in accomplishing the assigned task. It also includes an analysis of the arrangement of the workplace, tools, and equipment. Conditions of work, such as ventilation, lighting, noise, and control of obnoxious or dangerous gases, are usually surveyed and improved.

After studies of work methods have been made, the time required to do the task may be determined. Time study is used not only to measure the savings made by motion study but also to compare two or more motions or sets of motions to determine which requires the least time. Neither motion study nor time study is complete until workers who are assigned to the task have been trained in the new methods.

Motion studies are made to improve the methods of doing the various tasks. A task may be defined as a definite unit or piece of work to be done. The task should be distinguished from a job, which is an assignment of tasks to any one worker. The tasks that make up a job possess certain similarities, and they differ in some important respects from the tasks making up any other job.

MOTION STUDY

The work of making motion and time studies is usually combined with some other activities under the title of industrial engineering. In some companies, the standards are set by a standards department or a methods and standards department. While the duties assigned to the department will vary, they might include such activities as methods improvement, estimates of labor cost for new products, investigation of new procedures and new methods, assistance in plant layout, analysis of materials-handling problems, training of workers and management personnel in methods improvement, and operation of the suggestion system. Related activities that may be assigned to the industrial engineering or standards department include job evaluation and incentive methods of wage payment.[1]

Purposes of Motion Study. Motion-study techniques were developed in great detail by Frank B. Gilbreth and Lillian M. Gilbreth, who were interested in eliminating useless motions and particularly the body motions. An increase in output naturally resulted from the improvement. Another result is the reduction in the amount of time required to manufacture a product. A shortening of the construction period increases the rate of turnover of work in process and decreases the overhead cost per unit. The savings are greatest when the motion-study technique is applied to the bottleneck operations, for greater output may be achieved from other workplaces all along the line. This improvement usually results in improved morale, since wasted efforts and exasperating delays create a feeling of frustration.

The objective of motion study is sometimes described as that of finding the one best way to perform a task. This statement needs qualification, however, because workers differ in many respects, such as height, weight, strength, length of arms, manual dexterity, ability to use both right and left hands, and physical condition. Motion study may provide the method for optimum performance under conditions prevailing

---

[1] H. B. Maynard, "Work Measurements," *Factory Management and Maintenance*, Vol. CXVII, No. 8 (1959), pp. 61–67.

when the study was made. Differences between individuals may later require some modification in the methods prescribed for any task.

Analysis of Motions. Before an attempt is made to simplify a task, the investigator should see precisely what the worker does in performing the work. For example, the elements of the work of cutting gears with the hobbing machine, which was referred to in Chapter 6, might be as follows:

1. Walk to machine.
2. Place arbor of work between centers.
3. Advance hob to work.
4. Engage feed.
5. Cutting by machine.
6. Stop machine when work is completed.
7. Run hob back.
8. Remove arbor of work from machine.
9. Inspect.

While the machine is making the cut, the worker may prepare the next arbor of work. He may also perform steps 1, 2, 3, and 4, or 6, 7, 8, and 9 on another machine doing similar work.

Therbligs. As a part of the analysis of the task the entire operation is studied, and the separate motions are listed. The three basic phases of any task are: *Get ready,* or preparation; *Do it,* or operation; and *Clean up,* or completion. These parts of the task are further subdivided into elementary motions which vary with the task, although all tasks consist of different combinations of the same elementary operations.

The Gilbreths found that any task can be performed by a combination of eighteen detailed motions, which they called "therbligs." The word "therblig" is Gilbreth spelled backwards, except that the last two letters in the name are not interchanged. The therbligs and their definitions are as follows:[2]

THERBLIG	DEFINITION
Reach	Consists of reaching for an object.
Move	Consists of moving a tool or a part. The object may be pushed, shoved, carried, or moved in the hand.
Grasp	Consists of taking hold of an object.
Position	Means to put material into place for processing, or to line up a part for assembly, or to put a tool to the material for use.

---

[2] The therbligs listed here are the revised basic motion elements adopted by a committee sponsored by the American Society of Mechanical Engineers.

THERBLIG	DEFINITION
Disengage	Consists of separating two or more parts.
Release	Consists of letting go of a tool, a part, or an assembly.
Hold	Consists of retention of material or part in a fixed position with either hand.
Do	Consists of assembling two or more parts or of applying a machine or hand tool to the purpose for which it was intended.
Examine	Consists of viewing, examining, or testing a part or an assembly to determine whether it meets required standards.
Change Direction	Consists of changing the line or the plane along which Reach or Move is made.
Pre-position	Consists of locating a tool or part preparatory to the beginning of the next therblig.
Search	Means the movement of the eye or hand in an attempt to locate an object.
Select	Consists of locating a part or a tool.
Plan	Consists of mental processes of operator preparatory to beginning the next cycle of operations.
Avoidable Delay	Consists of stoppage of work activity for which the operator is responsible.
Unavoidable Delay	Consists of waiting for material or repairs to the machine or for the machine to make a cut.
Rest to Overcome Fatigue	Consists of seating oneself, changing position, or other activity or relaxation.
Balancing Delay	Means delay of one hand caused by differences in the time required by two hands to perform separate motions.

In the improvement of work methods, a complete cycle of therbligs is charted for both the right and the left hand. A simple motion chart for one hand in signing a letter is shown in Figure 37. In performing this

Name of Therblig	Motion
Search	Look for pen.
Reach	Reach for pen.
Select	Choose a pen for use.
Grasp	Grasp pen with hand.
Move	Move pen to letter.
Position	Put pen into position for use.
Do	Sign name.
Move	Return pen to holder.
Release	Release pen.

FIG. 37. Chart of Motions in Signing a Letter

task, the person may keep the left hand idle, or he may use it to hold the paper in position. A simple motion chart for both hands is shown in Figure 38.

LEFT HAND		RIGHT HAND	
Name of Therblig	Description	Name of Therblig	Description
Move	Get part No. 1	Release	Aside finished piece
Position	Position part No. 1	Move	Get part No. 2
Hold	Hold for right hand	Assemble	No. 1 and No. 2
Do	Help right hand	Do	Weld
Move	Give to right hand	Grasp	Take from left hand

FIG. 38. Motion Chart for Both Hands

The reason for the reduction of an activity into its elements and for the designation of each element by name is to determine whether a more economical sequence is possible and also to determine what steps may be eliminated. The therbligs that do not contribute directly to production should be especially scrutinized. For example, the therblig *Search* may suggest that parts have not been properly positioned for use. The therblig *Select* may be eliminated by teaching the worker to take parts from a certain part of the container or the pile. *Unavoidable Delay* may be eliminated by changing the sequence of motions or rearranging the workplace in order that one hand may not be required to wait for the other to complete an operation, or by permitting the worker to attend two machines if the delay is due to the time required for the machine to process the part. *Avoidable Delay* is due to causes that may be eliminated. The therblig *Plan* may be eliminated or reduced by training the worker in the sequence of operations and by posting the sequence in front of him. The therblig *Hold* may be eliminated by providing a fixture for holding.

Principles of Motion. The principles of motion are used as a guide in the improvement of any task. They were first published by Frank B. and Lillian M. Gilbreth in 1923 and have been only slightly changed since that time. One group of motion principles pertains to the motions of the right and left hands. One principle is that work is most effective if both hands begin their therbligs simultaneously and also complete them at the same instant. Less effort is required of the worker if the motions of the arms are in opposite and symmetrical directions and the motions are made simultaneously. If the arms are moved in the same direction, the worker must exert some effort to maintain the balance of the body, and he becomes tired sooner. Both hands should be used productively except during rest periods, although the idleness of one hand may be necessary at times because of the nature of the work. If both hands are idle because the worker must wait for the machine to process a piece or because he does not have material, an effort should be made to provide optional work to utilize the time, or to relax to overcome fatigue. Hesitation at any point should be studied to determine the cause, and an attempt should be made to eliminate it.

Other principles pertain to the work of the observer. He should record the time required for the therbligs during each performance of the task. The variations in the time required should be listed. The causes of significant variations should be determined and eliminated if possible by rearranging the workplace or changing the sequence of the therbligs.

Some principles pertain to fatigue. One principle states that unnecessary fatigue should be prevented. The least fatigue is caused by finger motions. The next in order are finger and wrist motions; then finger, wrist, and lower arms; then upper arm motions; and finally body motions. The work should be planned to confine the motions to the least possible classifications. For the reduction of fatigue, the hands should be relieved of any work that can be done by the feet or other parts of the body.

Several principles of motion pertain to the layout of the workplace. If possible, materials and tools should be located within the normal grasp area, which is bounded by the two arcs made by the hands and forearms as pivoted from the elbows. The maximum comfortable work area is bounded by the two arcs made by the arms extended full length. If the materials are further away, the worker will be required to get out of his chair or walk to reach a part. Materials and tools should be placed in definite locations (pre-positioned) to reduce the therbligs designated as search, find, and select. The arrangement of the materials and equipment should make possible a rhythmic set of therbligs and reduce the amount of planning required. The part required at the beginning of a cycle should be placed near the point of release of the finished piece at the end of the last cycle.

Some of the principles of motion pertain to the equipment or the machine. Incoming materials or parts which may be moved to the workplace by conveyors should be deposited as close to the point of use as possible. In some cases the machine may be designed to eject the finished part or the assembly without any effort on the part of the worker. In other cases, the worker may dispose of the part by means of "drop delivery." By this method the operator releases the finished work in the position in which it was completed without moving it to dispose of it. The part drops into a container or moves through a chute to a container or conveyor.

A workplace that has been designed for economy of motions is shown in Figure 39. The chair provides support for the back. The height of

Courtesy of Victor Adding Machine Co.

FIG. 39. Workplace Planned for Economy of Motion

The worker is making a subassembly for an adding machine.

the workplace is planned in relation to the chair. Most of the work can be done with parts that are available within comfortable reaching distance. In this illustration, the work cycle has been lengthened to permit the worker to assemble a number of parts. A possible reason for the longer work cycle is the larger number of parts required to make an adding machine.

The Methods Improvement Program. In the organization of the program for methods improvement, the first step is the selection of a task to be studied. The person in charge of the program should look for tasks that interfere with the orderly flow of work and unduly increase costs. In some cases, operations may be slowed because of the time spent in moving materials or in finding and positioning the right tools. The selection of the task for improvement will determine the possibilities of savings in the immediate future and in later months.

Next, a flow process chart is prepared for the entire operation. This chart, which was discussed in relation to plant layout, shows the flow of materials through all of the steps required for processing. All of the operations, including move, store, process, and inspect, are listed and described. The distances moved and the time required may be indicated. The data entered in the chart are summarized to indicate the total number of processes, storages, moves, inspections, and delays. The purpose of the process chart is to determine that the work is properly organized and that each step is necessary. The flow of work may be changed to eliminate unnecessary operations, shorten moves, reduce delays due to storage, provide for more economical methods of handling materials, or combine two or more operations into one. A revised process chart is then made of the improved method.

A study is next made of the methods used at each workplace. The arrangement of tools, the motions used, and the flow of materials are studied to see that they conform to the principles of motion. A motion study may be made to show the present method of doing the work, and the motions are studied in an effort to develop a better method. A way may be found that eliminates or reduces the number of such therbligs as search, select, unavoidable delay, hold, examine, or plan. The sequence in which the motions are performed is questioned. Attention is given to the arrangement of tools, containers, and materials. New tools and equipment may be provided. After the changes have been made and the motions have been improved, a new chart is prepared to show the new method of performing the task.

In working out the improved method, the person making the study takes into consideration both the technical and the human problems. The technical aspect concerns the cost and the greater efficiency of new tools and equipment that may be installed. The cost of the new equipment is compared with the ultimate savings to determine the advisability of purchasing it. The present facilities should be used unless economies from new equipment can be demonstrated.

The human problems pertain to the attitude of the worker who will be affected by the change. People usually resist change because they cannot be sure how it will affect them, or they may fear that it will have an adverse effect. Since the purpose of methods improvement is to reduce costs, they may expect that one or more workers on the job will be laid off or transferred. To gain their co-operation, they should be told how the change will affect them. The study will be most successful if they are willing to offer suggestions for improvement.

Worker resistance will be encountered if the new method implies criticism of the foreman or the workers who have been using the old method without questioning it. The motion-study man should be careful not to suggest or imply that the person who originally planned the workplace and the work methods was incompetent. He should refrain from taking full credit for any improvement but should regard the new method as the result of joint participation. He should give attention to safety regulations and working conditions as well as economy of method.

Training the Worker. After the best way to perform a task has been determined, all workers at that work are taught the easiest and quickest way, and all of them are expected to use it. Frank Gilbreth contended that a person who began his training to become a bricklayer should work fast from the beginning, even though his work was not up to standard in quality. He said that, if necessary, a skilled bricklayer should follow the beginner, tear down the bricks, and re-lay them. He held that the making of simultaneous motions was the most important feature of the work and that a worker who began by working slowly could not easily learn to work fast at a later time. If he began by working rapidly, Gilbreth said, he could later perfect his motions and attain quality and accuracy. Observers in other fields have not always agreed with this point of view; and some contend that correct motions and accuracy of work, as in typewriting, should be sought from the beginning, even at the sacrifice of speed.

An instruction sheet is prepared for use in training the worker. It indicates the method of performing the task as developed by the motion study. It gives a description of the work to be done, including the specifications for the part and the tolerances or variances that are permitted. It describes the material to be used in the processing and identifies them by number, size, or other exact means. The machine and the machine tools to be used are indicated; and a drawing of the machine after it has been set up may be included, together with any special instructions for operating the machine. Finally, the motions to be performed by the left and right hands and, in some cases, by the feet are listed; and the names of the therbligs for each motion are given.

Economies of Motion Study. The savings effected by motion study have been demonstrated many times and are no longer the subject of controversy. They arise from improvements of the workplace and conditions of work, the elimination of useless motions, and the development of more effective motions. Motion study also requires that management pay greater attention to the selection of workers in order that they may be willing and able to learn new methods. Since motion studies cost money, management should regularize employment as much as possible to reduce the cost of training new employees.

Motion studies effect the greatest economies if a large number of workers are engaged in the same type of work. A reduction of 25 per cent in the time required, for example, means greater dollar savings when more workers are employed in the same operation. If the task is not changed from one year to another with changes in design of the product or changes in equipment, the economies are increased because the savings are continuous. The amount of training, skill, or experience required of the worker is also a factor because jobs requiring such traits are highly paid. Better balance in the output of different work stations may be achieved by increasing output at bottleneck operations.

The worker gains from motion study in that he is usually given an opportunity to increase his earnings. Motion-study economies may be reflected in increased profits, lower prices to consumers, or higher wages to workers. Just how the economies are distributed depends upon the supply of goods in the market, the competitive position of the company in the industry, the strength of labor organizations, and other factors. The long-run effect is also different from the short-run effect. Taylor, Gilbreth, Gantt, and other pioneers in management agreed that, to secure the co-operation of workers in making the economies, a part of the savings had to be passed on to them as higher wages.

The Gilbreths found that motion studies increased the interest of the worker and made him more alert and more efficient.[3] During the period when motion studies are being made, the effect is educative. The worker learns to think of all activity in terms of motions and elements of motions. When he is later assigned to a new task, he learns the work faster with comparatively little coaching.

As for monotony, the Gilbreths said that a feeling of monotony results from a lack of interest rather than from repetitive motions. Interest is created by motion study. Worker attitude is improved by the elimination of useless and ineffective motions. A feeling of satisfaction and accomplishment results from doing the work in an efficient manner. The change is usually reflected in more suggestions from workers for methods improvement, increased enrollment in training courses, a more alert staff of junior executives, and an increased interest in management. The worker also gains from the elimination of such motions as walking back and forth, stooping, twisting the body, and lifting heavy materials. These motions are the most wasteful and also the most tiring.

Objections to Motion Study. The most serious objection to motion study is that it prescribes a fixed set of motions and tends to destroy initiative, creativeness, and interest in the work. Although some motion-study men attempt to gain worker co-operation by having him make suggestions, the technique remains autocratic in nature. The industrial engineer who makes the study leaves no freedom to the worker. He prescribes the setup of the machine, the layout of the workplace, the tools to be used, the arrangement of materials and parts at the workplace, and the motions of the right and left hands. The worker has no responsibility beyond following instructions.[4] Under such limitations,

---

[3] Frank B. Gilbreth and Lillian M. Gilbreth, "The Effect of Motion Study upon the Workers," *Annals of the American Academy of Political and Social Science,* Vol. LXV (1916), pp. 272–76.

[4] See B. B. Gardner and D. G. Moore, *Human Relations in Industry* (3d ed.; Homewood, Ill.: Richard D. Irwin, Inc., 1955), pp. 393 ff.

the worker is unlikely to develop a sense of belonging. He may feel that management regards him as a machine or a factor of production rather than as an individual.

Management may defend motion study by saying that modern industry, with its machine production of standardized products in quantity, does limit the freedom of workers and all other persons in the organization. Both laborsaving machinery and work standards limit the opportunity for creativeness in order to gain greater productivity. Furthermore, a worker who is left to his own devices will usually fall into a fixed pattern of motions. Motion study attempts to see that he adopts efficient instead of inefficient motions. To overcome worker objections, it is important that the right approach be made at the time the study is made and later when workers are trained in the new methods.

Some persons contend that motion study is unsound because it disregards differences between workers. Workers differ in natural abilities, training, and education. Psychological and manual dexterity tests show wide differences in people. To require all workers to use the same set of motions may create nervous tensions similar to those caused by requiring a left-handed child to write with his right hand. This criticism may be valid in some cases; but it clearly would not apply to most phases of motion study, such as the elimination of stooping, bending, lifting, and other tiring motions.

Another phase of the motion-study technique to which objection is sometimes made is the combination of the motions made by two or more workers to form a single set of motions. If one worker has found a short cut at one phase of the operation and another worker at another phase, the motion-study man may combine the two short cuts to get a more efficient method than either worker had before. Psychologists point out that the new series of motions may be impossible to attain, and that the rate at which one muscular pattern functions in one person is not necessarily an indication of its possible speed in another. It is also pointed out that the rate of output is not always a safe basis for judging the effect upon fatigue, since the nervous system may be seriously affected by a rigidly enforced pattern of motions. The increase in production that follows the making of motion studies may be the result in part of the introduction of an incentive method of wage payment and other changes which accompany the study.

Because a fixed set of motions may cause nervous strain, it has been suggested that motion studies should be undertaken primarily to make the work less tiresome. The studies might increase the pleasure the worker derives from the work by enabling him to work effectively and to develop a sense of rhythm. The possibility of an increase in production should be regarded as a secondary objective. Moreover, motion studies should not attempt to force all workers to adopt a standardized set of motions regardless of their differences. Instead, the studies should suggest lines of improvement which the worker might accept or adapt to his own requirements.

Effect upon Employment. The economies of motion study are expected not only to reduce fatigue but also to reduce the time required for the task. Some workers may be displaced. Provision for the transfer of such workers to other jobs may become necessary, and the transfers may be facilitated by a program of retraining. The effect is much the same as the effect of technological unemployment which may result from the introduction of laborsaving machinery. Protection of the earning power of workers who are displaced by motion study is necessary if their co-operation is to be gained.

WORK SIMPLIFICATION

The motion-study technique has been modified by the use of a new approach to the worker, which is sometimes called "work simplification." This modified technique is based upon the idea that worker co-operation is necessary to the success of methods improvement and that the way to gain worker co-operation is to permit his participation. This approach not only evades the traditional objection that scientific management is autocratic but also seeks to obtain worker suggestions for methods improvement.

The work simplification program is usually directed by a time-study engineer who is selected because of his interest in the work and because of his ability to gain co-operation. He works with small groups of ten to fifteen people, and he may continue with one group after another until he has reached all of the employees in a section. In some cases, participation in the program may be limited to foremen, assistant foremen, and others in the management. A regular meeting one hour in length may be held each week on company time, and suggestions for methods improvement are requested as the program proceeds.

After an initial discussion of objectives, the group may study the use of process charts, and each member may be asked to prepare a chart of operations with which he is familiar. The operation at any one workplace is then subjected to detailed analysis through motion studies and the listing of the motions made by the worker. In most cases, the members of the group are able to suggest improvements. To be effective, the program should stimulate a continuing interest in methods improvement.

When the workers are brought into the program of work simplification, the study of methods improvement may begin with the individual task. To dramatize the idea, one or more members may be asked to perform a simple task such as inserting pegs in the holes in a block. Many different methods may be used, and the conclusion that all ways are equally effective would obviously be incorrect. The director of the study would then demonstrate the best method. Different methods of removing the pegs and returning them to a box might also be demonstrated. This simple illustration usually arouses much interest and causes workers to question all traditional methods of performing different tasks. The principles of motion are subsequently developed, and applications are made. In return for constructive suggestions, rewards are usually given under the company suggestions system.

HUMAN ENGINEERING

As explained in Chapter 10 in connection with machine design, a machine should be built with a view to ease of operation. Some of the principles of motion economy as developed by the Gilbreths also pertain to the layout and arrangement of the workplace and the design of the machine. The study of machinery and equipment and their adaptation to the needs of the worker are phases of human engineering.[5]

A simple illustration of the possibilities of human engineering is shown in Figure 40. In the illustration, the material was fastened in small bundles, loaded on a truck, pulled to the storage area, and stacked on the floor by manual labor. The movements of the worker's hands may be traced by the lines in the picture. These lines were made by means of lights affixed to the worker's hands in accordance with a technique that the Gilbreths perfected. By another method, the materials may be fastened to form a single bundle, placed on a pallet, and moved to the storage area by means of a worker-propelled lift truck. They can be unloaded in a single operation; and when they are again moved, the pallet and load can again be picked up and moved by one operation. This improved method not only reduces the number of motions but also eliminates the work of lifting and carrying.

Human engineering precedes motion study and work simplification

---

[5] Jack W. Dunlap, "Human Engineering: What It Is and What It Can Do for You," *Factory Management and Maintenance,* Vol. CXI, No. 1 (1953), pp. 96–99.

Courtesy of Signode Steel Strapping Co.

FIG. 40. Motions Required for Movement of Materials in Small Bundles

by adapting the machine and the work environment to the needs of the operator. It includes not only machine design but also the arrangement of the aisles and passageways, lighting, ventilation, the use of color, noise control, communication systems, and the length of the work cycle. Human engineering also recognizes the limitations of the worker in such respects as the keenness of visual perception, his ability to withstand the effects of fatigue, his intellectual capacity, and the quickness of body movements. The engineer attempts to control and to change the work environment to fit the needs of the operator. He studies those aspects of the work that might be overlooked by the observer who makes a simple motion study. Human engineering does not represent a new development, since the Gilbreths and Henry L. Gantt, in particular, studied the entire worker environment. It represents a different emphasis.

WORK SAMPLING

Work sampling is a method of evaluating employee work loads, the performance of workers, machine utilization, methods of materials handling, and the various plant services by means of random observations of employee activities and machine performance. The observations are made at various times throughout the day and on different days in order that they may constitute a representative sample of plant conditions.

Initiating the Program. For a program of work sampling to succeed, the authorization and the support of top management are required. Unless such an endorsement is obtained, persons at the lower levels in the organization will not properly co-operate. Union acceptance is also usually required. To gain the co-operation of the union, the industrial engineer will meet with union officers, including shop stewards, to explain the objectives and the methods. Workers may object to work sampling because they regard it as a form of spying by the management. Their objections may be overcome by explaining the program and by agreeing to omit the names of individual workers from any reports that are made of the results.

Information Gained by Work Sampling. The nature of the observations made in work sampling will vary with the observer and the nature of the work. In most cases, however, the observer attempts to determine the time spent by the worker in various general types of activity and the lost time of a machine. The observations may provide data for evaluating performance as follows:

The observations would show the time spent in direct productive work. During this time, the worker was at the machine or the machine was performing the work on the material or parts.

The observations would also show the direct delay, which is defined as the time spent by the worker at the workplace but not in the performance of the task. The reason for delay would be indicated in each instance. Causes for delay would include waiting for tools, waiting for materials, poor scheduling, waiting for transportation, and talking with the foreman or other persons.

Time spent in transit would also be separately recorded. The worker might leave the workplace to go to the tool crib, the materials storeroom, or the office of the foreman.

Another category is preparation time of the machine, or the set-up time. This time could be included in operation time if the periods are short. In work sampling, the results are more meaningful if the set-up time is separately recorded.

Personal needs would include the time of the worker away from the workplace for a variety of reasons, such as washing up before quitting time, going to the rest room, or getting a drink.

A separate category called *Not Observed* would indicate the time during which some worker, usually one of a group, was not seen and not observed. This classification provides a check on the alertness of the observer himself in obtaining the desired information. If the time classified as *Not Observed* exceeds a reasonable figure, the reasons for failure to observe should be investigated.

Uses of Work Sampling. Before any conclusions are drawn from the observations, the observer should review the results to determine whether sufficient observations have been taken and the results are representative of the usual activities of workers and of machine utilization. Attention may also be directed to unusual conditions that may have prevailed during the time when the observations were made, such as emergency work, power failure, delayed deliveries of materials, or overtime work. The results are summarized and reviewed with foremen and interested executives. In some cases, worker performance may have declined when the observations were started because of their suspicions or fear. Later, the program should result in increased productivity and lower unit costs.[6]

QUESTIONS

1. Explain uses for motion and time study other than for determining the pay for a task.

2. A manufacturer says: "A reduction in the time for a task ultimately results in a saving of brick and mortar." Explain the meaning of this statement.

3. Should a worker who is learning a task begin by working as fast as possible and improve quality as he learns, or should he first strive to do quality work and attempt to build up speed later?

4. Why should the worker be interested in improving the motions he performs in doing a task? Why might he object to an improvement in the motions?

5. Should workers be required to use a fixed set of motions regardless of their individual differences and preferences?

6. Do workers welcome interruptions because they stretch out the work, or do they prefer that the work proceed in an orderly and efficient manner?

7. Who benefits from a reduction in the time required to perform a task and the increased production that results?

8. How is the saving from motion study affected by the existence of "bottlenecks" in the production line?

9. Do workers always work in the most efficient manner they know? How does this fact affect their co-operation with motion study?

10. Suggest efficient methods of performing the following tasks: (*a*) loading brick in a truck; (*b*) replacing light bulbs in ceiling lights; and (*c*) removing dishes of food from a refrigerator.

---

[6] C. N. Wiggins, "Work Sampling in Maintenance," *Factory Management and Maintenance*, Vol. CXVII, No. 12 (1959), pp. 72–76.

11. Show the relation of human engineering to motion study.

12. Why is work sampling especially suited to the establishment of standards for maintenance work?

CASES

38. METHOD OF COLLECTING TRASH ON THE STREET

The manager of trash collection of a municipality has been investigating the following methods of collecting trash from the street:

1. Sweepers using wide brooms would collect the trash in small piles, with two or three piles in each city block. Trucks would follow sweepers, and workmen would scoop up the trash and throw it into the truck.

2. Each truck would be accompanied by three workmen. Two workmen would walk at a brisk pace along the street and push wide brooms in front of them. Each workman would walk ten steps and then manipulate the broom to make a small pile of trash. The other man would perform the same operation for the next ten steps while the first man would carry his broom across the space swept by the other. The truck would follow a short distance behind the men at a slow speed. A third man would stand on the running board of the truck with a wide but lightweight scoop; and he would pick up the trash at each pile and throw it over his shoulder into the truck. Since the piles would always be the same distance apart, he would be able to develop a rhythmic motion. Workers would alternate positions to reduce fatigue.

3. Workmen would push hand trucks along the street. Each workman would have a broom and a shovel which he would use to sweep trash and throw it into the truck. Hand truck would be emptied into trash cans on the sidewalk. Trash cans would be emptied into a truck once a week.

4. A truck equipped with a vacuum device would be used to pick up trash by suction. The only labor would be that of the truck driver.

Questions:

1. How can the manager determine which is the best method?
2. Under what circumstances might each method be preferable?
3. What information not given in the case might be required for a decision?

39. THE TIME-STUDY MAN

Patrick O'Bern majored in industrial engineering at the technical school and regarded himself as especially proficient in time study. He made a number of such studies in nearby factories and offices before he completed his college course. In all of these studies, production standards had been established by the industrial engineering department of the plant, and Patrick's estimates of proper standard time, after adjustments and allowances, were always close to the estimates used by the company.

When Patrick graduated, he accepted a position with a shoe company in the Middle West. This company had initiated a program of wage payment by piece rates, and time studies had been made for many tasks. Where studies could not be made immediately by the industrial engineering department, each foreman made estimates of the proper time for the tasks in his department. After the industrial engineer compared the estimated task time with past production records, the estimates were used to set temporary piece rates. The foreman explained to each worker the manner in which his piece rate had been set and informed him that new rates would be set as soon as the industrial engineer made accurate time studies.

When Patrick reported for work, he called at the office of the employment manager who had interviewed him at the college. The secretary told Patrick that the employment manager was in conference and would be busy the rest of the day. He had left word that Patrick should call back at starting time the next morning. Patrick spent the rest of the day unpacking his clothes and arranging his room. The next morning when he reported, the employment manager was on the telephone. After Patrick waited for 30 minutes, he was shown into the office. The employment manager escorted him to the industrial engineering department and introduced him to the engineer, who gave him copies of the manual on company policy, the union contract, the company organization chart, and such job descriptions as were available. Patrick was given the rest of the day and all of the next day to study the materials.

During the next month, Patrick accompanied the industrial engineer to one of the manufacturing departments and observed how a time study was made. He made separate observations of his own and separate allowances for delays, also ratings for skill and effort. Usually the final time as set by Patrick agreed fairly closely with the estimate of the industrial engineer. The first task that was studied independently by Patrick was one of the finishing operations. When Patrick reported to the department, he learned that the foreman and all of the workers in the department were of Czech nationality and that they had worked in shoe factories in Europe before coming to the United States. The foreman showed Patrick to the machine and informed the workers that Patrick would make a study of the operation. The workers talked excitedly in a foreign language, and one remarked in English that Patrick was going to set a new rate for the task that would pull the company out of the red. Patrick made no reply but continued his observation of the work, which consisted of dyeing, waxing, and polishing the soles of the shoes.

After a few minutes, he told one of the workers he was ready to make the study. He completed the timing for the study, but the worker continued to polish the sole of the shoe at the machine. The workers then exchanged glances and made several remarks in a foreign language. The comments must have been humorous as they caused considerable laughter. Patrick took his slide rule from his pocket and made some computations to determine ratings and allowances. The workers made further remarks in their native tongue, and Patrick assumed that they were talking about the slide rule. Patrick informed the worker that the task was completed after the fourth round of brushes against the shoe and that the correct time would be computed on that basis.

When Patrick arrived back at his desk, the industrial engineer was talking to the foreman of the finishing department on the telephone. However, Patrick quietly made his computations and figured the final time. He placed his computation on the desk of the engineer who looked at the figures and compared them with the foreman's estimate. He then informed Patrick that his estimated time was about 60 per cent of that of the foreman. The foreman had informed him by telephone that Patrick had objected to the complete finishing operation, which was necessary to maintain the quality of the product. For this reason, the engineer said that the original time estimate of the foreman would be used.

Questions:

1. What mistakes, if any, were made in this case?
2. How could the difficulties have been avoided?

19 Time-Study
Techniques
and Procedures

THE establishment of a standard time for a task by means of observations made with the use of a stop watch is one of the most controversial techniques of management. To many persons, time study is the most important feature of the management system as developed by Frederick W. Taylor; and Taylor himself regarded it as fundamental to scientific management. His incentive system of wage payment required that a standard time be determined; and time study led him to develop production planning, standardization of materials and equipment, and other mangement methods.

The advocates of time study admit that, although the technique is widely used, its acceptance has been "grudging and tenuous" and has been "accompanied by much hostility."[1] Organized labor opposed it from the beginning, and in 1913 Congress passed a law prohibiting the use of the stop watch in government establishments. This provision was inserted in all federal appropriation acts for many years thereafter.

Time study was first used for setting standards and measuring work performance for workers who were engaged directly in production. Later the studies were extended to various types of staff or service activities. The technique has been used to establish standards for receiving and handling materials, shipping the finished product, servicing tools and dies, inspection work, housekeeping, and maintenance. In

---

[1] Ralph Presgrave, *The Dynamics of Time Study* (2d ed.; New York: McGraw-Hill Book Co., Inc., 1945), p. 1.

related activities, it is used for clerical and other office work and in plant protection.[2]

THE TIME-STUDY PROGRAM

Although Taylor developed the time-study technique, he was not the first to use the stop watch in timing workers engaged in manufacturing work. M. Perronet, a Frenchman, in 1760 listed the operations necessary to make pins and timed each task for the purpose of ascertaining the cost.[3] However, the studies seem to have been over-all observations rather than observations of element times. The technique was not further developed, and Perronet's experiment seems to have been an isolated incident. Charles Babbage made similar studies in England in 1830.[4] There is no evidence of the continuous use of the stop watch for studying tasks until 1881, when Taylor used it at the Midvale Steel Company. The first book on the subject appeared in 1920 and was a reprint of a series of articles.[5]

Taylor got the idea of time study from a teacher of mathematics at Phillips Exeter Academy while he was a student. The teacher had established an average time for the solution of each problem. From this experience, Taylor thought an average or standard time for doing any task could be established.

Uses of Time Study. Time studies may be used to set up a standard, regardless of how the worker is paid. Taylor's idea as to such a standard is expressed in the following statement: "The average individual accomplishes the most when he either gives himself, or someone else assigns him, a definite task, namely, a given amount of work which he must do within a given time; and the more elementary the mind and character of the individual the more necessary does it become that each task shall extend over a short period only."[6]

Time study is often thought of as a phase in the fixing of piece rates or the establishing of some other basis of incentive wages. Although wage determination is one use of time-study data, it is not a part of the work of the time-study man. Money values introduce an entirely new

---

[2] "The Truth about Wage Incentives," *Factory Management and Maintenance,* Vol. CXVII, No. 4 (1959), pp. 74–84.

[3] V. S. Karabasz, "The Analytical Study of Production Jobs," *Annals of the American Academy of Political and Social Science,* Vol. CXIX (1925), pp. 80–84.

[4] Robert Lee Morrow, *Time Study and Motion Economy* (New York: Ronald Press, 1946), p. 73.

[5] Dwight V. Merrick, *Time Studies as a Basis for Rate Setting* (New York: Engineering Magazine Co., 1920).

[6] F. W. Taylor, *Shop Management* (New York: Harper & Bros., 1903), p. 69.

problem with which time study in itself is not concerned. The standard money rate for any work depends upon such additional factors as bargaining with the union, the supply of labor, wage levels in the community, and the skill required of the worker who performs the task.

The standards set by time study are used for many purposes in addition to providing data for setting wage rates. In planning for the flow of work, the planning department uses the standards to estimate the time that will be required for work at each workplace. Work for each machine can be scheduled, and completion dates for production orders can be estimated. Deliveries of finished goods to customers can be planned with the assurance that the schedules can be met.

Time standards supply information on machine capacity for purposes of machine replacement. As explained in Chapter 10, the computation of costs per unit of product by the use of the old machine in comparison with the estimated unit costs with the new machine is based upon data of the number of units that can be produced within a certain time. Production standards are useful in planning plant layout because one objective in layout is a proper balance between workplaces. Balance means that machines and workplaces produce approximately the same number of units per hour or per week. When converted into monetary costs, production standards are useful in making bids on sales contracts.

Other uses of production standards relate to the control of operations within a department. The efficiency of a worker is judged by his ability to meet the standard, and foremen are sometimes judged by the percentage of workers in a department who meet or fail to meet the standards. If workers are paid by the hour, the standard would indicate what the labor cost of the product would be if all workers produced the standard number of units per hour. If costs exceed this amount, management knows that the standards are not being met.

Production standards assist management in eliminating the differences between the requirements of various tasks. The standards should be set in such manner that a worker at one task can render a satisfactory performance as easily as any other worker at any other task. No work should be unusually easy or unusually difficult in comparison with other work.

The department that is responsible for the setting of standards by time study may also be responsible for related activities requiring the use of standards. In one company, for example, the standards department makes motion and time studies, revises the standards when necessary because of changes in methods of work, makes studies of new tasks and work done on new equipment, prepares the payroll, makes cost investigations for purposes of preparing bids on contracts, and prepares cost estimates for the use of management in establishing sales prices on new products.

Relation of Motion Study to Time Study. Taylor never made time studies without first making improvements in the layout of the workplace, prescribing machine tools, and making other such changes as were required.[7] Frank and Lillian Gilbreth, who perfected the techniques of motion study, believed that time studies were misleading unless they were preceded by a thorough study of both the conditions of work and the motion elements. Their method was to study and improve not only the workplace, equipment, working conditions, and arrangement of materials, but also the motions made by the worker.[8] If the worker is to be guaranteed against a reduction in the standard time or in the piece rate, such studies are necessary. Otherwise, the worker may himself improve the motions and increase output to such an extent that the standard would be useless. Because motion study and methods improvement precede the taking of time studies, the time-study man should be skilled in manufacturing methods, machine tools, materials, and conditions of work as well as time-study techniques.

Time study may be made without motion study when an entire plant is changed to standards set by time study. Time studies might also be made for an entire plant when a new factory is constructed. In any of these cases the number of studies to be made immediately would preclude complete motion studies for every task. Such study of tasks as might be made would be less thorough and less elaborate than is implied by a motion study.

Time studies are sometimes made without motion studies when continuous changes in layout, equipment, product, or materials alter the requirements of a task. If a part of a department is already working under standards set by time study, the methods department is under pressure to complete studies of new tasks as rapidly as possible. Since the motion-study man cannot keep pace with the time-study man, and since some tasks do not justify the cost of a complete motion study, standards may be set for some tasks without motion study.

Time-study men realize the hazard of setting standards without motion studies, but they contend that the errors are negligible. The reasons are that abbreviated motion studies are made by time-study men;

[7] Taylor, "The Present State of the Art of Industrial Management," *Transactions of American Society of Industrial Engineers*, Vol. XXXIV (1912), pp. 1199–1200.

[8] Frank B. and Lillian M. Gilbreth, "Time Study and Motion Study," paper read before New York Section of Taylor Society, December 15, 1920.

that operators follow fairly well-defined patterns of motions; and that workers know that a loose standard will eventually be changed, regardless of earnings or subsequent performance.[9]

Because of the cost, time-study standards may not be set for all tasks in a department. In most productive departments the maximum number of tasks which justify such standards is estimated to be 95 per cent. Standards are sometimes set, with or without time study, for a wide variety of tasks, such as emptying wastebaskets, trucking supplies from storage, cleaning and replacing cuspidors, cleaning the corners in the stair wells, and replenishing supplies in the washroom.

The Time-Study Man.   The person who makes time studies is usually attached to the industrial engineering department. As preparation for his work, he should have an understanding of such technical subjects as manufacturing methods, machine feeds and speeds, the principles of motion, methods of rating worker performance in terms of average or above or below average, mathematics as it pertains to shopwork, the writing of reports, the uses of time standards, and methods of using the results of earlier studies in setting new standards. In the area of human relations, he needs to understand worker attitudes, methods of gaining greater co-operation, methods of oral and written communication, personnel policies, and labor union attitudes. To qualify himself for the work of making time studies, he should have some experience in the type of work for which he is expected to set standards. Such experience would prevent him from making errors in the technical aspects of the study. It would also give him an understanding of general shop methods and worker attitudes. Time-study men are usually recruited from shop operating jobs, but many of them gained their previous experience in clerical work, supervisory positions, and various departments performing staff functions.[10]

Personal Qualifications.   The time-study man also requires certain personal aptitudes. Because he performs a staff function, he must have the co-operation of foremen and other line executives in making time studies and in making the production standards effective. In many cases, the foreman prefers a loose standard that the worker can easily meet because loose standards do not interfere with the smooth operation of his department. The fact that the loose standard results in higher labor cost and also increases the machine time may not disturb the foreman. As long as the loose standard is retained, the higher labor cost and

---

[9] Presgrave, *op. cit.*, pp. 133, 140–43.

[10] "Important Facts about Time Study Men," *Factory Management and Maintenance,* Vol. CXI, No. 2 (1953), pp. 126–27.

manufacturing expenses may not be known to the management. The time-study man should attempt to gain the co-operation of foremen by showing them that proper standards will assist the company in maintaining its competitive position and will benefit all persons associated with the company.

The time-study man also needs to gain the confidence and co-operation of the worker. He should attempt to show the worker that standards established by time study are fair because they make the necessary allowances for fatigue, delays, interruptions, and other unusual factors. He should also show how improvements will increase wages and provide more jobs within the company by strengthening its competitive position. The person who arouses suspicion and antagonism cannot make proper studies. Good human relations constitute an important element of time study.

MAKING THE TIME STUDY

The making of the study requires attention to the department in which the study will be made, the selection of the task and the worker to be observed, the equipment to be used, and the recording of the observations made. Each of these phases of the study is important.

Selection of the Department and the Task. If no time studies have previously been made in the plant, the first step is the selection of the department and the task for beginning the studies. Much depends upon the choice of the task for the first study, since the time-study man is sometimes regarded with suspicion by the workers. This suspicion may be shared by the foreman, who is close to his men and is under pressure to get the work out. He may regard the entrance of the time-study man as a reflection upon his ability to manage his own department. The situation is one which calls for tact, sympathy, and understanding on the part of the time-study man.

Some of the considerations in selecting the task or the department for making motion studies were considered in the preceding chapter. These criteria are the number of persons at the task, their rate of pay, the possibility of changes during the next year, and the relation to other work in the production line. Another factor is the type of workers and their attitude toward the studies. If the foreman has a close personal relationship to his men, and if he is convinced of the value and the desirability of the studies, the department might be a good place to begin. Another factor is the rapidity with which tasks can be studied. To convince workers and management of the economy and fairness of the studies, it may be desirable to begin to show results as soon as possible.

Another factor in the choice of a department to begin the studies is the possibility of raising output and increasing wages. The results of the first studies are certain to be subjected to the greatest scrutiny. The possibilities of savings to the company are also a factor. The time study must be justified in dollars and cents and not merely by percentage increases in output per worker per hour. Although sensational or stunt performances should be avoided, the first task to be studied should be one that can be improved through motion study; and the worker should benefit by an increase.

Selection of the Worker. The person chosen for the study may be the best worker or an average worker. The type of worker observed is supposed to make no difference in the standard which is finally set, because allowance is made for skill. Gilbreth never made a time study of any but the very best workers. In fact, his studies were based upon a synthesis of the motions of the best workers. He said that judgment supplants measurements when a mediocre worker is used and that no allowances can be made for inefficiency. The willingness of the worker to cooperate is also important, because no allowance can be made for indifference or false motions. The achieving of worker co-operation requires tact, sincerity, and fairness on the part of the time-study man as well as the co-operation of supervisors. The understanding of union officials is also helpful.

In practice, time studies are usually made of the average worker instead of the very best. The justification for this procedure is that workers do not understand the method of making allowance for skill, and they are likely to think that the standard is to be set so high that it will be impossible for them to make it. The study is usually made of a worker who is engaged at the task, regardless of his skill. To ask an especially trained person to do the work while a study is being made would appear to be unfair. It is generally agreed, however, that time studies should not be made of a worker who is new at the work, a nervous person, or a person who is working with especially valuable material which he might spoil through poor workmanship caused by nervous strain or excitement.

The selection of the worker depends in part upon the workers themselves. When the studies are begun, a volunteer for the first study may be asked for. Each worker may hesitate for fear of losing the respect and the good will of his associates, and the personal friendship and influence of the foreman becomes important. If the standard is judged to be fair, and if the worker who is transferred to an incentive wage based upon the time study is able to increase his earnings, the others are more likely to be willing to have studies made. In no case should an attempt be made to take studies without the knowledge and co-operation of the worker.

Time-Study Equipment. The usual equipment for making time studies consist of a stop watch, a time-study sheet, and a board for holding the watch and the sheet.

Stop watches are made to record either fractions of a minute or fractions of an hour. The watch that records fractions of a minute has a large hand which makes one revolution in a minute and a smaller hand, similar to the second hand on an ordinary watch, which moves one space for each revolution of the large hand. The dial for the large hand is marked off into ten spaces, each of which is 1/10 of a minute. Smaller markings indicate a time length of 1/100 of a minute. The watch that records fractions of an hour has a large hand which makes a complete revolution in 1/100 of an hour, or 0.6 of a minute. It permits measurement in units of 1/10,000 (0.0001) of an hour. The watch that records hundredths of a minute is the type most commonly used. Such a watch is illustrated in Figure 41.

The sheet for recording the observation contains spaces for listing the motion elements of the task and for recording as many observations as may be considered necessary. Spaces are also provided for all oth-

Courtesy of Meylan Stopwatch Co.

FIG. 41. Decimal Stop Watch

er information pertaining to the task and the observations made, such as the speed of the machine, the depth of the cut in certain types of machine operations, the tool used, the material, the day and hour when the observations were made, the name of the observer, the employee, and the department. After the studies have been completed, entries are made on the sheet for the average time, the allowances made, and the standard time. The observation sheet is illustrated in Figure 42.

The watch may be fastened to the edge of a board on which the record of readings is kept, or it may be held in the left hand by means of a leather strap that is wrapped around the second finger. The advantage of holding the watch in the hand is that the board may be put

TIME STUDY RECORD

FILE NO. 111-395
WM NO. 265-AH-44-A
OPERATION NO. 30
DIVISION
1

DESCRIPTION OF ELEMENTS INCLUDING NAME AND NUMBER OF TOOLS, FIXTURES AND GAGES	SPD.	FD.	LEN.	CUT	TIME IN DECIMAL MINUTES AND RATINGS										AVER. TIME	RTNG. FCTR.	ALLOW. AT 100%
					1	2	3	4	5	6	7	8	9	10			
1. Pick up piece from bench					.05	.06	.05	.05	.04	.07	.05	.06	.04	.05	.05	100	.05
2. Break edges on ends, round one (1) corner to 1/8" radius	#80 stone wheel				.60	.58	.62	.60	.59	.60	.60	.64	.60	.61	.60	100	.60
3. Break edges on sides	#80 stone wheel				.32	.40	.32	.35	.38	.34	.40	.36	.37	.37	.36	90	.32
4. Burr edges on sides and ends	#80 Rag. Theo				.25	.24	.27	.24	.30	.31	.28	.27	.32	.30	.28	90	.25
5. Set side					.03	.03	.02	.02	.02	.01	.02	.03	.02	.02	.02	100	.02
SUB-TOTAL																	1.24

NET TIME PER 1 PCS. 1.24
18 % ALLOWANCE .22
TOTAL STD. TIME/ 1 pc. 1.46
SET-UP TIME/ 14.00

DEPARTMENT 111	SPEEDS, FEEDS, CUTS, TOOLS, FIXTURES, GAGES, MACHINE AND METHOD APPROVED BY:	GEN. FOREMAN	FOREMAN	SET-UP MAN Rooney	QUAL. CONTRL	SECTION 111	FILE NO. 395	SHEET NO. 1 of 1
WORK STATION	STARTING TIME 1:40	STOPPING TIME 1:56	ELAPSED TIME	PCS. COMPLETED 1	MACHS. PER OPER.			OPERATION NUMBER 30
DATE 8-15-47	EMPLOYEES' NAME Gloeckner	CLOCK NO.	CLASS	JOB EXPERIENCE	NO. OF HELPERS			PART NUMBER 265-AH-44-A
STUDY BY E. Fowler	MATERIAL SAE X 1020 CRS	TYPE AND GRADE	DIMENSIONS 7/16 x 1" x 1-7/16"	WEIGHT	SOURCE			
APPROVED BY E. Hall	MACHINE MAKE AND TYPE Polish Jack	MACHINE NO.	SIZE	LOT SIZE 240				
OPER. SPEC. NO.	OPERATION NAME Burr ends and sides and radius			ORDER NO. 42607				
PART SPEC. NO. 10.00 / 1.00 E	PART NAME Block							

FIG. 42. Observation Sheet for Time Study

in the pocket or laid down, while the watch is protected in the hand. Some time-study men use two or more stop watches, which are fastened to the board. It is usually considered best to keep the equipment as simple as possible to lessen the suspicion and the mystery which are likely to surround the studies. In any case the nature of the equipment is secondary, for the important feature is the accuracy of the observations made. A board used to make observations is illustrated in Figure 43.

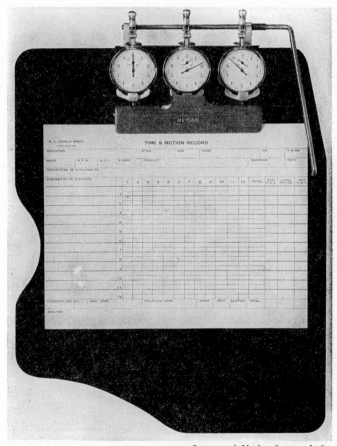

Courtesy of Meylan Stopwatch Co.

FIG. 43. Board Used for Making Observation of Times

Recording the Element Times. In making the observations, the time-study man usually stands to the side of the worker, because all suggestion of secrecy or underhandedness is thereby removed. For similar reasons a position in front of the worker may be preferred to a position behind him. If the worker stands at the work, the observer should also stand. Throughout the study an effort should be made to remove the "social distance" which is likely to exist between worker and observer.

The observations are made of the time required for each element and not of the over-all time for a task. To make a study, it is necessary to divide the task into its elements in a manner described in the preceding chapter. The smallest length of an element that can be successfully observed is usually considered to be 1/10 of a minute. If element times are very short, the errors of the observer in reading the watch and making the recordings are likely to be greater than the variations in the time required by the worker.

The observations may be made by the "snapback method." By this method, the hand of the stop watch is returned to zero at the end of each element. When the worker completes an element, the observer reads the watch, presses the stem to return the hand to zero, starts the watch for timing the next element, and records the time for the element completed. The observation sheet shown in Figure 42 was prepared on the basis of timing by the snapback method. Some time-study men regard this method as highly unsatisfactory because of the possibility of error in making the readings and recording the times while also manipulating the watch. The Gilbreths rejected the entire procedure because of the possibility of error. They contended that the errors of the observer in reading the watch might easily equal the elapsed time for the performance of the element under observation. Moreover, they said that the errors could not be corrected by averaging the results of several studies because this procedure might have the effect of cumulating the error.

The advantage of the snapback method is that the observer can use his recordings as a guide as he continues with the timings. For example, if one reading of an element is much longer or much shorter than the other readings, the observer can see this at once. He can then investigate the cause, which might be an error on his part, stalling on the part of the worker, a sudden burst of speed, a failure of the worker to conform to a lax standard which he had set for himself, or any one of several other causes. Any isolated instances of improved methods of work should be studied to determine whether they can be duplicated and made habitual. Unless the observer knows the situation as he proceeds, he is said to be "flying blind."[11]

Another method frequently used is the "continuous-run method." When this method is used, the stop watch is permitted to run continuously; and the observer records the reading of the watch at the end of

---

[11] Presgrave, *op. cit.*, p. 42.

each element. When one cycle of operations is completed, the watch is allowed to continue to run as the worker proceeds with the next cycle. This process is kept up until an entire series of observations has been made. The elapsed time for each motion element is computed by subtracting the reading of the watch at the end of an element from the reading at the beginning.

The advantage of the continuous-run method of timing is that the observer is required to account for all time, including delays and interruptions. He is also relieved of the necessity for starting and stopping the watch at any time during the observation. This method is the one most commonly used.

In accumulative timing, two watches are used. The two watches are mounted on a board in such a manner that, by pressing a lever, the observer can stop one and start the other. He may then read the watch while the hands are stopped, and the reading may therefore be more accurate. Subtractions are unnecessary. The principal objection to this method is the complexity of the equipment, which tends to alienate the worker.

Other Types of Equipment. To eliminate any errors that might be made by the observer in using a stop watch, other kinds of equipment may be used. If the element times are very short, a motion picture of the operation may be taken to show an electric clock as well as the worker and the machine. The clock should indicate time to a fraction of a second, and the motion-picture camera should be stepped up to take more frames per second. The picture is run on the screen after the observations have been completed. The projector can be stopped at any point, and the timing can be accurately observed. If any element time appears to be too long, the picture can be rerun; and the cause of the delay can be determined. Pictures of the worker performing the task are useful in training employees and in considering any subsequent complaint from workers about difficulties in meeting the standard as set for the task. The use of motion pictures for motion and time studies was first perfected by the Gilbreths. The method is now rather widely used. It is frequently referred to as "micromotion study."

Another type of motion-picture camera, which is driven by a motor at a fixed rate of speed, permits the measurement of the time required for each element of motion in fractions of a second or a minute. A different kind of device for making a record of the element times is the time-recording machine. This machine consists of a small box or cabinet equipped with a paper tape and recording keys. The tape is drawn through the box at a predetermined speed. The observer records the element times on the tape by depressing the keys. The elapsed time is indicated by the scale and the markings on the tape.

Number of Observations. The number of observations to be made of a task depends upon such factors as the length of the cycle and the time required to make the observations, the number of elements in the cycle, the skill of the worker, the consistency or variations in the observations made, the number of people employed at the task, the study made of the workplace and the motions prior to the timing, and the use to be made of the standard time. If the motions of the worker and the time required at the task are partially controlled by machine time or an assembly line, the observations may be fewer in number.

Although consistency in results may be an indication that the worker is skilled and that the results are reliable, this is not necessarily the case. Presgrave warns that unusually high consistency is open to suspicion that the worker has deliberately timed each element by counting to himself, observing a wrist watch, or pacing himself against a revolving part or a recurrent noise.[12] While the observer strives for the co-operation of the worker, he cannot always be sure that he has attained it.

If the observer makes an excessive number of observations, he is wasting his own time at unnecessary work, and the elimination of unnecessary work is a principal objective of the entire study. Time-study work should be as efficiently conducted as the time-study man expects the other departments to be. If the observer makes an insufficient number of observations, his standards may be too tight or too loose because they are based on inadequate samples. As a general rule, it is better to take too many observations than too few. Two short studies taken at different times are considered better than one long study.

QUESTIONS

1. Is time study concerned only with the setting of the standard time without reference to the pay for a task?

2. Should the worker whose work is observed be average or highly skilled?

3. A worker is nervous and cannot perform the task well while observations are being made. How can a standard be set for the task?

4. Is special effort required to gain the co-operation of the foreman for the making of time studies? Explain. What can be done to gain his co-operation?

5. Why are observations made of each element rather than the entire task?

6. What is the significance of the statement that the time-study man cannot perform the task in the time which he sets for the work?

7. What is meant by social distance? Does it affect the results of time studies?

---

[12] *Ibid.*, p. 182.

8. How can the worker mislead the time-study man and get a loose standard for a task? Does the time-study man need to know the technical aspects of the work?

9. What are the qualifications of a good time-study man?

10. Compare the snap-back method of making the observations with the continuous-run method from the point of view of accuracy of the recordings and the ease of detecting variations in the element times.

11. What determines the proper number of times the task is observed?

12. In setting a standard, does the time-study man take into consideration any differences in time that might be required by different people?

CASES

40. IMPROVED METHOD DEVELOPED BY A WORKER

In a pottery factory, various products such as flower pots, jars, and bowls were molded by machines. On most such units, tiny cracks would appear where the side of the unit touched the bottom, and occasionally cracks would appear in the side, beneath the handle, or near the top of the jar. Such defects were due to imperfect mixes of the material, which proved to be stubborn or unyielding in the forming operation. Before the units were glazed and passed to the oven for heat treatment, they were inspected and the cracks were filled with a portion of the mix.

The foreman had devised a method of filling the cracks by the use of a small trowel. The worker dipped the trowel into a bucket of the mix, picked up a small amount of the material on the point of the trowel, and touched up the crack in the manner similar to the method used by a bricklayer in smoothing the mortar between the bricks. When the time-study man timed the operation, the worker used this method and a standard time was set which seemed fair to the worker and would enable him to earn more than the usual $10.00 per day for this kind of work when the hourly wage was used. A check of the operation a month later showed that the worker was earning about $12.50 per day. This rate of earnings was considered satisfactory. The worker was using the method that had been used when the operation was timed.

Six months after the standard time had been set, the time-study man learned that the worker on the operation was earning about $45.00 per day. Investigation disclosed that the worker had devised a new method of performing the task. He added a small amount of water to a portion of the mix to make it more pliable, and he then worked up a small ball of the material in his hand. Holding the ball in the palm of his hand, he presssed it gently to extrude a small amount beneath his thumb which he used to spread the material and to fill the crack. He used the trowel only in a few instances to reach into small crevices. In this way, he was able to produce about four times as much work as the standard required.

Questions:

1. Was the time-study man at fault in setting a low standard?

2. Should the standard be corrected, or should the worker be permitted to earn as much as he can with the existing standard?

41. ARBITRATION OF TIME-STUDY STANDARDS

The ABC Metal Working Company owns and operates one plant which employs about 800 workers. Shortly after World War II, the company added to its staff a time-study man, who was authorized to make time studies and to set production standards in co-operation with foremen and plant executives. In 1949, the employees were unionized, and the union immediately began to take an interest in time-study standards. The union representatives have frequently argued that time-study standards are too tight and that a worker may injure his health by working at the speed required by the standard. The disputes concerning work standards have arisen as a result of the complaints from various workers.

In 1959, the union succeeded in getting a provision into the union contract which requires the arbitration of disputes over work standards. The contract provides that when such a dispute arises, the arbitrator shall hold hearings within seven days of the referral of the dispute and that he shall render a decision within seven days after the conclusion of the hearings. The arbitrator was given no authority to revise a standard, and he could decide only that a standard was fair or unfair. If he should decide that a standard is fair, the standard is to be considered an approved standard. If he should decide that it is unfair, he is expected to state the respects in which it is unfair and the basis of his disapproval.

When the provision for the arbitration of work standards was suggested by the union, it was strongly opposed in the management conference by the time-study man, Frank Ross. Mr. Ross contended that managerial efficiency was not a proper subject for arbitration. He said that the workers and the union objected to many standards that were fair and easily attainable. Management's function, he said, was to establish the controls over productivity and to determine the standards. The management had the right to expect workers to conform. Any employee of the company must be measured by company standards. If an arbitrator approves a loose standard, Mr. Ross said, the worker will be overpaid; or if he pegs his earnings to get only the going rate, he will put less time and effort into the work than is fair and reasonable.

Another fact pointed out by Mr. Ross was that once the standard was approved by the arbitrator, it could be changed only with the greatest difficulty, if it could be changed at all. However, a change in the standard might become necessary after a period of time because many small improvements in the manufacturing methods and processes could reduce the time required for the task. If a loose standard should be approved by arbitration, a discrimination in favor of one worker or a few workers would exist for an indefinite period of time.

When the company agreed with the union that time-study standards could be submitted to arbitration, Mr. Ross resigned. J. W. Gibbs was appointed to his position. One of the first standards established by Mr. Gibbs was challenged by four workers who performed the task. The union joined them in the complaint. The arbitrator who heard the case was a professor in a local technical school. When he observed the worker performing the task by the prescribed method, the elapsed time was 15 per cent more than the standard time. However, the arbitrator thought that the pace of the worker could be increased and that the standard could be attained with reasonable effort on the part of the worker. The decision of the arbitrator was therefore in favor of the company.

After the decision had been rendered, the arbitrator went to the workplace to talk with the men. While he was talking to them, one worker called to another and said: "Al, I am going to show the man what I can do."

He asked the arbitrator to time him while he did the work. He performed the task in 75 per cent of the time that had been established by the standard, and he repeated this performance two additional times. The other workers were amused by the incident.

Questions:

1. Should the company have agreed to arbitrate the question of time-study standards?

2. Should Mr. Ross have resigned?

3. What difficulties may arise from the arbitration?

20 Setting
the Standard
Time

IN establishing the standard time for a task, the industrial engineer follows four general steps: First, he studies the motions being made by the worker. Second, he improves the motions and determines the best method by improving the layout of the workplace, eliminating delays, determining the best sequence of motions for the right and left hands, and instructing the worker in the improved methods. Third, he observes and records the time required for each element of the task. Finally, he establishes the standard time by averaging the element times, rating the worker for skill and effort, and computing allowances for delay. The first three steps have been considered in preceding chapters. The fourth step will be considered in the present chapter.

DETERMINING THE STANDARD

The time required by the worker in performing the task while the observations are being made does not constitute a standard. It represents the data for the computation of the standard. The standard would be determined by a procedure similar to the following:

1. Discard the observation times for each element which were exceptional because the times were unusually short or unusually long.
2. Take an average of the observation times for each element.
3. Add the element times to determine the total time that would be taken by the worker who was observed, provided he could work continuously without interruption.

4. Rate the worker who was observed on the basis of his skill and effort. Usually the rating requires an increase in the elapsed time to determine the standard, although the rating could require a decrease in the elapsed time.

5. Make allowance for various delays, such as personal needs, fatigue, and interruptions for various causes.

Each of these steps requires further explanation.

Exceptional Observations. Abnormally long or abnormally short times might be caused by errors of the observer in reading the watch or in ending a motion element at a precise point. Very long times might also be caused by awkward movements, intentional slowing down, interruptions and distractions, defective materials, necessary adjustment of the machine, and numerous other factors. Abnormally short times might be due to a sudden burst of speed on the part of the worker or by an unusually favorable work cycle. Workers often unconsciously speed up because they see a break in a run of work or possibly because they wish to make up for poor performance at an earlier stage. If a worker takes material from a bin, his performance will vary slightly as he works from one end of the pile to another. Some of the therbligs may be abnormally short because of the ease of finding, selecting, and grasping materials that do not rest against other parts; but these therbligs may not be discarded. The observer decides which are so long or so short as to be unrepresentative.

Computing the Time for an Element. The time for an element may be computed by the use of the median, the arithmetic average, or the mode. The median is determined by ranging the recordings from shortest to longest and selecting the middle one. The arithmetic average is computed by adding all the recordings and dividing by the number of observations made. The mode is the figure which occurs most frequently. If the mode is used, the abnormally long and short recordings need not be discarded, since they will have no effect upon the final result. Exceptional observations will usually not affect the average if the median is used, since a very long or a very short recording merely counts as one observation more or one observation less than the middle figure.

The choice of the average depends in part upon the results of the observations and the pattern of the recordings. Suppose, for example, that the time-study man has made twenty-five observations and the times for the first motion element are as shown below:

```
0.08   11111   11111   11
0.09   11111   1111
0.10   1111
```

The motion element was performed in 0.08 of a minute 12 times; in 0.09, 9 times; and in 0.10, 4 times. The mode is 0.08, which seems to be a typical performance. The arithmetic average is 0.0868, but the average is clearly inaccurate beyond the second decimal place because the smallest time recorded by the watch was 0.01 of a minute. The median is 0.09.

The second element might assume a pattern like that shown below. The average is 0.12, regardless of whether the mode, the arithmetic average, or the median is used. A symmetrical distribution of this kind is not the usual result.

```
0.10   11
0.11   11111
0.12   11111   11111   1
0.13   11111
0.14   11
```

A more common distribution is shown in the third illustration below. The reason for this type of distribution is that the variations in time are due principally to mistakes, fumbles, and interruptions which serve to lengthen the time required.

```
0.15   111
0.16   11111   11111
0.17   11111
0.18   111
0.19   11
0.20
0.21   1
0.22   1
```

In this illustration the mode is 0.16, and the median the same. The arithmetic average is 0.17, if all of the timings are included. The median or the mode is probably the best average, unless the long performances were caused by poor materials or some other factor beyond control. If the cause cannot be corrected, the arithmetic average should be used; or perhaps more observations should be made.

When an element time has been computed for each motion element, the times for the various elements are totaled to determine the total average time. However, this figure is not to be confused with the standard time for the task, which is yet to be determined.

Performance Rating. The time required by the worker who was observed in the study requires a further adjustment before a production standard can be established. If the worker was above average in skill and performed the task at an unusually high speed, the time he required to do the work must be increased to determine a standard that is fair. If the worker was only average and worked at an average pace, the elapsed time may be decreased to determine the standard. The rating for skill and effort is probably the most difficult phase of motion and time study because it depends largely upon the judgment of the time-study man. Some authorities state that performance rating is the only part of the determination of work standards that remains to be put on a scientific basis.

A common method of rating workers is a point system based upon an output of one hour. The amount of work that an average worker, thoroughly familiar with his job, could do is referred to as 60 points. A worker who could do 10 per cent more than the average would be assigned 66 points. If the worker who was observed and timed was rated 70, he is 10/60 better than the average. The total time, therefore, would be increased by 10/60 to determine a fair time for the average worker.

Many other rating systems are in use. One well-known system rates workers as superskilled, excellent, good, average, fair, and poor, with percentages of production assigned to each grade. How accurate such rating systems are in practice has not been determined. The rating of the worker for skill is called the "leveling factor."

The time required for a task is affected not only by the worker's skill but also by the effort he puts forth to perform the task. A skilled worker may move slowly, either by nature or by intent. The effort of the worker when he first begins the task and before he has completed his warming-up period or when he is tired is not the same as at other times. Two persons who walk down the street, run, or deal a deck of cards do not necessarily exert the same effort. Although Gilbreth believed that no corrections could be made for mediocre effort, such corrections are often made. The justification is that this procedure enables the time-study man to make his studies at any time, regardless of the worker at the task. Readings are converted to normal by means of a percentage adjustment.

One method of rating is to grade the effort of the worker as excessive, excellent, good, average, fair, and poor. Another method classifies effort as killing, excellent, good, average, fair, and poor.

The effort rating, sometimes referred to as the "correction factor," is usually combined with the rating for skill. A worker of average skill working with average effort is expected to produce 60 points of work in an hour. If the worker who is timed is rated 80, he is 20 points above the average. The time which an 80-point worker requires is increased by 20/60 to determine the time of the average worker.

The leveling and correction factors are here assumed to be applied to each task. However, they may be applied to each element in the task. This procedure might be desirable in case the worker is more highly skilled on some parts of the task than others. The rating factor might also be applied to each element in case elements of different workers are combined to determine a rate on a new task without time study. A third variation is the selection of a specific timing for each element which represents the rating of the worker. For example, if his skill and effort are to be rated 10 per cent above average, a timing of each element is selected as the typical performance of the worker at that level. This selection is made when the observations are recorded on the time-study sheet.

The problem in rating is to maintain consistency from day to day and from one task to another. Errors in rating will result in gross inequities in the time assigned for different tasks. Because of its importance the rating is sometimes made by three persons—the time-study man, the foreman, and an engineer. It is found that the ratings are usually in agreement if the effort is about 100 per cent of average. If the performance is much above average, the usual tendency of the time-study man is to assign too low a rating. If performance is much below average, the tendency is to assign too high a rating.[1] In each case, the error is made in the direction of average performance. Although a few persons may work at an average or normal rate, most workers will work above or below average speed. For this reason, special training may be given to time-study men, foremen, and others who rate the performance.

Motion-picture films have been widely used in checking the assigned ratings. The films show workers performing various routine tasks in machine tending and assembly work. The proper rating for the performance shown has been determined by averaging the ratings as assigned by several hundred persons. When the film is run in the projector at a prescribed rate of speed and performance is rated by the student observer, both the observer and his superior can see the nature of the error made.[2] However, the rating for skill and effort continues to be the least scientific phase of time study.

[1] S. M. Dix, "Improve Your Time Study Rating," *Factory Management and Maintenance,* Vol. CX, No. 1 (1952), pp. 124–25.

[2] Some of the well-known films of this kind have been made by the Society for the Advancement of Management.

Allowances.   The worker cannot be expected to continue at the task, day after day, at the speed which he maintained while the observations were being made. Numerous factors in the work situation will prevent such a continuous rate of production. The factors naturally vary from one task to another, and they are so numerous that separate allowances cannot be made for each one. Some factors for which allowance is frequently made are as follows:

1. Personal needs.
2. Adjusting the machine or changing tools.
3. Time to set up or adjust the machine for new work. The worker is sometimes paid for set-up time as if it were a separate task; but if set-up time is short, the time is included in the standard for the task.
4. Miscellaneous interruptions, such as accidents and conferences with the supervisor. A worker's production is affected by accidents at nearby workplaces as well as those in which he himself is involved. The allowance should include time out for the treatment of minor cuts and scratches, even though the worker in question has never had an accident. Time required for oiling the machine and for keeping records is included under this classification.
5. Multiple machine interference. If a worker supervises the operation of two or more machines, he may not be able to keep their operations completely synchronized. Both machines may be stopped at the same time, and one must remain unattended until the worker starts the other. A standard which assumed that only one machine would require attention at a time would be unrealistic. The concept of multiple machine interference was explained in Chapter 10 (page 184).
6. Faulty materials or tools. Motion study and time study assume that materials, tools, and equipment are standard; but at times variations may be expected.
7. Fatigue. Fatigue varies with the length of the workday, the type of work, conditions of work, rest periods, and other factors. The allowance is necessary, but the proper amount is uncertain. Time required for the worker to develop rhythm or to get into the swing of the task is included in the fatigue allowance.
8. Defective work. If the worker is required to rework defective products or is allowed no credit for the spoiled product, an allowance may be necessary for this factor in order that his production for the day may be satisfactory.
9. Delay. Delay may be caused by machine breakdown, lack of materials, interference with production at a preceding operation, lack of power, or failure of the foreman to assign the worker a task. These causes are usually the fault of management. Such an allowance results in the inclusion of the cost of delay in direct labor cost, and for that reason an allowance is objectionable. Another method is to list delay separately and to record the cost as indirect labor. The amount of delay should be known for use in making the budget, determining standard costs, and making cost estimates. However, a time-study allowance is frequently made for unavoidable delays.

The allowance may be stated as a percentage or as an amount of time, such as 0.05 of a minute. It usually is a percentage of the average time taken. The amount of the allowance may vary from 10 per cent on office work to 35 per cent on some types of hot and dirty work. The percentage should be determined on the basis of observations and studies of conditions in various types of work. For an illustration of the method of computing the total time, see the observation sheet for time study in Figure 42 (page 370).

The amount of the allowance for fatigue and delay is clearly related to the method of making the observations of the task and the selection of a typical performance. For example, if the time-study man knows that he can add 10 per cent to the time taken in making allowance for delays, he may make comparatively loose observations of worker performance. If the allowance is as much as 20 per cent, his observations and the selection of the kind of average to employ can be made in such a way that observed time is much less. His objective in each case is a standard that will enable the worker to produce a fair amount of work in a day.[3]

ESTIMATING THE TIME STANDARD

The standard time may be set by a method which is known as estimating, which uses the results of previous time studies. Two such methods are available: standard element times and predetermined time standards.

Standard Element Times.   After many time studies have been made, standard times may be established for elements which are common to many tasks. When new work is to be run, the standard time is set by assembling the necessary elements and their standard times. For example, in operations performed on a lathe, standard element times may be established for such element times as the following: select rough casting, pick up casting, insert in chuck (holding device), tighten chuck, bring tool to position, and various other necessary elements. On a new task, standard data may be available for all of the element times; or a study may be necessary for some one element, such as the cutting time of the machine. Standard element times are used whenever they are available in order to maintain uniformity with other jobs as well as to save the cost of making a complete study. However, the time-study man must be sure that the standard elements are the same as those of the new task.

---

[3] Rating and Allowances in Time Study," *Advanced Management,* Vol. XXIV, No. 7 (1959), p. 28.

By the use of standard element times, the cost of a new product may be estimated prior to production. The product engineer would first design the parts which are necessary to the finished product. He would then list the operations necessary to make each part, such as cut a piece of the necessary length, drill holes, ream (enlarge or shape the holes by turning), finish or mill the edges, press, crimp, and solder. Standard element times are arranged for assembly as well as for fabrication. In this manner the standard labor cost is estimated. Overhead cost is estimated on the basis of the standard time, together with data for manufacturing expenses. Material cost is estimated from market prices or bids from vendors.

Using standard element data to build up the cost of operations, parts, subassemblies, assemblies, and the completed product has been compared with using the letters of the alphabet to build up words, sentences, paragraphs, and the complete essay or book. Once the elements are known, a new product may be completed by a rearrangement of the elements.[4] The method of standard element times originated with Frederick W. Taylor.[5] It is now in quite general use.

Another use of standard element data is the determination of piece rates in advance of production. When the design of the product is changed each season, and when the seasons are relatively short, the fixing of piece rates before the work is put into production is especially desirable. For example, a manufacturer of knit goods, such as mittens, scarves, and stockings, had 250 designs of colored embroidery work, which were changed each year. To permit the piece rates to be used as soon as production was started, the time-study man conducted a series of experiments on various designs and types of work. He found that the basic motions used to make the various designs were the same and that the length of the stitch made no difference. The time required to make a design varied with the number of stitches, the placement or positioning of the stitches, differences in the weight of the fabric, and the simplicity or complexity of the design. Standard times and piece rates were set by multiplying the number of stitches in a design by the standard element times and adding or subtracting a percentage to allow for variations in fabrics and in complexity of design. Time for threading needles was computed by the use of other standard element times.

---

[4] H. K. Hathaway, "On the Technique of Manufacturing," *Annals of the American Academy of Political and Social Science,* Vol. LXXXV (1919), pp. 231, 246.

[5] Frank B. Copley, *Frederick W. Taylor* (New York: Harper & Bros., 1923), Vol. I, p. 227.

This procedure not only resulted in advance determination of piece rates but also in a reduction in the number of complaints of unfairness in the rates.[6]

Standard element times have other advantages. They result in fairer standards for different tasks. The standards are set more quickly. Time-study men can use their time to better advantage by making careful studies of elements that are common to many kinds of work. After the basic studies have been completed, only occasional studies need be made of new motion elements in other types of work.

Predetermined Time Standards. An adaptation or extension of the method of standard element times is the development of predetermined time standards computed from fundamental manual motions. Several well-known systems of this kind are available. They are called basic motion time study, elemental time standards, motion-time analysis, methods time measurement, and work factors. Each system provides tables of time standards for the basic motions, which can be used to determine the total standard time for various tasks without further use of the stop watch. The tables show the time required for each element under any conditions of work. The standard can be used in any industry or company, provided that the basic motions and the conditions of work are the same as those under which the standard was fixed. Such standards are used for machine operations, bench work, line-paced assembly work, inspection, and materials handling. A few companies use them for repairs and maintenance tasks.

Predetermined time standards are characterized by the extreme care of the methods engineer in analyzing motions and standard times. For each motion element, a different standard is set for each of the varying conditions under which the motion is made; and in using the standards, the engineer studies each task to determine the proper time. For example, the conditions under which a worker might reach for an object are as follows:

Reach to object in fixed location.
Reach to single object in location that may vary slightly from cycle to cycle.
Reach to object in a group.
Reach to very small object or where accurate grasp is required.
Reach to indefinite location to get hand in position for body balance, or next motion, or to get it out of the way.

Tables of data for basic motions performed under varying conditions

⁶ Ralph P. Kreuter, "Standard Times for Handicraft Jobs," *Factory Management and Maintenance*, Vol. CIX, No. 11 (1951), pp. 94–97.

have been compiled for move, turn (including turning motions requiring the application of pressure), grasp, position, disengage, and release. One system recognizes only three fundamental arm motions, and the type of motion depends upon the manner in which the motion ends. A motion may end in impact, such as hammer against nail or other object. Another type of motion ends in the air without impact. Examples include drop delivery, the end of an upward stroke with a hammer or other tool, and the release of a part that is thrown into a box or a chute. The third type of arm motion ends with the act of grasping or placing an object.

Although any arm motion can be classified into any of the three groups, each type appears in endless variations. The objects moved may be heavy or light in weight. They may be fragile or sturdy. The objects grasped at the end of an arm motion may be large or small. If they are piled together in a box, the operator must select the object to be grasped. In other cases, no selection may be required. Some arm movements might require that the eye follow the movement, and other movements do not require the operator to look carefully. In a series of arm motions, the eye may follow the arm for some motions and not for others. All of these variations must be taken into consideration in arriving at the standard time for a motion element. Each system of predetermined time standards provides tables and formulas which can be used in the study of any task.[7]

Most companies use predetermined time standards to supplement studies made with the stop watch. In some cases, the predetermined standards are checked by studies in which the stop watch is used. A verification of time study in the shop may be desirable to satisfy an employee or a union representative, and to develop confidence among the engineers who may not entirely trust the accuracy of predetermined standards. Frequently the stop-watch procedure may be used to set standards for machine-paced work which is not covered by the standard tables. In some cases, the stop watch may be used for a part of the operation while tables are used for the rest of the work.

The setting of the time for a task by predetermined standards requires a thorough understanding of the procedure. People should be selected for the work because of their ability to profit by training. Consultants may be employed to train time-study men, foremen, and others in the system. Some companies send key personnel to conference schools where the system is studied and practice in the techniques is given.

---

[7] G. B. Bailey, "The Theory and Practice of Predetermined Time Systems," *Advanced Management*. Vol. XXIV, No. 5 (1959), pp. 5–11.

Some companies employ consultants to handle the entire project of introducing predetermined standards. Special provision would then be made for keeping the standards revised when tasks are changed or new work is begun.

REVISING WORK STANDARDS

Work standards may be expected at times to be either too tight or too loose because they are established by one person who observes the methods used and the time taken by another. Standards may be inaccurate at the time they are computed, or they may become inaccurate as a result of improved methods or increased effort on the part of the worker who develops greater skill or puts forth more effort. The need for revision from time to time is therefore the usual experience.

The Tight Standard. If the worker is unable to make the standard, a study should be made of the task over a period of a day or more. Inability to meet the standard might be due to such causes as slow set-up of the machine, too much time taken for personal needs, delay in receiving materials, or materials lacking in uniformity. In some cases the worker might not have been properly trained; or for other reasons, he might not be following the best methods. The machine might be out of adjustment, or the worker may be stopping the machine too frequently to make adjustments. The standard might be too tight because the leveling and correction factors were too low, or allowances may be too small. Appropriate steps should be taken by the standards department to correct any difficulty, regardless of whether the trouble can be traced to the time-study man, the worker, or some member of a line or staff department.

The complaint of the worker who believes a standard to be unfair is frequently made through the office of the union steward. If neither the worker nor the steward is familiar with the methods of time study, they may be unable to understand the basis for a standard which is fair and reasonable. A solution which some companies have found successful is to give a short course for shop stewards. Such a course is designed to impart an understanding of the method rather than to develop trained time-study men. Stewards who have completed a short course of this kind may arrive at an intelligent decision on the merits of a rate that has been challenged. Many labor unions also provide courses of training in time study for their shop stewards and other union representatives.

Unions may check or review a production standard at the time it is set without waiting for a complaint to be made by a worker. In some cases, the union representative may check the calculations made by the time-study man in making the study. Occasionally a union officer will make his own study, which he uses as a check of the standard as set by the management.[8] If a standard is believed by the union to be too tight, a complaint is made when the initial study is completed.

Some companies have agreed to provisions in the union contract which provide for the arbitration of disputes concerning the accuracy of standards which the worker and the union regard as too tight. The contract provides for the appointment of an arbitrator who will hear the arguments of management and the union and who will make his own investigation of the standard. On the basis of the arguments and his own study, he will render an opinion. After a standard has been approved by the arbitrator, it is accepted by both management and the union. If the arbitrator decides that the standard is too tight, management may proceed to make a new study and to set a revised standard. Time-study men usually object to the arbitration of production standards because such a standard is a measure of efficiency. A standard that has been approved by an arbitrator cannot be revised even though experience demonstrates that it is very loose.[9]

Revising Loose Standards.   When many work standards are known to be loose, any one of several procedures may be followed.[10] The standards may be revised one at a time, the old standards may be retained and tighter standards may be established for new work or for changed work assignments, or a plant-wide program may be initiated. Any method may arouse the opposition of workers and unions who may fear an undermining of the wage structure and the layoffs of some workers. Probably the most practical procedure in such cases is a general revision. The requirements for successful revision are the development of a plan; the explanation of the plan at the proper time to management personnel, workers, and union representatives; proper guarantees to workers against layoffs and wage cuts; and provision for handling grievances arising under the program. The reason usually given for the revision of work standards is that inequities in wage payments need correction. A further argument is that a rigid wage structure and fixed production standards may put the company at a disadvantage in meeting competition. Sometimes all of the companies in an area may

[8] "The Truth About Wage Incentives," *Factory Management and Maintenance,* Vol. CXVII, No. 4 (1959), pp. 74–84.

[9] James J. Foley, "How Not to Handle Productivity Disputes," *Harvard Business Review,* Vol. XXXVII, No. 5 (1959), pp. 68–80.

[10] For discussion of the difficulties of correcting a loose standard, see William F. Whyte, "Economic Incentives and Human Relations," *Harvard Business Review,* Vol. XXX (March, 1952), pp. 73–80.

find themselves at a disadvantage in meeting price competition because of loose standards that cannot be changed.[11] Both the company and the worker may be affected by such a situation.

Criticisms of Time Study. Objections to time study relate to the method of fixing the standard time. Some of the severest criticisms have come from psychologists. The objections made to time study are not to be regarded as invalidating the technique, for time study has unquestionably proved its value to management.

One objection is that allowance is not easily made for differences in day-to-day production. Such differences are due to lack of sleep, exercise, fatigue, digestion, and possibly a "psychological periodicity." Production also varies according to the hour of the day. Furthermore, allowance is not easily made for differences in the capacities of workers. Many variables are not measured but estimated—for example, the degree of effort, degree of skill, working conditions, and fatigue. The number of observations to be made is left to the judgment of the time-study man. Another uncertainty is that the line between a normal time value and an abnormal time value is indefinite.

The criticisms of time study may be summed up in the statement that the time-study man must rely upon his judgment rather than scientific measurement in the fixing of the final time. However, this criticism can be made of many other management methods. Judgment is required in valuing inventories, determining depreciation allowances, interviewing and rating applicants for employment, and evaluating jobs. The criticisms of time study indicate only that much skill, training, and experience are required of the man who makes the studies.

QUESTIONS

1. Would the unusual element times be very long or very short? What might cause some element times to be unusually long?

2. How can the practice of disregarding the unusually long element times be justified?

3. Compare the arithmetic mean, the median, and the mode as methods of averaging the observation times for each element.

4. Can a reliable standard be established on the basis of observations made of an average worker who works at moderate speed?

5. Distinguish between the leveling factor and the correction factor.

6. Distinguish between performance rating and the making of allowances.

---

[11] See George P. Schultz, "Decision Making: A Case Study in Industrial Relations," *Harvard Business Review*, Vol. XXX, No. 3 (1952), pp. 105–13; Bruce Payne, "A Program for Cost Reduction," *Harvard Business Review*, Vol. XXXI, No. 5 (1953), pp. 71–82.

7. Under what conditions would an allowance be made for setting up the work, and when might set-up time be timed as a separate task?

8. How is the standard time for a task affected by tolerances and the closeness of inspection?

9. Explain the interest of the following persons in time-study standards: foreman, inspector, production planning and control clerk.

10. Should the allowance for delays include time lost because of accidents? Is such an allowance fair or accurate?

11. What use may be made of standard element times?

12. Distinguish between standard element times and predetermined time standards.

13. Why do time-study men object to the arbitration of standards which the worker or the union claim are too tight?

14. What should the management do about a standard which has become very loose because the worker has found an easier and quicker way to perform a task?

CASES

42. CORRECTION OF LOOSE PRODUCTION STANDARD

In the plant of the Sleepwell Mattress Company, the bottleneck operation was the job of sewing reinforcement bindings in the mattress. In the making of a mattress, the cotton batting and the wire coil unit were inserted in one end of a mattress cover, and the open end of the cover was then closed by a sewing operation. To hold the entire unit in position, reinforcement bindings were sewed at various places in the mattress. The machine at which this work was done was manually operated. The worker placed the mattress on a metal platform which constituted a part of the machine. When the mattress was in proper position, the worker moved a lever; and the machine ran a strong cord through the mattress from top to bottom, pulled it tightly to hold the parts firmly, and tied and cut the cord. To prevent the cord from cutting the mattress cover, the machine placed a leather tufting under the string on each side of the mattress. This operation was repeated for as many reinforcements as were required.

The piece rate at the reinforcement machine had been set after a study of the task had been made by the time-study man, who had observed a skilled worker making average effort to do the work. The rate was fixed at an amount that would enable a skilled worker to earn $12.00 per day at the job. The first man who was placed at the job was unable to keep up with the flow of work from preceding operations, although his piece-rate earnings averaged about $9.50 per day. He was transferred, and William Compton was given the reinforcement job. Compton proved to be very fast at the work, partly because he knew how to grasp a mattress to lift it to the machine, and also because he figured out a method of determining the proper spacing of the reinforcements. He could place a mattress in proper position by reference to the design on the material of which the cover was made. For example, some of the material was striped; and without counting the stripes, Compton was able to estimate the proper location for each reinforcement. A part of the increased production by Compton was due to his willingness to work at high speed. He needed the money because of the sickness of a child, and he thought that he could consistently make good wages if he applied himself to the work.

Because of Compton's ability to produce an unusually large number of mattresses, the reinforcement machine ceased to be a "bottleneck." Mattresses no longer piled up at that workplace. Compton's earnings averaged about $24.00 per day. The time-study man, who regularly inspected the earnings of workers on tasks for which he had set standards, retimed the work and found that the adjustment for skill and effort had been too large. He therefore recommended that the piece rate be reduced in order that Compton should earn no more than $12.00 per day. When Compton complained, the foreman showed him the following statement in the company manual:

"No rate setter is perfect. The mistakes which he makes are made on the up side as well as the down side. No employee thinks it is wrong to adjust a rate upward when a mistake on the down side has been made. There should be just as fair recognition of the necessity and the right to make a downward adjustment in the rate as an upward adjustment."

Questions:

1. Should the rate be adjusted? Give reasons for your answer.

2. Would the worker readily accept the explanations given in the maunal? Why?

3. May rates be adjusted downward as readily as they may be adjusted upward? Why?

43. DEVELOPMENT OF STANDARD ELEMENT TIMES

The Argyle Company operates a fleet of lift trucks which move and store materials stacked on pallets. To enable the company to evaluate the work of operators, to provide information for a bonus system, and to achieve more effective utilization of the trucks, the standards department compiled a set of standard element times which can be combined to establish a standard time for any task without any further use of the stop watch.

The elements required for the operation of a lift truck were analyzed and found to consist of the following: get into truck and be seated, start motor, put into gear, gain acceleration, travel, apply brake and bring to a stop, lower fork, pick up load by raising fork, gain acceleration with fork loaded, travel with fork loaded, bring truck to a stop with fork loaded, raise and tilt fork, deposit pallet. The standards department developed standards for each of these elements under varying conditions. The studies were made outside the production area in order that employee and other traffic might not interfere. Allowances for delay were made after the basic data had been developed. Since the standards were established for the maximum speeds of trucks, further adjustments were required because of safety requirements.

In making the studies, the standards engineer marked off spaces 10 feet in length along a course which totaled 150 feet. He found that when the truck was traveling without load, it gained its maximum speed after traveling 60 to 100 feet, depending upon the size of the load. After the truck got under way, the travel time was proportionate to the distance. These experiments were made with varying loads, and in each case the time required was determined by the stop watch.

To determine the proper time required to bring the truck to a stop, allowance was made for the size of the load. A quick stop for a loaded truck might cause the load to fall off the fork. The driver was instructed to apply the brakes in a safe manner when he reached the beginning of the course while traveling at the maximum speed. Experiments were made to establish safe acceleration speeds with varying loads before the timing was done.

The time required to raise the fork with varying loads was determined for varying distances in increments of six inches. These studies were made by marking the spaces on a column in the storeroom and then having different sized loads lifted to each level. Detailed tables were prepared to indicate the time required.

The standards engineer found that the performance varied with the make and size of the truck. A Clark truck, for example, did not perform in the same manner as a Ross truck. Different times were also required for large trucks and small ones. Complete studies were therefore made for each type of truck. Adjustments in the element times were made for traffic interference, safety, and delays. With these standard element times, the standards department was able to determine in advance the time that would be required for any work of moving and stacking materials and withdrawing them from the storeroom.

Questions:

1. What are the advantages of standard element times as developed in this way?

2. What objections, if any, can be made to them?

PART VI
WAGES
AND
INCENTIVES

21 The Problem of Wages

W AGE determination is one of the vital problems of management. It is of great significance to the workers and their families because their standard of living depends upon the wages paid. The status of the worker within the factory and the standing of his family in the community also depend in part upon his wages in relation to the earnings of others. Both the amount of earnings and the method of payment are important. Social significance is attached to such distinctions as being paid by the month and being on the office payroll.

To the employer the problem of wages is important not only because wages are a part of the cost of the product but also because an equitable and satisfactory settlement of the wage question is a factor in the establishment of proper personnel relations. Controversies over wages are not the sole cause of industrial strife, although they are a frequent cause. Industrial strife is costly to the employer and should be prevented if possible.

Some of the questions relating to wages are as follows:

What determines the general level of wages? Are wages fixed by economic law?
How does the employer determine the amount of wages?
What can workers and management do to increase the amount of wages paid?
What are the relative merits of payment on an hourly basis, by piece rates, or by some type of bonus system?
How are the wages in various jobs or trades determined?
What factors influence the amount paid to one worker in comparison with another?

These and other questions of similar nature will be considered in this chapter and the following chapters.

THE ECONOMICS OF WAGES

The question "what determines the level of wages" has long been discussed by economists, and several theories have been advanced. The best-known wage theories are the marginal productivity theory, the commodity theory, the functional theory, and the theory of relative bargaining strength.

The Marginal Productivity Theory. The marginal productivity theory of wages is usually explained by reference to agriculture. If a farmer with a given amount of farm equipment and livestock has been producing a stated amount of grain or other crop, he may more than double the output of the land by employing an additional worker. As he employs additional workers to cultivate the same land, the product per worker will ultimately begin to decline. The farmer may profitably employ additional workers as long as the wages paid are less than the proceeds derived from the sale of the increased product. Ultimately, the increase in the product resulting from the employment of an additional worker will just suffice to pay the wages. The last worker employed is marginal. The amount of increased production attributed to him is the marginal productivity. His wages tend to equal the value of the product attributed to him. His wages would also determine the wages of all other workers, provided all persons on the farm are doing similar work.

The marginal productivity theory is a good explanation of wages in an agricultural economy. In industry the application might imply that a manufacturer could add one or more additional workers and that he would continue to expand his plant, if wages were so low as to afford a profit from an increase in output. The manufacturer might also use more workers by operating his plant for more hours of the day. His difficulty would arise in the marketing of the additional output or perhaps in the purchasing of raw materials. However, if manufacturers and farmers generally were able to employ more workers, the product could be sold to other workers, who would have increased purchasing power and would in turn produce more materials and goods for sale to others. Thus, demand and supply would tend to be equalized.

The marginal productivity theory assumes competition between workers for jobs and between employers for workers. It assumes that, because of this competition, the worker will be paid all he is worth to the employer. A perfect operation of the theory would also require some practical method of measuring the contribution of the marginal worker. This theory has had wide acceptance among economists.

The Commodity Theory. The commodity theory of wages regards labor as an article whose price is fixed in the market in the same way that the price of any article of merchandise is fixed. When the supply of labor is increased in relation to demand, wages decline. When the supply is decreased in relation to demand, wages increase. A change in demand, in comparison with the supply of labor, will affect wages in a similar manner.

Labor differs in many respects from such a commodity as coal or lumber. Labor cannot be separated from the personality of the worker. The employer cannot purchase the skill and brawn of the worker without taking into his plant a human being with all of his emotions, prejudices, antagonisms, and other attributes. Furthermore, the value of the services of an individual depends in part upon what is paid in wages, for it has been demonstrated many times that an increase in wages may result in better service and lower unit costs. Labor is immobile in that the worker has his personal and family ties to a community. He does not readily move from one job or one factory to another merely because of the lure of slightly higher wages. On the other hand, he may change jobs on provocations which appear to the employer to be unjustifiable. Labor is perishable, and services not sold each day are forever lost. Labor also differs from a commodity in that it constitutes both supply and demand. An employed worker sells his services; and he must have food, clothing, and shelter in order that he may live. The wages paid him are spent for the products of workers in various industries. The commodity theory is therefore not an adequate explanation of the factors that determine wages.

The Functional Theory. The word "function" as used in the name of this theory means a magnitude or trait that is closely related to another magnitude and that varies with it. The functional theory holds that wages depend upon the pecuniary, industrial, and economic factors of the industry.[1] The amount paid workers in an industry depends upon two factors: (1) the efficiency of the industry and its methods of production, and (2) the ability of wage earners to discover and to appropriate income in competition with other groups. In other words, the amount an employer can afford to pay depends upon the state of the industrial arts and the general level of industrial efficiency; but the workers may not receive their share unless they know how much the

---

[1] This theory was first advanced by Walton H. Hamilton and Stacy May, *The Control of Wages* (New York: George H. Doran Co., 1923).

employer can afford to pay and unless they make their demands for higher wages and other benefits.

The efficiency of industry is affected by the development of the technique and the science of management, the extent to which machinery and laborsaving devices have been perfected and utilized, and the manner in which the plant is organized. The amount of wages the industry can pay is also affected by the costs of raw materials, the salaries paid to managers, and the prices for which the products of the industry can be sold.

The functional theory of wages is very realistic. Instead of the hopeless outlook for raising wages which is presented by the other wage theories, the functional theory makes possible a constructive program. To raise wages, labor unions should do two things: First, they should co-operate with management in increasing production, eliminating waste, and introducing the most economical methods. Second, they should demand their share of the product by pressing for higher wages. This program would result in the increase in the wages of all workers rather than in increased wages for one group at the expense of another.

Relative Bargaining Strength.   The level of wages in a trade or an industry depends in part upon the extent to which employers are organized and by express or tacit agreement refrain from bidding competitively for labor, or the extent to which they actively compete for labor. Labor itself may or may not be effectively organized to press its demands for higher wages.

If one large employer dominates the labor market in a town or industrial area, the level of wages established by him may by tacit or expressed agreement be observed by other employers in the area. Other employers may pay somewhat higher or lower wages as the occasion seems to them to require, just as one company may decide to sell its product for a little more or a little less than the prices of its largest competitor. In that case the large employer occupies a position comparable to that of a monopolist. He fixes the price and lets the supply of labor be what it will. If more labor is required, he can draw more workers into the labor market by increasing wages. The higher wage would cause more persons to move into the area. It would prevent young persons from leaving; and it would cause wives, daughters, and others who previously were unemployed to seek employment. The employer thus pays what is necessary to obtain the help he needs.

If labor is well organized and the employers are not organized, the situation is reversed. The union may demand a high wage and thus fix the price of labor. The employer is then required to adjust his business to the wage level. If he is unable or unwilling to employ all potential workers at the established wage, some workers remain idle for the time being. The union will seek to control the situation by various restrictions upon admission to the trade and upon union membership and by stretching out the work to make more jobs. Thus the union fixes the price of labor and possibly the amount of work done in a day, and it permits the volume of employment to find its own level.

If both employers and workers are well organized and each achieves a monopolistic position, the situation resolves itself into a contest of strength between the two forces. In such a contest, there is an upper limit beyond which the wage level cannot go without threatening workers with the loss of their jobs. Within certain limits the level of wages is fixed by bargaining.

WAGE CRITERIA FOR THE EMPLOYER

The individual employer does not gain much assistance from the economic theories of wages. His difficulty arises from the fact that he cannot measure the contribution to the product which is made by any one employee. For example, if fifty-five separate operations are required in the manufacture of a pair of trousers, the garment is not complete without all operations. The sales price of the finished product must be divided among a great many persons, including, in addition to the fifty-five workers in the trousers factory, the sales manager and his assistants, the employees in the accounting office, the maintenance men, the employees in the power plant, the stockholders, the creditors, and many others. The employer lacks a definite rule to guide him in the allocation of the proceeds of the sale, and he must use some practical criteria which approximate fairness and justice. Possible criteria are as follows:

What is necessary to get workers.
The cost of living.
The ability of the employer to pay.
Working conditions in the plant.
Nature of the job.
Skill and personal qualities of the worker.

What Is Necessary to Get Workers. Each employer may have established his wage rates by bargaining with workers individually or collectively over a period of several months or years. In that case, he pays what he is compelled or induced to pay. Such rates have no relation to the worker's contribution to the manufacture of the product and no relation to sales prices. If the employer finds that he is unable to retain workers after they have been employed, he might attempt to correct the situation by wage increases.

When the employer pays what he considers necessary to recruit and maintain his work force, he usually measures his wage rates against the wages paid by other firms employing workers of similar capacities in jobs comparable in their mental and physical requirements and in their agreeable and disagreeable factors. He might attempt to pay a little more than a neighboring employer if jobs in his plant are more disagreeable or more tiring.

Wages are known to vary somewhat between plants within an area and between plants in different sections of the country. Variations in wage rates between plants within an area are certain to cause dissatisfaction, unless the differentials are offset by regularity of employment or some other factor. Variations between wage rates in different sections of the country are generally interpreted by labor leaders as proof that wages in one area are too low. However, the difference might be offset by other advantages to workers in the low-wage area, such as paid vacations, retirement allowances, sick benefits, and stabilized employment. If the total compensation of workers actually differs, several explanations are possible. The training and efficiency of workers may not be comparable, the employers may be too inefficient to pay high wages, or the supply of workers may be excessive as compared with the opportunities for employment. An excessive supply of workers would ultimately be corrected by a movement of industry into the area to take advantage of the low wage rates or by a migration of workers out of the area. The removal of geographical wage differentials by legislation might be unwise because they may serve a desirable economic purpose.

Cost of Living. If wages are based upon the cost of living, a minimum standard is assumed for food, clothing, shelter, medical care, and other items. Some minimum budgets estimate the living costs on the basis of facilities that a public welfare agency might consider necessary to the maintenance of comfort and decency. In the preparation of a minimum budget, it is usually assumed that the wage earner must support a family of four. According to the census data, however, the number of employed persons is greater than the number of families in the United States. In many families, two or more persons are gainfully employed and in other families, no one is gainfully employed. Many wage earners are not members of families. They may reside in boarding houses or institutions.

Other assumptions in estimating the wage rate necessary for a minimum budget relate to the regularity of employment, the amount of overtime work, the type of living quarters, the ages of the children, the nature of the transportation facilities, and other such considerations. Such budgets can be used only as general criteria. They do not apply to individual situations.

If the employer is engaged in interstate commerce, he is required to pay the minimum wage prescribed by the federal Fair Labor Standards Act, except that apprentices and learners are subject to special requirements. The minimum wage is presumably based upon a minimum budget. In the hiring of workers, the employer must decide whether the applicant is worth the minimum wage. This provision may result in the exclusion of some persons from the ranks of the employable.

Wage differentials between city and country and between various sections of the country are usually justified by differences in the cost of living. The practice of increasing the salary of an employee when he marries or when a child is born into the family rests largely upon the justification that the cost of living has increased, although a raise may be justified on the ground that persons with dependents are more likely to be stable and reliable and less likely to be floaters. The cost of living is also recognized in the practice of giving preference to persons with dependents in layoffs, rehiring, and perhaps promotions.

Labor leaders have usually opposed the basing of wages solely upon the cost of living.[2] The objective of labor is to gain for workers a larger percentage of the output of industry. Its leaders argue that as industrial production increases, the real (not money) wages of workers should be increased to enable the larger volume of goods to find a market. The objective is a constantly rising standard of living for labor. However, unions frequently support their wage demands by data on increases in living costs. They point out that rising prices reduce real wages unless money wages are increased accordingly. A formula for wage increases in proportion to increases in the cost of living was first included in the contract between General Motors Corporation and the United Automobile Workers, C.I.O., in 1948. Similar provisions have been included in contracts between unions and managements in the railway transportation and other industries.

The proposal to allow increases in wages in proportion to changes in the cost of living raises a number of general problems. An increase in wages that is made to compensate for rising prices would probably have

---

[2] For discussion of the use of cost-of-living data in wage negotiations, see Sumner H. Slichter, *Basic Criteria Used in Wage Negotiations* (Chicago: Chicago Association of Commerce and Industry, 1947), pp. 10–18.

the effect of further increasing the demand and causing further increases in prices. If all incomes are raised to compensate for changes in the cost of living, and if the output of goods is not increased accordingly, the only effect would be the distribution of the same supply of goods to the same persons in the same proportion. In practice, some persons will not receive cost-of-living increases. Such persons include many salaried workers, annuitants, pensioners, and persons whose income is subject to price control, such as landlords. The usual effect is therefore a gain for some groups at the expense of others. The problem becomes most acute during periods of monetary inflation when rapid advances occur in the sales prices of the products of the company, the cost of living, and all other items included in the price level. During such periods, wage increases are necessary and desirable, even though the incomes of some groups lag behind the general increase. Individual employers can only minimize the effects of inflation when the difficulty is due to causes in the national and international fields. The remedies can be provided only by the government through a control of banking policies, credit, borrowing, and spending.

Closely related to the question of the cost of living is the demand of unions that "take-home pay" be maintained after overtime work has been eliminated. The demand for an increase in hourly wages to compensate for the loss of overtime pay is supported by the argument that such an increase is necessary to prevent a decrease in living standards. This argument overlooks the fact that workers expect an increase in pay when hours of work are increased. In considering a demand for maintaining take-home pay, the employer should consider the rates of wages paid by competitors, the effect of the elimination of overtime work upon productivity, and the existing level of wages.

Ability of the Employer to Pay. One of the arguments made by labor unions for wage increases during periods of prosperity is that wages should be increased because employers can afford to pay more. The increase in wages, it is contended, can be paid from profits without the necessity for price increases. According to this argument, which requires "a look at the books," those employers who are making sufficient profits should increase wages. If an employer is not making profits, he will be relieved of the demand for a wage increase and will be permitted to pay lower wages than other employers.

The argument that wages should vary with profits can hardly be sustained. An employer whose business is well managed cannot be expected to pay higher wages than his competitors. If he did so, he would have no incentive for introducing laborsaving methods because the gain would accrue to labor. Moreover, every employer would have a different scale of wages for the same job. All workers would seek employment where wages were highest, and they would refuse to work where the wages were low. Neither the union nor the individual workers would approve a low wage scale for an inefficient employer.

In an economic system based upon the profit motive, the profits of efficient employers can be expected to exceed the profits of the less efficient. Profits provide the incentive for good management. They are the compensation for producing goods at a cost below the prices that consumers are willing to pay. If workers are to receive as wages all or a part of the profits in excess of a stated percentage, some standard of a fair rate of profit must first be agreed upon. This procedure would place all industries in a category similar to that of a public utility. The method is subject to both theoretical objections and practical difficulties.

Profits are the most fluctuating factor in the national income. They increase sharply during periods of prosperity, and they decline during periods of depression. Wage rates normally fluctuate over a much narrower range. Workers cannot expect their wages to increase during periods of prosperity by a percentage that is comparable to the increase in profits because wages do not decrease by comparable percentages during periods of depression.

Over a period of years the ability of industry to pay higher wages is increased by technological changes and better management. The benefits of the greater productivity and decreased costs may be shared by the management, the stockholders or owners, and the workers. Consumers of the product may ultimately enjoy a part of the benefits through lower prices. A large part of the higher standards of living of workers from year to year is explained by the greater productivity. A definite provision for annual increases in wages was first included in the contract between General Motors Corporation and the United Automobile Workers in 1950. The promise of an annual increase of 3 cents per hour for all employees is called the *annual improvement factor.* The willingness of the employer to guarantee such an annual increase in wages is predicated upon his belief that he can continue to lower costs through technological improvements and better management. He makes a substantial gain in productivity through the existence of the agreement itself because the union agrees not to call a strike for a period of years. The employer can regularize production without fear of interruptions due to labor trouble.

Effect of Work Conditions. One employer may reasonably expect to hire workers at lower wage rates than another if he offers them better working conditions. It is impossible to give a complete enumeration of the conditions of work, but they include lighting, heating and cooling the air, noisy or dusty conditions, monotony of work assignments, methods of materials handling, provision of coffee breaks or rest periods, and the general attractiveness of the workplace. The opportunity to earn additional income through overtime work, employment on odd shifts, or increased production under an incentive system of wage payment are also important. Another factor is the use of various financial benefits in addition to the regular wage, such as payment for holidays or annual leave, sick benefits, pensions, and group life insurance. The worker is also interested in the stabilization of production and employment, and wage payments under a guaranteed annual wage plan. These features of the managerial program have been discussed elsewhere. They are mentioned here to call attention to the fact that the worker is interested in many phases of the job besides the rate of wages.

Nature of the Job. In any plant there is not one wage rate but there are many wage rates. Some jobs require greater skill and more training, education, and experience than others. Some jobs subject the worker to heat, cold, moisture, accident hazards, or other unfavorable conditions. Some require heavy lifting or muscular exertion; and others require care in the handling of materials, tools, or equipment. Some jobs cause the worker to soil or possibly to ruin his clothing, while others permit him to wear clean clothing. The technique of evaluating the various factors in a job for the purposes of fixing wage rates and also for purposes of employing workers is called "job evaluation."

Several devices are used to vary the wages paid to workers on various jobs. A piece-rate or bonus method of wage payment is one such device. Payment by the piece requires that standards be set to indicate the amount of work which represents a fair day's work. Payment by the piece also requires that individual production records be kept. Employee records are kept to indicate absences, tardiness, spoilage, and other significant facts, both favorable and unfavorable. All factors in the record of the employee should ultimately be reflected in monetary or other rewards.

Ability of the Worker. Workers who are employed at similar jobs are not necessarily worth the same to the employer. They will differ in their productivity, regularity of attendance, accident record, spoilage of materials, ability to shift to other types of work, ability to help train new workers, and many other respects. The employer may therefore rate his workers as well as his jobs in order that he may pay them in accordance with their value to him. However, the payment of different rates of pay to various workers on the same job because of differences in their personal traits creates the possibility of favoritism and subjects the employer to the charge of discrimination. The attempt to pay on the basis of merit frequently causes such a wave of dissatisfaction and complaints that most employers consider this basis of payment at the employee level as impractical.[3]

BARGAINING ON WAGE RATES

The wage paid to the individual worker is determined when he is employed. His pay depends upon the pay for the job, which may be a part of the general wage structure as determined by the employer with modifications as worked out in negotiations with a union. In most manufacturing industries, the wage rates may be adjusted from time to time in negotiations to eliminate inequities or to grant wage increases in all job rates. The worker may get an increase because he qualifies for a higher rated job or because all rates are increased in the negotiation for the annual contract or upon action by the employer. In some industries, the union contract may run for more than one year, and the employer may voluntarily grant a general increase before the contract expires. Sometimes the union may be asked to agree to a general reduction in all wage rates when a contract expires; and in emergencies the workers or the union may be asked to take a general reduction in pay during the period of the contract. Such a request may be presented as the only alternative to closing the plant for an indefinite period, selling the business, or moving to another location.

When the representatives of the union and the management enter into wage negotiations, each side will advance such arguments as seem to support its case in view of existing circumstances. If the price level has been increasing, the union may argue that a general wage increase is needed to maintain standards of living. If prices have been stable or are declining but profits are good, the union will say that the company is able to pay more. If neither of these conditions exists, the union may be able to point to other companies or other industries that have raised wages. It may argue that wages paid by the company are inequitable because of poor working conditions, odd work shifts, or other reasons. If conditions do not seem to support a demand for a general wage in-

---

[3] See William E. McCauley, "Destruction of the Merit Increase," *Advanced Management*, Vol. XIX, No. 7 (1954), pp. 19–25.

crease, the union may press its demand for a guaranteed annual wage, higher pensions, or other benefits.

The representatives of the company also adapt their arguments to meet the conditions of the moment. If the price level has been stable, they will point out that a wage increase is not necessary to maintain standards of living. If the profits of the company have been small, they may argue that a general wage increase will endanger the solvency of the company and may require a reduction in the size of the work force. If the situation will support the argument, they may contend that a wage increase will cause an increase in the cost of the product that will put the company at a competitive disadvantage.

According to the common pattern of negotiation, the representatives of the company and the union meet in conference. After the usual informal exchanges, the union representatives may express their interest in the welfare of the company, and the representatives of the management may express similar feelings about the workers. The union representatives then state their requests for wage increases and other concessions. A large union with a research department will support its demands with statistical and other data. Frequently, the union will ask for much more than it expects management to concede. When the union requests have been stated, the management may describe the serious effects upon the company if wage increases and other benefits are granted, and it may ask for time to study the requests. At the next meeting, the management representatives return with counterproposals. If the price level has been increasing and profits are good, an acceptable middle ground may be found. If the company can pass along the higher costs to the consumer in increased prices for the product, agreement may more easily be reached. The higher wage may also be offset by reductions in costs, by improvements in methods introduced by the management, or by increased production as a result of worker co-operation.

If the parties cannot reach an agreement, the assistance of the United States Conciliation Service may be requested. The mediator will talk with the representatives of the two sides in a joint meeting. He then talks privately with the representatives of each side to determine what concessions each is prepared to make. If he knows to what extent each side is making demands for bargaining purposes, he may more easily bring them together. Frequently, one side or the other is pleased to resort to mediation as an excuse for retreating from too demanding a position. In extreme cases, however, a solution to wage and other controversies may be reached only after a strike.

QUESTIONS

1. Workers are sometimes reminded of the wage-cost spiral, which means that increased wages cause higher costs and the higher costs lead to higher prices and further demands for wage increases. Is this relationship close and are the consequences always as indicated?

2. Might a worker want a wage increase if prices subsequently advance by the same percentage as his wage increase? Why?

3. Does the marginal theory of wages assume that all workers are equally efficient? To what extent are the assumptions valid?

4. How does labor resemble a commodity and how does it differ?

5. Does the value of the services of a worker change when his wage is increased? Explain.

6. Do living standards of workers determine wages, or do wages determine living standards?

7. Is the pay of a worker determined largely by the nature of the job, or is it determined by the personal qualities of the worker as reflected in merit rating?

8. Can the pay of a worker be determined by the amount of his contribution to the value of the product? Explain.

9. How is the pay of a worker related to his status in the community?

10. How is the relatively high level of real wages in the United States explained? Is it due to the strength of organized labor?

11. Do workers join unions because they expect unions to get wage increases for them? If not, why do they join?

12. How does the employer determine the amount of wages to pay for any job, such as file clerk, truck driver, or janitor?

13. If the employer is making a high rate of profit, can he be expected to pay higher wages than other employers in the area?

CASES

44. EXTRA WORK ON SATURDAYS

Charles Wolfe held a job which was classified as general helper in the maintenance department. The union contract listed the work hours, but it also stated that a worker could be given extra work on Saturdays provided he agreed to come to work. The opportunity for such work was given to workers in the order of their seniority because not all of the maintenance workers were needed on Saturdays. Charles frequently accepted the chance to work, and he was glad to make some extra money.

Usually the Saturday work consisted of light housekeeping chores, such as removing scrap and waste, sweeping around the machines and in the aisles, washing windows, replacing warning signs, and painting stair railings, corners of steps on the stairways, and markings along the aisles. One Saturday morning when Charles reported for work, he was told by the foreman that he was expected to clean the metal drip pans under the machines, which were coated with oil and grease. When he was assigned to this work, Charles told the foreman that he had not agreed to do this kind of work and that a worker with less seniority should be assigned to do this dirty work. The foreman replied: "You were called in to work today because of your seniority, but your job is that of helper. You are expected to do any work of this kind that needs to be done. You have two hours to get this work done, and when I come back, I want to see all these drip pans clean."

The foreman returned later to find that nothing had been done to clean the drip pans. Investigation disclosed that Charles had checked out at the gate immediately after the foreman had left him. On Monday when Charles reported back to work, the foreman called the personnel director to his office and then called Charles to come to the office also. When Charles learned that the conference was being called to discuss the incident of Saturday, he asked to be permitted to call in the union steward.

The foreman related the facts pertaining to the work assignment on Saturday, and Charles did not deny the facts. The foreman asked the personnel director if he thought the refusal called for a disciplinary layoff, and the personnel director said he thought it did and the duration should be five days. The union steward protested the penalty because Charles was not required to work on Saturday. He was free to work or not to work as he chose, and in this case, he had chosen not to work. The reply of the personnel director was: "Charles was free to work or not to work on Saturday, and on Friday he elected to work. When he agreed to work, the foreman did not attempt to get any one else to come, but he depended upon Charles. When he comes in for Saturday work, he is required to accept all work assignments that are included under his job classification. Moreover, he had no right to leave the plant without the permission of the foreman. He gets a layoff without pay."

The decision of the foreman and the personnel director was referred to the plant superintendent in accordance with the usual company procedure. The plant superintendent approved the recommendation. The union steward referred the case to the executive committee of the union. The union requested that the case be submitted to an arbitrator as provided by the union contract.

Question:

We as the recommendation of the foreman and the personnel manager the correct decision?

45. REVISION OF JOB DUTIES

At the plant of the A. C. F. Smith Company, the work of the finishers of wood cabinets consisted of waxing, polishing, and inspecting cabinets that were used for radio and television sets. Each finisher was required to inspect the cabinet when he had finished polishing it and to see that it was free of scratches or other imperfections and that the finish was otherwise of acceptable quality. The workers on this job were paid on a piece rate with a guaranteed hourly wage.

The crating and shipping foreman reported to the plant manager that many of the cabinets received for crating did not meet the standards of quality as set by the company. Since considerable time and expense would be involved in returning the cabinets to the finishing department, the foreman of the crating department had assigned a man to the work of retouching and refinishing cabinets. When the plant manager heard of this situation, he asked that the job of overinspector be created in the finishing department, and this person would see that all cabinets met the required quality standards. Any cabinets that were found to be below the standard would be referred back to the finisher who had done the work, and he would be required to correct the defects.

In the job description that was used as a basis for the job evaluation, the work of the finisher was described as including finishing, polishing, and inspecting. The union contract stated that the point value and the piece rate for any job could be revised by the company if the job was changed as a result of a change in the design of the product or the method of manufacture. Since the company regarded the revision of inspection methods as a change in manufacturing, it reduced the piece rate for the job of finisher.

The union challenged the reduction of the piece rate. It alleged that the finishers had been doing the inspecting for four years, that the company had no right to narrow the work cycle, and that the finishers were being asked to take a pay cut to provide money to pay the inspector. As the company and the union were unable to reach an agreement on the matter, they referred the case to an arbitrator in accordance with the provisions of the union contract.

The arbitrator held that the reduction in the piece rate could not be made by the company because methods of manufacturing the cabinets had not been changed. He ruled that a change in manufacturing would mean a change in the physical work elements, such as new materials, new machinery, new tools, or new processes. A different assignment of the work of inspection did not constitute a change in manufacturing methods as defined in the contract. As a result of the ruling, the old rate was restored and the worker was held entitled to payment at the old rate for all cabinets finished during the period while the case was being contested and arbitrated.

Question:

Was the arbitrator correct in his ruling?

46. VARYING CAPACITIES OF WORKERS

At the Office Appliances Company, parts for computing machines are processed in one part of the plant. About 2,000 parts are required for one machine. After the parts have been inspected, they are transported to another part of the building for assembly. Because the machines are light in weight and the assembly work requires considerable time, the machines in process of assembly are moved by the workers from one bench to the next. When a worker has completed work on a machine, he picks it up and carries it to another bench for the next operation.

At one work station, three workers are employed on one phase of the assembly. The three workers perform the same operation on different units of the product. One of the workers, Albert Ross, has developed good use of both hands and can perform the assembly operation in six minutes. The other workers are slower, and they see no reason for trying to work rapidly. Consequently, Albert can do the assembly work on three machines in about eighteen minutes while the other workers take several minutes more for three machines. This arrangement enables Albert to take a break and to sit down, to drink a cup of coffee, or to take a smoke in the smoking area when he wants to do so. If work accumulates at his work station while he is absent, he soon catches up after he returns. Usually, he keeps work supplied to the next work station, but he expects the other two workers who perform the same operation to keep their work moving and to prevent any delay.

Albert has been subjected to considerable pressure from the other workers who want him to remain at his station and to keep working. Since he is unwilling to help them with their work, they think that he should work more slowly because his pace may cause management to establish a lower standard time for the work and to put more pressure on all workers to follow a faster pace. As a result of the situation, Albert often finds that the workers are not friendly toward him. He is subjected to similar pressures from other workers along the line.

The foreman has observed that Albert often takes a break while the other two assemblers continue at their benches. He has talked to Albert about his production record and the breaks, and he has urged Albert to follow a slower pace in order to keep things moving smoothly in the department. Although he has not expressed his anxiety, he thinks that if the time-study man should make another study of the task and set a shorter time, one of the workers might be dismissed or transferred to another job. Albert has promised to work slowly, but he finds that the parts just seem to slide into place without much effort from him. He cannot understand why the other workers require so much time.

Questions:

1. How can the attitude of the foreman and the workers be explained?
2. Does this situation require any action on the part of the foreman?

22 Wage

Systems

A large number of methods of wage payments have been devised. Some methods emphasize the amount of time spent on the job, and other methods provide for payment largely on the basis of production. Some methods vary the payment on the basis of time, quantity, and quality of work. Many companies use more than one method of wage payment because the requirements of various jobs differ.

Wage systems may be classified on the basis of the amount of bonus paid for increased production above a predetermined standard. From this point of view, wage systems may be classified into five groups, which are as follows:

1. No increase in wages for increased production. The systems of payment falling under this classification reward the worker for time on the job rather than the amount produced. The retention, transfer, or promotion of the worker may depend upon his production rate; but his pay from one day to another does not vary with his production. Three wage systems fall under this classification—the day or hour wage, the measured day wage, and the annual wage.

2. A slight bonus for production in excess of the standard but less than a proportionate increase. For example, a production of 5 per cent above the standard is rewarded by less than 5 per cent increase in pay. Examples are the Halsey plan and the Rowan plan.

3. An increase in pay in proportion to the increase in production. Examples are piece rates, the 100 per cent savings or premium plan, and the Bedaux plan.

4. An increase in pay which is larger than the percentage of increase

in production. Some plans which may properly be classed under this heading do not grant the higher rates for all levels of achievement but only at certain fixed points. For example, the worker may receive a sharp increase in pay when his rate of production exactly equals the standard with no more than a prorata increase in pay for additional output. An example of a system of wage payment which liberally rewards the worker for equaling or bettering the standard is the Gantt system. The Emerson plan also awards substantial bonuses and is therefore discussed under this heading. Under this plan the bonuses increase most sharply just before production reaches the standard rather than at the time it reaches the standard.

5. Profit-sharing and bonus plans, which provide for additional payments to workers not related directly to either time or production. These plans supplement some other method of payment, such as an hourly rate.

SYSTEMS THAT GRANT NO BONUS

Wage systems that fall under this classification reward the worker for the amount of time that he spends on the job rather than the amount of his production. His daily or hourly rate may be adjusted from time to time as the quantity and quality of his production increase or decrease. Nevertheless, on any one day, the pay is for time spent rather than quantity produced.

Advantages of the Hourly Rate. Both individual workers and labor unions have been inclined to favor the hourly rate, although not all of them have done so. One reason is that payment by the day gives the worker some feeling of security. He knows how much he will earn each day and each week or month, so long as he continues to be employed. He can therefore plan with some measure of assurance what he should be able to pay for rent, clothes, food, and other necessities. To the extent that he can budget his expenses, he has security and is relieved of fear and worry. His freedom from uncertainty is obviously an advantage to the employer as well as to the worker. The hourly rate permits the worker to emphasize quality of work. In any event, quality must be such that the product will pass inspection; but a worker on daywork can emphasize quality, whereas the worker on piece rates will think first of quantity.

The hourly wage tends to develop a solidarity of interest among the workers. Workers at similar jobs may be paid the same rates, and they can raise their rates by gaining a general wage increase. Workers on piece rates may increase their daily earnings by increasing production. Differences in daily or weekly earnings tend to destroy group solidarity because highly paid workers are less inclined to press for higher wages for workers whose production rate is low.

From the point of view of management, the hourly rate has other advantages. It requires a minimum of payroll work. To determine the amount due the worker, it is necessary to know only the rate per hour and the amount of time worked. The worker can readily figure his own pay when this system is used, and this fact is an added advantage to both the worker and the management. Many systems that are theoretically desirable on other grounds have been discontinued because they were confusing to the worker and required excessive payroll costs. Another advantage is that the hourly rate can be used in any type of work. If the worker does a variety of tasks, such as repairs and maintenance, the hourly rate may be the most logical method to use. Even if the worker is engaged in repetitive work, such as assembly line work, the hourly rate may be satisfactory because the production rate may be controlled by regulating the speed of the line.

Disadvantages of the Hourly Rate. From the point of view of the employee, a disadvantage is that superior workers are not encouraged to do their best. The hourly rate offers no inducement to the good workers to excel in production. The better workers may be inclined to follow a pace that enables them to avoid being criticized and that also protects slower workers. In fact, good workers sometimes permit others to take credit for some of their production. Workers or their unions often set informal production standards which are quite generally observed.

Daily earnings may be lower when payment is by the hour. The effect of the method of payment upon daily or weekly wages cannot be definitely determined since all wages are fixed in relation to earnings on other jobs or in other plants. However, if the rate fails to encourage the better workers to do what is for them a fair amount of work, the result is lower productivity. According to the functional theory of wages, lower productivity results in lower wages.

From the point of view of management, the hourly rate has additional disadvantages. Good workers may feel that the rate is unjust to them. When all workers on the same type of work receive the same pay regardless of their efficiency or their production rate, the better workers are inclined to feel that the rate is unfair. The employer is required to assume the greater part of responsibility for maintaining production.

The worker has little incentive to produce more than is necessary for holding his job. Labor cost on contracts cannot be accurately estimated. Standard costs are unreliable because the rate per piece is not fixed.

The Measured Day Rate. In the measured daywork plan the worker is paid a guaranteed daily rate plus a bonus which is determined by his individual performance. The guaranteed daily rate is the same for all workers on the same type of job. The bonus varies with the efficiency of the worker. The plan is usually so designed that approximately 75 per cent of the total pay is base rate and 25 per cent is bonus.

The bonus to be paid under the measured day rate is determined by rating each worker. Ratings may be based solely on productivity, or two or more factors may be used. Factors used in the rating may be productivity, quality of work, dependability of the worker, and versatility of the worker or his ability to do various kinds of work. The factors are weighted according to the requirements of each job. For example, productivity may be weighted 50 or 60 per cent, with the remaining percentages assigned in varying amounts.

The essential feature of the measured day rate is that the performance of employees is measured over a fairly long period, usually one to three months. The record of an employee in one period determines his rating during the ensuing period. His rate of pay during any period is determined solely by his performance during the preceding period and is not affected by his production during the current period. The plan protects the worker against loss of earnings due to breakdowns, poor scheduling, shortage of materials, and lack of customer demand. The worker has an incentive to increase production, improve quality, work regularly, and shift to other jobs in emergencies, because a good record will increase his rate and his earnings during the next period. It assures the worker a certain weekly income while offering an incentive for good work.

The measured daywork system differs from merit rating of employees in that productivity is heavily weighted and employees are rated at definite intervals. The rating is immediately reflected in the wage rate, and the change may be either an increase or a decrease. Merit-rating plans usually provide that pay rates may be increased as a result of the rating, but they usually are not decreased.

One advantage of the measured day rate is that it helps to break down the resistance of the employee to changes in the method of performing a task because a change in methods usually does not affect his pay. When the worker willingly adopts improved work methods, the industrial engineer can devote his full time to increasing productivity and worker efficiency.[1]

Annual Wage. Although payment on an annual basis has usually been limited to executives, a few companies have experimented with the plan of paying employees by the year. Interest in the subject of annual wages was increased after the close of World War II when the Congress of Industrial Organizations began to advocate the plan in an active manner. However, the labor unions for several years ceased to press their demands for the annual wage and became more interested in retirement pay. Later they revived the demand for the annual wage with considerable success. In 1955, the large automobile companies agreed to a modified plan for an annual wage, and many large companies in other industries followed their lead. Provision for some form of guaranteed annual wage was thereafter included in many other union contracts.

Annual wage plans assume several forms. One type of plan provides for a guarantee of a certain number of weeks of employment each year at unspecified job assignments. This guarantee is extended only to workers who have been with the company a stated number of months. A variation of the plan is a guarantee of a certain number of weekly or monthly pay checks of a stated amount. Payments are made even though the employer has no work for the employee to do. If the employer wishes to do so, he may transfer a worker to another task; or he may continue the payments without receiving any services in return. In this case the guaranteed annual wage is the equivalent of unemployment compensation for the duration of the guarantee.

The employer may also guarantee to maintain the income payments from week to week at a rate which fluctuates less than the hours of employment. The overtime of some periods is balanced against the hours of underemployment. If the peak season precedes the slack period, full payments may be made in the weeks of overtime work without provision for future deficits. Other plans provide for deductions from the pay in the overtime weeks to be held by the employer for credits against payments not earned by the worker during slack seasons. If wage advances in dull seasons exceed the amounts earned by overtime work in subsequent weeks, the indebtedness is canceled at the end of the year.

Another type of plan provides for some form of grant or aid during periods of low earnings. For example, the plan may permit the em-

---

[1] *Factory Management and Maintenance,* Vol. CXVII, No. 12 (1959), p. 63.

ployee to obtain a loan from the employer or to draw upon funds set aside for this purpose under the profit-sharing plan or through mutual benefit programs. This type of plan may also provide that employees with a specified number of years of service may be entitled to cash payments in layoff periods up to a stated percentage of the standard wage for forty hours per week. In 1955, for example, the American Can Company and the Continental Can Company agreed to guarantees which raised the unemployment compensation to 65 per cent of the usual take-home pay. These payments were to continue for the full fifty-two weeks of each year. In these two companies, the money for the payments is contributed entirely by the employer. In some instances, however, the payments have been made from sums deducted from the earnings of other workers who are provided with work of more than a stated number of hours per week.

A company plan for unemployment compensation necessarily conforms to the legal requirements, which vary with the state. In some states, the employer cannot raise the unemployment compensation as provided by law because the worker is not entitled to state benefits if he is being paid by his employer. Where this interpretation is given to the state law, the worker who is laid off may first draw state unemployment benefits for a stated period and then he becomes entitled to payments under the annual wage plan of the employer. After a period of time, he may again receive state unemployment benefits.[2]

An advantage of a guaranteed annual wage, from the point of view of the employer, is that the greater security offered the worker relieves him of worry and thus makes him a better worker. Workers have a greater loyalty to the company. Increased loyalty reduces labor turnover and results in a higher level of efficiency. The plan eliminates one distinction between the office workers and the factory workers by raising the social status of factory workers. Moreover, workers are less inclined to oppose technological changes. Although the employer is free to reduce his working force at the beginning of the next contract period, the situation may be corrected by the normal labor turnover or business expansion. Investment in plant and equipment is decreased, provided that the employer is able to utilize his productive equipment at a more nearly uniform rate the year round.

In instituting a plan for a guaranteed annual wage, the principal question for the employer is whether he can eliminate seasonal and cyclical variations in production to the extent necessary to finance such

---

[2] See Edward D. Wickersham, "Repercussions of the Ford Agreement," *Harvard Business Review*, Vol. XXXIV, No. 1 (1956), p. 6173.

a guarantee. In some industries, such as the processing of oysters or the canning or freezing of fruits and vegetables, production cannot be stabilized because the supply of raw materials is subject to seasonal variations. In other industries the stabilization of production might be effected by inducing customers to spread their orders evenly over the year, by producing and storing the product in anticipation of demand, or by dove-tailing the production of two or more commodities that have different seasonal peaks. To stabilize the demand in an industry such as the steel industry would require that customers stabilize their production. The principal customers of the steel industry are automobile companies, construction companies, railroads, public utilities, and oil companies. Stabilization for some of these companies is difficult, and the development of a substitute material which might be produced by a steel mill in the dull season is impractical.

Storing the product in anticipation of an increased demand at a later season or year would cause increased expenses for storage space, interest on idle capital, record keeping, handling costs, and possible deterioration and obsolescence. A further difficulty is the anticipation of the probable demand for various sizes, colors, grades, shapes, and finishes of product. While some employers have been able to stabilize their production, many of them have found it cheaper to permit plants to be operated at less than capacity for a part of the time than to attempt to produce goods in anticipation of the busy season.

Since most employers have considered it unprofitable to stabilize their labor force, it may be assumed that their costs would be increased by such a plan. The feasibility of the guaranteed annual wage, therefore, depends upon the answers to such questions as whether employers can find ways to reduce operating expenses to offset the increase in labor costs, whether prices can be increased to cover the increased costs, and whether the margin of profit is great enough to absorb the increased costs without forcing firms into bankruptcy. The answers to the above questions would obviously not be the same for all industries. The annual wage is practical for some companies and in some industries but not in all of them.

SYSTEMS THAT PAY A SMALL BONUS

A few systems of wage payment grant the worker a small bonus for production above a designated standard, but the bonus is less than the percentage increase in production. For example, an increase of 10 per cent above the amount set by the standard would be rewarded by something less than a 10 per cent increase in pay. Two well-known systems of this kind are the Halsey premium plan and the Rowan plan. These methods of wage payment are generous with the time allowed but not with the premium paid. With both systems the standard time for a task is established on the basis of past performance and not by time study.

Halsey Plan. Under this plan of wage payment, the worker is paid a guaranteed hourly wage plus a percentage of the wages for the time saved. If he completes a task in less than the standard time, he is paid the wages for the time taken plus from one quarter to one half of the wages for the time saved. Since the worker is free to begin another task as soon as he finishes any one task, he is enabled to increase his hourly rate. He is paid by the hour on those tasks where he requires more than the standard time.

To illustrate the method of the Halsey plan, assume that the standard time for a task is 10 hours and the worker is paid $1.00 per hour. If he takes 10 hours to finish the task, he is paid $10.00. If he takes 9 hours, he is paid $9.00 plus a premium of, say, one third of the wages for the time saved, or a total of $9.33 for the task. See Table 3.[3]

TABLE 3

THE HALSEY PLAN

(Standard Time 10 Hours)

Time Consumed (Hours)	Wages on an Hourly Basis	Premium	Total Cost of Work	Worker's Earnings per Hour
10	$10.00	None	$10.00	$1.00
9½	9.50	$0.17	9.67	1.018
9	9.00	0.33	9.33	1.036
8½	8.50	0.50	9.00	1.058
8	8.00	0.67	8.67	1.084
7½	7.50	0.83	8.33	1.111

The reason for the small increase in the earnings per hour is that the standard is based on past performance. It is, therefore, not difficult for the worker to do most tasks in less than the time set. The scanty bonus makes for permanence in the standard. Earnings on the various tasks are not seriously out of proportion, even though the standards are inaccurate. The unfairness in the standards is not carried over into earnings

---

[3] This table follows the form of one prepared by F. A. Halsey in his article, "The Premium Plan of Paying Labor," *Publications of American Economic Association*, Vol. I, No. 2 (1896), pp. 75–88, 82. The article appeared first in *Transactions of American Society of Mechanical Engineers*, Vol. XII (1891), p. 759.

per day or per hour. This feature of the plan permits it to be used as a temporary basis of bonus payment prior to the completion of time studies. If some jobs have been placed on a bonus plan and workers in other departments would also like to earn a bonus, they may be paid by the Halsey premium plan without subjecting the entire program to the risk of failure.

The Halsey plan, in effect, amounts to a reduction in the piece rate as the performance of the worker improves. This fact is apparent from an examination of the total cost of the work, as shown in Table 3. However, the plan is not stated as a series of decreasing piece rates, since that would probably raise objections. The method of statement presents the plan in a much better light.

The Halsey plan was at one time rather widely used, but it has declined in popular appeal and is now seldom used. One objection to the plan is that it permits the continuance of standards that are inequitable and unfair. It makes possible a policy of drift on the part of management. It does not require that management set its standards carefully. Furthermore, the plan does not offer sufficient incentive to the worker. Of the total pay, too much is base pay and not enough is bonus. Experience indicates that if a bonus plan is to encourage the worker to put forth his best efforts, incentive earnings should be from 25 to 30 per cent higher than daywork earnings.[4] In the Halsey plan the base rate is too near the maximum earnings possibility. It may also be argued that the plan is unfair. If the saving in time is the result of worker efforts, the worker should be paid the entire amount. If the saving is due to an inaccurate standard, the fault is that of management, and the worker should not be penalized.

Rowan Plan. The Rowan plan, like the Halsey plan, fixes the standard by past production rather than by time study; and it provides for a small bonus for better-than-standard performance. It provides that the wages for the time taken will be increased by the same percentage that the time set for the task has been reduced. For example, if the worker completes the task in 10 per cent less than the standard time, he is paid for the time required plus a bonus of 10 per cent of his wages for the time taken. The pay for a 10-hour task completed in 9 hours by a worker whose rate is $1.00 per hour would be $9.00 plus 10 per cent of $9.00, or $9.90. As in the Halsey plan, the rate for the task has been reduced. However, the reduction is less under the Rowan plan than it is under

---

[4] Ralph Presgrave, *The Dynamics of Time Study* (2d ed.; New York: McGraw-Hill Book Co., Inc., 1945), p. 124.

the Halsey plan. Stated as a formula, the Rowan plan provides for payment of wages as follows:

$$\begin{array}{c}\text{Wages for} \\ \text{the task}\end{array} = \begin{array}{c}\text{Wages for the} \\ \text{time taken}\end{array} + \left(\dfrac{\text{Time saved}}{\text{Standard time}} \times \begin{array}{c}\text{Wages for the} \\ \text{time taken}\end{array} \right)$$

The justification of the Rowan plan is embodied in the statement that the bonus bears the same relation to the base pay for the task as the time saved bears to the standard time. The Rowan plan is somewhat more liberal with the worker than the Halsey plan because the bonus is larger for performance slightly better than the standard. For deductions in the standard time of 50 per cent or more, the Halsey plan is more liberal; but the worker cannot be expected to reduce the standard time to that extent. Under the Rowan plan a worker can never double his base pay because the bonus is a percentage of the wages for the time taken. This plan has most of the advantages of the Halsey plan and is subject to the same limitations.

QUESTIONS

1. What are the advantages of the day rate from the point of view of the worker? Do all workers prefer this method of wage payment?

2. What are the advantages of the day rate from the point of view of the employer? What are the disadvantages?

3. Why do unions usually prefer the day or hour rate?

4. Under the guaranteed annual wage, an employer may be required to pay for labor services that he does not need and may not be able to use advantageously. How can he afford to make such payments?

5. Do casual workers fill a social or economic need?

6. What factors are taken into consideration in determining the rating of the worker under the plan of the measured day rate?

7. Compare the Halsey and the Rowan plans from the point of view of the size of the wage payments.

8. The effect of both the Halsey and the Rowan plans is to decrease the pay for a task as worker performance improves. How can such a method of wage payment be justified?

9. Would the worker have less difficulty in understanding the fairness of the Halsey plan, or would he more readily understand the Rowan plan?

10. Which method of wage payment would require more work in the payroll department?

11. Why might an employer favor the guaranteed annual wage?

12. Does the employer have an obligation to provide financial support for the entire year when he needs the services for only a part of the year?

CASES

47. PREMIUM PAYMENTS UNDER HALSEY AND ROWAN PLANS

The standard time for a task is 4 hours. The hourly rate of the worker is $1.50. In doing the work on different days, the worker performed the task in various times as follows:

Day	Hours Taken
1	4.5
2	4.0
3	3.8
4	3.5
5	3.0

Required:

1. Compute the pay under the Halsey plan. The premium is 33⅓ per cent.
2. Compute the pay under the Rowan plan.

48. GUARANTEED EMPLOYMENT

In October, 1959, the Drury Hoe and Rake Company informed the union that the hours of work would be reduced from 40 per week to 32 because of a lack of orders. The union officers advised that the company plan would be ineffective because the men would stretch out the work and thereby force the company to return to a 40-hour week. The management then suggested to the union that it give the company a free hand in shifting men to maintenance, yard work, or any other work available. This proposal was presented to the workers at a meeting of the union, and they accepted it.

After the new agreement was put into effect, productivity increased 10 per cent. The management believed that the increase in production was due to a realization on the part of workers that they would not work themselves out of a job and also to a belief that the profit position of the company was not good. The management increased its efforts to sell the larger volume and to avoid paying employees for maintenance and other work not immediately productive. The result was that the employees were kept busy at regular productive work for the remainder of the year, and no transfers of employees were necessary.

Questions:

1. Was the company right in accepting the suggestion of the union, or should production policies be determined without consultation with union officers?
2. How might the increase in production be explained? Did it indicate that employees had previously been loafing on the job?

23 Wage Systems— Continued

IN the preceding chapter, two general classes of wage systems have been considered. These were, first, systems which provide for no increase in pay with increased output and, second, systems which provide for a small increase or small bonus. In this chapter the third and fourth classes of wage systems will be considered.

SYSTEMS THAT PROVIDE FOR PAYMENT IN PROPORTION TO OUTPUT

When this type of wage payment is used, any worker who increases his output is rewarded by an increase in pay of the same percentage as the percentage increase in production. Wage systems of this type include piece rates, the 100 per cent premium plan, the Bedaux system, and group piece rates. When any one of these methods is used, management is required under the federal Wage and Hour Law to guarantee a stipulated minimum wage per hour.

Piece-Rate Plans. The piece-rate plan of wage payment provides for an established rate per unit of output. Separate rates are set for each operation. The 100 per cent premium plan is a form of piece rate with a guaranteed hourly wage. The worker is paid for the time required for a task and is also paid a bonus of 100 per cent of the time saved. For example, a worker who is paid $1.00 per hour may be assigned to a job on which the standard time is 30 minutes. If he does the task in 25 minutes, he is paid for the 25 minutes taken and also for the 5 minutes saved. The effect of this plan is, therefore, to fix a rate of 50 cents for the task with a guaranteed wage of $1.00 per hour.

Bedaux Plan. This plan is also a modified piece-rate system with a guaranteed hourly wage. It differs from the straight piece-rate system in that each task is standardized by being assigned a number of "B's" (for Bedaux) according to the number of minutes required to complete it. A "B" is defined as follows: A fraction of a minute of effort plus a fraction of a minute of relaxation to overcome fatigue, the total being equal to one minute of effort.

Thus a task which requires 15 minutes of work, including time necessary for relaxation, is said to be worth 15 "B's," and a task which requires 20 minutes is worth 20 "B's." During any payroll period the total minutes spent at work are compared with the total "B's" completed. The worker is paid for the "B's" completed if he is above standard. Otherwise, he is paid at the hourly rate.

Some variations of the Bedaux plan provide that the foreman may share in the bonus paid for the "B's" earned above the standard. To illustrate, assume that the worker is employed 40 hours during the week. His standard of work would be 60 "B's" in each hour, or a total of 2,400 "B's." If he has completed 2,460 "B's," he is entitled to a bonus of 60 "B's," or one hour of pay. He may receive three fourths of the bonus and the foreman one fourth, on the theory that the foreman has helped the worker to make the standard. This system is usually opposed by the workers because it encourages the foreman to put pressure on the men.

An advantage of the Bedaux plan is that it can be used in any department and in any type of work, and it can be used for a worker who shifts from one type of work to another. The reason for its adaptability is that all types of work are converted to a common denominator through the device of the "B" and the unit of work.

Group Piece Rates. A group of workers may be paid for their total production on a piece-rate basis, provided that the work of one is dependent upon the work of another, as in line fabrication or assembly work. If the workers are guaranteed an hourly rate and the hourly rates vary, the amount to be paid each worker may be determined as follows:

1. Total production of the group multiplied by the piece rate equals the total amount to be paid to all workers.
2. Total amount to be paid minus hourly earnings equals bonus.
3. Bonus divided by total hourly earnings equals the bonus percentage.
4. Earnings of each worker multiplied by the bonus percentage equals the amount of the bonus in dollars.

To illustrate the group bonus plan, assume that workers are paid hourly wages and are permitted to work for a bonus on the basis of 2 cents per piece. During a stated payroll period the group produced 100,000 pieces. Their wages on an hourly basis totaled $1,600. The pay of a worker who earned $120 on an hourly basis would be determined as follows:

```
Total amount due all workers, 100,000 × 2 cents..........$2,000
Deduct wages on an hourly basis........................  1,600

Bonus above hourly wage...............................$  400
Bonus percentage, $400 ÷ $1,600......................      25%

Pay of the worker on an hourly basis, $120 × 25%........$   30
Add earnings on an hourly basis.......................      120

        Total  Pay.......................................$  150
```

When this system is used, an increase in the hourly wage of all workers does not affect the total earnings of the group. It affects only the distribution as between the hourly wages and the bonus. If some workers receive an increase in their hourly wage rates while others do not, the effect is a redistribution of the total earnings of the group, since the amount of the bonus and the percentages are changed.

A variation of the group piece rate provides for the payment of an hourly wage to each worker and an additional bonus for each unit produced. At the end of the year the bonus is distributed on the basis of the number of hours worked by each employee during the year. To be eligible to share in the bonus fund or "kitty," the employee must have a record of 90 per cent "presenteeism"; and he must not have participated in any unauthorized strike or other work stoppage. Employees who have not been on the payroll for ninety days or more are usually ineligible to participate.

Attitude of Labor Unions. Many labor unions oppose piece rates. Piece rates are an indirect recognition of the prevailing wage rate in that the employer fixes the rate at that figure which he thinks will enable the employee to earn a fair wage for a day's work. The time set is therefore subject to all the limitations of time study. In industries that are subject to frequent changes in style or product design, it is not easy to keep changes in rates abreast of changes in the work. If designs change from year to year, a wage scale must be scrapped for a new scale when new designs are put into production.

The earnings of workers on piece rates are decreased by the inability of management to stabilize production, to maintain a steady flow of work, or to keep machines in repair. This problem is especially acute in industries that bring a series of models into production or that are unable to stabilize production because of fluctuating demand. Piece rates are also unfair to workers when the production run varies greatly. If the worker can produce five hundred units without having to change tasks, he can make better earnings than he would make on a run of one hundred units on each of five different tasks of the same standard time.

Piece rates often lead to speeding up on the job. In a seasonal industry where the amount of work to be done is definitely limited, such as in certain branches of the clothing industry, each worker is likely to rush through his work to produce as large a number of pieces as possible before being laid off. In such an industry, speeding by workers on piecework can be prevented only by a plan for allocating the work.

Piecework makes it more difficult for the workers to present a united front to the management. The better workers who earn a satisfactory wage may be unwilling to strike for more money or to risk an interruption of work by making demands upon the employer. The foreman can discriminate against the workers he dislikes by putting them on work where the standards are tight and by putting his favorites where the standards are loose.

Workers fear that the piece rate will be cut if they increase production. If some workers demonstrate to management that an increase in production is possible, management may cut the piece rates in order to keep down daily earnings. Workers believe this to be true even though no rate reduction has occurred in the plant; but it is true, however, that cuts in piece rates have sometimes followed increases in output.[1]

Unions seek various forms of protection for workers on piece rates. They may take an active interest in management methods to prevent interruptions in the flow of work and to see that the worker has an opportunity to earn a satisfactory daily wage. The result has been in many cases that the unions insisted that outside consultants be asked to recommend changes in policies or that the management itself make certain improvements. Unions have concerned themselves with difficulties which prevented workers from making fair piece-rate earnings in such industries as coal mining, textile manufacturing, clothing, window glass, foundry work, and carpets. The conditions with which the unions have been concerned include the following:

---

[1] F. W. Taylor was compelled by the directors of Midvale Steel Company to cut piece rates under such circumstances. See N. I. Stone, "Wages, Hours and Individual Output," *Annals of the American Academy of Political and Social Science*, Vol. LXXXV (1919), pp. 120, 131.

Inadequate, obsolete, or poorly maintained equipment.
Unsatisfactory working conditions.
Insufficient or unsatisfactory material.
Faulty methods of doing work.
Avoidable delays.
Obstructions caused by other workmen.

Some unions prefer piecework to daywork. The preference is based upon a number of factors. Some unions, as in coal mining, recognize that supervision of individual workmen by the employer is not practical. Since each worker is placed upon his own responsibility, piecework is the only feasible method of payment. However, the worker may be paid on an hourly basis for travel time or for odd jobs, such as timbering.

Piecework relieves the employee of pressure from the foreman to get out production. When the worker is paid by the day, management uses various devices to assure itself that production is up to standard in both quality and quantity. Consequently, the worker may be gradually speeded up until he is turning out much greater production for the same pay. Under piece rates a worker has a chance to follow his own pace. If the pace is a leisurely one, the employer may not make serious objections.

Many unions recognize that competition from other shops, particularly nonunion shops, is so keen that the employer cannot grant general increases in daily or hourly wage rates. The piece rate permits the employee to increase his earnings with no increase in labor cost. Where work is uniform from one plant to another, as in certain branches of the clothing industry, the piece rate enables the union to eliminate discrimination in the rates paid by various employers. Day rates do not permit the same uniformity, unless the union can fix the amount of the daily production as well as the daily wage.

Workers tend to benefit by numerous small improvements in the task which enable them to increase output. Many such improvements are not of sufficient importance to justify a cut in the rate. In the aggregate, improvements in work methods may result in substantial increases in earnings. Some improvements result from changes made by the employer, and some result from short cuts developed by the employee or taught him by fellow workers.

The employer is more likely to retain older workers if he pays them by the piece. The loss to the employer when he keeps the older man is limited to machine time, although in some cases one slow worker may cause a slowing down of others. Workers who take off a few minutes from work in the middle of the day are also less likely to be criticized by the foreman, even though the practice is a violation of the rules, because labor costs cease when the worker stops work.

INCENTIVE WAGE SYSTEMS

While the piece rate rewards the worker by paying him an increase in wages in proportion to his increase in production, some plans allow the efficient worker an even higher percentage increase. Usually, the increase in pay comes just at the point where the worker measures up to the established standard. If a worker does a task within the standard time, he gets a very large increase in his pay. Under most plans the bonus is not regularly distributed for small increases in efficiency but is granted for any performance within the standard time. Although the plans of wage payment that liberally reward the worker for increasing production are not the only systems that provide incentives, these plans are commonly referred to as "incentive systems."

Basic Principles. Incentive wage plans are based upon four principles, which are as follows:

1. The task is large and clearly defined. This principle requires that the standard time be fixed by time study rather than by past performance. Taylor believed that the standard should be so high that it could be met only by workers who were better than average. While practice varies somewhat in this respect, close attention and unusual skill are usually required of any worker who completes the task in the standard time.

2. Standard conditions of work are maintained by the management. Standard materials are issued, tools are kept in repair, and the machine is maintained in good operating condition at all times. In addition, the management sees that a steady and continuous supply of materials is moved to the workplace. Failure to meet the standard cannot, therefore, be ascribed to management. Performance becomes a matter of worker efficiency and application to the task.

3. The pay for worker success is high. Since the task is large and clearly defined, an inefficient worker cannot make the standard as he might do under the Halsey or Rowan plans. The management can afford to be generous with the pay because it is not generous with the time allowance. A further reason for the high rate of pay is that if the worker can perform the task within the standard time, he uses the machine or the workplace for a relatively short time. The machine becomes available for another task with the result that cost per unit is

decreased. As the cost of machine time per hour increases, management can become more generous with the bonus or the piece rate.

4. The penalty for failure to meet the standard is severe. Under most incentive plans, the worker is expected ultimately to reach the standard, but the penalty for failure varies. The difference between the guaranteed wage and the earnings of the worker who is standard or better is so great that workers make every effort to reach the standard. Under all incentive plans, the worker who does not ultimately reach the standard is expected to change to some other job. Typical incentive plans are the Gantt task and bonus plan and the Emerson efficiency wage.

Gantt Task and Bonus Plan. According to the Gantt plan, the worker who does the task within the standard time is paid for the standard time (not the time taken) plus a bonus of 25 per cent or more of the wages for the standard time. To illustrate, assume that the task time is 1 hour and the worker is guaranteed $1.00 an hour plus a bonus of 30 per cent. A worker who completes the task in 60 minutes is paid $1.00 plus a bonus of 30 per cent, or a total of $1.30. A worker who does the same task in 55 minutes is paid the same amount, $1.30. Thus the plan provides a piece rate for standard workers and an hourly rate for substandard workers. Like Taylor, Gantt made up a sharp distinction between the worker who did the task in a little less than the standard time and the one who required a little more time. Under both plans the standard was so high that a worker could not expect to do the task in much less than the time set.

Emerson Efficiency Wage. The Emerson plan was designed by Harrington Emerson, whose work was referred to in Chapter 1 (see p. 17). This plan guarantees the worker a daily wage and a bonus according to a graduated scale. The percentage of bonus increases as performance nears the standard. The efficiency of the worker is not computed on the basis of daily performance but is averaged over a payroll period of a week, two weeks, or a month. The efficiency is determined by the ratio of total standard time on all tasks completed to the total time taken by the worker. For example, a worker who required 90 hours to complete tasks with a total standard time of 80 hours would have an efficiency rating of 80/90, or 88.89 per cent.

The scale of bonuses permits a small premium to be paid to the worker who is $66\frac{2}{3}$ per cent efficient, but the bonus rate increases sharply as the performance of the worker nears standard. Above 100 per cent efficiency the bonus increases by 1 per cent for each 1 per cent increase in efficiency.

The Emerson plan has the advantage of relieving the worker of the fear that on any one task he may barely fail to make the standard. It offers encouragement to the learner because the bonus begins at a low level of performance. However, the worker has a strong incentive to continue his improvement because of the sharp increase in the rate as he nears 100 per cent efficiency.

The principal disadvantage of the Emerson plan is its complexity. The worker has difficulty in computing his pay under this plan, and a considerable amount of work is required by the payroll department. It does not offer the same incentive for sustained effort as the Taylor or Gantt plans because the efficiency rate is an average for the period. This objection may be minimized by posting each day the efficiency rate of each worker for the preceding day.

Requirements of a Successful Plan.   An essential requirement for success is the establishment of a fair standard for the task. The setting of the standard involves the improvement in work methods, careful timing, and fair allowances and adjustments for skill and effort. If standards are loose, workers may be able to earn a high wage with production only slightly above the pace of other workers who are on daywork or on a tight standard. Once the incentive rates have been set, they are not easily changed, particularly if the workers are unionized.

Another requirement is that the method by which the pay is figured should be simple enough that workers can verify the amount of their earnings by making their own computations. A lack of understanding of the method by which their earnings are determined will only increase the dissatisfaction which may arise because take-home pay is decreased by numerous deductions for such reasons as federal and state income taxes, social security taxes, union dues, bond purchases, and donations to charity.

To be successful, the wage plan should provide for a premium scale that is large enough to encourage continuous worker co-operation and interest. The amount of the bonus should depend upon worker effort rather than conditions beyond his control. For example, a company that based the bonus of maintenance workers on the volume of plant production paid high bonuses during a period of prosperity, and the workers were pleased with the plan. When production decreased through no fault of the maintenance men, dissatisfaction became widespread. To relate the earnings to worker effort, management should plan the flow of work to avoid interruptions due to poor scheduling, shortages of materials, machine breakdowns, and other such causes. To prevent the sacrifice of quality by the worker in his effort to earn extra pay for quantity production, management should establish and maintain quality standards. To assure continuous interest in incentive pay, bonuses should be paid as soon as possible after they are earned.

From the point of view of the management, the requirements for wage computation and record keeping should not be too complicated. Some methods that seemed to be satisfactory from the point of view of the workers have been discarded because they greatly increased the work of preparing the payroll.

Maintenance of the Plan. A wage incentive plan that is satisfactory at the time of its adoption will soon become inadequate unless it is maintained. If the task is changed as a result of a new design of the product, the purchase of a new machine, or other developments, the effect on the production standard should be determined. Some persons believe that any change in the task requires a change in the standard because a series of small changes may in time result in gross inequities in the pay rates. Others state that the task should be retimed only when the change is perceptible, say 5 per cent. If workers object to their inability to earn a bonus, their complaints should be investigated without prejudice. A worker who complains that his bonus has been incorrectly computed should be given an explanation of the method of calculating his pay. Workers who are unable to make a bonus should be helped to make the standard by proper training or by whatever action may be necessary.

Evaluation of Incentive Plans. Experience indicates that incentive plans result in increased production, higher wages, and lower unit costs. Reports to the War Labor Board during World War II showed that on the average the introduction of an incentive plan was followed during the next ninety days by an increase in production per man-hour of 40 per cent. A later survey of a number of firms by the American Management Association showed that where a company had changed from an hourly rate to an incentive plan, production was increased 20 to 50 per cent. Many other reports indicate similar increases in production. Much depends upon the rate of the bonus, the circumstances under which the change in methods of wage payment is made, and possibly other factors.

For reasons previously suggested, most labor unions prefer the hourly wage to an incentive plan. One objection is that the wage incentive plan is superimposed upon a wage structure that is not scientific. For this reason the incentive plan alone will not correct inequities in the wage structure. The rates or bonuses are not scientifically determined because the base rate is usually the result of tradition or bargaining methods. It is also said that the bonus does not compensate the worker for his increased effort and that the speed may injure his health. Although not really a serious objection, it is said that the wage standards are set by engineers who could not make a bonus if they were to work under their own standards. Furthermore, wage incentive plans disregard variances between the capacities of workers, since all are expected to reach a high standard. The plans also do not allow for variations in output from day to day and from hour to hour. Another objection is that wage incentive plans result in a continuous simplification in the methods of work, with a resultant decrease in the need for craftsmanship on the part of the worker. It is a part of a larger movement for making work routine and repetitive.

PROFIT-SHARING AND BONUS PLANS

Profit sharing is not a complete system of wage payment because it assumes that the initial wage payments are determined by hourly or day rates, piece rates, or some other plan. The worker gets a share of the profit as an additional lump-sum payment at the end of the month, half-year, or year. Monthly payments have the advantage of promptness, but the accounting difficulties of figuring monthly profits cast serious doubts upon the advisability of such a plan. The share of profits due to each worker may be paid in cash or stock of the company or may be credited to an employee retirement fund. Payment may be partly in cash, partly in stock, and partly in retirement benefits. Usually, an employee must have been with the company six months or longer to participate in the distribution. The termination of employment during the year, whether voluntary or otherwise, usually cancels all participation rights. Layoffs or leaves of absence are not considered termination of employment.

Several plans for the sharing of profits may be distinguished. The labor dividend may be a stipulated percentage of the profits before taxes or dividends are deducted. The amount paid to any employee may be determined by his wages or salary or by the total unit credits in accordance with a plan such as the following:

```
For each $100 of annual compensation....................  1  unit
For each year of continuous service......................  1  unit
For each 6-month term on the junior board of directors during
    the current year.....................................  5  units
For supervisor...........................................  5  units
For assistant department manager........................ 15  units
For specialized personnel ............................... Various
```

Payments to employees may be made after a stipulated dividend has been paid on the capital stock. The amount paid to workers may vary from 25 to 50 per cent of the profits after dividends. Before the distribution is made, the total payment is apportioned to various groups of workers and salaried personnel on the basis of their rates of pay. Payment to workers is usually in cash, but payment to salaried employees may be partly or entirely in stock.

Payments of profits to employees may also be made in proportion to the dividend paid on the stock. Employees may be paid a dividend on their annual earnings equal to the percentage earned or paid on the common stock of the company. This method would usually pay the employees about 25 per cent of the profits.

The advantage to the employer of a profit-sharing plan is that it encourages a moderate degree of co-operation. In small companies, it has tended to break down the distinctions between crafts and to encourage workers to assist in any work that needs to be done. It makes workers interested in the elimination of idle time of men and machines and in the reduction of spoilage and waste. It results in a reduction of labor turnover. To the employee, profit sharing probably has the advantage of increasing annual wages.

Disadvantages of Profit Sharing. One objection to profit sharing is that the profits are not directly dependent upon the efforts of any one employee. A worker cannot increase his personal share of profits by application to the job because earnings are distributed among so many persons. Moreover, profits may be made or lost by many factors not under the control of workers as a group, such as prices and discounts, expansion into new territories, the development of new products, budgeting of sales and expenses, production planning, and business prosperity or depression. Good and poor workers are rewarded in the same manner without distinction or discrimination. The inefficient worker receives the same share as the efficient, provided that his hourly or daily wage rate is the same.

Workers share in the profits but not in the losses. Some attempt has been made to secure an agreement from workers that in case of emergencies or failure of the corporation to make profits, employees will accept reduced compensation or fewer hours of work or will make other sacrifices until the emergency is past. However, substantial sacrifices cannot be expected of workers during lean periods; and they are likely to find other jobs if company losses are deducted from their pay. The fact that the company shares the profits but bears all of the losses is not a serious objection to profit sharing. The plan can accomplish its purpose of giving the workers an incentive to increase production or reduce cost without an accompanying loss-sharing plan.

The reward is too uncertain and too long postponed to be effective. A possible payment at the end of the year does not stimulate the worker to much greater effort throughout the year. Payments are sometimes made at more frequent intervals, but monthly payments are usually considered impractical because of the uncertainties of accounting methods. Monthly computations of profits are especially difficult in an industry that is subject to marked seasonal fluctuations.

Workers eventually look upon a year-end distribution as a matter of right. If they do not receive such payments, they may consider that somehow they have not been fairly paid for their labor.

The accounting practices used by management in determining profits are likely to be misunderstood by the workers. Many accounting practices are a matter of opinion, and any one of several methods may be acceptable to accountants and to management. Items which may be questioned are depreciation expense, maintenance and repair charges, and inventory valuation. Workers usually cannot see why the profit and loss statement should include such expenditures as those for research, public relations, long-range planning, and budgeting. A profit-sharing plan has often proved to be a source of friction rather than a means to better industrial relations.

Christmas Bonuses. Many companies that do not have a profit-sharing agreement regularly pay a bonus to their employees near the end of the year. The bonus is a gratuity, but the amount may be based upon annual wages or salaries. Employees are usually classified into groups according to the number of years of service, with the oldest employees receiving the largest bonuses. If the bonus is paid near the end of the calendar year, it is called a Christmas bonus.

Bonuses are designed to develop the loyalty of employees and to decrease labor turnover. Since the amount varies from year to year, employees cannot rely upon it as a means of meeting their Christmas bills or of paying other obligations. If payments are made regularly, employees may regard the bonus as part of their wages.

QUESTIONS

1. Under what circumstances might the 100 per cent premium plan be preferable to the piece rate?

2. For what types of work are piece rates particularly suited?

3. A foreman states that the piece rates put pressure upon the foremen rather than the workers. How can this opinion be justified?

4. Would the piece rate cause workers to follow a fast pace at their work? How might it result in a more leisurely pace on the part of the workers?

5. The Taylor piece-rate plan reduces the rate for the worker who is below standard. The Halsey plan reduces the rate for the worker who is better than standard. How can the two methods be fair and reasonable?

6. Why do workers fear that an increase in output when they are paid by the piece will result in a reduction of the rate? Should management ever reduce the piece rate?

7. If workers are unable to make high earnings under a bonus plan because management is inefficient, should the workers or the union assist management to improve working conditions?

8. Should the union ever employ a management consultant to improve conditions in the management?

9. Why are good working conditions especially required for the success of efficiency wage plans while they may not be necessary to the success of the Halsey and Rowan plans?

10. A worker who is paid by the Gantt plan with a 25 per cent bonus is guaranteed an hourly wage of $1.50. Determine his pay for a 2-hour task completed in the following time periods: 2.5 hours, 2 hours, 3.8 hours, and 3.7 hours.

11. In some branches of the clothing industry, the season is short and the amount of work is limited. Workers who are paid by the piece sometimes work very fast in order they may get as much of the work as possible. Should the company encourage this effort on the part of workers? What should it do about the situation?

CASES

49. PROFIT SHARING BY FORMULA

The profit-sharing agreement of the Daisy Manufacturing Company provides that 30 per cent of the net profits before taxes will be paid to a trust company for the benefit of employees. The trust company distributes one half of the payment to employees and holds the remainder in a retirement fund for their benefit. Distributions of profits are made annually.

The amount paid to any employee is determined by the number of hours worked. To share in the distribution, the employee must be on the payroll at the end of the year. The total amount to be distributed is divided by the number of hours worked by all employees entitled to share in the distribution to determine the profit distribution per hour. Hours worked by any employee multiplied by the profit distribution per hour equals the payment to be made to him. An amount equal to the cash distribution is credited to each employee as his equity in the retirement fund. Retirement fund equities cannot be withdrawn by the employee but must be used for the purchase of an annuity. In case of death the equity of the employee is payable to beneficiaries.

Questions:

1. What is the merit of the plan of the Daisy Manufacturing Company?

2. What are the limitations of the plan from the point of view of the company?

50. PROFIT SHARING WITHOUT FORMULA

The Ramsay Corporation shares its profits with its employees each year but has no formula for determining the amount. Each year the board of directors pays dividends to the stockholders and also a "dividend on wages" at such rates as seem fair to the directors. If dividends to the stockholders are reduced or passed in any year, the stockholders are considered to be entitled to extra dividends in the next year before profit distributions are made to employees. If the money of stockholders has been used for risky ventures in any year, they may receive extra dividends as compensation in the case the ventures are successful. If the board of directors believes that earnings have been increased because of plant operating efficiency, profit distributions to employees may be increased without any increase in dividends paid to stockholders.

Each year the company holds a meeting of jobholders just as it holds a meeting of stockholders. At the annual meetings, as well as in the communications during the year, the plan and the profit position of the company are explained. The company considers that the plan is a success and that employees believe the management to be fair with them.

Questions:

1. What is the merit of the plan of the Ramsay Corporation?

2. What are the limitations of the plan?

24 Job Evaluation

JOB evaluation is a significant management technique in the field of personnel relations. Its essential purpose is to reduce or eliminate differentials in pay that are not due to differences in the job. Its basic principle is that an employee who works at a difficult, hazardous, dirty, or lifting task should be paid more than an employee who works at an easy job in safe, pleasant surroundings and that the pay should be determined by the various requirements of the job.

The pay for any job is high or low only by comparison with the pay of other jobs or in comparison with some factor in the work situation. Consequently, when a worker says that he is not paid enough, he may mean that the correct differential has not been maintained between his wages and the pay of other employees in the company or between his pay and that of persons doing similar work in another plant in the community. A system of wage payment which aids in establishing fair differentials between jobs should avoid underpayment for some jobs and overpayment for others. It should grant increases in the wages for advancement to jobs that have been given a higher rating under the plan. It should also provide an incentive for employees to prepare themselves for more difficult jobs because a logical wage scale has been established. Because it reduces complaints of discrimination in wages, employee satisfaction should be increased; and labor turnover may be decreased. The plan should reduce the opportunities for favoritism on the part of foremen in recommending wage increases.

INFORMATION FOR JOB EVALUATION

Before jobs can be evaluated, agreement should be reached concerning the definition of a job. A job may be defined as a group of positions which are similar with respect to their major or significant tasks. This definition permits the inclusion of positions with minor differences under the same job title and reduces the number of jobs to be evaluated. For example, although the duties assigned to workers at various workplaces on an assembly line may vary slightly, the various positions might be included in a single job provided that the duties are similar and require about the same degree of skill, education, and experience.

A job may also be defined as a group of positions which differ materially from any other group of positions with respect to their major or significant tasks. To illustrate, the duties assigned to a carpenter's helper would differ in some material respects from the duties of a carpenter, a plumber's helper, or any other job. What constitutes a material difference in duties may be a matter of opinion. Frequently, a union prefers a job definition that permits of the inclusion of a large number of positions because seniority becomes more significant and the possibility of discrimination between workers for personal reasons is reduced.

Types of Job Information.   Several types of job information may be compiled in organizing a job-evaluation program. A first step in compiling job information might be a list of titles of jobs. A set of job definitions might also be prepared. A job definition consists of a brief statement of the duties assigned to each job. The definitions might be expanded to include a complete and detailed statement of all of the tasks of each job. A job description includes duties, conditions of work, and requirements of the job. It also indicates relationships with other people, such as the nature of the supervision, the number of persons the worker supervises, if any, and the staff departments with which he will have contacts. The group relationships are frequently as significant as technical skill and knowledge.

The job description usually follows a prescribed form in order that all essential information may be included. It shows such information as the following:

Title of the job.
Department in which the work is done.
Duties performed and percentage of time devoted to each type of work.
Number of persons supervised and extent of the supervision.
Amount of supervision received.
Machines and equipment used.
Relation of the job to later operations.
Material processed and its value.
Reports and records prepared.
Promotion opportunities.
Initiative and ingenuity required.

Personal qualifications desirable, such as sex, age, etc.
Effort required.
Mental requirements.
Physical requirements.
Length of time required to learn the work.
Experience desirable.
Accident hazards.

The job description should be prepared in specific rather than general terms and should indicate precisely what is done, how it is done, why it is done, and under what conditions it is done.

A job specification is a written description of the job in relation to the worker. It shows the abilities and the qualifications that a person should possess in order to do the work. Job specification has been called a "man specification" because it relates to the occupant.

The compiling of the information should precede job evaluation because the persons evaluating the jobs should first agree on the requirements and conditions of work. Unless descriptions are prepared, various members of the committee will have varying concepts of the meaning of such terms as toolmaker, crib tender, or lacquer sprayer.

METHODS OF JOB EVALUATION

Four methods of evaluation may be distinguished. They are job ranking, job classification, factor comparison, and the point system. The point system is the method most commonly used.

Job Ranking. Evaluation by the ranking method means, as the name indicates, the arranging of the various jobs in the order of their difficulty, responsibility, and other requirements. Each member of the job-evaluation committee independently ranks the jobs from the highest to the lowest. The usual procedure is to begin by identifying the highest and the lowest jobs and gradually to work toward the jobs in the middle. The ranks assigned by different members of the committee are compared, possibly revised, and averaged to determine the final rank. A partial ranking might be as follows:

1. Toolmaker, first class.
2. Toolmaker, second class.
3. Electrician, first class.
4. Machinist, first class.
5. Plumber and steam fitter, first class.
6. Lathe operator, first class, intricate.
7. Milling machine operator, first class, complicated.

8. Milling machine operator, ordinary.
9. Bench assembler, first class.
10. Bench assembler, second class.
11. Watchman.
12. Gateman.
13. Inside laborer.
14. Sweeper.

Although the job-ranking method is the simplest of the methods of evaluation, it is subject to several serious objections. Because each rater must be familiar with all of the jobs to be rated, it is difficult to find qualified raters. Since the method does not provide a definite basis for the ratings, the rankings are likely to be made on the basis of prevailing wage rates. The assignments of rankings are difficult to justify in case workers or union officials challenge a pay rate. The rankings do not indicate the differences or the amount of spread between the pay of the various jobs. For these reasons the job-ranking method is usually regarded as unsatisfactory.

Job Classification. This method consists, first, of setting up various classes of jobs according to the duties, responsibilities, and experience required by the work and, second, of assigning each job to a class. The method has had more general use in the evaluation of clerical and office jobs than of factory jobs. A well-known plan provides for six classes, as follows:

CLASS	DESCRIPTION
1	Work of office- or messenger-boy character.
2	Simple operations. Use of few definite rules. Routine operations performed under close supervision.
3	Requires recognized clerical ability.
4	Requires complete and intensive knowledge of a restricted field.
5	Requires knowledge of general policies and principles of management. May require long experience with the company.
6	Work of a highly technical or confidential nature or of semiexecutive supervisory character.

After the classes have been established, the committee will assign each job to a class. If a more definite differentiation is desired, the jobs with each class may be ranked. This procedure is an improvement over either the ranking or the classification method used independently, but it is subject to most of the limitations of the job-ranking method.

Factor Comparison. This method evaluates all jobs in terms of a rating scale based upon fifteen to twenty-five key jobs. The relative rank of the various jobs is determined in relation to a monetary scale. The procedure includes the following five steps:

1. The factors to be used in the rating plan are determined, such as mental requirements, physical requirements, and skill.

2. The key jobs are selected. For such jobs, the present pay is believed to be fair in relation to the requirements of the work.

3. The key jobs are ranked under each of the factors. For example, the job which has the greatest mental requirements is ranked No. 1 under that factor. The same job might rank as No. 7 under physical requirements, with other rankings under each of the other factors.

4. The total payment for any job at existing rates is apportioned to the various factors in accordance with the ranking of each job under that factor. To illustrate, if a patternmaker is paid $2.76 an hour, a painter $1.80 an hour, and a drill press operator $1.50 an hour, the payment might be attributed to the job factors in the manner illustrated:

Factor	Patternmaker	Painter	Drill Press Operator
Mental requirements	$0.80	$0.30	$0.26
Physical requirements......	0.30	0.32	0.24
Skill....................	1.00	0.56	0.42
Responsibility............	0.48	0.32	0.34
Working conditions.......	0.18	0.30	0.24
Total Pay, Present Rates..	$2.76	$1.80	$1.50

If a key job is found to be improperly paid for any factor or for total requirements, it is dropped from the list, and another job is substituted.

5. Other jobs are evaluated in relation to the key jobs. The job of machinist, first class, for example, would have mental requirements only slightly below that of patternmaker and might be assigned 70 cents for that factor. Physical requirements might be somewhat greater and might justify pay of 36 cents. Skill required of the machinist might be less and might justify payment of 96 cents for that factor. This process is continued until the total hourly wage of each job is determined. Each factor for each job is compared with the same factor and the pay for all other jobs. Although the total pay for key jobs agrees with existing wage rates for the key jobs, it does not necessarily agree in the case of other jobs.

While the factor-comparison method results in more equitable rates for various jobs than ordinary methods of rate setting do, it is subject to some objections. It begins with the assumption that selected key jobs are properly paid in relation to each other. The fact that the rating is stated in monetary terms is objectionable because a change in the prevailing level of wages requires a change in all the rating tables. However, the method has been successfully used by many companies.

Point System. In the point system several factors common to all jobs are used as a basis for evaluation. The factors are weighted according to their importance. The number of factors used in any plan varies from 4 to 40. The usual number is 10 to 12. The factors most frequently used are experience, education, skill, physical effort, working conditions, responsibilities for material and equipment, and accident hazards. The weights assigned to all factors may total 1,000 points, or the total may be as low as 100. The total points should be a large number if many jobs are to be evaluated, but it is not necessary that the total be a round number, such as 500 or 1,000.

Each factor is divided into degrees or grades. The meaning of the factor and also of each degree is carefully defined. For example, educational requirements might be divided into five degrees, with requirements as follows: lowest degree, ability to read and write; second degree, grade-school education; third degree, technical-school education; fourth degree, high-school education; and fifth degree, college or special.

If educational requirements are weighted 50 points, the various degrees would be evaluated with a spread of 10 points from one degree to the next. Intermediate degrees are recognized in the evaluation. The number of degrees in various plans ranges from four to seven. Some authorities recommend an even number to avoid the tendency of some raters to assign the middle rating when they are unable to form a definite opinion. The number of factors, the weights assigned, and the number of degrees vary with the company and the requirements of the jobs.

Figure 44 shows a job-evaluation plan with six factors and five degrees for each factor. The differences between the degrees and the points assigned are indicated in the table. An instruction manual for use by raters should be prepared to give a detailed description of the plan, the factors, and the degrees. The maximum points in the illustration total 400. However, it is not to be expected that any job would receive the maximum evaluation on all six factors.

Before the evaluation plan is considered complete, a few jobs should be evaluated by the rating committee. The original plan may be revised as a result of the experience in rating the first jobs. After the point values of the first jobs have been determined, the title of each job

FACTORS	1	2	3	4	5
EDUCATION REQUIRED	READ AND WRITE 10	GRADE SCHOOL 20	TECHNICAL SCHOOL 30	HIGH SCHOOL 40	COLLEGE OR SPECIAL 50
EXPERIENCE REQUIRED	0 TO 3 MONTHS 15	3 TO 6 MONTHS 30	6 TO 9 MONTHS 45	9 TO 12 MONTHS 60	OVER 12 MONTHS 75
MENTAL EFFORT	SLIGHT 10	BELOW AVERAGE 20	AVERAGE 30	HIGH 40	VERY HIGH 50
PHYSICAL EFFORT	VERY LIGHT 20	MODERATE 40	AVERAGE 60	ACTIVE 80	STRENUOUS 100
WORKING CONDITIONS	NO UNDESIRABLE CONDITIONS 10	SOMETIMES UNDESIRABLE 20	ONE OR MORE UNDESIRABLE CONDITIONS 30	CONTINUOUS EXPOSURE 40	CONTINUOUS AND EXTENSIVE EXPOSURE 50
RESPONSIBILITY FOR MATERIALS AND EQUIPMENT	LESS THAN $1,000 15	$1,000 TO $10,000 30	$10,000 TO $25,000 45	$25,000 TO $50,000 60	OVER $50,000 75

FIG. 44. Job Evaluation by the Point System

evaluated should be entered in the rating manual as an illustration of the degree requirement. For example, if the job of tool set-up man is rated as fifth degree under the factor of experience, the title of that job should be used as an illustration for the guidance of subsequent raters.

The evaluation of six representative jobs is illustrated in the chart shown in Figure 45. The factors used in the evaluation and the weights assigned to each factor are indicated in the scale of values at the right in the illustration. The total value of all factors is 1,000 points, and the highest rated job is assigned 645 points. The high evaluation of the job of tool set-up man is due principally to the mental development, skill, accuracy, experience, and mental effort required.

The evaluation will usually result in a wide range of point values for the various jobs. To avoid the confusion which would result from having a different pay scale for each point value, a limited number of labor grades should be established. For example, 10 labor grades might be established with definite point values within each grade. Grade 10 might include all jobs with point values of 175 or less. Grade 9 might include jobs with point values from 176 to 185. The number of points included within a grade usually increases with the higher grades. The limits depend upon the jobs to be graded.

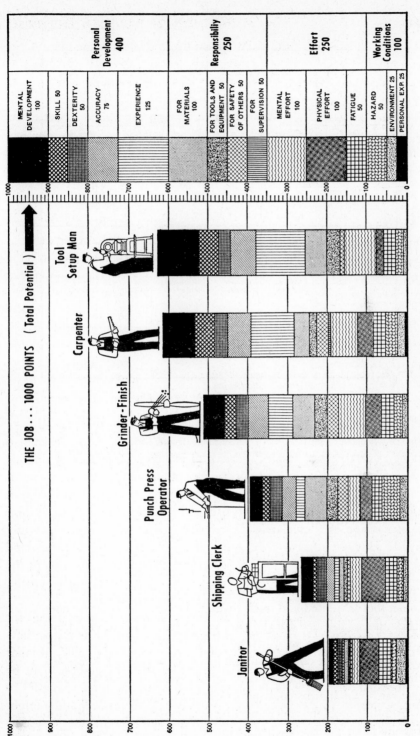

FIG. 45. Illustrative Job Evaluations

In the discussion of the point system up to this time, the question of pay has not been considered. Because wage rates have often been a haphazard process, the pay for many jobs will be found to be out of line with the points assigned under the job-evaluation program. This fact can be graphically demonstrated by the preparation of a chart which shows the existing pay rate and the points assigned to each job. Such a chart is shown in Figure 46.

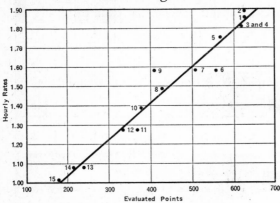

FIG. 46. Method of Showing Relation of Prevailing Wage Rates and Job-Evaluation Points

From this chart, management can easily see which jobs are out of line. Key: 1—machinist, first class; 2—tool set-up man; 3—welder; 4—carpenter; 5—engine lathe operator; 6—assembler, gang leader; 7—grinder, finish; 8—drill press operator; 9—truck driver; 10—milling machine operator; 11—punch press operator; 12—turret lathe operator; 13—shipping clerk; 14—unskilled labor; 15—janitor.

Usually, the pay rates for the various classes of jobs are determined after a survey has been made of comparable jobs in the same industrial area. In making the survey, the job-evaluating committee submits job descriptions for a limited number of companies and requests information as to wages paid for similar jobs by the other employers. A visit is made to the plant of each company to which such an inquiry is sent to determine the requirements of the jobs and to establish the fact that the requirements are similar. The committee must inquire into any supplementary pay, such as bonuses, overtime pay, paid vacation, paid group insurance, pension or retirement plans, and other financial aids. Because an increasing number of companies are interested in labor market surveys, the information is sometimes tabulated and made available to the co-operating companies. The rates established for the various grades, which are based upon the results of the survey, may be at, below, or above the rates paid by other companies. For example, an employer who guarantees a yearly wage or who guarantees a stated number of weeks of work each year might pay rates which are somewhat below the community level.

Another problem which must be decided in establishing rates of pay for the labor grades is whether to establish one or several rates of pay for each grade. One of three plans may be followed:

1. A single rate may be established for each grade. All jobs within the grade are paid the same rate regardless of their point values.

2. A maximum and a minimum rate may be established for each grade. The minimum rate is the starting rate. The pay of an employee is established by periodical rating of his qualifications and accomplishments. A variation of this plan would grant wage increases within the range established for the job at time intervals determined by the rating of the employee. For example, if the normal time interval between wage increases is six months, an outstanding employee might be given an increase after three or four months, a satisfactory employee after six months, and a passable employee after nine or ten months. The various gradations of employee ratings would be determined by assigning point values for ratings on various tasks.[1]

3. A maximum and a minimum rate may be established. The pay of an employee on the job is advanced to the mid-point of the scale by reason of seniority, with advances at predetermined intervals. Advances beyond the mid-point are based upon merit.

When the evaluation of a job indicates a wage rate which is higher than the existing rate, the wages should be advanced in accordance with the evaluation. If the existing rate is higher than the rate called for by the plan, the problem is more difficult because it is usually unwise to reduce the pay of an employee as a result of the evaluation of his job. One solution is to train the employee for a higher rated job and to transfer him to it without loss of pay. The job made vacant by the transfer is filled by transferring a worker from a job with a lower rating. Another way out of the difficulty is to pay present employees the existing rates and, as vacancies occur, to employ persons at the lower rates.

MAKING THE PLAN EFFECTIVE

The success of job evaluation requires that steps be taken to inform workers of the way the new plan will affect them and to meet objections as they arise. An essential requirement for success is the sincerity of the mangement in its desire to deal fairly with workers in the matter of job assignments and wage rates.

Disseminating Information as to the Plan. If the union has participated in the formulation of the plan, the task of informing employees of its purpose and its application is made much easier than would

[1] E. F. Fisk, "Tying Pay Raises to Merit," *Factory Management and Maintenance,* Vol. CXVI, No. 9 (1958), p. 108.

otherwise be the case. Employees may be informed through the plant periodical, the local newspapers, group meetings, the bulletin board, and booklets or leaflets. Appeal is made to the sense of fairness of employees, who will readily agree that the pay should not be the same for all jobs. While the factors and the weights assigned may be subject to differences of opinion, the plan of increasing the pay as job requirements increase will usually be accepted. An illustration of the method of explaining the job-evaluation plan is shown in Figure 47.

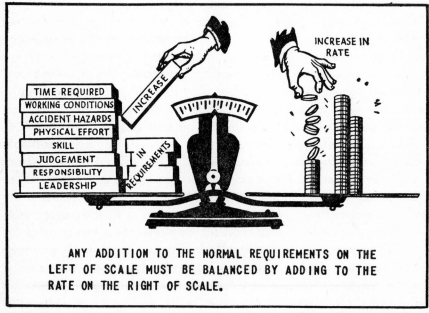

INCREASE IN RATE

TIME REQUIRED
WORKING CONDITIONS
ACCIDENT HAZARDS
PHYSICAL EFFORT
SKILL
JUDGEMENT
RESPONSIBILITY
LEADERSHIP

INCREASE

IN REQUIREMENTS

ANY ADDITION TO THE NORMAL REQUIREMENTS ON THE LEFT OF SCALE MUST BE BALANCED BY ADDING TO THE RATE ON THE RIGHT OF SCALE.

Courtesy of Armstrong Cork Co.

FIG. 47. Drawing Used to Explain Job-Evaluation Plan

This drawing was used in a pamphlet on the job-evaluation plan which was prepared for distribution to employees.

When the evaluation plan is explained to employees, they should be told not to expect that the plan will cure all the ills in the rate structure. They should also be told that, while no one will receive a pay cut, some will not receive raises. Attention should be centered upon the fact that the plan is designed to fix compensation by uniform measurement rather than by individual bargaining.

To obtain the support of foremen, several advantages of job evaluation may be pointed out. The plan should reduce the amount of dissention and criticism. False accusations of discrimination can no longer be made. The program does not strip foremen of their authority but helps them to evaluate and measure jobs.

Maintaining the Plan. The job evaluations will soon become obsolete unless they are revised. New jobs will be added, and existing jobs will be changed. Points assigned to jobs may be challenged by the union and by workers. Such jobs should be restudied and reclassified, if necessary. Requests for re-evaluation of a job may come from foremen, time-study men, or other persons.

LIMITATIONS OF JOB EVALUATION

While the technique of job evaluation is vastly better than haphazard opinion, it is not to be inferred that it is perfect. Job evaluation is not scientific in the sense that it is exact. Opinion enters into the selection of factors, the assignment of weights, and other phases of the program. Job evaluation does not provide a basis for determining the amount of the total income from sales that should properly be paid to the worker individually or to workers as a group.

Need to Get Workers. Probably the greatest weakness of job evaluation arises from the fact that any employer will ultimately be required to pay a sufficiently high rate of wages to attract workers and maintain the work force as a group. If the rate for a job as determined by job evaluation does not attract a sufficient number of workers for some jobs, the rate may require revision regardless of point values. Although this difficulty may be met in part by the labor market survey, wage problems of this kind may still arise, particularly in a changing economy.

Relation to Employee Rating. The principle that wages go with the job rather than the individual is sound. However, the personal traits of the worker are also important. Such traits include regularity of attendance, quality of workmanship, observance of safety regulations, and willingness to help in an emergency. Personal qualities may become a factor in wage determination as a result of an employee rating system, but the wage rate will be determined largely by the job.

Attitude of Unions. As might be expected, labor unions do not accept the technique of job evaluation as an adequate solution to wage problems. They tend to regard it as an arbitrary yardstick for ranking jobs in relation to each other. They say that by using this method, management merely determines the pay of a job in relation to other jobs in the same plant. Even for this purpose, however, they contend that the value of job evaluation is limited because the weights assigned to the different factors are arbitrarily determined. The final ratings are not scientific, and the point values of a job are not necessarily fair and equitable in relation to the point values of other jobs. Furthermore, labor unions say that the general wage level in a plant may not properly reflect the cost of living, the ability of the employer to pay, and other criteria that properly affect the wage structure. To some unions, the use of points, factors, degrees of a factor, and community wage surveys merely provides a "smokescreen" by which management may introduce an element of confusion and attempt to avoid genuine collective bargaining and realistic wage adjustments. These criticisms suggest that job evaluation does not provide a complete answer to the question of wage determination.[2]

QUESTIONS

1. Is dissatisfaction with wages largely caused by a low level of wages or by discrimination in rates of pay?

2. How does job evaluation attempt to deal with dissatisfaction with the wages paid?

3. Can a person who works at a job that is poorly paid raise his wages by working hard and doing the work as he is expected to do? How can he best raise his wages?

4. Do workers receive good wages for working at a job where working conditions are bad and the accident hazard is great?

5. What are the advantages and the weaknesses of the job-ranking method of job evaluation? Of the job classification method?

6. Is the worth of a job to the company determined by the value added to the product by the job? Explain.

7. Why is high point value given to a job with high requirements for education, experience, and skill?

8. Labor unions have alleged that the point values assigned to a factor are purely arbitrary. In what respect, if any, is this charge justified?

9. How is allowance made for fringe benefits in the job-evaluation procedure?

10. How are the results of the community survey used in determining the pay for a job?

11. How does the efficiency rating or merit rating of a worker affect his pay when the point system of job evaluation is used?

12. How can the employer adjust the wage rates of workers whose pay is shown by the job evaluation to be too high? What does he do about wage rates that are found to be too low?

[2] See Edward N. Hay, "The Attitude of the American Federation of Labor on Job Evaluation," in Paul Pigors, C. A. Myers, and F. T. Malm, *Readings in Personnel Administration* (New York: McGraw-Hill Book Co., Inc., 1959), pp. 405–12.

CASES

51. LAUNCHING A JOB-EVALUATION PLAN

The Brinkley Spring and Wire Company has had considerable difficulty over requests of employees for wage increases. An argument frequently made by employees was that their wages were not sufficiently higher than wages paid certain other employees whose jobs required less skill and experience, permitted them to work in more pleasant and desirable working conditions, or made less physical and mental demands. The plant superintendent, the foreman, and the personnel director, in conference with the worker and the shop steward, frequently found themselves unable to explain differentials in pay. After dealing with a number of such cases, they decided that wage differentials were largely the result of bargaining with employees and union officers and that a general revision was needed. The president authorized that a job-evaluation program be undertaken for the jobs of the 750 employees. The plan selected was a widely used point system which had been especially developed for the metal trades.

As the personnel manager did not feel qualified to supervise the program, the company employed a job analyst who had recently organized the program of another company. Since the job analyst was not familiar with jobs in the Brinkley Spring and Wire Company, he requested that two men be selected from the plant to work with him. They would be able to continue the program after the job analyst had completed his work if the management found this arrangement to be desirable. One of the men selected to assist the analyst was a former time-study man and the other was a cost estimator. These men were selected on recommendation of their supervisors, who rated them high on analytical ability, ability to express themselves, ability to handle people, and enthusiasm for their work.

The plant superintendent informed the foremen and other people in management of the nature and purpose of the program. After the analyst was employed, he attended the regular meetings of the supervisors and explained to them what the plan would be and how they would be affected by it. He emphasized the fact that they would be able to discuss intelligently with employees any complaints concerning wages. No wages would be reduced as long as an employee now holding a job remained on it. Ultimately, the hope was that a rational wage structure could be achieved. The program was also explained to union officers and employees.

Before undertaking to evaluate any job, the analyst spent two days with his assistants discussing the theory of job evaluation and the procedure to be followed. The assistants were then asked to write descriptions of jobs with which they were familiar. They were told to include all data that would be used in assigning points to jobs in the evaluation plan. The writing of the descriptions and the discussion of the jobs by the analyst and his assistants extended over two days more.

The next step was the making of a job evaluation by the analyst with the aid of the foreman of the department. For the first study the analyst chose the job of drill press operator, with which he was thoroughly familiar. The assistants observed the methods. On the next job the analyst and the assistants made the

ratings, and the three evaluations were then compared. This method was continued for two days, during which time five jobs were rated. Then the analyst
watched while the assistants made evaluations of other jobs. The training of the
assistants extended over a total of fifteen days.

The work of evaluating the various jobs continued under the supervision of
the analyst who checked the job descriptions, the degrees of each factor, and the
points assigned. The assistants obtained their information concerning each job
from the foreman, the worker, and their own personal observation. They discussed each rating and the point values with the foreman and explained the reason
for the ratings assigned. Foremen were given the opportunity to object to any
rating. Workers were not told what the point values of their jobs were because no
wage rates were assigned and no wage scale had yet been made.

The study of the jobs by the analyst and his two assistants continued over a
period of five months. At the end of that time management agreed upon a wage
scale in money to be assigned to the jobs. This wage scale required a few wage
increases. The new scale was explained in a general meeting of employees, and a
booklet describing the plan and its results was distributed. Each foreman was
given information concerning the results of the evaluation of all jobs in his department. He personally explained to each employee how his job had been evaluated and how his job fitted into the new wage scale. In accordance with the
original plan the company granted a wage increase where the point value of the
job indicated that the worker was entitled to an increase. No wages were decreased.

After the analyst left the company, one of the assistants continued the program
by investigating requests for the revision of point values assigned to jobs and
studying new jobs as they were created. His work gradually decreased as the
number of complaints became less. However, the management believed that he
should be retained indefinitely in the personnel department.

Questions:

1. Why did the company find a program of job evaluation necessary?
2. What might it hope to gain by such a program?
3. How would the average wages paid be affected?
4. Do you approve of the procedure followed?

52. PAY OF FOUNDRY WORKERS

The National Metal Products Company produced a varied line of metal products for sale to machine manufacturers. The departments of the factory were
designated as patterns, foundry, forge shop, machining, finishing, and assembly.
The company had established a wage scale according to the job-evaluation plan of
a well-known trade association in the industry. The plan provided for a total of
500 points of which 250 were assigned to skill, education, and experience. The
maximum number of points on working conditions was 25, and the maximum
for safety was also 25.

Despite the careful assignment of point values to various jobs and the construction of a logical wage scale in view of community wage levels, the company
experienced considerable difficulty in the foundry. Most of the foundry jobs

were assigned the maximum of 25 points for working conditions because the foundry was hot and dirty in summer, and it was subject to drafts of hot and cold air in winter. The men were exposed to serious accident hazards because of possible burns on legs, feet, hands, arms, or face. Workers did not like to wear protective helmets, shoes, leggings, and gloves, although they were expected to do so.

For many years, the workers in the foundry had been immigrants from a country of central Europe, or the descendents of such immigrants. However, immigration had dwindled until few immigrants of that nationality were available, and the young men were desirous of finding work that would give them greater social status. Young men of other nationalities or of American birth could not be induced to accept foundry employment at the wage rate provided by the job evaluation program. Furthermore, the employment manager doubted that persons of other nationalities would be accepted by the group presently employed in the foundry.

The problem of foundry wages and employment was discussed at a meeting of the foreman, the plant superintendent, and the personnel manager. The foreman argued that the test of a job evaluation plan lay in the attractiveness of the wage rates to prospective employees. He suggested that the point values assigned to foundry jobs be disregarded and that wage rates be substantially increased. The personnel director thought that the difficulties arose because of poor supervision, a failure of management to air-condition the foundry, and the lack of mechanization. He urged attention to these aspects of the problem. The plant superintendent thought that too many persons of one nationality had been employed. The work was regarded as lacking in status because it was associated with the one group. He would mix different nationalities and would promote a recruitment program more effectively. He also suggested that if the situation did not improve, he might recommend the closing of the foundry and the purchase of castings from other companies.

Required:

Evaluate the various proposals.

PART VII

PERSONNEL
RELATIONS

25 Personnel Activities

INDUSTRY is devoting an increasing amount of attention to the problems of human relations. Reasons for the growing importance of this phase of management may be found in the growth of labor unions and in the greater amount of federal and state labor legislation. Of equal importance, however, is the recognition of the necessity for improving personnel relationships. The greater variation in efficiency among plants within an industry is in the human element. It is probably easier to equip a plant with the right machines, materials, buildings, and layout than it is to provide a corps of trained and loyal workers who are integrated into an effective organization. A company that is equipped with efficient machines and buildings may be wrecked by dissatisfaction, strife, unrest, slowdowns, and excessive labor turnover. An efficient work force with a high state of morale is essential to success.

Although the problems of personnel management permeate the entire organization and cannot be segregated and managed by a separate department, the general policy has been to establish a personnel department to study workers and their problems, to formulate policies concerning workers, and to assist in the handling of personnel activities. The work of the personnel department in no way minimizes the need for the practice of sound methods of dealing with human problems on the part of the foreman and other persons in the line organization. On the contrary, it indicates that management regards the problem of manpower as being so important as to require the aid of specialists in the field.

PERSONNEL FUNCTIONS

The personnel manager is not a supervisor or a boss except insofar as the employees in his own department are concerned. He cannot give orders to either the worker or the foreman. His authority over activities in the shop is limited to assisting the foreman in dealing with problems as they arise and in advising with top management concerning policies as they relate to personnel. He manages directly none of the work of production but only those activities that concern employees, such as recreation, health, and cafeteria service. The personnel manager cannot issue commands but can only advise. If his recommendations are not followed, he can refer the problem to a higher executive; but he cannot take direct action.

The foreman may be irritated by the interference of a representative of the personnel department. A further irritation may arise as a result of communications within the organization. In the absence of staff departments, all communications concerning conditions in a manufacturing department originate with the foreman; and some unfavorable facts may be suppressed or glossed over through the averaging or totaling of weekly or monthly production figures or other data. The staff departments, on the other hand, are anxious to straighten out difficulties and to report them to officers up the line in order that they may prove how useful they are to the organization. The foreman would prefer not to report his difficulties and problems which the personnel department may want to play up as justification for its existence. This situation requires tact on the part of the personnel manager.

The personnel function increases in importance with the size of the company and the plant. In larger companies, there is danger that the top executives will lose sight of employee desires and interests and that the employees will misunderstand the motives of top management. The difficulty is due in part to the existence of a number of horizontal levels in the organization. In multiplant companies the plants are smaller and the local management may establish fairly close personal relationships with the workers. In such a company the personnel manager at the main office formulates general personnel policies which are made effective through a local representative or personnel manager at each plant.

Development of Personnel Function. The first personnel departments, as explained in Chapter 1 (p. 18), were no more than employment departments. Although their activities were slightly expanded prior to World War I, the scope remained rather limited. In 1916 a progressive personnel manager explained that the purposes of his department were to improve human relationships and to reduce labor turnover through employment and placement activities. The employment department sought to develop a better labor force by studying the requirements of the various jobs and by employing people who could best meet the requirements. Since new employees were not always fully qualified for their jobs, the employment department carried on a limited amount of training. Exit interviews with departing employees were designed to find instances of poor placement and to eradicate the causes of employee dissatisfaction with their work.

After World War I personnel work steadily expanded. Many new techniques were devised, and old methods were improved. Notable progress was made in methods of selecting and training workers; and personnel activities were expanded to include numerous employee services, employee counseling, job evaluation, merit rating, and other activities.

Relations with Unions. Union relationships have become exceedingly important, and the personnel department necessarily concerns itself with the union, although the top executives also participate in the handling of such problems. In most large manufacturing companies, the relations between the company and the union, or unions, are stated in a formal contract. Negotiations with the union in relation to the contract are conducted in close consultation with the top executives, and the personnel manager may participate only to the extent of rendering advice. The contract includes a wide variety of provisions. It would always provide for the recognition of the union as the bargaining agent of the employees, or a part of them. It also defines the groups of workers for whom the union is authorized to bargain. It usually provides for the checkoff or the deduction of union dues and assessments from the pay of employees. Miscellaneous clauses provide for seniority rights, the conditions under which seniority rights may be lost, the manner of spreading work to prevent layoffs, the order in which workers will be laid off, discharges, and promotions. Other provisions pertain to extra payment for nightwork, odd shifts, overtime, paid vacations, holidays, and other compensation. The contract sometimes provides for various phases of working conditions, such as health, safety, and sanitation. The contract states the date when the agreement will become effective, the duration, the date of termination, and the method of renewal.

In day-to-day relationships with the union, management is represented by the foreman with the assistance of the personnel department. The foreman receives complaints from workers and usually settles difficulties without any necessity for consulting anyone else. Some questions may be referred to the superior, who may be the plant superintendent or the general foreman. If the complaint is not handled by the foreman in a manner that is satisfactory to the worker, the problem may be referred to the personnel department by either the worker or the union representative. If the difficulty is not settled in the personnel department, the worker or the union may appeal to the next level of the company organization. It is important for both the company and the workers that grievances be settled at as low a level in the organization as possible.

Organization for Personnel Relations. A possible organization for personnel and industrial relations is shown in Figure 48. As indicated

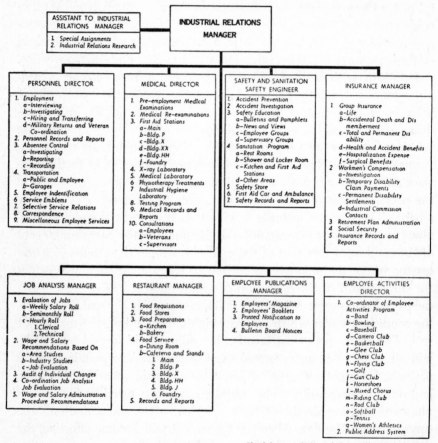

Used by permission of Caterpillar Tractor Co.

FIG. 48. Organization of Personnel Department

by this illustration of the organization within the Caterpillar Tractor Company, the head of the department is called *industrial relations manager* rather than *personnel manager*. Moreover, the departmental organization in this company should not be regarded as fixed because the details of the organization vary with the company. The Caterpillar Tractor Company has an unusually elaborate program of personnel activities.

PERSONNEL OBJECTIVES AND POLICIES

The principal objective of early personnel departments was to reduce labor turnover by proper methods of selection, placement, and transfer when necessary. This objective still remains one of the principal aims. However, personnel work is now directed also at developing a loyalty to the company and an understanding of its problems. This objective is accomplished by a manifestation of a genuine interest in the worker and a recognition of his worth as an individual. Activities that are designed solely to develop loyalty to the company or to create a better understanding of company problems will usually be recognized as such by the worker and branded as propaganda. The union is likely to denounce such a program as a snare to trap the worker and to undermine the position of organized labor. Consequently, the work of the personnel department should be motivated by a sincere interest in the worker as an individual. Loyalty to the company and improved morale should be by-products of policies that can be justified on other grounds.

Furthering Company Objectives. The personnel manager is expected to criticize or evaluate a proposed program or policy from the point of view of the effectiveness of the work force. However, he cannot afford to put himself in the position of opposing changes that will benefit the company. He is, after all, a part of the management; and his purpose is an increase in company profits. The personnel manager is therefore in a very different position from that of an officer of the union. While both are expected to oppose policies that would be detrimental to the worker, the personnel manager cannot become a partisan. The employee, therefore, cannot expect him to carry a controversy up through the higher levels of management as the union may do. The personnel manager himself can never be sure how far he may safely go in advocating or urging concessions for a worker, since he may undermine his own position. The worker, therefore, is likely to regard with some suspicion the representations of management that the personnel department exists for the protection of his interests.

Developing an Efficient and Loyal Work Force. To increase the co-operativeness of the worker, the personnel department should have an understanding of the worker and his problems. The more significant wants and interests of the worker have been discussed in Chapter 7 (p. 120). His most pressing interests concern working conditions, supervision, security, and pay. The view of the average worker is limited in scope, but he feels keenly concerning the things which he does see. From his point of view, the most important representative of the management is his supervisor. In a less significant position are the members of the personnel department, the time-study and standards department, and other staff departments with which he comes in contact. Top management, although actually more significant, is farther removed and assumes a less prominent position. The attitude of the average worker is also profoundly affected by the fear that his job and his future are insecure. A management that can offer security will profit in many ways from an improved worker attitude.

A personnel program should take cognizance of the fact that the worker belongs to the group. The procedure for selection and placement of workers will fail unless due allowance is made for that fact. White persons may not readily accept a Negro; Polish workers may not accept a Greek; and men may resent the employment of women in jobs that they regard as men's work. Group solidarity is often based upon religion, social relationships, club membership, or nationality. Experience has shown that the existence of groups is essential to plant solidarity and stability. New enterprises which have not established a group relationship are plagued by excessive absenteeism, a high rate of turnover, and low morale.

Every person desires the respect of his fellows: This desire is most keenly·felt in closely knit groups, although it exists in all societies. How much work a person does may be more affected by what the group expects than it is by the score he makes on intelligence or manual dexterity tests. This significant fact should be recognized in the formulation of personnel programs. It may work for or against the interests of the company.

Employee attitudes and loyalty are affected by all of the experiences of the worker in the company and his contacts with supervisors, fellow workers, representatives of the personnel department, and other persons. The greatest influence upon morale is probably exerted by the foremen because their contacts are most frequent. The personnel department must have the co-operation of operating executives to bring about changes in working conditions or to correct inequities. However, the personnel director can exert much influence by helping to keep line executives informed, making recommendations for new policies, and showing the importance of worker attitudes.

Statement of Personnel Policies. Recognizing that the worker is interested in the general policies that guide the management in its dealing with employees, many companies have formulated a statement of their policies and have made them available to any interested person. The statement may be brief, since it consists of general principles that require application to specific problems. It usually makes reference to the interests of employees, the public, the managmeent, and the stockholders. For example, the statement of one company includes the following:

The following principles and procedures comprise the company's labor relations policy:

Recognition of the individual worth of each employee, and of his need for self-expression and self-improvement.

No discrimination by the company or its employees against any employee because of membership or nonmembership in any church, society, fraternity, or union.

Training of employees for more important work; promotion based on demonstrated ability.

A policy of at least matching prevailing rates for similar work in comparable operations in the community, as well as prevailing conditions of employment. Changes in living costs are also taken into consideration.

An adequate grievance procedure, together with well-established rules for discipline and discharge.

A genuine belief in collective bargaining principles—with the employee individually or with his accredited representative.

Continuity of employment, limited only by the work load and by the competence of the individual.

The promotion of effective health, sanitation, and safety programs.[1]

The statement of policies is usually supplemented by a more detailed statement of company rules and regulations and by descriptions of special services and benefits. The most common booklet of this kind is the employee handbook. Handbooks differ considerably in their methods of presenting the information. Some are formal, factual, and dignified in their approach; and others are informal, friendly, and conversational in tone. Some give a great deal of information about the company, its product, its history, and its financial condition. Some stress rules and regulations; and others emphasize recreational activities, credit services, and other benefits provided for employees.

Responsibility for Human Relations. Although the personnel department has as its objective the improvement of personnel relations, its authority is limited to such activities as advising with top management concerning problems as to policy in the field of human relations, co-operating with the operating departments on personnel problems, assisting in the development of sources of labor supply, supervising methods of selecting workers, and assisting the operating executives in the handling of various problems in the field of personnel. In cases of difference of opinion between the operating executives and the personnel manager,

---

[1] The full statement includes thirteen provisions similar to those quoted.

the higher executives would usually be inclined to agree with the operating executives because they are responsible for getting out the work, meeting production schedules, and keeping down costs.

Qualities of Personnel Manager. To perform his work effectively, the personnel manager should have an appreciation of the problems of human relations and an understanding of what is required to establish harmonious relationships. He should also be able to convince other executives to accept right principles and to put them into practice. The proper principles would include a recognition of the dignity of the individual, fairness and impartiality in dealing with people, and freedom from racial or other prejudices. He should realize the costliness of error in dealing with human lives, and he should understand the importance of protecting a worker and the company from financial loss.

To establish good human relations, the personnel manager should be able to appraise a situation and to arrive at a sound judgment in the midst of controversy where emotional feelings run high. He should be willing to express his point of view, even to top executives. At the same time, he should be tactful and diplomatic. He should be willing to permit the foreman or the worker to have the credit when a difficulty has been satisfactorily handled. This attitude on his part is not easily developed because he may be anxious to convince top management that he is rendering a worthwhile service to the company.

The personnel director is expected to develop a program for improving the morale of employees and establishing better relations with them. However, in most cases, such a program means more paper work for the foreman and other line personnel in the preparation of reports of employee performance, the rating of employees on their efficiency or promise of further development, the preparation of descriptions of jobs in the department, and the assembling of other data. The personnel director must steer a difficult middle course to perform his function properly without arousing the opposition of operating personnel.[2]

Most of the proposals of the personnel director would require a change in operating methods, procedures, or practices. For example, the personnel director might wish to inaugurate a new program of training, merit rating, counseling with employees, or accident prevention. People naturally resist changes, and the personnel director will be required to find ways of overcoming resistance. While the methods will vary with the people and the circumstances of the situation, he may find it desirable to consult with operating executives in the working out of the

---

[2] See Dalton E. McFarland, "Dilemma of the Industrial Relations Director," *Harvard Business Review*, Vol. XXXII, No. 4 (1954), pp. 123–32.

details of a change. He should consult them early enough to permit them to make suggestions that will be incorporated in the plans. If he permits operating executives to assist in the development of a program, he may give them a feeling that the plans are at least partially their own.[3]

Evaluation of Personnel Work.   Management usually accepts personnel activities as being essential to the success of any large company. However, the value of personnel work is not easily determined because any improvement in human relations is usually the result of the work of many persons and because the results of personnel work are intangible. Some measurement of the gains in relation to costs may be achieved by studying labor turnover, production records, absenteeism, labor costs, and profits. The results of some activities such as a safety program or employee training may be stated in dollars and cents and compared with costs.[4] A substantial part of the benefits will be reflected in the human values, such as greater self-respect of the individual, an appreciation of fair play, and the intangible factor of employee attitudes.

Index of Employee Relations.   Some companies have attempted to compute an index of employee relations by converting such data as the figures for labor turnover, absenteeism, tardiness, scrap, accidents, and grievances into percentages, with figures for an earlier year taken as 100. The various series are then averaged to compute one figure which is used as an index. In this way, the company attempts to evaluate the success of its employee relations program from year to year. A company that owns and operates several branches or plants may undertake to compare the programs of the various plants by the use of such an index.

While an index of employee relations may have some value, it should be used with caution. The success of any program depends upon many factors that are not under the control of the industrial relations manager or even the persons in the operating division. Moreover, employee attitudes and opinions may not be reflected in any of the data that are used in the computation of the index. Many of the intangibles are impossible to measure even though they are important.[5] The management is concerned with various aspects of quantity of production,

---

[3] See Paul R. Lawrence, "How to Deal with Resistance to Change," *Harvard Business Review*, Vol. XXX, No. 3 (1954), pp. 47–57.

[4] See Robert Saltonstall, "Evaluating Personnel Administration," *Harvard Business Review*, Vol. XXX, No. 6 (1952), pp. 93–104.

[5] See Chris Argyris, "The Organization: What Makes It Healthy?" *Harvard Business Review*, Vol. XXXVI, No. 6 (1958), pp. 107–16.

quality of the product, cost, and human relations which may be affected by the personnel program but are not determined entirely by such activities.

QUESTIONS

1. It has been said that the personnel director faces a dilemma in that a strong personnel program will require much paper work of the foreman, which they dislike, and that a weak program will fail to accomplish the purposes of the personnel department. Explain the two alternatives, and indicate how the dilemma may be avoided.

2. The personnel director faces a problem with regard to company policy. The policy is determined by top executives, sometimes without the consent of the personnel director, and the support of the personnel director is required in carrying out the program. Explain methods of handling this problem.

3. The personnel director is expected to explain personnel policies to the workers, and he is also expected to support company policy. Can he expect workers to come to him for the settlement of grievances if he is partisan, favoring the company in every instance?

4. Is the personnel director expected to improve human relations throughout the plant? How can he do so when his relations with foremen and workers are not constant and close?

5. The union claims to be the only organization that protects the interests of the worker as a human being and not as a factor in production. Is this a fair statement? Can the company become too human in its dealing with workers? Explain.

6. Is the most important role in the communication of company policies to workers properly played by the personnel director or by the foremen?

7. How can the management know whether the personnel department is worth its cost to the company?

8. Will workers listen to statements of the personnel department in defense of company policy, or do they dismiss such statements as propaganda? How can the company develop the proper attitude on the part of workers?

9. What is the responsibility of the personnel director regarding proposals by other executives for programs that would lower employee morale? If they consistently criticize such proposals, may they become branded as obstructionists?

10. Some companies do not publish statements of personnel policies because they wish to meet any new situation in the light of the circumstances of the moment. Defend or criticize.

11. What is the responsibility and the authority of the personnel director regarding working conditions that might be injurious to the health of workers?

CASES

53. COMPANY RULES CONCERNING ABSENCES AND TARDINESS

The personnel director of the Apex Spring and Wire Co. was concerned about the number of absences and the amount of tardiness. After discussing the problem with the plant superintendent, he called a meeting of the foremen to discuss possible changes in the rules. It was generally agreed that absences and tardiness were excessive, and various suggestions were made for correcting the situation.

One foreman suggested that absences and tardiness reflected a low level of morale and that all phases of management practices and policies should be re-examined. He mentioned methods of selecting persons for employment, the induction procedure, methods of handling grievances, wage rates and bonuses, and methods of supervision. The personnel director thought that the proposed corrective measures were too broad and that attention should be directed to particular problems.

Another foreman thought that the present rule concerning tardiness was too severe and that the rule should be relaxed. According to the present rule, a worker who did not report to work promptly at starting time was required to report to the front office and receive a warning slip before reporting for work. He was further penalized by loss of pay for $1/4$ hour. The penalty tended to build up resentment because it was unfair. The foreman thought that a period of grace might be permitted and that the worker who arrived no more than five minutes late should be allowed to begin work without penalty. In his department, the foreman said, the workers were not on an assembly line and they could begin work at any time. The plan of permitting a grace period was being followed in another plant, and the workers often made up the five minutes by extra work at the lunch period or at quitting time.

To reduce absenteeism, a foreman suggested that the company should establish a number of days of sick leave each year, and it should agree to pay the employee his regular pay if his absences were due to illness. The number of days of sick leave would depend upon the number of days of service with the company. An employee who did not take all of his sick leave during any year would receive pay for the days not taken by the end of the year. This plan had been tried for clerical workers, the foreman said, and it had almost eliminated absenteeism.

Another foreman suggested that a coffee break should be instituted. He said that the employees managed to take a break each morning and each afternoon on one excuse or another, and he thought it would be better if they all took a break of the same length at the same time. Another foreman said that the company paid for eight hours of work each day and was entitled to that amount of production time. The suggestion was made by another foreman that the institution of a coffee break would not only reduce absenteeism but would also increase production.

The method by which coffee was supplied to many workers at one time was discussed. The coffee could be placed on a table in pitchers, and each worker could serve himself and drop his money into a box under the honor system. According to another plan, coffee breaks in various departments could be staggered with one department stopping work at a time. Still another plan would provide for one worker from a department to go to the cafeteria and get coffee for all of the workers at one time. It was also suggested the company install automatic vending machines where each worker could serve himself after dropping a nickel or a dime into a slot. If a worker wanted to bring coffee from home in a thermos bottle, he would be permitted to do so.

The personnel director thanked the foremen for their suggestions and stated that he would discuss the problem and their suggestions with the plant manager.

Required:

1. Evaluate the suggestions made by the foremen.

2. Was the procedure of the personnel director in asking foremen for suggestions the proper way to handle the problem?

54. ENFORCEMENT OF COMPANY RULES

The J. C. Hardy Co., Inc., published a book of rules and regulations and gave a copy to every employee. One of the rules stated that any employee who was unable to report for work should notify the foreman before work time on the day he was absent. The rules also stated that excessive absence from work would constitute reason for discharge. The company had a contract with a labor union which provided for the arbitration of controversies which could not be settled directly by representatives of the company and the union.

Although the company has attempted to deal fairly with its employees and to demonstrate an understanding of their problems, it has experienced considerable difficulty with the rule concerning absences. The difficulties arise because employees present reasons which seem to them to justify prolonged or frequent absences. The company has found it difficult to make exceptions to the rule or to define the exact meaning of excessive absences.

To cite some examples of the difficulties, Charles Wilson took a trip over the week end to a city forty miles away. He drank too many beers at a tavern, got into a fight, and was jailed on several counts including drunkenness in a public place, disturbing the peace, attacking another person, resisting arrest, and assaulting an officer. Because he was unable to pay his fines, he spent thirty-five days in jail. He notified the company of the reason for his absence after the fifth day. The company notified him while he was still in jail that he was discharged, although the rules did not state that an employee would be discharged for being sent to jail.

Howard Annis was required to be absent from work frequently because his mother was an invalid and his brother was a mental case. Both his mother and brother had spent considerable time in hospitals but had been sent home because of the expense. Over a period of a year, Howard had reported for work an average of only nine days each month. Although Howard always notified the foreman in advance that he would not report for work, he was discharged for excessive absences. Howard's personal file showed that he had been warned ten times that excessive absences constituted cause for discharge.

Ralph Clayton, a stock handler in the storeroom, requested permission to be absent on Thursday and Friday because he wished to take part in the wedding of a high school friend. He needed the two days for rehearsals, a luncheon, and parties given by himself and others. His request was denied because he was needed for inventory taking. Since the plant would be closed until the inventory was completed, his services were considered to be necessary. He took the time off anyway and was therefore discharged.

In all three of these cases, the arbitrators upheld the right of the company to discharge the employee. **In rendering the decision concerning Howard Annis,** the arbitrator commented as follows:

"The company cannot operate its plant without its employees, and it requires the services of a worker at each work station along the line. Regularity of attendance is necessary to the planning of the flow of work. While the company can provide some flexibility in its work schedules, the reassignment of work because of absentees increases costs and places serious burdens upon the foreman and the personnel manager. The interests of the company and the work force as a whole outweigh the desires and interests of one employee and may demand some sacrifice on his part."

Although the company was upheld in these cases, the management knows that arbitrators do not follow precedent and that another arbitrator may render a different decision in another case that is similar. The personnel manager therefore requests the policy committee to consider the following questions:

1. How many absences are required to constitute excessive absence?
2. Does the period over which the employee is absent make any difference?
3. Is the nature of the job a factor in the absences?
4. When should warnings be given? To how many warnings is the employee entitled?
5. Is the company required to take any steps other than to issue a warning?
6. Should the company request the co-operation of the union in correcting the practice of absenteeism, or is a notice to the union sufficient?

Questions:

1. Were the discharges justified?
2. Should the company attempt to make its rule more definite?

55. INCREASE IN LABOR TURNOVER

When Alex Jones became personnel manager of the Heath Company, he was able to obtain the support of the president, Mr. Thomas Heath, in making a number of changes in personnel practices and policies. He developed a comprehensive plan for improving relationships with people in the community by his speaking engagements, by holding open house on certain days when people could visit the plant, and by organizing a company basketball team. He checked the procedure for interviewing applicants for jobs to assure that interviewers were courteous and considerate. In many other ways, he attempted to improve the selection procedure and the method of inducting new employees to their jobs. In time, Mr. Jones organized various service activities for the convenience and comfort of employees.

Mr. Jones began the tabulation of certain statistical information pertaining to the work force, and he regularly discussed with Mr. Heath certain of the statistical data. One series of such data pertained to labor turnover. An index of turnover was computed as follows:

$$\text{Labor turnover} = \frac{(\text{Number of separations} + \text{Number of accessions} \div 2 \text{ x } 100}{\text{Average number on the payroll}}$$

The index was computed each month. The turnover rate usually fell between

5 and 6, whereas it had been about 10 before Mr. Jones came to the company.

In his discussion of the turnover figure with Mr. Heath, Mr. Jones was careful not to take credit for the improvement. He pointed out that employee attitudes were affected by all of the methods of supervision, the physical and economic security of employees, and other factors. However, Mr. Jones was quite sure that Mr. Heath gave him credit for much of the improvement.

Recently, Mr. Jones received the turnover figure from the clerk who computed it, and he was disturbed to learn that the figure had increased to 7.6. He began immediate investigation to determine the cause since he knew that Mr. Heath would expect an explanation.

Questions:

1. What are the possible causes for the increase in labor turnover?

2. Is the index reliable as a measure of the success of personnel methods and policies?

26 Employment
of
People

THE employment procedure was the first phase of personnel work to receive the attention of management, and it has increased in importance in recent years. Under present labor laws and strong union organization, a worker who is once employed soon achieves a claim upon his job which makes it difficult for management to discharge him. The importance of employment procedures is increased also by the policy of promotion from within, since future executives may enter the service of the company by way of the employment office.

SOURCES OF LABOR SUPPLY

The development of sources of supply for applicants should be regarded as the first step in the process of employee selection because the preference of one source instead of another results in the elimination of persons who are not available in the source that is developed. The employment department is not interested in appealing to all possible applicants but prefers a group that represents partial selection. The larger the number of applicants the greater is the cost of selection in both money and time. The employment manager therefore begins his selection by cultivating some sources and neglecting others. However, additional sources may be utilized in busy seasons or in years of increasing production.

Inside Sources. A position that is vacated by separation of an employee is often supplied by transfer or promotion of another worker.

Vacancies may also be filled by the employment of persons who formerly held jobs with the company. Less risk is taken in employing such
persons than would be involved in employing persons whose records
are not known within the company. A closely related source is the
recommendation of a person who is presently employed. This kind of
recommendation may be dependable because the person now employed
is familiar with the qualifications and the interests of the person being
recommended and also with the working conditions within the company. An employee might hesitate to recommend a person who will
not succeed.

Outside Sources. Many sources of employees are available outside
the company. If the company has a reputation in the community as a
good place to work, some qualified applicants may appear at the employment office or make application by mail without any effort on the
part of the employment department. Employment agencies may also be
used to direct applicants to the company upon request of the employment manager for workers possessing certain skills. Employment agencies are either public or private. Public agencies are supported by state
or federal taxation. Private agencies charge a fee which is usually paid
by the applicant. The reliability of employment agencies varies widely;
some use discretion in the selection of the persons whom they recommend, while others are less careful.

Representatives of the company who search for persons with desirable
qualifications are used by many companies. Scouts frequently visit colleges to solicit applications from graduates in chemistry, engineering,
business administration, and other courses. However, the soliciting of
the employees of other companies is regarded as unethical, unless it is
done with the knowledge of the other employer. Labor pirating may
result in retaliation to the detriment of both companies.

Advertising for applicants by newspaper, radio, or television is a reliable source for many types of workers, particularly in larger cities.
Some employers use advertising only when other sources fail to supply
enough applicants. Specialists in such fields as accounting, time study,
costs, and budgeting may often be reached through trade and professional magazines.

Requirements for Good Sources. Every employer must decide for
himself which sources of applicants he should use at any particular time
for the kinds of jobs and the conditions that prevail in his plant. The
sources used should provide a sufficient number of applicants but not so
many that the work of interviewing and selecting the qualified persons

is too great. A source is unsatisfactory if too many persons that clearly are unqualified make application for employment.

A company should use a source of labor supply that will enable it to employ people with suitable technical qualifications who will work for the wages paid, who will associate with the other workers on the job, and who will prove to be satisfactory. The employer should determine the number of applicants obtained from each source of supply, the number who are accepted for employment, and the number who are found by experience to possess the desired qualifications.

METHODS OF SELECTING WORKERS

When a worker is needed, the foreman may prepare a requisition for help. After the requisition has been approved by the division chief, it is sent to the personnel department. The employment section has on file the job descriptions and job specifications for the various jobs. The employment section may also have on file an application from a qualified person. If so, that person is invited to call. For higher ranking jobs, some of the present employees may be available by transfer or promotion. If the job cannot be filled by a present employee or an applicant previously interviewed and investigated, it may be necessary to select a worker from those currently making application.

Methods for selecting workers are not expected in every case to result in the employment of applicants who will succeed and the rejection of those who would fail if employed. Employment methods cannot be expected to rank or to grade workers in a manner that would be predictive of the degree of success. Employment methods can be considered to be good if they make possible the classification of applicants into three groups: those likely to succeed on the job, those likely to fail, and those whose success is doubtful. In the following paragraphs, some of the methods used in selecting employees will be described.

Preliminary Interview. The preliminary interview is the initial greeting of the applicant by the receptionist together with a brief discussion of the purpose of his visit to the employment office. Its purpose is to find what type of job the person is seeking, to inform him whether such a position is available, and to instruct him to fill out an application blank if that is the proper procedure. When no job suited to the applicant is open or in prospect, the applicant should be told that this is the case in order that he may save his time. This plan is desirable for both the applicant and the company.

Application Blank. The application blank should be filled out by the applicant. The information requested may be classified into four groups. Some information is designed to identify the applicant and to make it possible to communicate with him later. This information includes name, address, date and place of birth, telephone number, business address, social security number, and color of hair and eyes. Other information is designed to indicate the kind of job for which the applicant is suited and the prospects of success. This information is difficult to evaluate because it varies with the job and is in many cases a matter of opinion. The information of this type may include sex, height, weight, citizenship, marital status, number of dependents, education, languages spoken, military record, physical disabilities sustained in service, home-ownership, employment experience, and machines operated. Other data requested on the application blank are desirable to enable the employment section to verify statements made. This information consists of names and addresses of former employers and persons named as references. Finally, some information may be used by the personnel department to serve persons employed. The data include fraternity or lodge affiliation, athletics or sports activities, musical instruments played, and hobbies. Unless the applicant understands the purpose of such questions, he may regard them as an intrusion. He may refuse to answer such personal questions as whether his wife works and whether he is a vegetarian. The applicant may also think it unfair to ask what was his salary in his last position and what is the lowest salary he would accept.

The uses of the application blank are indicated in part by the information requested. The information may also be used as a basis for opening the interview, since the interviewer knows the name of the applicant and something about his education and experience. It makes for a better interview by eliminating any necessity for recording personal data. If no suitable opening is available when the application is received, the blank may be filed for future reference. If the applicant is hired, the blank becomes a part of his permanent file.

Letter of Application. Applications for positions, particularly those in the staff departments, are frequently received by mail. They supply personal information concerning the applicant and also afford some basis for judging his ability, unless the applicant had assistance in composing and writing the letter. Letters of application are necessarily supplemented by other methods of selection before the employment contract is completed. Their value is that they may indicate whether personal interviews, letters of recommendations, tests, and investigations are desirable.

Employment Interview. One purpose of the employment interview is to get information from the applicant. An attempt is made during the interview to reach an opinion as to the applicant's general ability; his technical training and experience; his success in positions previously held; his physical defects, if any; his health; and other qualifications varying with the job and also the interviewer. The personal traits and the experience of the applicant are compared with the job specifications or the man specifications which were previously established. The interviewer also attempts to determine whether the applicant would be able to make friends with the other workers and to become a good member of the organization.

Another purpose of the employment interview is to inform the applicant concerning the job and the company. The interviewer should undertake to sell the job to the applicant but not to oversell it. He should point out both the desirable and the undesirable features. The applicant especially wants to know the rate of pay, the hours of work, the duties, the conditions of work, the possibilities of promotion, the probable duration of the job, the dates of paydays, accident hazards, uniforms or clothing required, and many other facts concerning employment. However, the interviewer should not take time to inform the applicant if he decides that the applicant is not qualified.

The information which the interviewer imparts to the applicant is obtained from statements of company policies, rules, and regulations and also from the job description. As explained earlier, the job description shows what the worker does, why he does it, how he does it, and the working conditions under which the work is done.

The interview is also intended to create a friendly attitude toward the company on the part of the applicant. A person who is to become an employee should receive favorable first impressions. In handling large numbers of applicants day after day, the interviewer sometimes forgets that each applicant approaches the employment office with anxiety and perhaps timidity. A rejected applicant should leave the employment office with the feeling that the management appreciates the worth of an individual and that the company would be a good place to work. This attitude is very desirable not only because persons seeking employment need sympathy, encouragement, or perhaps vocational guidance but also because the number of rejected persons residing in the community may, after a period of years, be large enough to affect the attitude of the public toward the company. By showing courtesy, sincerity, and a personal interest in the applicant, the employment section can exert a strong influence upon the public relations of the company.

The interview may be conducted in an informal conversational manner. When this method is used the interviewer discusses the various features of the job and attempts to get the applicant to talk freely about himself. Without a fixed procedure, he lets the discussion follow a natural course. Before the interview is ended, he undertakes to learn from the applicant any facts which have not been adequately considered.

In another type of interview, which is called the aggressive or offensive interview, an attempt is made to put the applicant to a test to see how he will handle himself in a trying situation. For example, the interviewer may ask the applicant why he considers himself qualified for the position. He may constantly ask other questions which put the applicant on the defensive. This type of interview may fail to accomplish the three purposes previously stated. When the procedure followed in the employment office becomes generally known, the method will become ineffective for accomplishing whatever purpose was intended. This system is usually regarded as having little to recommend it. As Herbert Moore has said, the interviewer "should avoid being an authoritative impertinent cross-examiner who puts the applicant on the defensive and prevents a natural expression of hopes and interests."[1]

The interviewer may follow a fixed set of questions and record the answers as they are given by the applicant. This method is often used when no application blank is required of the applicant, and it is also used to obtain additional information not requested on the blank. The information may be recorded during the interview or after the applicant has departed. However, the usual patterned interview attempts to obtain so much detailed information that the record is necessarily made as the interview proceeds.

The interviewer may evaluate or grade the applicant on the basis of the various qualities required, such as personal appearance, conversational ability, enthusiasm, general knowledge, attitude toward the company, and experience in the job for which the applicant is being considered. The applicant may be rated separately on each trait, and the ratings may be recorded without averaging. Another method is to figure a total score for each applicant on the basis of the ratings assigned on each quality. A total score should be used with caution because a low rating on one quality might in fact completely disqualify an applicant.

Recommendations. Letters of recommendations are widely used but almost universally discounted. Their value is limited unless the person

---

[1] Herbert Moore, *Psychology for Business and Industry* (New York: McGraw-Hill Book Co., Inc., 1939), p. 96.

writing the letter knows what qualifications are important for the position and can judge the kind of person who will succeed in it. Furthermore, he is presumed to know the applicant well enough to speak of his qualifications and to be sufficiently honest to say what he believes. Letters of recommendation may fail on any one of these counts. The applicant may be expected to give as references the names of persons who will write favorable letters.

The honesty and sincerity of the person making the recommendation may be affected by the circumstances under which he is asked to write. His recommendation may be assumed to be least frank if the letter is requested by the applicant and is given to him for forwarding to the employment officer. Such letters are of little or no value. The letter has more value if it is requested by the applicant but is sent directly to the employment officer. This type of letter is occasionally of some value. It should be judged by the faintness of praise given the applicant or the enthusiasm manifested by the writer. The recommendation has most value if the inquiry is received from the employment officer and a confidential reply is made directly to him.

If an inquiry is made to persons whose names are given by the applicant as references, a form may be included which calls for answers to a number of questions. The form attempts to elicit information as to the experience, skill, and personal traits of the applicant. The questions asked might, for example, pertain to the type of work for which the applicant is qualified, his industriousness, his habits, his moral character, and his integrity. Such an evaluation of an applicant may be useful in some cases, especially if the results are not entirely favorable.

Personal Investigation.   An investigation by the employment section may be made by personal visitation or by telephone. It is used to verify statements made on the application blank and during the interview. Personal investigations sometimes reveal dishonesty, excessive drinking, and other serious facts which would otherwise not be detected. Since the applicant may request his associates to tell only certain things concerning him, the scope should be broad enough to prevent collusion. Questions which are asked should be of the type that cannot be answered by "Yes" or "No." The investigator might ask, for example, what the nature of the responsibility of the applicant was or what programs he initiated or completed.

Two objections may be made to the personal investigation. First, it is too costly to be generally used. Second, the wrong kind of questions asked of landlords or business associates may cause them to believe that the applicant is suspected of wrongdoing. To avoid this danger, the questions should be worded with care; and the investigators should be trained to follow prescribed methods.

Mental Tests. Mental or general intelligence tests have been the subject of much controversy and much experimentation. While opinions differ, most authorities consider that the tests are of value, provided that they are carefully prepared and administered and that exclusive reliance is not placed upon them. The use of mental tests in employment assumes, first, that intelligence is important for the job and, second, that the tests measure intelligence. As for the first assumption, a high degree of intelligence is not necessary for all jobs. In some types of work a person of lower mental capacity may be more satisfied and more willing to stay on the job than an ambitious, aggressive person of high mental capacity. Persons with low test scores should not be placed in jobs where they might cause great damage to materials or equipment or where they might cause themselves or fellow workers to be injured. If the tests measure intelligence, a distinction should be made between intellectual capacity and achievement, that is, between ability to learn and present experience, education, and training. An example of a short general intelligence test is given in Figure 49.

GENERAL INTELLIGENCE TEST

Check the one best answer to each of these questions

1. A nose is to a man as a snout is to a:
    Dog.... Cat.... Pig.... Fish.... Bird....
2. Write a number after each word to show the order in which it should be used if a good sentence is to be made of all the words.
    embankment ( ) train ( ) down ( ) lost ( ) an ( )
    people ( ) lives ( ) rolled ( ) many ( ) the ( )
    and ( ) their ( )
3. A place in which to eat begins with:
    m.... c.... i.... o.... f....
4. 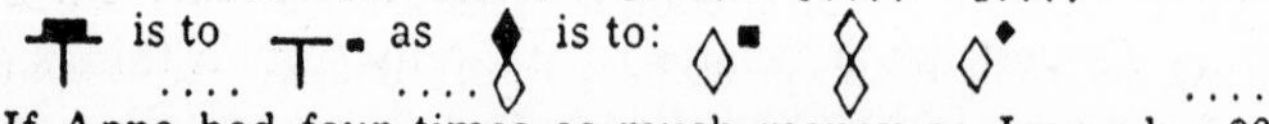 ⌐ is to ⌐. as ◆ is to: ◇■ ◇ ◇•
5. If Anna had four times as much money as Jean plus $8. she would have $24. How much money does Jean have?
    $4.... $8.... $12.... $16.... $64....
6. A and B had a race. B had a start of 30 yards, but A ran 4 yards while B ran 3. A won by 40 yards. How long was the course?
    150.... 350.... 320.... 280.... 240....

FIG. 49. A Short Intelligence Test

Designed by Donald E. Super for publication in *Look* magazine, Vol. X, No. 24 (1946), p. 55. Reproduced by permission of the author and editor.

A good test should meet certain requirements. The directions to the candidate should be clear and concise. If questions have varying weights, the weighting should be indicated. Separate instructions should be given to true-false, matching, completion, and multiple-choice questions. The test should require a minimum of writing. Each question should include only one basic point or idea, and only one correct answer for each question should be possible. Statements should be positive or contain single negatives. Double negatives should be avoided. The number of questions should be large enough to reduce the possibility of chance scoring. Questions should be so difficult or so numerous that few or no persons will measure perfect. Few should make scores of zero. The range of grades should be as wide as possible to permit the ranking of the applicants.

In giving the test, the examiner should endeavor to quiet the fears of the candidates, since the results may be affected by their nervousness. All should start and stop at the same time because the time required is important in the scoring. Interruptions during the test should be prevented, if possible. Grades should be assigned, and the candidates should be ranked. If the group is sufficiently large, the candidates should be classified into percentiles for purposes of comparison with other groups of persons taking the test. It is usually considered inadvisable to tell the people their rank on the test because they may attach too much significance to slight differences. If the applicants are a select group, as a result of eliminations at earlier steps in the employment procedure, the results of the tests may be misleading. Tests should not be given to executives. Such a procedure would likely result in criticism of the whole program by those who made low scores.

Special Aptitude Tests. Numerous tests have been perfected to test special or particular ability which may be necessary to the performance of a specific task. Special aptitude tests usually require the use of especially designed equipment or mechanical devices. Tests are available for measuring such capacities as space comprehension, distance judging, quickness of motor responses, ability to distinguish colors, and manual or finger dexterity. Some of them test abilities that may later decrease in effectiveness, such as tests of vision. Others test abilities that may be developed by training, such as manual dexterity or memory. When used in conjunction with other methods of selection, special aptitude tests have much value.

Trade Tests. Trade tests, sometimes called "achievement tests," attempt to measure the knowledge of a trade skill in performing certain types of work at the time the tests are given. They are not intended to determine the ability of the applicant to learn. One type of trade test consists of a list of questions which are asked orally by the examiner. The advantage of this type of test is that it eliminates the danger that the applicant will misunderstand the questions. Persons who are not accustomed to take written examinations may do best on the oral examination. Care may be required in making the test standard.

The trade test may include pictures of tools or parts which the applicant is asked to identify or explain. This type of test is practical and can be made as difficult as desired. The test may be unfair if the tools or machines used are of a different make or model from those which are familiar to the applicant. A short test is shown in Figure 50.

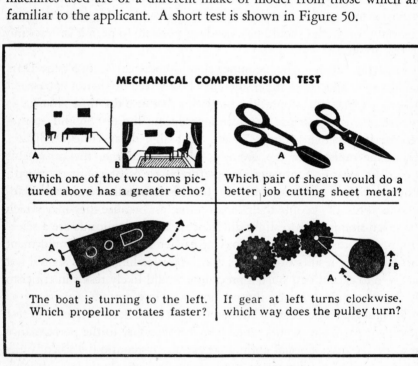

FIG. 50. A Short Mechanical Comprehension Test

A good type of trade test is the performance test, which requires the applicant to perform a small task which is similar to the job. This kind of test has been standardized, and the time allowed the applicant has been established by repeated use. Rules for scoring indicate the penalties for errors and omissions. Performance tests are usually expensive to design and administer.

Situational Testing. Since the best test of an applicant would be experience on the job, an effort may be made in the employment procedures to reproduce the working environment and to try out the applicant under such conditions. On the technical aspects of the work, this procedure may be very successful. For example, the applicant may be asked to take dictation and to type a letter, to operate a machine, to use a micrometer, or to drive a truck. His reaction to various aspects of a working environment cannot be easily tested, but some such tests are possible. A bus company may place the applicant in the seat of a bus, flash motion pictures of traffic conditions on a screen in front of him, and record the speed of his reactions in using brakes, steering wheel, accelerator, or horn. An applicant for a sales position may be interviewed under trying conditions to see how he will respond. A prospective supervisor may be required to direct two or more workers in performing simple tasks. Such tests must be carefully planned if they are to be worthwhile.

Testing the Test. A test can be properly used for selection, placement or other purposes only if the test scores bear some relationship to subsequent performance on the job. Performance may be measured by any one of several criteria, such as quantity of work, quality of work, time required to reach standard performance, regularity of attendance, safety record, or ability to adapt to new situations. Inasmuch as a test is usually designed to measure a specific trait, the record on the job may be compared with the extent to which the employee is found to possess the trait tested.

The relationship between the test scores and subsequent performance

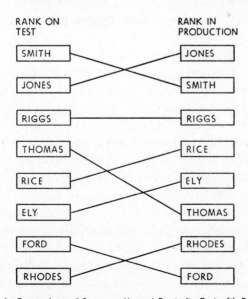

FIG. 51. Simple Comparison of Score on Manual Dexterity Test with Production Record

may be measured statistically by the computation of the coefficient of correlation. However, a simple measure of the relationship may be made by ranking the employees by their test scores and ranking the same persons again by their performance on the job as determined by any one criterion. This kind of comparison is illustrated in Figure 51. This diagram shows a fairly close relationship, since a test may indicate no more than capacity to do rather than willingness to work or to co-operate. A limitation of this type of comparison is that it cannot make allowance for the extent of differences in test scores or subsequent performance of the employees.

Physical Examination.   Physical examinations may be used for either the selection and rejection of applicants or their placement in work suited to their physical abilities. In hazardous industries, physical examinations may be desirable in order that workers may be protected from injuries due to their inability to hear or see well or to do heavy lifting, or due to their susceptibility to certain diseases. To be effective, examinations should be given at regular intervals and not merely at the time of their initial employment.

One purpose of the physical examination is to reduce employment and training costs by selecting workers who are qualified and who will profit from the training. Accident rates may be reduced by the proper placement of new employees. Another purpose of the examination is to reduce illness and absenteeism and also claims for compensation due to illness or disease existing at the time of employment. Fellow workers and customers may be protected from exposure to infectious diseases.

Physical examinations may be complete, or they may be limited in scope. They usually include tests of blood pressure, heart action, lungs, chest X ray, and eyes and ears; and they may include urinalysis. In a small plant the examination may be given by a local physician who is employed on a retainer basis. The examining physician may be asked to indicate whether the applicant can perform work that requires lifting, standing, walking, climbing, use of one or two hands, use of hands and feet, or exposure to dust, fumes, heat, noise, or moisture.

Use of Selection Methods.   Employers differ not only in the methods used in the selection of workers but also in the order in which the methods are used. Some applicants are rejected at each step in the employment procedure, and the steps that eliminate the greatest number of applicants should therefore be placed early. Another reason for early rejection of unqualified persons is that unqualified applicants should be informed of their rejection as soon as possible in order that they may seek employment elsewhere. Another factor in the procedure is the time required and the expense incurred. Cost considerations suggest that some tests might be deferred until many of the applicants have been rejected and fewer applicants remain to be tested. The employment procedure therefore requires careful study by the personnel manager.

INTRODUCING THE WORKER TO THE JOB

The final step in the employment procedure is the introduction of the worker to the job. This phase should not be neglected, for many separations result from failure of the applicant to become adjusted to the new situation. One objective of the induction procedure is to make the new employee feel that he is a part of the company and that he belongs to the group. It should also impart additional information concerning the company and the job. The induction procedure of one large employer provides that the applicant, after being employed, signs an employment card, payroll forms, and forms required by the government for purposes of social security and income tax deductions. He is next assigned a clock number and is given a temporary pass. He is instructed to return within two weeks for a permanent pass. The employment manager then gives an induction talk to a group of new employees. He gives the essential facts concerning company history, explains how the company started and how it expanded, discusses the policies of the company toward its employees, and explains the position of the factory in relation to the entire organization of the company. At the conclusion of his talk, he gives each new employee a copy of the union contract and a safety booklet. At this same meeting, new employees are welcomed by the personnel manager, who endeavors to make them feel at home as a part of the organization. The employee is then taken to the department to work. He is introduced to the superintendent, who explains the work of the department and the safety rules. The foreman inducts him into the job, shows him the locker room, washroom, and other employee facilities, and tells him how to get tools and materials. The foreman also tells him what to do if he is injured, how his pay is figured, and what his hours of work and his lunch period are.

The employee is then introduced to the timekeeper and shown how to punch the clock card. After he has been introduced to his fellow workers, he is given job instruction by the foreman and begins work.

Later, the employment manager writes a letter to the worker at his home. The letter is to be read by all members of the family and is designed to gain their loyalty to the company. After two weeks, the employee reports back to the employment section for his permanent pass.

At that time an effort is made to learn whether he has had any difficulties and whether he is in need of further assistance. Employee services not explained on the first day, such as clubs and recreation facilities, are then discussed with the worker.

EVALUATION OF SELECTION METHODS

Although the reliability of any one method of employee selection cannot easily be determined, some information may be gained by determining the reasons why employees are not retained by the company, why they quit, and why they cause trouble. For example, if new employees lack technical skills, the need for additional or improved tests in this area may be indicated. If they are involved in a large percentage of the accidents, either the selection methods or the induction procedure might need revision. If new employees fail to make the necessary social and mental adjustments, the fault might be found in the employment interview, the investigation of previous experience of the applicant, or the test of social interests. Much opportunity for improving the selection procedure may exist in any area.

The usual experience indicates that employment methods are more reliable in measuring or estimating technical skills than in measuring character traits, social interests, and ability to make adjustments. Although the difficulties of employees may have developed after the applicants have passed through the employment office, the facts indicate that most employee failures are due to such weaknesses as problem drinking, emotional disturbances, mental illness, accident proneness, violation of company rules and regulations, excessive absenteeism, vandalism, interpersonal frictions, and other manifestations of emotional difficulties. Weaknesses in character traits are most difficult to detect at the time of employment. Methods of detecting them and ways of avoiding such difficulties in employees will continue to require much study and research.

QUESTIONS

1. How can the employment manager know the qualities required for the various jobs throughout the plant? Can he get the necessary information from the job descriptions and the job specifications?

2. It has been said that the purpose of the employment interview is to get information, to give information, and to make a friend. Explain the types of information to which reference is made and indicate how the interviewer may make a friend.

3. Should the personnel director have experience on the various jobs in the plant before he undertakes personnel work? Why or why not?

4. The application blank frequently asks the applicant to list all of the jobs he has held since he left school and to give the reason for leaving in each case. Can he be expected to tell the truth if he has been discharged?

5. It has been said that the employment procedure is satisfactory if it enables the management to classify the applicants into three groups: those likely to succeed, those likely to fail, and an intermediate group whose possibilities are uncertain. Explain the limitations that cause the results of the procedure to be questionable.

6. How should the employment interview be conducted for the proper accomplishment of its purposes?

7. "Letters of recommendation are sealed with a shrug and opened with a smile." Explain the meaning of this statement. Does it indicate that the letter of recommendation is without value?

8. Before an applicant is offered a job, he may be taken to the place where he will work, introduced to the foreman, shown the machine or desk, and introduced to persons who work nearby. Why is this procedure desirable?

9. Is the induction of a new worker principally the work of the personnel department, or is it the work of the foreman? Do other workers play any part in the induction?

10. How can a company know whether or not its selection procedure is effective and economical of the time of applicants and company personnel?

11. What does the applicant want to know about the company and the job before he is employed?

12. One company always asks the applicant why he wants to work for the company. What would be a good answer to this question? What would be a poor answer?

CASES

56. THE WORKER AND THE UNION STEWARD

For many years the Wilkins Company had managed its personnel activities through a personnel department without a union. The company had what it considered a good program of personnel activities and services, and the management considered the morale of the work force to be high. However, a union representative succeeded in obtaining the required number of signatures of employees favoring a vote on the question of establishing a local of the national union. When the vote was taken, 78 per cent of the workers voted for the establishment of a union. They also voted for requiring all employees to join within a period of 30 days after their employment. This provision applied to persons on the payroll at the time the union was established at the plant.

One of the employees opposing unionization was Eva Meyer. Eva was well known to the personnel manager as well as the foreman because she had frequently become involved in difficulties with other workers. Her file in the office of the personnel department disclosed that she was 27 years of age. Her record

in high school was unusually good, and her family had intended to send her to
college. However, her father, who was a member of the faculty of a small
college, died when she was 16 years of age. Her mother obtained a position as
a clerical worker with the idea of providing for the further education of Eva.
Her health did not permit her to continue work, and Eva began a course in a
secretarial school. Partly because of a dislike for the work and partly because of
financial problems, Eva left the secretarial school to accept a job in a local manufacturing plant. She had held three such jobs before she came to the Wilkins
Company.

Although Eva did good work, she was not popular with the other workers.
When she first came with the company, the other girls had invited her to parties
and double dates. She always declined because she said she did not believe in
mixing work and social activities. She tended to become more and more isolated
from the social activities within the plant. She irritated the other girls by working until quitting time while the other workers took a few minutes at the end of
the day to wash up and prepare to leave. By doing so, she earned the name of
"five o'clock special." The other girls suspected that she was an informer because
she was seen talking with the foreman occasionally, and the foreman seemed to
know a good many things about what was going on in the department.

When the question of unionization came up for discussion, Eva talked against
the proposal. She said the workers were getting more than a union could ever
have obtained and that the workers had not been required to spend their money
for initiation fees and dues to get plant services. She said the workers would
just be throwing their money away for nothing and that a union would merely
antagonize the management. She expressed her views to the workers, the foreman, and the personnel manager. When the results of the voting were announced, Eva expressed her indignation and contempt in words that were clearly
understood, as she said, "How foolish can you be?"

The business agent of the union, Solomon Golding, appointed Rosa Stein as
the union steward in the department for the purpose of accepting applications
for membership in the union and attending to other problems of organization.
Rosa and Eva had previously had several encounters. Three weeks before the
end of the period for signing up with the union, Rosa called upon Eva and
handed her an application blank. Eva tore the blank into shreds, threw the pieces
into Rosa's face, and declared that she would never join the union. Later, Mr.
Golding called upon her, told her that she would be required to join, and gave
her another blank. He received a rebuff as Rosa had done. On the last day for
joining the union, Eva stopped Rosa in the department and asked for an application blank. Rosa stated that she had used up all of the blanks and that Eva
would be required to get one elsewhere if she could.

The next morning, Rosa went into the personnel office and informed the
director that Eva was fired. Furthermore, she said that she wanted to tell Eva
herself and that she would tell her as soon as she reported for work. "She can
report to the pay office and see about picking up her last check," Rosa said. The
personnel director asked the reason for the outburst, and Rosa proceeded to tell
him the whole story. When she had finished, the personnel director said that the
union steward could not discharge a worker and that any action required would
be taken by himself. If Eva wanted to join the union and was prevented from

doing so on the last day because she was not given a blank, she could still join. If the union did not wish to accept her, the case would be referred to an arbitrator and the union would be expected to make up to her any wages lost while she was laid off. Rosa left the office, stating that she would take up the question with Mr. Golding.

Required:

Evaluate the issues raised by this case.

57. EMPLOYMENT PROCEDURE

The employment manager of the Haley Company considered his procedure for handling applicants for jobs to be unusually complete and reliable. When Azile Wilkins applied for a position as secretary to the plant engineer, she completed an application blank listing her personal history, her formal education, and her employment record. She held a high school diploma and had graduated from a local secretarial school. She had held four clerk-typist positions since she finished school. The reason given for leaving each position was increased pay in the new position. She was currently unemployed. Her record seemed to be quite favorable.

The personal data showed that Azile was 22 years of age and unmarried. She lived alone in an efficiency apartment in a good neighborhood. She paid $60 a month rent. She had lived at this address for three months. The apartment building was about a mile from the plant. Bus service to the plant was direct, requiring no transfers. Her mother and father were divorced and her mother had remarried.

Azile was interviewed by a woman interviewer who filled out a personal evaluation sheet. She was rated high on personal appearance, neatness of dress, ability to express herself, initiative, mental alertness, and attitude toward other people. The interviewer dictated two paragraphs of a test for typists. Azile took down the dictation in shorthand and then neatly typed the material in good time with only two errors.

Azile was referred to the plant engineer for a personal interview. She made a favorable impression upon him. Before she was hired, the employment manager called her former employers. He received the information in each case that Azile had left to make more money elsewhere. Three days after the interview, Azile was informed by telephone that she would be offered the position, and she reported for work the next day.

Azile's performance as personal secretary seemed to be entirely satisfactory. The letters and reports were neatly typed, she kept up to date on all of the work of the office, and she attended to all the office details, such as keeping the office calendar, answering the telephone, filing correspondence, sharpening pencils for the engineer each morning, and interviewing callers. She was liked by other girls employed by the company.

After Azile had been in the office about three weeks, the plant engineer noticed that she was taking a great deal of interest in the drawings for a new type of engine on which the engineer was working. On one occasion, he reprimanded her for listening on the extension telephone while he was discussing the plans with the production manager. Later, he observed her putting a manila envelope in the top drawer of her desk. As she started to leave the office, he saw her put the envelope in the large purse which she always carried on the street. He inquired about the envelope; and when she seemed evasive, he required her to open the envelope, which was found to contain the drawings for the engine. Azile admitted that she had arranged to lend the plans to a competitor company, who would permit her to return them the next morning.

Under questioning, Azile admitted that she desperately needed money. She was behind with her rent and with installment payments on furniture, the television set, and her winter coat. Creditors were on the point of repossessing almost everything in her apartment, including her wardrobe.

Questions:

1. In what respects was the employment procedure inadequate?
2. What should be done about Azile?

27 Changes in the Work Force

CHANGES in the composition of the work force result from many developments, some of which have been considered in preceding pages. Transfers and layoffs may be caused by the installation of new machines, which was considered in Chapter 10. Workers may leave their jobs for any one of several reasons, including dissatisfaction with working conditions, hours of work, methods of supervision, production standards, wage rates, and other aspects of management which have been discussed. In some cases, management is required to lay off workers because it has been unable to stabilize production and employment. This problem will be considered in later chapters. Changes in the work force also result from retirement, which will be briefly treated in Chapter 29. In the present chapter, attention will be directed to some of the problems that arise in connection with transfer, promotion, demotion, layoff, and discharge.

TRANSFER OF WORKERS

Transfers may be made from one job to another or from one department to another. One reason for transfer is an expansion in the volume of business of one department accompanied by a decline in another. Seasonal variations require similar short-time transfers. For example, a department store may transfer salespeople from the millinery department to books or porch furniture to meet changes in seasonal demand. Transfers may also be made to enable workers to leave blind-alley jobs or departments whose promotional opportunities are limited. For purposes of training executives, some employees may be transferred from one department to another in order that they may receive experience in many different kinds of work. Workers who have completed training programs may be transferred to give them opportunities to use their training. Transfers are also advantageous if the worker dislikes the duties of his present job. For example, a clerical worker may prefer shopwork, or a machine tender might prefer a bench job. A transfer of a worker who has been unable to co-operate with his foreman or his associates is more difficult to justify. Occasionally, transfer affords the best permanent solution of personal difficulties.

Transfer usually provides opportunity to the worker to increase his pay or to advance within the organization, although this is not necessarily the result. A worker who is transferred because his job has been dispensed with as a result of the introduction of laborsaving machines or a change in the design of the product or the introduction of new methods of production may be given a job with a lower rating or a tighter standard. In that case the transfer may result in lower earnings. This situation is frequently the subject of a clause in the union contract which may provide that employees shall not be subject to reduction in rates because of a transfer from one classification to another, except by mutual agreement between the company and the shop committee of the union. A clause which is somewhat more favorable to management permits the union to challenge the reduction in pay and to present the matter to an appropriate committee.

PROMOTION, DEMOTION, AND LAYOFF

In the minds of some persons, promotion means an increase in authority over persons or the expenditure of money and perhaps a change in title. It may also mean an increase in wages or salary on the present job. The worker may consider that he has been promoted if he is given a higher rated job or is transferred to a location carrying greater prestige or less exposure to undesirable working conditions. The social prestige of an incumbent may be increased by the granting of special privileges or exemptions, such as a special place to park his car, or exemption from the requirement to punch the time clock.

Every person wants promotion, provided it means only increased pay, greater prestige, or better working conditions. Many workers do not want increased responsibility or greater authority in the making of decisions. Their reasons are that responsibility means care and perhaps worry and that such a promotion carries with it the possibility of failure.

Another reason that a person might not want a promotion is that it might mean a transfer to a night shift or other odd shift. Even though such a job carries an increase in pay, the pay differential might not be sufficient to compensate for the inconvenience. A transfer which also represents an advancement may increase the risk of being laid off because the person holding the next higher job in the chain of promotion may be able to take the lower paid job in case of a cutback in the labor force. For the same reason, workers have sometimes attempted to take their jobs out of the chain of promotion and to make them into blind-alley jobs.

The Promotion Chart. Every worker should know the directions in which he may be transferred or promoted. If his present position offers

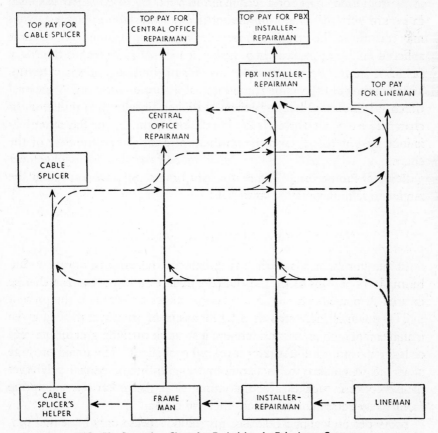

FIG. 52. Promotion Chart for Technician in Telephone Company

(PBX means Public Branch Exchange. Lines of promotion are solid. Lines of transfer are broken.) Chart by courtesy of George O. Clark of the Chesapeake and Potomac Telephone Co.

a chance of promotion only by transfer, the worker should know what the situation is. Blind-alley jobs may include those of office boy, mail clerk, telephone operator, elevator operator, doorman, and some stenographic jobs. Mr. and Mrs. Gilbreth recommended that a promotion chart be prepared for each job showing all possible directions of development and promotion. This chart, which they called "the glory chart," was to be made a part of the personnel record of the worker. It was to be shown to him at regular periods of counseling, when his work was reviewed with him and vocational guidance was given.[1] The promotion chart does not make provision for advances due to off-the-job training. For example, a stenographer might become a cost accounting clerk or a production control clerk as a result of the completion of special training courses.

A promotion chart for a technician in a telephone company is shown in Figure 52. This chart shows that if a person starts as a lineman, he may transfer to the position of installer repairman, frame man, or cable splicer's helper as indicated by the broken lines. If he makes the transfer after he has been advanced in pay as a lineman, he may transfer at approximately the same wage rate as his pay as lineman. This relationship is indicated by the horizontal broken lines in the middle of the chart. The top pay for each job in relation to the pay of the other jobs is indicated by the distances from the top rectangles to the base of the chart.

Basis of Promotion. The reasons for promoting a worker are many. An increase in pay may be awarded for performance on the present job or after a specified number of months of satisfactory experience. Salary advances may also be based upon age or the completion of a training program. Promotion to a position requiring greater responsibility for machinery or materials or the supervision of the work of others should be made on the basis of the qualifications of the person for the increased responsibility.

The union is interested in the promotion of employees because the management might discriminate against union members or union officials in promotions. An employee who thought that union activity would close the door to his advancement with the company would have little interest in working for the union, since the union offers a career to very few persons. The union, therefore, often insists that wage rates be subject to review by a board composed of representatives of the company and the union or that union approval be required for all promo-

---

[1] F. B. Gilbreth and L. M. Gilbreth, "The Three Position Plan of Promotion," *Annals of the American Academy of Political and Social Science,* Vol. LXV (1916), pp. 289–96.

tions to supervisory positions. Another provision that has been incorporated in some union contracts is that no person can be promoted to a supervisory position unless he is in good standing with the union when the promotion is made.

Merit Rating in Promotion. A company may regularly rate its employees for merit as a basis for promotion and also for deciding upon transfers, determining the need for training programs, evaluating the results of training, and counseling with employees. The rating of employees may be designed to evaluate the ability of the person to learn, to adapt himself to changing conditions and duties, or otherwise to render a satisfactory performance. A rating of this kind could provide information that would be useful in determining whether a person should be promoted to a position of greater authority and responsibility.

	EXCELLENT	GOOD	FAIR	POOR
ABILITY HOW WELL IS EMPLOYEE QUALIFIED FOR THE JOB? Consider knowledge and understanding of the work, skill, judgment, capacity to learn, follow instructions and accept responsibility.	Outstanding. Far above average. Little improvement could be expected.	Not outstanding, but entirely satisfactory. From average to above average.	Barely satisfactory. Below average. Considerable need for improvement.	Unsatisfactory. Far below average. Not up to minimum requirements.
EFFICIENCY HOW WELL DOES THE EMPLOYEE PRODUCE? Consider quality and quantity of work, care of equipment and supplies.				
PERSONAL QUALIFICATIONS HOW WELL DOES THE EMPLOYEE CO-OPERATE? Consider conduct and temperament, ability to get along with others, willingness and dependability.				
PHYSICAL QUALIFICATIONS HOW WELL IS THE EMPLOYEE QUALIFIED PHYSICALLY FOR THE JOB? Consider health, physical handicaps and lost time.				

Courtesy of Caterpillar Tractor Co.

FIG. 53. Rating of Performance on Present Job

On the other hand, the rating might be designed to evaluate the success of the person in performing the duties of his present position. His rating under such a plan might indicate that he should have an increase in wages or a promotion to a higher grade or rank. It might not indicate whether he would be successful in a higher position in which the requirements would be different. A rating sheet that provides an evaluation of performance on the present job is shown in Figure 53.

Merit ratings are usually made by more than one person. Shop employees may be rated by a committee composed of the foreman, the personnel director, and the division chief. In order that ratings in different departments may be consistent and fair, the raters should be trained in the methods and the purposes of the plan. If raters are not trained, foremen will not rate their employees on the same basis.

A merit-rating system is no better than the raters make it, for it is a method whereby one person or a few people rate other people. Certain pitfalls should be pointed out to the raters in order that they may be avoided. One of the dangers is the *halo effect,* which means the tendency to give a person a high rating on all traits because he has received a high rating on some qualities. One way to minimize the halo effect is to rate all employees on one trait before proceeding to the next.

Central tendency is the practice of giving an employee the middle rating regardless of his merits. A possible reason for this tendency is that the rater fears criticism from the employer or from his own supervisor. The central tendency may be minimized by using an even number of degrees for a trait, such as four or six.

Another possible danger is *leniency.* A rater who knows the personal difficulties of an employee may assign a high rating because of sympathy. The use of a rating committee of two or three persons is designed to correct this tendency. The construction of the rating scale may also discourage the tendency toward leniency. This is accomplished by reversing the scale for each successive trait. On the first trait, for example, the highest rating may be indicated at the extreme right; and on the second, the highest rating may be indicated at the left. This arrangement of the scale also minimizes the halo effect.

The possibilities of *racial or other bias* should be recognized. There is also the possibility that, in an effort to be fair, the rater may be unnecessarily harsh with his friends and lenient with persons against whom he might be biased. These dangers can be minimized by the training of raters.

New employees may be rated at the end of sixty days of service. Other employees may be rated once every three months, once every six months, or once a year. Some companies rate at irregular intervals. Ratings are subject to review by the plant superintendent or other executive in case they are challenged by the worker or the union.

A plan for employee rating cannot be expected to eliminate all dissatisfaction. It is humanly devised and administered for the rating of human beings, and it is subject to human limitations. As Gardner and Moore say, merit systems "do not seem to work quite according to theory."[2] One difficulty is that the management does not always include in the rating scale those things for which it is willing to pay. If an employee's production record is low, the company may be unwilling to increase his pay merely because he is given a high rating on co-operativeness, dependability, or other such traits. Earnings are also limited by the evaluation of the job, and consistent effort on the part of an employee to improve his rating will not bring an increase in pay if he has reached the maximum for his job. Pay raises are affected by economic conditions, the general trend of wages, and the cost of living. The number of pay raises that a foreman may get for his men is determined in part by his budget. If he asks for too many increases, his supervisors may be inclined to charge him with leniency in making the ratings. Another limitation is that workers whose ratings are lowered seldom receive reductions in their pay. Pay cuts are so serious to the affected workers that the business may fare better when employees whose ratings are poor are paid at their established rates of pay, unless they are transferred to lower rated jobs.

Employees or executives should not be promoted to positions of higher rank merely because they are well qualified for their present positions and have received high ratings for performance. Promotions in rank advance people to positions with different duties which require different traits or qualities. To be qualified for promotion, the employee or executive should possess the traits required by the new position. The same statement applies to transfers.

Seniority Rights. Seniority may be a recognized factor in promotions, wage increases, discharges, layoffs, rehiring, preferences as to shifts, and preference in the scheduling of vacations. Management usually objects to making promotions on the basis of seniority because the oldest worker may not be the best one and may not have the personal qualities necessary for the higher position. Persons who would make good executives may be unwilling to start at the bottom of the organization and to wait for vacancies, as they would be required to do if positions were always

---

[2] Burleigh B. Gardner and David G. Moore, *Human Relations in Industry* (3d ed.; Homewood, Ill.: Richard D. Irwin, Inc., 1955), p. 190.

filled by promoting the person with the longest service. To prevent discrimination against union members, the union may ask that seniority be one factor in promotions. This objective may be accomplished by a provision that representatives of the union and the company will agree upon six persons who are qualified for promotion and that the man in the group who has the greatest length of service will be promoted. Even this provision is objectionable to management, which considers the making of promotions to be its own prerogative.

The principal seniority rights are the right to the job in case the work force must be reduced and the right to be taken back first when the work force is increased. In other words, layoffs are in the reverse order of seniority, with the workers most recently hired laid off first; and rehiring is in the order of seniority, with the workers of longest service rehired first. The right of workers who have seniority to choose the shifts they prefer may result in putting newly employed workers on night, Sunday, or holiday work. This provision makes many kinds of work unattractive to young women. If they refuse certain kinds of work or night and Sunday shifts, they may not acquire the seniority which would give them the right to ask for more desirable jobs or shifts.

Even though the management policy as to seniority has been established, there remain several questions concerning the acquisition and termination of seniority rights. To have seniority, it is generally agreed that the term of service should be unbroken. When the worker quits or is fired, he loses his seniority and must again start at the bottom if he is re-employed. Workers who are temporarily laid off or go on strike do not lose their seniority, but such time does not count in figuring months of service. A worker who is called back after being laid off and who fails to return within a specified number of days usually loses his seniority rights. Continued absence may also cause a loss of such rights.

The strict observance of seniority as a basis for laying off and rehiring workers has significant effects for the worker, the employer, and the community. The seniority rule discourages the movement of workers from one company to another or from one place to another. Persons who have been laid off are inclined to remain in the community in the hope that they may soon be rehired. The effect is to increase the labor reserve in the industry and to decrease the effectiveness of the total labor force.

The number of men who are affected by technological change is increased. A worker whose job is dispensed with because of technological change takes the job of a junior employee who in turn takes the job of a worker with less service. Without seniority rights, only the worker who is no longer needed would be affected. The effect of seniority rights is to increase the opposition to technological change. This situation creates management problems because the shifting of workers tends to impair morale, increase uncertainty, lower production, and increase the interest of workers in make-work practices. The pressure for the recognition of seniority rights comes largely from the union, and the question of how seniority will be recognized is one of the major concerns of the union.

Observance of seniority rights makes discharge a severe penalty because the discharged worker must start at the bottom of the seniority scale with another company. Seniority rights prolong the working life of the worker because older workers are retained when the force is reduced. Workers are less willing to strike if they think that seniority rights may be threatened.

Pension plans receive wider support because workers are more inclined to remain with one company long enough to earn participation rights. Men having seniority are encouraged to join the union in order to protect their rights.

Demotion. Demotions should be avoided because of the effect upon the individual. The person who has been advanced in rank or status and then put back in his former position is likely to be dissatisfied with himself and his employer. The necessity for demotion may be avoided by advancing on a temporary basis a person being considered for promotion. He may be promoted for a trial period during the absence of the regular incumbent because of illness, vacation, or other reasons.

Failure to receive a promotion which was expected or believed to be merited may have as serious an effect upon a person as a demotion. A change which is generally regarded by the associates or subordinates as a decrease in authority also has the same effect as a demotion, even though an announcement is made that the change is only a reorganization. For example, the shifting of a division or an activity from the authority of one executive to another or the placing of office workers in the same building as shopworkers whose jobs are regarded as inferior in status may be regarded as a demotion, even though no changes are made in rates of pay.

The person who has been demoted is likely to lose interest in his work and may ultimately be lost to the company. If the worker can find another job with similar rates of pay and working conditions, he is likely to leave. If he remains with the employer, he may cause trouble by creating dissatisfaction among the other workers, violating company rules when he considers it safe to do so, absenting himself from work when he feels like it, filing charges of discrimination with the union steward, and possibly increasing his participation in union activities in order that he may build up his self-confidence and overcome his feelings of frustration.

Layoffs. A decrease in the amount of work available may require the laying off of a number of the workers or a reduction in the hours per week of all of the workers. The plan to be followed may be left entirely to the employer, or an agreement may be included in the union contract. Some unions prefer not to assume responsibility for the decision, since the efficient workers or the workers having seniority may consider a spreading of the work unfair to them, while older, less efficient workers may regard a spreading of the work as a fairer solution. Unions that wish to have a voice in the decision contend that if the decision is left to the foreman, he may play favorites; that the men may be required to be subservient in order to hold their jobs; and that control by the union is necessary to prevent the workers from speeding up in order to justify their retention. A union contract may make provision similar to the following:

When a decrease in the force is necessary because of lack of work, the employees hired during the last 6 months (or year) shall be laid off. If further reduction is necessary, the hours of work shall be reduced but they shall not be less than 35 hours per week. When further reduction is necessary, employees hired during the last two years shall be laid off. When further reduction is necessary, the hours of work shall be reduced but they shall not be less than 30 hours per week.

The agreement may make provision for further reduction in the work force or for further reduction in the number of hours per week.

When the reduction in amount of work is temporary, a spreading of the work may be preferable in order to avoid throwing the full cost of reduction upon a part of the force. This arrangement enables the employer to hold his men, although it creates some problems in scheduling hours. In a declining industry, spreading the work does not solve the problem but encourages workers to retain their jobs at a time when they should seek full-time employment elsewhere. It causes a reduction in the weekly pay and lowers the standard of living of the workers and their families.

The company may seek in various ways to lighten the effects of necessary layoffs. One plan would provide for spreading the layoffs over a period of weeks in order that large groups of workers will not be looking for jobs at the same time. The industrial relations department may attempt to find openings for workers in other plants in the area or other plants in the same industry within a larger radius. It may also ask the assistance of public employment services or other outside agencies. Where this plan is followed, each suggestion is passed along to workers even though only one vacancy may have been reported.[3]

DISCHARGE

The dismissal of some workers is inevitable regardless of the care exercised in employment and supervision. Discharge should be used as a last resort after all other procedures have been exhausted. Positive action to prevent the necessity for discharge is a duty of management to both the employee and the community.

Attitude of the Union. The union recognizes the right of management to discharge workers for cause. This right is necessary for the security of management, for, unless management can dismiss undesirable workers, the company may eventually cease to operate efficiently. During a specified probationary period, which may be six months, management has an unlimited right to discharge. The firing of an employee during that period cannot be made the subject of a grievance under the union contract. This provision is desirable, since management should not have to justify the discharge of every probationary employee. After the agreed period, management retains the sole responsibility for discharges; but union members cannot be discriminated against because of their union affiliation.

Reasons for Discharge. Company rules and regulations usually specify the situations or acts of employees that constitute reasons for discharge. Two general causes are incompetence and social maladjustment. Incompetence includes lack of trade skill or knowledge, inability to meet production standards, excessive spoilage, poor quality of work, and physical limitations. Discharge for incompetence requires justification because management is presumed to have determined during the probationary period that the worker was competent.

Social maladjustment is the more common cause for discharge. The reason probably lies in the fact that employment techniques are more likely to detect the lack of technical skill than the lack of the necessary social or personal qualifications. Personal causes of discharge include assault on a supervisor or a fellow employee, general insubordination, continued violation of rules regardless of warnings, drinking liquor on

[3] "Relocation Plan Eases Layoff Shock," *Factory Management and Maintenance,* Vol. CXVI, No. 1 (1958), p. 87.

the premises, theft of property of the company or fellow employees, habitual lateness or absenteeism, troublemaking or clowning, accidents due to carelessness, and laziness or loafing on the job.

Company Rules Concerning Discharge. The company rules pertaining to discharge, as well as other rules, constitute a private system of control over the worker while he is on company property. Like any other set of regulations, the rules should be made known to the workers, and they should be fair and reasonable. The penalties for minor offenses should be less severe than penalties for more serious offenses. If an employee continues to commit the same offense after he has been warned or given some minor penalty, more severe penalties may be imposed. The company should not play favorites in assessing penalties, although mitigating circumstances may be considered.

Proof of Violation. In cases of alleged violations of the rules, the burden of proof rests upon the employer, who should be able to present clear and convincing proof that the employee was guilty of the alleged offense. Usually, the company cannot justify discharge by the accusation or statement of an employee unless other evidence can be produced. However, circumstantial evidence may constitute justification for the imposition of penalties as it does under the law of the state.[4] The record of the employee with the company may be used to support the charge that is made against him if proof can be offered to show that his record has been unsatisfactory. The personnel record of the employee may contain such data as the following:

Copy of warnings sent to the worker by the foreman, or memorandum of any conference with him at which he was warned.

Memorandum of attempt made by the foreman to help the worker correct his deficiencies.

Records of production, rejects, absences, tardiness.

Records of merit ratings of the worker and reports of conferences for discussion of how his rating might be improved.

Copy of letter notifying him of his discharge. The letter should state the reason for the discharge.

Report of physical examinations and results of aptitude or other tests.

The Preclearance Interview. Every worker who leaves or is discharged should be interviewed by a representative of the personnel department. Some companies send the worker's last pay check to the department and notify him to call there for it. It has also been found to

---

[4] "Tips to Successful Discipline," *Factory Management and Maintenance,* Vol. CXVI, No. 6 (1958), pp. 79–87.

be good practice for the man who interviewed him at the time of employment to conduct the exit interview. In the case of workers who quit, the preclearance interview is designed to get information on the causes for leaving. These data may assist in correcting undesirable shop conditions and in improving employment and training methods. In some cases the interviewer may be able to induce the worker to remain and to save the investment which the company has made in him through the employment, induction, and training procedure. An exit interview may also serve to prevent hasty decisions by the foreman. The foreman may be called in case the worker has had difficulties or misunderstandings with him. The difficulty may be corrected by changing the worker to another shift, improving work conditions, or removing an accident hazard. If the worker decides to stay, the foreman is put on notice that he has some responsibility to the worker. The interview may help to maintain the good will of employees and the public. It affords an opportunity to explain the regulations of the company which are misunderstood. Some departing employees may be given assistance in finding positions elsewhere in case a worker is leaving the city, or possibly in overcoming personal difficulties.

Report of Termination. The personnel department attends to the various details pertaining to the termination of employment. To make certain that no necessary action is omitted, it may prepare a termination report on which the various steps are checked. This report would show that the following details had been completed:

Company pass returned.
Union notified.
Group insurance canceled.
Deductions for social security, income tax, and union dues verified.
Company store notified, bills paid.
Personnel record posted.
Addressograph department notified.

INDEX OF CHANGES

Changes in the work force are usually measured by indexes of labor turnover. An index of total turnover may be computed as follows:

Add the accessions and the separations.
Divide the total by two.
Divide by the number of workers at the end of the period.
Multiply by 100.

An index computed in this manner reflects both accessions and separations. No distortion results if persons who leave are replaced by other workers. The index may be misleading if the total number of workers is increasing because the volume of production and employment is expanding, or the total is decreasing because the volume of production is declining. Separate indexes are therefore computed for accessions and separations.

Indexes of Accession. Accessions are caused principally by two developments, replacements for people who leave and additions to the work force. Separate indexes may be computed to show the effect of each set of changes. A replacement rate would be computed by dividing the number of persons hired as replacements by the average number of workers and multiplying the result by 100. The index indicates the number of persons hired as replacements for each 100 persons in the work force. An index of the expansion of the work force may be computed by dividing the number of new hirings by the average number on the payroll and multiplying by 100. The replacement index plus the index of expansion would indicate the total accession rate.

Indexes of Separation. Separations are caused by quits, discharges, layoffs because of declining production, and miscellaneous causes. Separate indexes may be computed by dividing the number of separations for each cause by the average number of persons on the payroll and multiplying by 100. The sum of the four indexes would indicate the separation rate for all causes. The quit rate and the discharge rate are the most significant indexes of changes in the work force.

Using Turnover Rates. The indexes of changes in the work force require further analysis before management can determine their significance. The changes never occur equally in all departments or jobs. In some departments, the work force may be relatively stable while frequent changes are occurring elsewhere. The turnover may be greatest among younger workers, women workers, workers on odd shifts, or other groups. Research may be necessary to determine causes and corrective measures.

QUESTIONS

1. What costs or expenses are incurred as a result of labor turnover? Are these expenses the result principally of separations or accessions?

2. Are expenses increased by transfers? Explain.

3. Should a company post notices of vacancies in order that workers now with the company may apply for transfer? Why might the company prefer not to publish notices of vacancies?

4. Distinguish between a promotion and a transfer.

5. Why are definite rules necessary with regard to the beginning and the termination of seniority? Explain the nature of such provisions.

6. Distinguish between a rule and a policy. Illustrate.

7. Why may the recognition of the rights of the worker as a result of seniority benefit the employer as well as the worker?

8. Social maladjustment is a more common cause of discharge than incompetence. How may this difference be explained?

9. If a company is unable to provide full employment for all workers, would the management prefer to lay off some workers and provide full employment for others, or would it prefer to spread the work? Would the nature of the manufacturing processes affect the decision? What difficulties of scheduling might arise?

10. Has the worker been demoted if his job is abolished as a result of mechanization and the worker is given other work at lower pay?

11. Why would the management prefer not to demote a person?

12. Executives are usually asked to resign; they are seldom fired. What is the difference?

13. How do seniority rights affect the utilization of the work force and the earnings of the entire body of workers?

14. What objections might be made to the use of a promotion chart for every job?

15. How would executive development programs for college graduates affect the chances of promotion of persons who have attempted to work up within the organization? What problems are created by the use of such programs?

CASES

58. SENIORITY RIGHTS OF A TOOL CRIB ATTENDANT

The machine shop foreman at the Rexford Company found that work had fallen behind schedule and that some men in the department would need to work overtime for three hours to assure delivery of the product at the scheduled date. The machinists agreed to stay for the required time. However, the tool crib attendant, James Boone, asked to be relieved of the assignment because of other commitments. The foreman then decided that the men could obtain the necessary tools before quitting time and that the tool crib could be closed during the overtime period.

The next day the union steward filed a complaint, alleging that the second man on the list, William Allen, should have been given the work in the tool crib and that Allen was entitled to three hours of overtime pay because he had been improperly passed over. The foreman contended that the union could not file a complaint and that only Allen himself could claim the extra pay. Furthermore, the foreman alleged that the company was not required to keep the tool crib open during the overtime period. After the company and the union failed to reach an agreement on the questions at issue, the case was submitted to an arbitrator as provided by the union contract.

The arbitrator held for the union on the first question. He said that the union represented all of the workers and could file a claim for any one of them. On the second question, the arbitrator decided that the seniority rule would apply only in case work was assigned to some other worker not having the necessary seniority. The contract did not require that an attendant be kept on duty in the tool crib.

Question:

Was the decision of the arbitrator correct?

59. SENIORITY RIGHTS IN PROMOTION

The contract between the Woodward Company and the union contained a clause which gave the worker with the greatest seniority the right to a new job provided he possessed the necessary qualifications. The company followed the practice of posting notices of vacancies on the bulletin board, and any worker who thought that he had the necessary qualifications could apply. The applications were reviewed by the personnel director and the foreman of the department where the new job existed. The decision of the personnel director and the foreman could be challenged by any worker who thought that he was not given fair consideration, and the grievance could be handled through the usual procedure. On one occasion a new job was created as a result of the purchase and installation of a new machine. Continuous operation of the machine was important not only because of the overhead expense resulting from the cost of the machine and the space it occupied but also because of the place of the machine in the production line. The management therefore decided that two essential traits of the operator were technical skill and dependability.

The personnel director received bids for the new job from only two workers, and both of them seemed fully qualified by training, experience, and technical ability. William White had been employed in the plant 28 months and had a perfect record as to safety, attendance, and observance of company regulations. Ralph Jones, the other applicant, had a record of 43 months of continuous service. However, Jones had been reprimanded twice during the past year for failing to wear goggles while using a grinding machine and for failing to notify the foreman of his inability to report for work on one occasion. Jones had also been given disciplinary layoffs for punching the time clock for another worker and for gambling on the premises. Consequently, the personnel director and the foreman awarded the new job to White.

When Jones learned of the decision, he immediately filed a complaint with the personnel director and the union steward. He contended that he already had been disciplined for an alleged violation of company rules. Denial of the new job constituted double punishment which was unfair. He met the requirements for the job and his seniority entitled him to it. The union supported him in his claim.

The personnel director pointed out that the job required not only technical ability but also dependability and a willingness to assume responsibility. He argued that the record of Ralph Jones indicated a lack of these essential qualifications.

The dispute was appealed through the usual grievance procedure and finally was submitted to an arbitrator in accordance with the provisions of the contract. The arbitrator held that the company had not violated the contract in awarding the job to William White because dependability could properly be regarded as one requirement for a job. The arbitrator expressed the opinion, however, that a record of disciplinary action should not always bar an employee from promotion.

Questions:

Was the decision proper and fair to all parties concerned?

60. REASONS FOR DISCHARGE

The Atlas Company had difficulty obtaining female clerical help during the busy season. The company asked the assistance of the state employment service, and it also ran advertisements in the local newspapers. After all other sources had been exhausted, the company arranged with the women's club to discuss its employment opportunities and the nature of the work at a meeting of the club. The meeting was open to any one who wished to attend. At the meeting, the personnel manager explained the requirements for some of the jobs, the working conditions, the hours of work, and the pay and benefits. The women who were present showed much interest in his talk and asked many questions.

The personnel manager arranged for three employees to be present to discuss the advantages of working with the company. These young women had been employed by the company in several different jobs and could discuss the problems from the worker point of view. Their presentations seemed to be very convincing.

Present in the audience was Mary de Luca, who was employed as a sorter and inspector in the packing department. Mary had come to the meeting on her own initiative. After the meeting had been under way for some time, Mary arose to discuss her experience with the company. She said she had been employed for 18 months and had had no increase in pay during that time. Her supervisor used rough language in talking to her and had sworn at her on two occasions. She was required to stand at her work, and the lunch periods did not allow adequate time to eat. The work piled up at her work station, and she had to work at a pace that in time would be injurious to her health. She advised the women to look elsewhere for employment if they wanted to work.

The next morning, the personnel manager inquired into Mary's record and found that she had filed three complaints with the foreman, who described her as a troublemaker. The foreman also said that Mary had started several rumors concerning other workers and that the reports had no basis in fact. The foreman and the personnel manager decided that she should be discharged.

When Mary reported at her work station, she was called into the office of the foreman who told her that her services were no longer needed. A replacement had already been hired for her job. Mary retorted that the company could not fire her for exercising her right of free speech, which was guaranteed to her by the Constitution of the United States. She said she could say what she pleased outside the plant. After a stormy session, she announced that the business agent of the union would see that she was restored to her position.

The business agent called the personnel manager and asked for a conference to discuss Mary's case. He contended that Mary had a constitutional right to say what she pleased at a public meeting and that the company would be required to reinstate her. The personnel manager replied that Mary had violated her obligations to the company in speaking as she did. While she could not be prevented from speaking, she had relieved the company of any obligation to her.

When the personnel manager brought up the question of Mary's unsatisfactory record with the company, the business agent declared that her record was entirely irrelevant because she was not fired because of her record. He said that she could not be dismissed for a series of minor incidents, and that the company would have overlooked her record if she had not spoken up at the meeting. Furthermore, he said, the personnel director had been negligent in not reporting to the union any criticism the company may have made of Mary's conduct. He said that the union would have helped to correct minor infractions of company rules if they had been reported to him.

Mary's case eventually went to arbitration. The arbitrator held that although Mary was not subject to punishment under the laws of the state for her remarks, she had proved herself to be disloyal to the company and that she had purposely damaged the reputation of the company in the community. He upheld the right of the company to discharge her.

Required:

Justify or criticize the decision of the arbitrator.

28 Employee Training

IN the days of Frederick W. Taylor, employee training programs were not well developed by the management. Helpers or laborers were expected to learn principally from mechanics, bricklayers, or other skilled workmen with whom they came most in contact. Those workers who seemed most capable or who seemed to know most about the work were promoted by management.[1] This system was unsatisfactory because the worker learned the job well only when he observed and imitated a craftsman who used effective methods. Poor methods were perpetuated. An excessive amount of time was required for an employee to learn a job. In establishments where the foreman was expected to instruct and train the worker, the system was not satisfactory because the foreman might be a poor teacher. Moreover, as Taylor showed, the foreman had so many duties that he neglected some of them. Employee training was a responsibility that he often neglected.

OBJECTIVES OF TRAINING

While the development of management methods has simplified the work of the person who tends a machine, it has resulted in the organization of staff departments and has complicated interdepartmental relationships and thus increased the need for employee training. Even on routine work, as Gilbreth showed in his bricklaying studies, workmen will use wasteful and inefficient methods if they are not properly taught.

---

[1] Henry L. Gantt, *Industrial Leadership* (New Haven: Yale University Press, 1916), p. 42.

Poor training or a lack of training may result in a low rate of production, poor quality, excessive spoilage, and low wages.

Although any one company may obtain a supply of workers who have been trained elsewhere, a training program is essential for the advancement of industry. In 1915, Richard A. Feiss, a well-known leader in the management movement, said that "skilled and fit men are not born, but made, and it is an essential function of any industrial organization to train men and make them fit for specific positions."[2] In 1917, Henry L. Gantt said that "the nation which does not so develop its industries as to produce men will not for any great length of time hold its place in the world. The men produced by industrial methods are far more important to the life of the nation than the wealth and luxury by which we set so much store."[3] Gantt was of the opinion that the training of employees should stress motivation as well as methods of work. Habits of industry, he said, are more valuable than knowledge and skill—"without industry, knowledge and skill are of little value and sometimes a great detriment."

The need for employee training has been increased by mechanization and the development of fully automatic machines. Special training may be required for such skilled craftsmen as patternmakers, toolmakers, set-up men, maintenance men, electricians, and inspectors. The necessary skills for some kinds of work can be acquired only through an apprenticeship program. Many jobs on the assembly line can be performed with little training, but other assembly-line jobs may require the experience of many months. Automation usually increases the need for employee training because it requires a change in job assignments.

The Training Program.   Training may be given to persons recently employed, to persons already employed and preparing for advancement, to present employees for improving performance in jobs now held, or to persons being transferred to other jobs. The nature of the training program depends upon the needs of the persons taking the training and the objectives of the program. The needs of newly employed persons may be met by a short period of instruction or by longer courses such as an apprenticeship course. The planning of a training program should begin with an analysis of the requirements of the work and the qualifications of employees. The program should be designed to correct any deficiencies.

Training may be general in nature and not specifically related to any

[2] Richard A. Feiss, "Scientific Management Applied to the Steadying of Employment," *Annals of American Academy of Political and Social Science,* Vol. LXI (1915), p. 106.
[3] Gantt, *op. cit.,* p. 37.

task. General training may be given to enable an employee to understand the basic or scientific principles of production. Examples are
courses in industrial chemistry, physics, shop mathematics, and economics. Training of this kind may provide avenues of growth for
employees who show promise or have demonstrated their ability to advance. General training may be intended to inform employees of developments affecting the industry, the company, or the product. Instruction of this kind is sometimes called "employee education" rather than
employee training.

TYPES OF TRAINING PROGRAMS

Many kinds of training programs may be organized according to the
nature of the work done, the need for new employees with special skills,
and the qualifications of the people who are available for employment.
The training may be given before the worker is assigned to a job, immediately after he reports to the foreman at the time he begins work, or
after a former worker has been rehired. The subject matter and the
methods of training depend upon the objectives of the program.

Vestibule Training.   The word *vestibule* means a passage or hall between the outer door and the interior of the building. Vestibule training means preparation for the job which is given immediately after the
employee has been hired and prior to his induction. The name of the
program indicates the time when the training is given rather than the
place where the school is conducted.

According to one plan for vestibule training, a small group of employees is given an intensive course in the function, design, manufacture, and assembly of the product. They are shown the relation of the
various operations to each other and the consequences of improper
workmanship at each step. After the preliminary instruction is completed, the members of the group are taught to make or assemble a
product. At the completion of the course of training, workers are transferred to the regular production lines, where they are taught some
specific job. A course of this kind may extend over three to five days
with groups of five to eight employees in each class.

Vestibule courses may consist of a production line which duplicates
the line or a part of the line in the factory. All workers in the line are
new employees. The instructor keeps records to show the progress
made by each employee. He observes the employee's patience, emotional stability, willingness to co-operate, and resistance to monotony
and fatigue. Production is secondary because instruction, training, and

placement are the primary aims. Supervision is closer than the foreman usually can give. The regular production lines are not slowed by the training program. The time and skill of the instructor are more efficiently utilized because all of the persons under his supervision are learners. The time spent by the employee in the vestibule school depends upon the time required to develop skill and speed at the work and the need for replacements.

In some vestibule schools, machines are set up for certain types of work but not for all operations. For example, a shirt manufacturer maintains a vestibule school in which cuffs, collars, pockets, or the main section of the shirt may be made. As the parts are finished, they are moved to the main production line for assembly. This plan permits the use of a smaller school at lower cost.

The vestibule school is a practical plan only for the large company. If a complete production line is established, balance in the line is not easily maintained. The labor turnover on some jobs is more rapid than on others, and more replacements must be trained for such jobs. Perhaps the greatest problem of the vestibule school is that of keeping abreast of developments within the shop. Any change in product design, machines used, layout and arrangement of workplaces, or sequence of operations in the shop should be matched by similar changes in the vestibule school. Unless the methods are identical, new employees will learn the wrong methods and will have a problem of relearning and readjustment when they transfer from the school.

Apprenticeship Training. An apprentice is a person who is bound by contract to work or serve for a stated time with a view of learning a trade. Formerly, such a contract was made with a master craftsman, who agreed to instruct and train the apprentice in the skills of the trade and to provide him with the means of subsistence. At the present time, such contracts may be made by a corporation. The apprentice is usually a minor who cannot make a legally binding contract, and his parent or guardian therefore signs with him. The apprentice studies to learn a trade rather than a job. A trade includes a number of jobs.

While practices differ among employers, the apprentice training offered by a large machinery manufacturer may be cited as an example. Four-year apprentice courses are provided for machinists, patternmakers, and foundrymen. Apprentices are on trial during the first six months. During that time, they must demonstrate their ability to continue the course. They are assigned to jobs in the plant as soon as they enter training, and the mangement sees that they are gradually advanced to more difficult jobs and learn to operate more complicated machines.

The apprentice machinist, for example, may begin with the speed drill or bench assembly. Later, he receives experience on milling machines, lathes, grinders, and shapers. Apprentices may attend classes three days a week where they study blueprint reading, geometry, trigonometry, applied mechanics, heat treating, tool design, and other technical subjects. Tools and books are charged to the apprentice, and the cost is refunded to him at the completion of the course. He is then advanced to the rank and pay of a skilled workman. A diploma is awarded attesting to the completion of the prescribed course.

Both labor unions and the federal government have interested themselves in the regulations governing the training of apprentices. The unions wish to prevent abuses in the program by employers who might use such training as a method of procuring cheap labor in large numbers. The government is interested in uniformity of standards and in the promotion of programs for training skilled craftsmen. An advantage to the apprentice is that he becomes more versatile and is less likely to become unemployed as a result of technological changes. Apprentices are paid while they learn, and they receive good wages after graduation.

On-the-Job Training. Much training is given on the job, where the worker is taught improved methods of work, care of machines and equipment, tooling and machine adjustment, and safety. In this type of training, the employee deals in realities and can be sure that the methods he learns are practical. Since the instruction is usually given by the foreman, the worker can be sure that he will not later be required by some other person to do the work in a different manner. The competition of other workers spurs him to put forth his best efforts to learn as quickly as possible. The disadvantages are the limitations of the time of the foreman and possibly his lack of knowledge of methods of teaching.

Foremen may need training in methods of work improvement and in ways of instructing workers to use the improved methods. A program of methods improvement for foremen would follow the principles and methods of process charts and motion study which were explained in Chapter 18. A generally accepted plan of methods improvement provides, first, that the foreman will break down the flow of work and separately identify the tasks performed by each worker. Second, the foreman is taught to inquire into the purpose of each step followed in the processing of the material and the performing of a task in an effort to make improvements. Third, he is taught to develop better methods. Finally, he applies the improved methods, instructs workers, and attempts to gain their co-operation. This procedure has been adapted from motion study methods as developed by the Gilbreths. It is stated in more detail as follows:

How to Improve Production Methods

Step I—Break down the job
1. List all the details of operations, moves, inspections, and delays, while operators are:
   a) Moving materials.
   b) Working with machines.
   c) Working with hands and tools.

Step II—Question every detail
1. Use these types of questions:
   Why is it necessary?
   What is its purpose?
   Where should it be done?
   When should it be done?
   Who is best qualified to do it?
   How is the best way to do it?
2. Question product design, material, material handling, layout, set-ups, tools and equipment, machines, operator qualifications, workplaces, and operations.

Step III—Develop the new method
1. Eliminate unnecessary details.
2. Combine details when practical.
3. Rearrange to get better sequences.
4. Simplify all necessary details.
   a) Make the work easier and safer.
   b) Pre-position materials, tools, and equipment at the best places in the proper work area.
   c) Use gravity feed and drop delivery.
   d) Let both hands do useful work.
   e) Use jigs and fixtures for holding.
5. Discuss your idea with others.
6. Write up your suggestion.

Step IV—Apply the new method
1. Sell your suggestion to the boss. Get his approval for a trial.
2. Sell the new method to the operators. Give it a fair test.
3. Consider safety, quality, quantity, cost.
4. Get final approval from all.
5. Put it into effect. Use it until a better way is developed.
6. Give credit where credit is due.

The improved methods may be developed by the foreman in cooperation with the workers on the job. Later, the foreman is expected to train others in the new methods. He therefore may require instruction in methods of training workers to work effectively. The foreman is told that the first step in teaching the worker to perform the task consists of preparation of the workplace, getting tools and materials, and finding out how much the worker needs to be taught. Second, the foreman attempts to gain worker interest and co-operation. Third, he shows the worker how to perform the task. Next, he has him use the proper method. Finally, he follows up the manner in which the work is being done and gives the worker any further instruction or assistance that he needs.[4] The method of teaching the worker is summarized as follows:

HOW TO INSTRUCT

First, the teacher makes the following preparation:

1. Decide what the learner must be taught in order to do the job efficiently, safely, economically, and intelligently.
2. Have the right tools, equipment, supplies, and material ready.
3. Have the workplace properly arranged, just as the worker will be expected to keep it.

Then, he should instruct the learner by the following four basic steps:

STEP I—Preparation (of the learner)
1. Put the learner at ease.
2. Find out what he already knows about the job.
3. Get him interested in learning the job.

STEP II—Presentation (of operations and knowledge)
1. Tell, show, illustrate, and question in order to put over the new knowledge and operations.
2. Instruct slowly, clearly, completely, and patiently—one point at a time.
3. Check, question, and repeat.
4. Make sure the learner really learns.

STEP III—Performance try-out
1. Test learner by having him perform the job. Correct errors.
2. Ask questions beginning with why, how, who, when, or where.
3. Observe performance and repeat instructions if necessary.
4. Continue until you know he knows.

STEP IV—Follow-up
1. Put him on his own. Designate to whom he goes for help.
2. Check frequently to be sure he follows instructions.

[4] From *The Training within Industry Report* (Washington, D.C.: U.S. Government Printing Office, 1945).

3. Taper off extra supervision and close follow-up until he is qualified to work with normal supervision.

Remember—If the learner hasn't learned, the teacher hasn't taught.

Training for Upgrading. Training for advancement may be given to employees, foremen, and executives. The courses may be designed to train skilled workers or supervisors, and several types of training may be given as parts of one program. A small company, for example, has given courses in metallurgy, metallurgical chemistry, public speaking, time study, operation-sheet writing, cam design, and work simplification. A larger company gives a two-year course in machine-shop work, a fourteen-month course in welding, and a three-year course in general office and production procedures. The courses are usually given on company time. Classes may meet for one or two hours each week.

Training makes extensive use of visual aids for demonstration and illustrative material. Charts, drawings, and pictures are widely used. Models of the factory layout are used to demonstrate the flow of work from one department to another. Motion pictures and slides are generally used for technical instruction and also in the safety program. Motion pictures are good, provided the subjects are carefully chosen. However, they should be used as supplementary aids rather than as the major part of the training work. The showing of the motion picture should be preceded by a period of instruction. The picture should illustrate the information presented in the instruction period. The value of pictures for instruction purposes decreases sharply after about fifteen minutes. Slides permit the picture to remain on the screen until the instructor and the class have concluded their discussion. Slides may also be designed to show cutaway parts of equipment and to demonstrate the method of machine operation.

Training in Safety. New employees are often given safety instruction, and other workers may be given refresher safety training. New employees, in addition to being given oral instructions, are frequently given a booklet of safety regulations with a perforated sheet which they are asked to sign and hand to the foreman as evidence that they have read the instructions.

Safety instruction is most effective if it is integrated with the training for the job. The employee is taught the proper way to do the task, which is the safe way. When safety regulations are made a part of job instruction, the worker is more likely to receive positive instructions rather than negative warnings. For example, instead of being warned not to hold a piece of metal with his hand while he bores a hole, he would be instructed that the first step is to fasten the piece firmly in the machine. Instead of being told not to push a chisel toward his hand while he trims a piece of wood, he would be instructed that he should clamp the piece of wood to the bench and direct the chisel in a certain manner. However, warnings of a negative sort may be necessary in addition to positive instruction. Employees are often subjected to a barrage of bulletin board posters, signs displayed at entrances or danger points, illuminated moving messages, and placards within or about the shop.

MANAGING A TRAINING PROGRAM

The management of a training program is the joint responsibility of the personnel department and the line. The program requires the support of supervisors and executives in the manufacturing departments because the training is given to benefit them in their work. They are expected to direct certain kinds of training. The personnel department is best qualified to handle various administrative details. In addition, top management should lend its encouragement and support.

Determining the Need for Training. Before a training program is undertaken, the need should be clearly established. Because the suggestion for training usually originates with the personnel department, line executives may be skeptical when the proposal is made. They may recall other occasions when training courses were conducted without apparent success. Training will require time and effort from the supervisors who are confronted with day-to-day problems that demand attention. If the need is not clearly shown, they may suspect that the personnel executive is urging the training partly to enhance his own prestige.

The need for employee training may be established in many ways, such as information gained from exit interviews, studies of labor turnover by crafts and by jobs, difficulties in finding jobs for people who are displaced by mechanization of production, and discussions with foremen. Shortages of skilled workers in certain categories may be disclosed by employment interviews and the difficulties of finding qualified workers for transfer to certain jobs. The accident record may indicate the need for training in safety. The period of time required for workers to make production standards or the inability of workers to keep work moving on schedule may indicate the need for other training programs.

Determining Objectives. The objectives of a program will influence the manner in which it is conducted. In general terms, three objectives may be distinguished: the impartation of technical knowledge and a broader understanding of technical processes, the development of special skills, and the modification of worker attitudes. More specifically, the training may be intended to achieve a reduction of learning time on new jobs, a reduction of waste and spoilage, an improvement in quality, a reduction of complaints and grievances, an improvement in methods of work, or an increase in production. Although a training program might have several objectives, it is not likely to be successful if they are not clearly defined.

Obtaining Instructors. In any type of training, instruction is most effective if it is given by the immediate supervisor. If the training is given by someone else, the learner may find that the methods are not approved by the supervisor or that some of the principles taught are not in agreement with his ideas. However, many technical courses, particularly in an apprenticeship program, are given by specialists. Some courses may be given by staff personnel. Much depends upon selecting the right instructors.

Responsibility of the Personnel Department. The personnel director usually does not give the instruction, but he may assist in many ways. He may suggest areas where instruction is needed and types of programs to meet the needs. He assists in working out the plans for the training, in obtaining literature, in selecting and training instructors, and in scheduling the program. By the use of tests, interviews, and personnel records, he assists in the selection of persons to be trained. He may provide the physical facilities to be used in training, such as rooms, blackboards, charts, slides, and other visual aids. After the training has been completed, the personnel department would make the necessary follow-up to determine the costs, results, and methods of improving the training in the future.

Rewards for Course Completion. Employees who successfully complete formal training courses should receive appropriate recognition or reward. The nature of the reward depends upon the type of course, the amount of effort required of the persons enrolled, and the duration of the course. Completion of an apprenticeship course should be recognized by formal exercises and the conferring of a diploma. For shorter courses a certificate of completion is frequently awarded. Even though grades may be assigned for purposes of personnel records, the grades are not shown on the certificate except perhaps for persons making exceptionally good records. The completion of any course is usually announced in the plant magazine, which is also used for much other publicity concerning the program.

More substantial rewards for course completion include some sort of monetary payment. Employees who buy books or other materials at the beginning of the course may be reimbursed upon satisfactory completion. Employees who take technical courses at night schools are sometimes repaid for the cost of the tuition. A wage increase is usually not given automatically but depends upon transfer to a higher position. The employee may also benefit through greater security or his ability to shift to a different kind of work.

Checking the Value of the Training Program. An attempt should be made to determine whether the program has accomplished its objectives. This evaluation is not easy. Cause and effect are not closely related where human relations are concerned. Conclusions as to the results of a training program are more reliable if the number of persons taking the course is large. Allowance should be made for any change in the work force during the time the training was given. For example, if women are employed for the first time, a comparison of the safety or the production record before and after the training was given will be inconclusive in establishing the value of the training. Changes in the work force may reflect such factors as age, color, or experience of employees.

The method of determining the value of employee training depends upon the nature and the objectives of the training program. The data which may be tabulated for this purpose are as follows:

Increase in the rate of output.
Reduction in the time required to complete a task.
Increase in the number of operators who meet the standards of production.
Decrease in the time required for new employees to reach the standard.
Decrease in the breakage of machine tools.
Reduction in the number of accidents.
Reduction in absenteeism.
Reduction in the rate of labor turnover.

QUESTIONS

1. How is the need for employee training affected by subdivision of the work into tasks that can be completed within a short time?

2. Is the need for training affected by the method by which the plant is laid out, namely, by processes or by products?

3. What is the advantage of the vestibule school? What difficulties may be encountered by the operation of such a school?

4. What is the responsibilty of the personnel department in connection with a training program?

5. What types of training are most likely to be accepted by the foremen and

the line executives? To what types of program may they give only formal support?

6. Why do labor unions want to have a part in the development of an apprenticeship program?

7. How is the need for apprenticeship programs affected by the rise of the factory system of production? In what areas is such training still needed?

8. Why are women usually not admitted to apprenticeship programs?

9. How should a worker be rewarded for the completion of a training program?

10. How can management determine whether a training program is worth its cost?

11. What types of training should be given by foremen?

12. How might a training program affect the rate of employee turnover?

CASES

61. CO-OPERATION WITH LOCAL SCHOOLS

At a luncheon meeting of the local chamber of commerce, Ralph C. Riggs, plant superintendent of the Chase Electrical Company, happened to meet the director of a local technical school. The director remarked that employees of the Chase Electrical Company enrolled in the school were good students. Mr. Riggs replied that he did not know of any employees who were enrolled. When the director recalled the names of three of the students, Mr. Riggs said he thought the director was mistaken as to the company as none of the men were employed at Chase.

Later, Mr. Riggs called the director and asked for the names of all of the students who were Chase employees. Comparison of the list of students with Chase payrolls showed that the three students mentioned as outstanding had left Chase for jobs in other companies where they could use their technical training to advantage. No one in the management at Chase knew that the men had completed courses at the technical school.

Questions:

1. How can the company keep informed of the training taken by employees in local schools or by correspondence?

2. What can the company do to encourage employees to take such training?

3. What department or person in the management should be made responsible for knowing that employees are taking technical courses?

62. TRAINING PROGRAM FOR A NEW PLANT

The American Electric Products Company planned to build a new plant in Waynesville, Missouri, which was a city of 28,000 population. The principal products of the plant were expected to be television sets. Workers with certain technical skills would be needed, and it was known that few people with the necessary skills were available in Waynesville. The total work force in the plant was expected to be from 1,200 to 1,500.

Before construction of the building was started in Waynesville, Mr. Hughes, the vice-president for manufacturing, discussed the problem of personnel with Mr. Lowe, the personnel director. Mr. Lowe, with the approval of the president of the company, immediately took up the matter with the superintendent of schools in Waynesville. He proposed that the city organize a program of adult education to train people in the necessary skills. Mr. Lowe agreed that American Electric Company would provide equipment and materials for the courses as well as instructors, and the company would provide a syllabus for each course. It would also meet any financial deficit that might be incurred by the school authorities. The superintendent of schools agreed to organize the program. He in turn secured the co-operation of the state employment service in recruiting adult students who might also become applicants for jobs in the new plant.

The superintendent rented a small office building for the school program. Prospective students made application through the local state employment office. All applicants were required to take a battery of tests, including tests of mechanical aptitude and mental ability. The tests were used for counseling and placement, but no person was rejected for training because of his test scores. Each student paid a fee of $1.00 for each course. American Electric Company made no promises of jobs for successful completion of a course, and the students did not promise to apply for jobs with the company. The director of public education in the city school system enrolled for all of the courses in order that he might better appreciate the problems of adult education for employment in a television plant.

The skills that were particularly needed in the new plant were those of assemblers on the production line, major repairmen, trouble analyzers, chassis circuit inspectors, and performance testers. The company prescribed the type of course that would be necessary for each skill. The courses included radio and television theory, electronics, and practice in bench and assembly work. The class schedules required attendance of three to six hours a day for four days each week. Both day and evening courses were offered, and a student could enroll for more than one course. The longest course, which covered the work of trouble analyzing, extended over five weeks for a total of 120 hours. The shortest course covered wiring and soldering in a total of 36 hours. Each student was awarded a certificate upon the completion of any course.

By the time the plant opened, 400 persons had completed one or more of the courses, and about 375 of these people were given jobs on the subassembly or final assembly lines or in some other work requiring the newly acquired skills. After the plant opened, the day classes were discontinued while night courses were retained. These courses were integrated with the regular trade and shop departments of the city schools. The local plant manager attributed the smooth organization of the work force in substantial degree to the training program in the school system.

Question:

What were the advantages of using the local school system for the training program?

29 Employee Services

EMPLOYEE services include those activities of a company that are designed to provide employees with facilities not directly related to production. They are intended to supply the social and other needs of employees that can best be met through group rather than individual action. They are conducted for the purpose of making the work force more efficient by fostering loyalty to the company and an interest in its activities, by building up a feeling of group solidarity, by developing a feeling of financial and personal security, or by meeting some other personal need. Employee service activities are of many kinds. No one company would provide all the services to be mentioned in this chapter, although most large companies would provide many of them.

Employee services may be grouped under four headings. They relate to health services, financial benefits, recreational services, and miscellaneous services that are designed to establish closer relationships between the company and its employees.

HEALTH SERVICES

It is estimated that the average employee in industry is absent from work seven days per year on account of illness. One of the absences is due to industrial illness and accidents and the other six days are due to illness to which the population in general is subject. The illness is not evenly distributed among employees, and both illness and accidents cause great suffering in individual cases. A comprehensive health program would include attention to many types of plant problems.

Improvement in Working Conditions. Features of plant facilities that relate to health include sanitation and rest room facilities, lighting, air conditioning, cafeteria and lunchroom facilities, noise, and the use of machines for doing heavy work. Some departments subject the worker to special health hazards, such as heat and cold, gases, dust, dampness, and poisonous substances. Diseases that are caused by conditions peculiar to industry are called "occupational diseases." The most common occupational diseases are dermatitis and lead poisoning.

Medical Services. The company may provide some health services for employees who are injured or who require the services of a physician. The medical services may be organized as a subdivision of the personnel department. However, the medical officer is a highly trained person; and his position is a responsible one. For these reasons, the medical services are sometimes organized as a major division. While this arrangement has much to recommend it, the effect may be to place too many executives under the supervision of the general manager.

The organization of the medical services depends in part upon the number of persons on the staff and the extent of the work. Very small enterprises provide no medical service at the plant, whereas some use the services of a local physician on a part-time basis. Some companies arrange for applicants for employment to report to a local physician for a physical examination, and other companies arrange for a physician to spend a part of each day at the plant. In larger companies a full-time physician may be employed. Another arrangement is to employ a nurse on a full-time basis to operate the dispensary, with the assistance of a physician on a part-time basis.

When first-aid services are provided, it is usually necessary to require that workers report for the treatment of minor injuries, such as cuts, abrasions, and burns. Workers may hesitate to ask for treatment of minor wounds. They may need to be reminded that an infection is cause for discipline, while an injury may not be cause for criticism.

Group Hospitalization and Surgical Benefits. To aid employees in meeting hospital expenses and surgeon's fees, many companies provide group insurance. Insurance premiums may be paid by the company, by the employees, or by the company and the employees jointly. One plan provides that each employee will pay a fixed sum each month, which is deducted from his pay. The remainder of the cost, which may vary, is paid by the company. Usually, no examination or statement of health is required of any employee who makes application for the insurance within thirty-one days of the date of employment. Employees who apply after the time stated may be required to pass a medical examination which is satisfactory to the insurance company. The protection afforded by the policy may include room and meals at the hospital for a period not in excess of seventy days, anesthesia, and certain other services not to exceed the amounts stated in the contract. The surgical protection covers the fee charged for any surgical operation, with a maximum of perhaps $150. The surgical allowance varies with the type of operation in accordance with a fixed schedule. The policy may specify that an operation is not covered by the contract if it arises in the course of employment. The employer bears the cost of accident or illness arising out of the employment, as required by workmen's compensation laws.

Group Life Insurance. The group life insurance plan usually provides for a scale of premiums and benefits which vary with the salary or earnings of the employee. New employees become eligible for protection under the group policy after a stated period, say three months, provided the employee is actively at work at that time and has made prior application. A part of the premium for the life insurance may be deducted from the pay of the employee, and the remainder of the cost is paid by the company. No medical examination is required for employees who make application within thirty-one days after the date they become eligible. While the protection afforded by group insurance depends upon the policy, income for a period of years may be paid to beneficiaries, or a lump-sum payment may be made. If death is due to accidental causes, the payments may be increased. If an employee becomes totally and permanently disabled before he reaches sixty years of age, specified payments are made to him. Disability payments are made without regard to the cause of the disability, which might be occupational or nonoccupational. The policy may also provide for payments to an employee who loses a hand or a foot or is otherwise maimed, even though he may not be able to prove disability.

A few labor unions have experimented with hospitalization and other types of group insurance. According to the usual plan, the members pay the premiums to the union, which manages the insurance fund and makes payments to workers who are entitled to compensation. Experience with such funds has usually been unsatisfactory because unions lacked statistical data on which to base assessments and benefits. Union officials were not trained in the management of the funds, which were sometimes improperly used for strike benefits. Consequently, unions have urged that money for the payment of benefits to workers should be paid by the employer. Three types of management for such benefit funds are in operation: those administered solely by the union; those administered jointly by the employer and the union; and those administered by a private insurance company, with premiums paid directly by the employer to the insurance company.

RECREATIONAL SERVICES

In some cases, particularly in urban locations, few recreational services may be provided by the company, while in smaller communities a more elaborate program may be developed. The activities may include a variety of sports, such as basketball, bowling, softball, and tennis. Social activities might include dinners, shows, picnics, and concerts. Clubs may be organized for stamp collecters, musicians, and camera enthusiasts. The programs may be financed by the company, by a benefit association supported by the workers, by club dues, or by profits from vending machines and lunchroom sales.

Recreational activities are necessarily adapted to the needs and interests of workers and the community. They are affected by the distance from workers' homes to the plant, shift hours and overtime work, and the other recreational facilities in the area. The program should have a minimum of support from the company, and it should in no sense be considered as paternalism or charity. The administration should be as democratic as possible with a maximum of participation by the employees. The program should be designed to provide recreation and competition of an amateur nature. It should not be permitted to become professional. A phase of the recreational program which should not be neglected is the possible liability of the employer for injuries sustained by employees who participate in athletic events. The employer may also be liable for injuries sustained by an employee in an automobile accident in traveling to or from such an event. The risk of injury is increased by inadequate training for athletic contests and failure to take adequate precautions to protect workers from injury. The employer is more likely to be liable if any pressure is placed upon an employee to get him to participate, if the games are played on the employer's premises, or if the employer has provided supervision for the activity. To reduce the risk, the employer may see that players are physically fit, discourage excessive zeal to win, and provide adequate medical care. Adequate records of injuries should be kept to determine whether sports are becoming too strenuous.

FINANCIAL BENEFITS

Financial benefits are provided in part by the health services because they may give the worker who is ill or who is injured by accident certain financial assistance. However, additional financial benefits may be provided in certain cases, or the workers may be encouraged to help each other financially. Several types of such services may be provided.

Retirement Plans. Many companies have long provided for the payment of retirement allowances to employees with a stipulated number of years of service. The enactment of the Social Security Act in 1935, which provided for old-age and survivors' benefits, did not cause a general abandonment of pension plans, as many persons had feared, but was followed by the adoption of pension plans by more companies. Possible reasons for the extension of retirement plans may be the recognition that payments under the Social Security Act are not large and that the law directed the attention of employers to the need for retirement allowances. Other possible reasons are the growing strength of organized labor and an increased feeling of social responsibility on the part of employers.

Retirement plans differ greatly in their provisions. Some plans cover all employees, and some cover employees earning in excess of a specified amount per year. Some cover only salaried employees earning in excess of a stated amount. In some cases, all the cost is paid by the employer, and in other plans a part of the cost is paid by the employee and a part is paid by the employer. Some plans provide for the establishment of a fund, which may be managed jointly by the employer and the employees. Some provide for the payment of the joint contributions to a trust company, which manages the funds and makes payments to the annuitants according to the plan. Some plans provide for the purchase of an annuity from an insurance company. In some cases, no fund is established, and the company merely pays its retired employees the agreed amounts and charges the payments to payroll expense as they are made. Unless a fund is established, the rights of employees may be lost as the result of a merger. Funds have sometimes been set up on an unsound actuarial basis.

Benefits to employees are usually based upon their annual earnings and the number of years of service. For example, one plan provides for the monthly payment of 1 per cent of the compensation in the year preceding retirement, multiplied by the number of years of service. Social security benefits are sometimes deducted from the payments made under the plan. Allowances may be payable in case the employee is disabled prior to the retirement age.

Employee Stock-Purchase Plans. Following World War I, many companies adopted a plan of selling capital stock of the company to employees. The price was usually somewhat below the prevailing market price at the time of the sale, and payment was made in installments deducted from the pay of the employee. The amount of stock which an employee was permitted to purchase depended upon his annual earnings. The purpose of such a plan was to foster interest in the company, to permit the employee to share in the profits, and to make the employee feel that he was a part of the company. Many of the plans were abandoned after the stock market crash of 1929.

During the 1950's, a large number of corporations adopted revised plans for selling stock to employees. An interesting example is the plan adopted by General Motors Corporation in 1955. According to this plan, any salaried employee with at least one year of service can invest up to 10 per cent of his annual salary. One half of the saving, together with a contribution of the same amount by the corporation, is used to buy stock of General Motors Corporation. Thus, the total amount invested in stock is 10 per cent of the salary. The other 5 per cent is used to buy government bonds. The dividends on the stock are not paid to the employee but are withheld by the corporation for further investment in stock. Amounts invested are used for retirement pay or may be returned to the employee if he leaves the employment of the company. The purposes of the plan are the development of a better employee attitude toward the corporation, the encouragement of thrift, and the provision of additional capital for the corporation. The plan permits the corporation to retain and to reinvest in the business a substantial sum. Income taxes are a factor in the plan because no taxes are paid by the corporation on the amounts retained and reinvested.

The most serious objection to stock ownership by employees is that the employee becomes dependent upon the company for both his job and the security of his savings. Common stock in any one company does not provide either stability of income or security of principal. A diversity of investments in senior securities might be preferable. When a company urges employees to buy stock, it may expect criticism if prices decline in the market to less than the purchase price. Disappointment in the stock investment may impair the confidence of employees in the management of the company.

Credit Unions. A credit union is a co-operative small-loan enterprise. The company credit union receives deposits of the savings of employees and makes loans in small amounts to other members of the group. Interest rates paid to depositors are higher than the rate paid on time deposits in banks and perhaps conservative investments in bonds. The charges on loans made to borrowers are low in comparison with charges made by small-loan companies. Under the usual plan of organization, the members elect a board of directors of five or more members, a credit committee, and a supervisory committee. The directors elect the president, the treasurer, and the secretary. These officers receive deposits, make loans, and manage the affairs of the credit union with advice and counsel of the two committees and a minimum of assistance from the personnel manager.

Credit unions made rapid progress during the decade of the 1950's. They have been encouraged by management because they help workers to solve their financial problems and to accumulate their savings.[1] Some employers believe that credit unions have contributed to the morale and the training of workers in financial management. Workers have been able to make considerable investments in credit unions because of the increased real wages and steady employment. The unions make their greatest appeal to workers who regard their relationship with the company as permanent. The principal problems for both the members of the union and the employer pertain to the soundness of the loan policy and the possibility of mismanagement.

SERVICES TO ESTABLISH CLOSER RELATIONSHIP WITH EMPLOYEES

All of the services to employees described in the preceding pages are designed to improve morale and they may help to establish a closer personal relationship between the management and the employees. However, additional services may be provided that are general in nature and cannot be included in any of the preceding classifications. Some of them will be described in the following paragraphs.

Employee Publication. A magazine published by the company in the interests of better personnel relations is usually referred to as an employee publication or plant magazine. One purpose of such a publication is to integrate the interests of employees and management by informing each group of the interests and activities of the other. However, most of the space and notices should concern employees rather than management. The magazine should also build up an interest in the company as a whole by informing the employees in various departments of the activities in all parts of the plant. It fosters a group spirit by recognizing the work of various departments in such matters as safety records, attendance, and production. It helps to build up a feeling of importance in the individual employee through notices of per-

---

[1] "Credit Unions Are Booming," *Factory Management and Maintenance,* Vol. CXVI, No. 4 (1958), pp. 134–35.

sonal events, such as marriages, births, wedding anniversaries, retirements, and vacations.

The plant magazine is usually published under the direction of the personnel department. Publication may be supervised by a joint committee of employees and management. Papers sometimes appear weekly and sometimes monthly. In a small business the reporting is done on a volunteer basis. The paper may be mimeographed or printed by a more expensive process. Most of the items are of a personal nature or relate to employee activities. The mentioning of the names of employees is good technique, although care may be necessary to avoid devoting an undue amount of space to the publicity seeker.

The employee publication is sent or distributed to employees without charge. The most successful method of distribution is to place the papers at the exits at quitting time in order that employees may pick them up as they leave. Papers should not be taken to workplaces or read in the plant. To emphasize the timeliness of the paper, surplus copies should be removed from places of distribution after two or three days.

The distribution of space in the magazine depends, in part, upon employee interests, and reader checks may be made to determine which topics have the greatest appeal. Some papers submit questionnaires to readers every six months to sample their opinions. Most of the space is usually devoted to personal items, such as weddings, births, company sports, hobbies of employees, vacation trips, and recreational activities. Some space is given to special features, letters to the editor, occasional educational subjects, and editorials. Pictures of employees at work, at home, or on vacation are usually featured.

Although the plant publication is usually read by employees, it does not discuss the problems in which workers are most interested, such as the settlement of complaints and grievances, possible cutbacks in production, seniority provisions, methods of evaluating jobs, changes in working hours, and improvements in working conditions. Perhaps the failure of the magazine to treat such matters is explained by the fact that other methods of communication may deal with them. Another reason is that the editor of the magazine is not included in the committees that consider company programs and policies and is not sufficiently informed to discuss the problems and interests of workers. Furthermore, the company is now required to give consideration to all pronouncements in the area of employee and union relations because of the requirements of state and federal law and the union contract. The failure of the company publication to discuss such problems contrasts with the policy of labor unions in keeping their members informed.[2]

Some companies have made use of the plant magazine to explain company programs and to establish better employee and community relations. For example, if employees are known to complain that prices in the plant cafeteria are too high, the company might publicize data as to the number of meals served, labor and food costs, and the net results of operation. If the company is criticized for the pollution of rivers or other water supply, it might explain what it is doing about the problem and the extent to which improvements have been made. If the company has developed programs to keep people employed who might otherwise have been laid off, the plant paper might be used to inform employees and other people in the community.[3] In most cases, however, the plant periodical is not used as a means of informing employees concerning such problems.

Plant Food Services.   Many large companies now provide some kind of food services inside the plant. Some companies operate a cafeteria, and others operate snack bars or lunch counters at convenient points. Other companies provide dispensing units on wheels, which make the rounds through the plant. Employees may make their purchases at the regular lunch periods or at other times which are usually referred to as "coffee breaks."

In-plant feeding is managed in any one of three ways. The company may manage the facilities at cost or perhaps at a small loss. Second, the facilities may be managed jointly by the company and the employees. Space is provided by the company for little or no charge. Any profit is used for employee activities, such as sports and social affairs. According to the third plan, the facilities are managed by a service company which specializes in operating plant food facilities. The service operates under the company name and is generally regarded as a part of the company that owns and operates the plant.

Company Stores.   Several types of company stores and purchase plans have been developed to meet the varying requirements of the employees. Some companies permit their employees to buy at a discount limited amounts of the merchandise in which the company regularly deals. To prevent the abuse of the plan, the company may stipulate that the merchandise must be used for personal or family use. Some companies buy from other manufacturers or wholesalers certain articles for resale to

---

[2] See Fred C. Foy and Robert Harper, "Round One: Union *vs.* Company Publications," *Harvard Business Review,* Vol. XXXIII, No. 3 (1955), pp. 59–67.

[3] William C. Halley, "Making Your Plant Paper Pay Off," *Factory Management and Maintenance,* Vol. CXIII, No. 10 (1955), pp. 138–40.

employees at cost. Such purchases are made on specific requests from the employee. The company may organize a co-operative store whose capital is supplied by the employees themselves. Co-operative stores are managed by the employees with a minimum of help from the company.

The most common type of store is company owned. Sales are made at cost plus a margin to cover operating expenses. In some cases the margin above cost has been so large as to amount to exploitation. Because some companies have taken advantage of workers by forcing them to buy from company stores, many states now prohibit the payment of employees in scrip which is redeemable only at the store. Such provisions are also frequently included in the union contract.

Many stores have not been successful. Company stores and employee purchase plans do not operate advantageously during periods when merchandise is in short supply. Too much time is spent by the purchasing department in trying to find scarce items. In times of rising prices, employee ill will may be created because the company is blamed for the high prices. The competition of well-managed stores in the community is another factor. In some cases the closing of company stores was considered necessary to the maintenance of good community relations because of objections made by local merchants.

Suggestion Systems. A suggestion system provides the machinery whereby an employee may contribute ideas for the improvement of conditions within the plant. In small companies the program for the soliciting of suggestions is frequently an organized campaign which terminates at a definite time. Large companies may conduct a continuous program for employee suggestions. The purposes of such a program are to encourage suggestions for the improvement of working conditions, to establish better relations between the management and employees through the exchange of ideas, and to direct the minds of all employees and officers toward work methods. Suggestions usually relate to proposed changes in tools, machines, workplace layout, and procedures for purchasing, storing, or issuing materials.

The management of the suggestion system is the work of a member of the personnel department. His duty is to solicit and investigate suggestions. No suggestion can be received through the suggestion system from foremen, engineers, time-study men, or other persons in the management group. Suggestions are made in writing on a form prepared by the company. Usually the suggestions are signed by the employees although some companies request that the suggestion not be signed. The person who makes the suggestion is identified by a number which appears on the form and also on a perforated slip which he detaches.

Acceptable suggestions are rewarded by a cash prize which may be 15 per cent of the savings for the first year. A minimum award may be established. In some cases, no measurable savings may be anticipated because the suggestion pertains to the prevention of accidents, the reduction of fire or health hazards, the improvement of the product, or a change in working conditions. The award for such suggestions may be based upon the value placed upon the idea by a committee of the management.

Employees should be informed of the type of suggestions desired. One plan is to publish a booklet describing the system and the method of its operation. One such booklet describes a suggestion as "a positive constructive idea to improve methods, equipment, and procedures; to make for safer and better working conditions; to reduce time or cost of an office, factory, or sales operation; or to improve either industrial or public relations." Another way of indicating to employees the type of suggestion desired is to print in the heading of the suggestion form the classes or groups of suggestions which are solicited. The employee checks the appropriate heading and then writes a description of the plan or change he suggests.

Some companies have found suggestion systems to be very successful. Others have tried and abandoned them. Reasons given for discontinuance are various. In some cases the value of the suggestions was not considered sufficient to cover the cost of the awards and the time spent in managing the plan. In other cases, foremen resented suggestions for improving conditions in their departments. If one worker made a suggestion for improving the job of another, the worker on the job resented it. Both foremen and workers sometimes attempted to show that the old way was better even after the committee had approved the suggestion. Suggestion plans are said to generate an individualistic attitude and to interfere with the development of a team spirit. The failure of some plans should be attributed to poor management or a lack of enthusiasm for the plan.

To assure success, the management of the suggestion system should be made the regular work of a capable person. All suggestions should be acknowledged as soon as they are received, and they should be promptly investigated. Some suggestions may be referred to the foreman in whose department the change would be made, or to a staff specialist who is in a position to determine the desirability of the proposed change. The person to whom the suggestion is referred is requested to estimate the cost of making the change, the cost of the tools or equipment that would be required, and the amount of the annual savings that would be realized if the suggestion should be accepted.

If a suggestion is not immediately accepted, the employee who submitted it may be interviewed and asked to explain it. If it still appears to be impractical, he should be told the reason for rejection. To encourage the co-operation of employees, some companies pay a small amount, perhaps $1.00, for suggestions that are not accepted. If a suggestion has merit but cannot immediately be made effective, it may be returned to the employee who submitted it, and he should have priority as to the suggestion for a period of twelve months. He may be asked to resubmit a suggestion after a year has elapsed. Employees who win substantial awards should receive proper publicity through the plant periodical and in other ways. The manager of the suggestion system should see that practical use is made of any suggestion for which an award is given.

Accident Prevention Programs. Accident prevention is usually included in personnel activities, although the program includes certain engineering aspects. The phases of safety work are sometimes referred to as the four E's: Engineering, Education, Enlistment, and Enforcement. The engineering phase includes the design of machines and equipment, the enclosure of moving parts, protection against falls through manholes, the design of safety apparel, and the development of rules of safe practice. The other E's are personnel activities. Education in safety is given as a part of the induction program, in connection with training on the job, and in connection with other personnel work. Enlistment refers to the continuous program that is required to convince people of the necessity for observing safety practices. Enforcement includes the investigation of accidents to determine the causes and to recommend measures to prevent similar accidents in the future.

A fifth E could be added—Evaluation of results. Improvement in safety performance may be measured by the number of accidents or their severity. The compilation of data pertaining to accidents requires first that a definition of accident be agreed upon. An accident is defined as an unplanned incident that results in injury to a person and a loss of time beyond the day when the incident occurred. Accident frequency is computed by the following formula:

$$\text{Frequency} = \frac{\text{Number of accidents} \times 1,000,000}{\text{Total labor hours worked}}$$

The reason the number of accidents is multiplied by 1,000,000 is that the formula usually results in a whole number which is easily understood.

Accident severity makes allowance for the seriousness of the accident. It is computed by this formula:

$$\text{Severity} = \frac{\text{Number of days lost x 1,000}}{\text{Number of hours worked}}$$

In the computation of the number of days lost, death or disability is counted as 6,000 days. A smaller number of days is assigned to the loss of a finger, a hand, a toe, a foot or other dismemberment. The accident rates are computed for the entire company, for each plant, and each department. The accident program requires the attention of each person who is exposed to accident hazards.

Employee Counseling. A personal service which members of the personnel department may render to employees is that of counseling. Methods and purposes of counseling differ according to the company and the interviewer. Three types of counseling may be distinguished. First, the counselor may attempt to aid the employee in the solution of his personal problems incident to his employment. This type of counseling service was widely used during World War II, when many persons were drawn into industry for the first time. Some of the problems with which the counselor might be concerned have been mentioned in connection with the discussion of induction of employees. They include methods of checking in and out, information as to rest periods, smoking rules, methods of wage payment and payroll deductions, clothing regulations, vacations, medical facilities, reporting of accidents, and method of applying for a social security number. Employees may also be assisted in the solution of community problems, such as housing, shopping, transportation, schools, nurseries, and banking. This type of counseling is most valuable during periods of rapid expansion of the labor force.

The counselor may also advise with the employee concerning his record and methods of advancement. When employees are rated by some plan of merit rating, their records should be reviewed with them after each rating. Their strong and weak points should be noticed, and methods of improving the rating should be discussed. The counselor may discuss with promising employees the possibilities of special training courses. The counseling interview is valuable in stimulating the interest of the employee.

In a third type of counseling, the counselor may endeavor to assist the employee in making a satisfactory adjustment to his work. The counselor does not attempt to give advice, and he does not argue with the employee. He listens, and by means of well-directed questions, he attempts to have the employee work out his own solution of the difficulty. The theory of this method is that the employee frequently rationalizes concerning his problems without realizing it. He permits his attitudes and his work to be affected by misfortunes at home, demotions, transfers which are interpreted as demotions, unemployment of other members of the family, disappointment in personal affairs, and numerous developments which are not relevant to the job. The purpose of the interview is to give the employee a chance to talk to an understanding listener, to reduce his emotional tension by talking it out, and to decide for himself the best procedure. Discussions are confidential, and the interviewer can take no action to correct a situation of which the employee complains. The method requires great skill and patience on the part of the interviewer.

This method of counseling resembles the procedure used in counseling with the general public, where the method is called "psychotherapy." The principal difference is that in industry the interviewer is less free to lead the employee to discuss all his personal problems than is a private practitioner in handling the case of a client who recognizes the need for a solution to his problems. The method has not been generally used in industry because of its cost.

Other Services. Many other services are being rendered by various companies to their employees. It is not possible to give a complete list; but they include company loans for housing, company housing projects, legal advice, and nurseries for the care of young children. The types of services depend upon the size of the company, the nature of the business, the location of the plant, the needs and desires of employees, and the attitude of the management. The services may vary from year to year according to changes in business conditions and the experiences of the company.

The benefits, pensions, and indirect wage payments may be extended in small amounts from time to time; and if management fails to compute the costs of each benefit that is granted, the total may eventually become a substantial amount. For example, one survey indicated that fringe benefits paid by manufacturing concerns totaled 16.8 per cent of the payroll, or $667 per worker for a year. The payments included legally required contributions for social security and workmen's compensation, pensions and other payments under contract such as group insurance and tuition refunds, paid rest and lunch periods, and payments for time not worked, such as vacations, holidays, sick leave, jury duty, funerals of members of the family, and national guard service. Other miscellaneous items were profit-sharing payments, special bonuses, and suggestion awards.[4] Large companies usually make more payments of this kind than small enterprises, and for this reason may be able to attract workers more easily. A small company is at a disadvantage in making guarantees of benefits over a period of years.

QUESTIONS

1. How can the management determine whether a proposed employee service is worth its cost to the company?

2. Some employee services should be offered only because the employees want them. How can the management determine in advance whether they want the service?

3. Should management provide services to employees because profits will be increased, or does management have some other objective?

4. Why should management wish the employees to have good food at the luncheon period? Would management be concerned that many employees make a lunch of sandwiches and soft drinks? Should management concern itself with the kinds of breakfasts employees eat?

5. What can the personnel director do to improve working conditions in the plant?

6. Is the personnel director concerned with plans an employee may make for his retirement, or is such preparation a personal matter with which the personnel director should not interfere?

7. Some companies have found that alcoholism is most prevalent among highly skilled workers who are very difficult to replace. Should they be concerned with this problem?

8. Should employees be encouraged to purchase stock in the company?

9. What types of suggestions does the company want submitted under its suggestions system? What types does it not want?

10. The personnel director finds that suggestions are not investigated until six months after they were submitted. He also finds that approved suggestions for which an award is given are often not put into practice. How can these difficulties be corrected?

11. Should the company make a charge for uniforms for a company baseball team? Should admission fees and dues be charged for membership in a club, such as a camera club or a garden club?

12. Why would a company want worker participation in the management of employee services where such participation is possible?

---

[4] "You'll Be Paying More for Fringe Benefits," *Factory Management and Maintenance,* Vol. CXIV, No. 4 (1956), pp. 82–83.

CASES

63. OPERATION OF A CAFETERIA

The Sievers Company had not provided cafeteria service because the number of employees did not seem to warrant the trouble and expense. The company employed only 130 employees in its busy season, and the number dropped to 110 during some months of the year. The company had no personnel department. An assistant to the office manager interviewed applicants for jobs, handled requests for transfer, and attended to the other personnel problems when the need arose.

Food service in the area adjacent to the plant was not satisfactory. Most of the eating places were of the small quick-lunch variety that featured cheap and poorly served foods. The time allowed to employees for the lunch period did not permit them to walk to better-class restaurants and for most of the employees the cost of good lunches was prohibitive.

The president authorized Mr. George Lucy, the office manager, to investigate and report on the possibility of a satisfactory plan for the operation of a plant cafeteria. Most of the people with whom Mr. Lucy talked advised against the provision of in-plant food service. They said that the cafeteria created too many problems for the mangement, would operate at too great a loss, and would result in too much employee dissatisfaction. However, Mr. Lucy was convinced that in-plant feeding was needed by the company.

Mr. Lucy developed a plan designed for maximum service at minimum cost. His plan was an adaptation of the plan of another small company in a nearby city. The Sievers Company would provide space in the basement of the building where a dining room could be equipped to seat 125 persons. A small kitchen would also be installed for the preparation of food. Bread, cake, pies, and other bakery products would be purchased from a local bakery.

To minimize food losses and to permit better planning of meals, employees would be asked to place their orders in advance. The names of all employees would be printed in the order of their payroll numbers on the left side of a sheet of paper, and the menu for each day would be written above the columns on the sheet. As each employee entered the plant each morning, he would merely place a check mark in the appropriate spaces opposite his name to indicate his order for the day. Spaces were provided where the employee could indicate the soup, meat and vegetable combination, the salad, drink, and dessert he desired. Only one kind of meat would be served each day. The orders would be complete by 9 o'clock each morning, and the cafeteria manager would know how many servings of each kind to prepare.

Prices would be set to cover only the cost of food. Since in most restaurants that serve plain foods the food cost is about half of the price charged, employees would be able to buy their noon meal for about half the amount they would pay in a public place. The company would furnish the space and pay the wages of the kitchen help.

To reduce the cost of labor in the dining room, no cashier would make charges or collect money. Payment for meals would be made by employees solely by coupons in denominations of five and ten cents which could be purchased in books of $3.00 value from the office manager. The coupons would be stamped with the payroll number of the employee. In the cafeteria, the employee would tear out and deposit in a box an amount of coupons equal to the price of his meal. As a verification, the office manager would sort out the coupons by payroll numbers and compare the total for each person with the price of the menu checked for the day.

All food would be served on plates and other dishes before the cafeteria was opened for service, and each employee would merely pick up the plate containing the food ordered. Beverages would be self-service from pitchers or pots, in the case of tea or coffee. To reduce congestion, the cafeteria would be opened to women employees at 11:55 A.M. and to men at 12 noon. As each employee finished eating, he would stack his dishes and place them on a table near the kitchen for the dish-washers. With these arrangements, the office manager thought that the cafeteria could be operated by three employees who would prepare and dispense the food and clean up the kitchen each day. Purchasing and accounting work would be handled by the assistant to the office manager and a clerical assistant in the accounting office, and no additional help in the office would be required.

To obtain suggestions on the operation of the cafeteria, the office manager recommended that a committee of three employes be appointed to work with him. The membership of the committee would be changed every three months. An effort would be made to appoint to the committee employees who were known to be dissatisfied with things in general. Mr. Lucy thought that if good food could be served at the prices suggested, more than 90 per cent of the employees would regularly eat in the cafeteria.

Required:

Criticize favorably or unfavorably the plan recommended by Mr. Lucy.

64. ADVANCE OF SALARY TO AN EMPLOYEE

Mrs. Mary Miles was employed as a secretary by the Otis Company on the basis of a personal interview, a practical test of dictation and typing, and the recommendation of her last employer. Her application blank disclosed that she had held five positions during the last two years, but she explained that she had obtained a better position each time she had moved.

Mrs. Miles soon demonstrated that she could take telephone calls and receive visitors satisfactorily and that she could do typing and filing very well. However, she soon came to be violently disliked by all the other girls in the office because she persisted in discussing all of the details of her troubles with her former husband. She seemed anxious to show that her separation from him was his fault and not hers. In talking with the other girls, she often used words that they regarded as undignified and unsuited for the relationships in the office.

The company paid its salaried employees by check at the end of each month. After Mrs. Miles had been with the Otis Company for two months and had received her check for the second month on July 31, she informed her supervisor that she had borrowed $1,000 from a pawn broker to meet the hospital bill of her mother. She had fallen behind in her payments, and if she did not have the money to pay him, her salary would be attached for the payment. She therefore asked the company to advance her salary for August. Within a month, she expected to get her debts straightened out. Reluctantly, the supervisor recommended that the advance be made, and the treasurer complied with the recommendation.

At the end of August, Mrs. Miles received no check because she had already been paid for the month. On September 1, she again requested and received an advance. The same was done on November 1. On December 1, the treasurer informed the supervisor that since the books would be audited at the end of the year, he was required to have all advances cleared. He therefore requested the supervisor not to approve another advance. Furthermore, the treasurer said that the "grapevine" had carried the word that Mrs. Miles was the recipient of special consideration in regard to salary payments. Although Mrs. Miles protested that her Christmas would be ruined and that she would be driven to the loan sharks, she was not given any further salary advances. The supervisor did not learn what arrangements Mrs. Miles was able to make.

Question:

Was the case of Mrs. Miles properly handled?

PART VIII
PROCUREMENT
AND
STORAGE

30 Purchasing

THE management of production includes planning the operations, making the plans effective by issuing orders for work to be done, and seeing that the plans are carried out effectively at low cost within the established time limits. Many of the steps required for production management have been described in previous chapters. Such steps include the design of the product and the establishment of standards for each product, and the planning of the facilities for production including types of machines and plant layout. Organizational relationships should also be defined, and the duties of each position should be determined. Personnel requirements at each level should be provided.

An important phase of the management problem remaining for consideration is the procurement of materials of the prescribed kind and quality in the proper quantities at the right time at the lowest cost consistent with the other requirements. Since the materials may have to be received into stock and held in the storeroom for an indeterminate time prior to use in production, procurement includes not only the placing of the purchase order but also the establishment of inventory standards and the control over quantities on hand and on order, the storing and the issuing of the materials for use in manufacturing. The present chapter is concerned with purchasing for production.

TYPES OF PURCHASES

Although the purchasing function may be regarded principally as a phase of the procurement of raw materials, the purchasing department may in fact make contracts for the purchase of four types of materials, parts, and other merchandise.

Materials for Fabrication. Merchandise of this type enters into the product with its form so changed that consumers may not recognize the material by either grade or trade name. Examples are lumber, grain, sheet steel, pipe, wire, wool, cotton, paint, and copper. Consumer acceptance of the trade name or the good will associated with the name of the manufacturer of the material is not important in the purchase of merchandise of this sort. The purchase of such materials is usually made by commercial grade or specification.

Merchandise for Resale without Fabrication. Some manufacturing enterprises occasionally contract for the manufacture of the product for resale. For example, a shirt manufacturer may contract for the manufacture of fancy shirts of certain designs for which the demand is seasonal. This arrangement enables the company to concentrate on the manufacture of shirts of stable demand. Many manufacturers purchase various types of appliances and other merchandise for sale to employees or members of the management at a discount. As explained in Chapter 29, some companies operate employee stores, canteens, or lunch counters where goods are sold as purchased. Parts, containers, and accessories may be purchased rather than manufactured. Examples are roller bearings, motors, carburetors, locks, tires, and tin cans. In all such cases, purchases may be made on the basis of brand, trade name, and consumer acceptance, as well as suitability for manufacturing.

Machinery and Equipment. The purchasing department usually makes purchases of machinery, furniture, office appliances, and other types of equipment upon requisition from the department for which the items are intended.

Supplies. This type of merchandise includes coal, fuel oil, cleaning supplies, lubricants, stationery, printed forms, athletic supplies, photographs, and literature for use in employee and public relations. Such purchases should be made on the basis of suitability for the purposes intended and of acceptability to the persons who will use the supplies.

THE WORK OF PURCHASING

In the purchase of materials and supplies, the first responsibility of the purchasing department is to locate sources of supply and to select the best and most reliable sources. It also should keep informed as to prices, the quality of various grades and varieties, and the amounts available at the prices quoted. It negotiates the purchase contract, arranges for delivery dates, and follows up the purchase order to see that the goods are received on the date wanted and are available on schedule. It attends to the details of compiling quotations for materials or bids on contracts, checks the invoices of vendors, and carries on correspondence with suppliers. It maintains records of bids received, prices quoted, and orders placed.

A number of activities are closely related to the purchasing function and are sometimes considered a part of it. For example, production planning requires the scheduling of the receipt of material for use in meeting production schedules. The design of the product, which is an engineering function, may depend upon the availability of certain types of materials, their cost, and the existence of standard materials, parts, and accessories. Purchasing is closely related to other procurement activities, such as traffic management, the handling of incoming shipments, storeroom management, and inventory control. Purchasing should also be co-ordinated with the activities of the departments for which the purchases are made.

The Timing of Purchases.   The work of purchasing is affected by the way in which the timing of the purchase order and the schedule for deliveries into stock are determined. In some cases, a reorder point is established for certain items of materials that are regularly used. When the number of units on hand falls to the reorder point as a result of withdrawals, an order for an additional supply is placed with a vendor.

For some types of material, a purchaser may place his orders for a stated amount for an entire year or season, and the exact dates for delivery are arranged as the season advances or as the need arises. For example, a fruit or vegetable canning company may place its orders for cans or other containers for an entire year in advance. Likewise, it may contract with a grower for vegetables or fruits, which are delivered when the vegetables are mature or the fruits are ripe. Similar contracts may be made for paper, coal, cotton, fabrics, and other materials. This arrangement assures the seller of his markets and gives the purchaser a dependable source of supply.

In some cases, the purchaser may contract separately for each order or each project that is planned in production. For example, a building contractor might order separately the doors, windows, structural steel, and plumbing supplies that would be used in each building or other structure. A garment manufacturer who plans for the production and sale of a fancy shirt or dress of a particular design might contract with the textile manufacturer for the textiles of a specified color, design, and thread count. Some of the materials used in the manufacture of a shirt, such as thread and buttons, might be purchased by the method of the reorder point, while the fabric which would be used only in one season might be dropped from the purchasing program as soon as the one order has been placed.

A plan for purchasing in large quantities without regard to specific needs over a period of time might be followed because of the possibility of a price rise or an interruption to the flow of production resulting from a strike or other such difficulty. This plan might also be followed for materials that are imported from abroad where regular or prompt deliveries cannot always be anticipated. Examples are cork, industrial diamonds, ivory, coffee beans, and hemp. This plan of advance purchasing is particularly advantageous if the item is not a large percentage of the total cost of the product but is essential for production. The adoption of such a plan would be a question of company policy.

Organization for Purchasing. The work of purchasing is usually placed under the direction of an executive with the title of purchasing agent. This title emphasizes the legal position of the purchasing officer as legal respresentative of the company in making purchase contracts. The purchasing agent may report to the chief executive as the head of a major division, or he may report to the vice-president in charge of manufacturing. The position of the purchasing function in the organization depends upon its importance to the enterprise. In some companies, such as meat packing, flour milling, or sugar refining, the cost of material constitutes such a large percentage of the total manufacturing cost that purchasing assumes a major importance. A mining company, at the other extreme, gets its raw materials from the ground and buys only certain supplies and equipment. In many companies, purchasing is placed in an intermediate position as a separate department but not a major division.

The organization within the purchasing department depends upon the extent of the activities for which it is responsible. If it handles only the purchasing function and none of the related activities of procurement previously mentioned, the principal activity would be that of letting purchase contracts. Each buyer under the direction of a purchasing agent would specialize in the purchase of a group of materials, such as finished parts, chemicals, and steel. The organization of the buying group would obviously depend upon the types of materials to be purchased. The buying group would be assisted by other sections which would attend to clerical details. A price and vendor section would maintain price information and data pertaining to sources of supply. A clerical section would keep records and check invoices. Other sections would follow up orders placed and prepare statistical research reports. The organization chart of the purchasing function in a chemical manufacturing company is shown in Figure 54. This organization chart

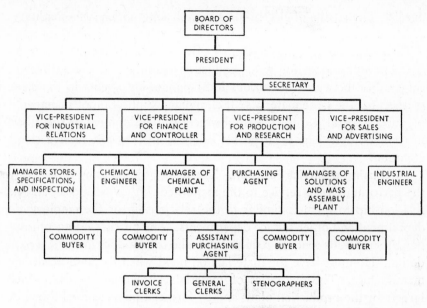

FIG. 54. Organization for Purchasing in a Chemical Manufacturing Company

also shows the place of the purchasing function in the general organization of the company.

In a multiplant company the principal question of organization for purchasing pertains to the extent to which purchasing is centralized. If each plant produces a different type of product, such as frozen foods, meats, or coffee, each plant may be permitted to make its own purchases. If all of the plants produce the same or similar products, such as shirts, wire and cable, or tin cans, purchasing is more likely to be centralized in the main office.

Centralized purchasing is usually preferred if the plan is feasible. Buying can be done in larger quantities at lower prices and easier credit terms. Materials and merchandise are more likely to be standardized throughout the organization. During periods of short supply, when materials are allocated by vendors or are controlled by a governmental agency, centralized purchasing may afford greater assurance of an adequate supply because the central office can devote more attention to negotiations with vendors and to governmental regulations. Purchase commitments and inventory plans may be controlled by the main office in conformity with production plans and financial requirements. In times of price uncertainties, many companies have found that programs of reducing inventories were not closely followed by local purchasing agents. The results of decentralized purchasing under such conditions can be disastrous.

Centralized purchasing has other advantages. It permits better co-ordination of production with production planning. It also eliminates competition between the various local purchasing agents in the same markets for the same materials. It eliminates duplication of managerial organization and permits the employment or development of specialists in commodities. The legal phases of the contracts will receive closer attention.

Purchasing a Service Function. The work of purchasing is primarily the performing of a service to the manufacturing departments, and its relationship to them is similar to the relationship of the employment department and other service departments. The purchasing agent must buy the materials that are required to make the product in the standard design. He must have the materials on hand when they are needed in manufacture. The quantities of materials purchased are determined largely by the production plans and by financial plans as established by the budget. The principal authority of the purchasing agent pertains to the selection of sources of supply, although company policy may limit his authority in this respect. Because the purchasing department is established principally to serve other departments, it may be properly regarded as performing a staff function.

PURCHASING PRACTICES AND POLICIES

The work of purchasing requires attention to several important questions of practice and policy. The first consideration pertains to the issuance of a purchase requisition. If a perpetual inventory is maintained, the inventory control group would issue the requisition when the supply on hand reaches the reorder point. The purchasing agent then selects potential sources of supply and issues a request for a quotation of price. After the quotations have been received and analyzed, the best source is decided upon with due regard for price, dependability of the vendor, transportation costs, and other factors. The purchase order is then issued and a probable delivery date is established. To insure delivery on the scheduled date, the purchasing department follows up the order and traces the shipment if it is delayed. The materials are inspected upon arrival, and the receiving report is checked against the invoice to verify quantities and quality of materials received. The invoice is also compared with the purchase order. If the invoice is correct in all of its details, it is approved for payment.

Some of the aspects of purchasing have been discussed elsewhere and do not require treatment at this time. Other purchasing practices and policies are treated in the following pages.

Developing Sources of Supply. The purchasing department is responsible for locating sources of supply, determining the relative advantages of the possible sources, and developing good relations with vendors. The purchasing agent may learn of possible sources from advertisements of vendors in trade magazines, interviews with salesmen who call upon him at his office, and advertisements or other solicitations received through the mail. He may also publish in newspapers and other periodicals a request for bids to be made by vendors, although this method has limited application. Frequently, engineers, research personnel, or others needing supplies and equipment may suggest sources of supply. In some cases, the purchasing agent may consult directories published by technical societies or trade associations. The classified lists in the telephone book constitute another useful type of directory.

The purchasing agent should strive to develop and maintain satisfactory relations with vendors after the initial contact has been made. The importance of good relations may manifest itself in prompt shipments, liberal credit terms, strict adherence to the specifications as set forth in the purchase order, advance information on price changes or material shortages, advice in planning for new developments in style trends, assistance in moving surplus stocks of materials, and in other ways. If supplies are difficult to get, the vendor may set up his own system of priorities and allocations with special advantages to customers who have dealt fairly with him. Such favors may sometimes be rendered by the salesman who calls upon the purchasing agent and sometimes by the personnel at the main sales office.

Certain practices of the purchasing agent may result in a loss of the good will of salesmen and the vendor whom they represent. He may refuse to see salesmen; he may require them to wait an unduly long time; or he may fail to keep an appointment for an interview. He may cut an interview short without permitting the salesman to explain his product. Another objectionable practice consists in asking the salesman to state his case in the presence of other persons in the reception room instead of the private office. He may ask for samples when he knows that no orders will be placed, or he may tell the salesman that the company is not in the market when purchases are being made.

Other objectionable practices of the purchasing agent may be of a more serious nature. He may make unnecessary and unreasonable delivery requirements which would disrupt the orderly planning of production of the vendor. He may place speculative orders with the intention of requiring delivery if prices advance and canceling the order if prices decline. He may attempt to obtain a low price which does not afford a fair profit to the vendor. He may bargain for a lower price by playing one vendor off against another and by misrepresenting the prices asked or the terms offered by others. He may use a quoted price on an inferior article to drive down the price on a better one.

Although the practices just referred to are unethical, other practices may be even more objectionable. The purchasing agent (and his company) might refuse to accept the delivery of merchandise ordered by raising some objection of a technical nature. He might reject good merchandise by alleging that it does not meet specifications, and he might refuse to compromise or to arbitrate. Although such an act might afford a basis for a lawsuit, the vendor might permit the practice in order to avoid the costs incident to litigation.

The practices of the buyer may be stated positively to indicate what he should do. He should be fair in quoting bids received from others, place orders far enough in advance to permit of delivery in the regular way instead of rush orders, and treat salesmen courteously and fairly. He should be fair in inspecting materials, accept delivery of goods ordered regardless of price changes, and be willing to arbitrate any differences.

Selection of Vendor. The decision to place an order with a vendor would depend upon a number of factors of which the most important would be the prices asked. In judging the price, however, the purchasing agent will take into account a number of related factors, such as discounts for larger quantities, the time when the vendor will expect payment without penalty, the cash discount or other deductions from the stated price, and the point to which the shipper pays the freight or insurance or other costs (f.o.b. point). A high freight charge because of a distant f.o.b. point, for example, may nullify the apparent advantage of a low quoted price.

Another factor is the reputation of the vendor as reported by other purchasers or as experienced by any one purchasing agent. Some vendors may ship materials differing from the goods ordered, and they may refuse to accept returns of materials. While such conduct may give rise to legal claims on the part of the purchaser, the better plan is the avoidance of such difficulties whenever possible.

Another closely related consideration is the reputation of the vendor for workmanship. If the vendor is recognized as the manufacturer of a quality product, the purchaser may be assured that the goods will be of the quality specified in the order. If the ultimate consumer can identify the part or the accessory after it has been built into the product of the purchaser, the good will facilitates the sale of the final product. For example, the good will attached to the name of the manufacturer of plate glass or tires may be a factor in the sale of the automobile on which they are mounted. If the final product fails to give good service to the purchaser or consumer, the poor performance may react upon the reputation of both the manufacturer of the part and the manufacturer of the ultimate product.

If the quality of purchased materials and parts is very important and tolerances are close, the purchasing agent may develop a rating for vendors which is based upon the percentage of items purchased from each source that fail to meet the prescribed standards. The development of such a rating requires the establishment of definite specifications, careful inspection of predetermined percentages of incoming materials, the keeping of records to show the quality of the items purchased from each vendor, and the computation of the rating. The rating may be used to determine the best sources of supply and to assist vendors in maintaining their standards of quality.[1]

In many cases, the amount the vendor can supply will enter into the decision to buy from a certain source. A low price on a small quantity may not be attractive if the vendor cannot provide sufficient materials to meet the requirements of the purchaser. The purchaser may at times buy his materials at a lower net price by placing the order for a large quantity with one vendor, even though a small manufacturer has quoted a low price on a small quantity. At times, however, a large manufacturer may prefer to place many orders with small suppliers to develop many sources. This plan makes for good public relations and may assist the company in meeting the criticism of government agencies which allege that large size is objectionable.

The guarantee of delivery when the goods are needed can be of great advantage to the purchaser in maintaining his own production schedules. The vendor may be able to assure delivery on schedule if he maintains an inventory from which regular deliveries can be made or if he has two or more plants that are equipped to produce and ship the materials as ordered. Prompt deliveries may also depend upon the extent to which the vendor has regularized his production and his willingness to take such corrective action as may be necessary to avoid or mini-

[1] "Helping Vendors Boost Quality," *Factory Management and Maintenance,* Vol. CXV, No. 12 (1957), pp. 88–90.

mize delays. Failure to make promised delivery dates may be due to labor difficulties, inability of the vendor to acquire materials for his own production, poor production planning by the vendor, or the acceptance of new orders while a large volume of unfilled orders is on hand.

The financial stability of the vendor may also be important. A purchaser who is interested in the development of a permanent source of supply would prefer that the vendor be sufficiently established and financed to assure stability. A vendor who is well established in the industry may be able to assist the purchaser in anticipating the trend of prices or styles and in avoiding the difficulties incident to strikes, traffic congestion, and other developments. Some vendors may offer constructive suggestions for using overstocks of materials, eliminating waste, reducing scrap, or improving the product.

Reciprocal Buying.   The purchasing agent may be expected to use certain sources because the company buys from its own customers. For example, an automobile company may buy tires from a certain rubber company because the rubber company buys the automobiles of the first company. A company making office supplies may buy its machines from a company to whom it sells. A paint company may buy its linseed oil and other materials from companies that use its paint. This practice is known as "reciprocal buying." Purchasing agents are usually opposed to the practice because they prefer to make their purchases on the basis of price, quality, or other details of the purchase contract. When reciprocal buying is practiced, the selection of vendors is made outside the purchasing department.

Commercial Bribery.   Commercial bribery is the name given to the practice of placing orders with a certain vendor because the purchasing agent has accepted gifts or "kickbacks" from the vendor. The purchasing agent should be entirely free to place orders with the best sources of supply. If he has accepted gifts from salesmen or vendors, he may be influenced, consciously or unconsciously, in the placing of orders. To free himself of any appearance of favoritism, he would do well to decline gifts of any kind. Commercial bribery is illegal as an unfair method of competition under the provisions of the Federal Trade Commission Act of 1914, although actually the practice has not been discontinued. Somewhat less objectionable is the acceptance of entertainment offered by salesmen, including gifts of liquor, cigars, meals, and theater tickets. Entertaining customers and giving small gifts are not legally considered to be commercial bribery.

What to Buy.   The first question to arise in determining what to buy concerns which parts or materials are to be purchased and which parts are to be manufactured. Every business is required to purchase some parts or materials from outside sources of supply. However, some companies purchase so many parts, subassemblies, and accessories from others that they become largely assembly companies, while others make a much larger percentage of the parts they need.[2]

Manufacturing the part may be preferred policy if the parts can be made at costs that are lower than prices asked by vendors. The manufacture of a part may also reduce the risk incident to an uncertain source of supply and may prevent an interruption of operations because of the lack of materials. Production of a part may make possible better planning of work and better integration of the activities of the various departments, and quality may be more closely controlled.

The purchase of a part may be an advantage if its manufacture requires a knowledge of specialized production methods or techniques, if a large capital investment is necessary, or if the quantity required by the purchaser is not large enough to permit low manufacturing costs. In some cases, parts or materials are purchased because the source of supply is located in a limited geographical area within or without the United States or because the materials are manufactured from a deposit of a natural resource which is limited. Examples are magnesium, aluminum, copper, lumber, and industrial diamonds.

Another question concerns the kinds of materials to be purchased. The specifications of materials are determined as a part of the work of the development of product design. As long as the product is made in the same design, the same kinds of materials may continue to be purchased. However, the question of materials specifications might be reconsidered if new materials become available, if shortages of certain materials develop, or if economies in production can be realized from changing the specifications. The specifications for manufacturing supplies can be changed without any effect upon the specifications of the product.

Some commodities are purchased by brand or trade name, some by sample, and some by specifications. Many commodities may be purchased by commercial grade, as established by the National Bureau of Standards, the American Standards Association, or other agencies. The use of specifications or the designation of a commercial grade in the making of purchases affords several advantages. Unless such specifications are used in connection with bids received from vendors, the purchaser has no reliable basis for comparing the bids. When the goods

[2] See Carter C. Higgins, "Make-or-Buy Re-Examined," *Harvard Business Review*, Vol. XXXIII, No. 2 (1955), pp. 109–19.

are received, the purchaser has no assurance that the material received from the vendor is of the quality ordered unless the contract was definite in this respect. Inspection of incoming materials is simplified when the goods received can be compared with a definite standard. Quality standards for production are more easily maintained if the same grade of materials is always used. If nonstandardized materials are used, manufacturing costs will probably be increased even in those cases where the quality standards of the product can be maintained.

Some incidental advantages may result from the use of specifications. The use of standard commercial grades may permit the purchaser to limit the varieties of materials carried in the storeroom and to reduce the dollar value of the total inventory. Turnover of inventory is increased, and clerical expense of purchasing, receiving incoming shipments, and maintaining inventory records is reduced. The use of standard materials also aids in the operation of a standard cost accounting system and in the establishment of production standards through motion and time study.[3]

As explained in Chapter 16, some variance in the quality of the product of any company is to be expected. In most materials, some dimensions or other qualities are important and the requirements must be rigidly adhered to. Some qualities are less important, and greater tolerances may be permitted. The quality characteristics of a material or part have been classified as critical, major, and minor. A critical characteristic is a quality that vitally affects safety and requires complete adherence to specifications. A major characteristic is less important but significantly affects the service, life or appearance of the product. The product must possess a high degree of adherence to specifications in regard to major characteristics. A minor characteristic is less important, and the product is required to possess only a general adherence to specifications in respect to such characteristics.

Inspectors and vendors should be instructed as to the characteristics which the purchaser considers as critical, major, or minor. The classification adopted by the purchaser may be affected by the difficulties of vendors in meeting close tolerances. To appreciate the difficulties of manufacturing according to specifications, the purchasing agent should have an understanding of machines and processes of production. One advantage of buying from two or more sources of supply is that the purchasing agent may acquire a better understanding of expected or permissible variances in quality.

---

[3] J. M. Juran, "Ten Basic Tools to Control Vendor's Quality," *Factory Management and Maintenance*, Vol. CXIII, No. 3 (1955), p. 126–29.

Checking for Quality. The purchaser may inspect 100 per cent of the items in a shipment, or he may determine the acceptability of a lot by sampling. Inspection by sampling requires the vendor to take a calculated risk that good lots may be rejected if the sample is not sufficiently large to permit a proper determination of the quality of the entire lot. If the risk is substantial, he will demand a higher purchase price for the materials. The buyer is therefore interested in seeing that the sample is sufficiently large but not too large. The risk of rejection because the sample is too small is called the producer's risk.

The maximum number of defective items in a lot which the buyer will permit is the lot tolerance percentage defective. If the sample is too small, the buyer may accept a shipment with more than the permissible number of defectives. This possibility is called the consumer's risk.

The buyer and the seller may protect themselves by agreeing upon a sample size and the permissible number of defective items in the sample. For example, they may specify a sample size of ten and an acceptable number of three. If the sample is found to contain three defectives or less, the lot is accepted. If it has four or more, the lot is rejected. The contract may provide for the inspection of a second sample if the first sample is found to contain more than the acceptable number of defectives. The proper size of the sample and the permissible number of defectives are determined by the use of mathematical formulas.

How Much to Buy. The quantity to purchase will depend in part upon the nature of the manufacturing processes and the relations with customers. If the company manufactures the product in a limited number of designs, the need for materials can be anticipated and the purchases can be planned to meet the requirements for production. In a job shop which manufactures the product to fill the order of each customer after the order has been received, materials and parts might be purchased as they are needed, or a supply of standard types of materials might be kept on hand to fill most orders. For example, a company that manufactures office forms and other office supplies could keep a supply of paper and carbons in a few qualities and sizes. A company that makes radiators for automobiles of current or older models could keep a supply of the materials commonly used.

The purchasing agent may attempt to buy large quantities of standard materials because the price is believed to be low. In such cases, purchases are made in anticipation of requirements at an indefinite future time, without regard to immediate needs. This practice is known as "speculative buying."

Speculative buying is widely practiced during a period of rising prices. The practice may be justified not only because a speculative profit may be realized from the advance in prices but also because it may make continuous operation of the plant possible during periods of short supply. However, speculative transactions may result in losses instead of profits; and excessive purchases may cause additional expenses to be incurred for storage, handling, insurance, and interest. In some cases, materials may decrease in value because of deterioration. Merchandise purchased on a speculative basis may become unusable as a result of changes in the design of the product. Many companies consider that, as an established policy, speculative buying is not sound.

The profits realized or the losses sustained from speculative buying may be entered in the accounting records and shown separately in the profit and loss statement. This result is accomplished by, first, recording the purchases in the general accounts and in the balance of stores records at cost and, second, charging purchases to operations at market prices prevailing when the materials are issued for use in production. The difference between cost and market price at the date of issuance is recorded as Gain or Loss on Purchases of Materials.

Forward buying differs from speculative buying in that the purpose is to achieve some advantage other than an increase in the price of the materials. Future needs might be anticipated in order to build up a reserve stock and avoid materials shortages. This practice might be followed for materials which are low in price but essential to production. These materials, called key materials, might be stocked in quantity when they are available and when shortages are anticipated because of transportation difficulties or for other reasons. Future needs for materials might also be anticipated to obtain the advantages of quantity discounts or to reduce freight charges that would be required on small shipments. Forward buying obviously involves risks.

Hand-to-mouth buying is the opposite of speculative buying. Inventory is kept as low as possible without interrupting current operations. The purpose is to avoid the costs incident to the carrying of large quantities of materials and the possible losses due to market declines. Many companies adopt this plan during periods of declining commodity prices.

Hand-to-mouth buying may result in definite advantages. The investment in inventories is lowered, and less inventory space is required. Inventory losses are minimized in case the design of the product is changed. If new and more desirable types of materials are offered in the market, the specifications or grades of materials are more easily changed. Furthermore, the purchaser has more frequent contacts with vendors and keeps informed of market developments.

Some objections can be made to the plan of hand-to-mouth buying. Quantity discounts may be sacrificed because prices on numerous small quantities may be higher than on fewer orders for large amounts. Freight charges are higher. Clerical expenses in placing orders, receiving shipments, checking freight bills, inspecting materials, and accounting for purchases are increased. Because similar expenses of vendors are increased, a certain amount of vendor ill will may be engendered. Any interruption in the flow of incoming materials may result in delays in production. If large orders are received unexpectedly from customers, deliveries may be delayed.

For most companies, purchases should be made in economical quantities and inventories should not be excessive. However, the practice depends in part upon the material and the conditions in the market. The amount to be purchased at any one time should be increased during periods of expanding business to provide for the increased rate of consumption of materials.

The Purchase Order.   In the making of purchases, a contract is negotiated between the purchasing agent and the sales representative of the vendor. The contract results from the making of an offer by one party and an acceptance by the other. The offer may be made by either the buyer or the seller, and the acceptance may be made by either party. The manner in which the contract is negotiated may become an important matter if a misunderstanding should arise concerning such details as quantities, quality, the payment of freight and insurance, and credit terms. To avoid misunderstandings, the purchase order or the sales contract should indicate the person who is making the offer and the person who is to accept, as well as the terms of the contract.

Although the purchase-order forms used by many firms do not specify any conditions other than quantity and price, the forms frequently include a number of conditions. For example, some firms protect themselves as to prices by specifying that the material cannot be billed at a price higher than the prices charged on the last shipment, that no charges will be allowed for crating or boxing, and that no drayage charges can be made by the seller. The purchaser may protect himself as to quantity by specifying that the acceptance is contingent upon inspection and that in case of rejection for quality no replacement can be made by the seller until another order has been received from the buyer. Other clauses might be included to protect the buyer against suit for infringement of patents or copyrights by the seller, to assure that excess quantities will not be shipped by the seller to be charged to the buyer, and that the seller will not draw a draft against the buyer to obtain payment.

One-Year Contracts. Some materials may be bought on contracts covering the requirements for as much as one year in advance. A contract of this kind would provide that for the stated period the vendor will supply on reasonable notice the full requirements of the purchaser, however large or small his needs may be. The contract relieves the buyer of the necessity for making any commitment for materials beyond the exact quantities he needs. He may order the materials on any time schedule according to the requirements of his business. The price is varied to allow for changes in material and labor costs of the vendor. With this type of contract the customer is assured a constant cost of material purchased. The advantage to the vendor is that he may undertake research or development work and may expand production facilities with reasonable assurance that the product can be sold at a profit.

One-year purchase contracts may contain a clause which permits the price to be increased or decreased if market prices change prior to the date of the delivery of the merchandise. Such a contract is legal, provided that it indicates the conditions under which the price is to be increased and defines the standard or formula by which the amount of the increase will be determined. The increase in price should be automatic, and it should not require further discussion between the parties. A vague clause which provides for a change in the purchase price on the basis of time studies or a cost analysis cannot be enforced at law. In deciding a controversy between two parties who had made a contract containing a tentative price schedule which was to be revised on the basis of a cost analysis, the court said:

> The cost analysis furnished only the basis for negotiation for a final revision of the prices—it did not provide an acceptable standard by which the court could give effect to the intention of the parties. . . . The prices stipulated were tentative and temporary, but they prevail until revised through the medium of supplemental contracts. The parties could not mutually agree upon terms of a supplemental contract, and we cannot make one for them.[4]

Formerly, some companies negotiated contracts covering their requirements for as long a period as five years. However, long-term contracts are questionable as to legality because they may be held to constitute violations of the antitrust laws. The objection of the courts arises from the fact that other sellers are excluded from a part of the

---

[4] *Beech Aircraft Corporation* v. *Ross*, 155 Fed. (2d) 615 (1946).

market as long as the contract remains in effect. In some industries, contracts are illegal if they require the purchaser to limit himself to one source of supply for a period of more than one year.[5]

INFORMATION USED IN PURCHASING

The clerical section of the purchasing department compiles various types of information for use in placing orders and in following up scheduled deliveries. The data used in placing orders would include files of catalogues, price quotations, and bids received. Records of purchases would show materials ordered, vendors with whom orders were placed, and purchase-order numbers. Orders currently outstanding are controlled through a follow-up file.

The principal problem in the maintenance of records and files in the purchasing department is the arrangement of catalogues, quotations, and price lists received from vendors in a form that makes possible the quick and easy location of quotations on any material desired. Unless a systematic plan of filing is followed, obsolete catalogues and quotations will accumulate; and much time may be lost in searching for information when it is needed. The choice of a filing system depends upon the size of the department and the amount of material to be filed. The following methods are used:

1. Catalogues and price information may be filed alphabetically by name of vendor. One file may be maintained in bookcases for large catalogues and leaflets.

2. The alphabetical file may be supplemented by a commodity file. In the commodity file a folder is kept for each commodity. A sheet which is inserted in each folder lists the sources of supply, as contained in the catalogue file. The commodity file serves as a cross reference and is used in connection with the catalogue file.

3. The catalogues and sales literature are filed numerically. Folders are used for small, thin pieces of literature. Each catalogue or folder is given a number. A card index, with cards arranged alphabetically, is used to show the name and address of each vendor and the number of the catalogue of the vendor in the numerical file.

4. Information pertaining to vendors is filed in cases or cabinets as it is received and is located by reference to an alphabetical index. The index card indicates the case, drawer, and folder number in which the

---

[5] *United States* v. *American Can Company,* 87 Fed. Supp. 18 (1949).

information is filed. For example, the file number 4-3-S4 might indicate:

4 Number of filing cabinet.
3 Number of drawer in cabinet number 4.
S Guide letter in drawer number 3.
4 Fourth catalogue behind guide S.

Adaptations of these methods are frequently found in practice. The essential requirement of any filing system is that the purchasing agent or the file clerk be able to locate quickly the catalogue of any vendor and the sources of supply for any commodity when the information is needed. The files should be reviewed regularly to eliminate obsolete information and to add supplementary information.

QUESTIONS

1. Is purchasing a staff function or a line function? Does it serve the manufacturing departments, or does it receive services from other departments? What difference does this distinction make?

2. Is purchasing a major or a minor function? Discuss with reference to particular industries.

3. When the various departments use the same kinds of materials and supplies, what economies may be gained by centralized purchasing?

4. To what extent can the purchasing agent determine when to buy, where to buy, what to buy, and how much to buy? Should he have complete authority in all four types of problems?

5. Contrast hand-to-mouth buying with forward buying in large quantities. Under what conditions would each method be desirable?

6. Mention materials or parts that might be purchased to meet specific requirements and upon receipt be moved directly from the car or truck to the production line.

7. If materials are purchased only upon specifications, is the reputation of the vendor for quality important, or should the vendor be selected on the basis of other qualifications?

8. Explain different ways of determining when to buy.

9. For what reasons might an order be placed with a supplier other than the lowest bidder?

10. How can the purchasing agent distinguish between small favors and gifts from a vendor that are permissible and the larger gifts that constitute commercial bribery?

11. What considerations enter into the decision to buy or to make a part?

12. How can the buyer afford to accept a shipment from a vendor without inspecting the entire lot? Illustrate.

13. What advantages might be gained by contracting for supplies or parts

for a period of five years in advance? Why do the Department of Justice and the Federal Trade Commission object to the practice?

14. How does integration affect the planning of production and the purchasing and sales programs?

CASE

65. PURCHASE PROGRAM FOR BULK MATERIALS

The General Specialties Company makes a varied line of metal products principally for the order of the customer. When the company was first organized, the plant manager permitted each foreman to requisition cleaning supplies, oil lubricants, coatings, solvents, thinners, paints, lacquers, and other such supplies. The foremen requisitioned by brand name the products with which they were familiar. Upon receipt of the supplies, they were sent to the foreman who had requisitioned them. As a precautionary measure, the plant manager himself requisitioned reserve stocks of some items which were placed in the general storeroom. These supplies were issued in case a foreman had failed to order a certain item or needed a supply in an emergency.

The system for the purchase of supplies was found to be costly in several respects. After the plan had been in operation for five years, the plant manager found that the company was buying 750 different items for cleaning, lubricating, painting, and other such purposes. Of these items, 75 were used for cleaning. Inspection was limited to the checking of the brand name and the counting of the number of containers. Chemical tests in the laboratory were not attempted because chemical composition was not specified in the purchase order. Prices of supplies varied considerably for items believed to be similar, although price comparisons were uncertain because composition was unknown. Quantity buying and planned purchases were not possible. Inventories were excessive. Frequently one department would be lacking in an item which was available in another department. Some of the supplies were much more effective and satisfactory in use than others.

To correct the situation, the plant manager and the purchasing agent agreed upon a study of the problems of bulk purchasing. First, they classified the supplies into five groups: lubricating supplies, waxes and coatings, paints and dyes (including ink, lacquers, and thinners), cleaning supplies and solvents, and chemicals. Each group of items was studied to determine which kinds of supplies were really needed to meet the requirements of the various departments. The assistance of the plant chemist enabled the company to establish chemical specifications for each kind of supply that was to be stocked. A symbol was assigned to each of the five major classifications, and additional symbols were added to indicate the particular item within the group, according to the method of mnemonic classification. For example, a particular shade of blue inside paint in one-gallon containers was designated as PI3B1. Requisitions and other forms designating the item would give the mnemonic symbol. All supplies would be kept in the central storeroom until they were requisitioned for use in a particular department. In some cases, the plant manager and the purchasing agent found that some of the supplies formerly used had required an excessive amount of labor cost in use.

For example, some cleaning supplies had required several applications in addition to scrubbing with a wire brush. The new item now to be used in all departments required merely spraying on the cleaning agent, permitting to stand eight minutes, and rinsing with warm water. In some cases accident hazards had been created by the use of highly combustible supplies. Some of these items were eliminated, and others were made subject to careful control. Other items that were found to create difficult problems of waste disposal were dropped. To supervise future additions to the authorized items and to eliminate items found to be no longer needed, a committee of plant management personnel was established. The membership included the purchasing agent, the plant manager, the maintenance manager, the accident prevention manager, and the chief chemist.

Questions:

1. What are the advantages of the new system?
2. What difficulties might be encountered?

CHAPTER

31 Inventory
Standards
and Control

THE materials used in the manufacture of the products of industry as a whole amount to 50 or 55 per cent of the total cost to manufacture. Because of its importance, much attention is usually given to the problem of inventory control. Effective control requires the setting up of procedures for the handling of each of the kinds of inventory, which are purchased parts, materials, supplies, and finished goods. The work in process of manufacture is also controlled through a system of production planning and control and a cost system, which will be considered in later chapters.

Purpose of Inventory Management. Effective inventory control should assure that stocks of materials and parts are not excessive. Large inventories result in the increase of certain carrying expenses, and the inventory may be subject to deterioration and obsolescence. However, the inventory should be maintained at a level that will prevent delays in production because of lack of materials of proper quality. Inventory control should also be designed to prevent waste of materials through carelessness in handling, dishonesty, or poor workmanship in processing. Inventory control should also yield information that may be used in financial planning. Such information includes the cost of materials per unit of product as well as total cost, supplies used in each department, inactive and obsolete materials in the storeroom, and value of inventories for purposes of the balance sheet and the profit and loss statement.[1]

---

[1] For discussion of various phases of inventory control, see John F. Magee, "Guides to Inventory Policy: Functions and Lot Size," *Harvard Business Review,* Vol. XXXIV, No. 1 (1956), pp. 49–60.

Good inventory management requires that attention be given to several phases of the problem. The kinds of materials to be used in production should be determined, and the specifications should be established. This phase has been previously discussed in connection with product design and purchasing. Standards may also be established for the quantity of materials to order for each item in stock. However, the management may decide upon a program of speculative buying if price increases appear to be likely. Control should also be established over methods and procedures for receiving, inspecting, storing, issuing, and moving materials. Such control might require that detailed records of the various activities be maintained.

Standard Quantities. Four standard quantities for inventory should be distinguished. The *maximum* is the largest quantity of any material that should be on hand at any time. It is the upper limit for the inventory of any item. The theoretical maximum would be the quantity on hand at the time the order is placed plus the usual amount ordered at one time. However, this maximum would be reached only when no items were used during the period while the additional supply was on order but prior to receipt. The anticipated maximum would be the amount on hand when the order is placed plus the amount ordered minus the anticipated withdrawals prior to the receipt of the new supply.

The *minimum* is the smallest quantity of any item which should be on hand at any time. It is the quantity which is considered necessary for emergency or unusual demand. The supply may go below the minimum if material used is greatly increased or the delivery of materials purchased is delayed. The minimum is sometimes referred to as the "margin of safety."

The *reorder point* is the quantity on hand when a purchase order should be placed with a vendor for an additional supply or a production order should be issued to the factory for manufacture of a product or finished part. The reorder point is established at that quantity which is believed to assure that the supply will not be exhausted before additional materials can be received. The reorder point would be fixed at the average consumption during the time required to place the order and to receive the additional supply into stock, plus the margin of safety.

The *quantity to order* is the economical quantity of a material or part to purchase. *The quantity to manufacture* is the economical quantity to manufacture in case a part or a product is manufactured for sale or for stock. When this quantity has been determined, all purchase orders placed with vendors or production orders issued to the factory are for the standard quantities. The standard quantity to order is revised when market or other business conditions change.

The relation of the inventory quantity standards to each other are as follows:

> Reorder point + Quantity to order = Theoretical maximum.
> Reorder point — Average consumption during the
> order period = Minimum.
> Minimum + Quantity to order = Anticipated maximum.

Determining the Quantity to Order. If materials are purchased for use in manufacturing goods to fill the order of the customer, the quantity to buy might be the amount needed for the one production order, with perhaps an allowance for spoilage and for defective items that might not be accepted by the inspector. In case this quantity is not sufficiently large for an economical purchase, a larger quantity might be purchased and the excess held for future orders of customers. However, this practice would usually result in waste because a variety of types of unusable materials would soon accumulate in the storeroom.

For materials that are bought by specification and that are used in making the product in standard designs, the manufacturer should establish a standard quantity to order. Such a standard is affected by many factors, some of which relate to all commodities in the inventory and some of which relate to the individual items. The more important factors which should be considered in determining the quantity to purchase are as follows:

I. General factors affecting the entire inventory
> General business conditions
>> Possible labor troubles of vendors
>> Shortages of supply in the markets
>> Transportation difficulties
>> The probable trend of prices upward or downward
> Prospects and plans for the individual business
>> Advertising and sales promotion plans
>> Financial resources available for investment in inventory
>> Storage facilities and materials-handling equipment available for storing materials
>> Possible revisions in the design of the product
>> Plans and prospects of competitors

II. Factors relating to individual commodities in the inventory
> Clerical costs of placing the order
> Space required in the storeroom and cost of space
> Possible deterioration in quality

Possible obsolescence due to changes in the design of the product or simplification and standardization of materials

Rate of consumption of the material

Freight and drayage on large and small quantities

Quantity discounts allowed by vendors which may result from manufacturing or other economies in the plant of the vendor

Cost of material and investment required

When a company produces parts or materials for stock, many of the same considerations affect the economical quantity to manufacture. However, manufacturing quantities are especially affected by the cost of adjusting the machine for varieties of styles or sizes and by the clerical expense required for the issuance of factory orders and for following their course from department to department until their completion and transfer to the finished goods storeroom. Labor costs are also increased when workers are required to make frequent changes from one order to another.

Some unit costs which affect the quantity to order increase with the size of the purchase order, and other costs decrease with the size of the order. Costs which tend to increase with the size of the order are:

Storage cost.

Interest on investment in inventory.

Insurance against fire and other hazards.

Possible spoilage or deterioration.

Possible obsolescence.

Unit costs which tend to decrease with the size of the purchase order are:

Invoice price per unit, because of quantity discounts.

Clerical cost of placing the order, follow-up, inspection, approving the order for payment, and accounting.

Freight and drayage.

Since the total cost of materials is the sum of the various elements of cost, the problem is that of determining the lowest total cost. Numerous formulas have been devised for computing the most economical size of the purchase order. One method is to compute for each item or each of several representative items the total cost for the year, on the assumption that orders are placed for varying quantities. To illustrate, if the total purchases for the year are $10,000, one order might be placed for $10,000, two orders might be placed at different times for $5,000 each, or twenty orders might be placed for $500 each. The costs with varying quantities might be as shown in Table 4. The margin of safety is omitted from this tabulation because it is constant, regardless of the size of the order. This table indicates that the lowest total cost is realized when four orders per year are placed for $2,500 each.

TABLE 4

COST OF MATERIALS WITH VARYING SIZES OF PURCHASE ORDERS

	NUMBER OF ORDERS PER YEAR					
	1	2	4	8	10	20
Size of each order.....	$10,000	$5,000	$2,500	$1,250.00	$ 1,000	$ 500
Average inventory of the item........	5,000	2,500	1,250	625	500	250
Discount for quantity..	5%	5%	4%	3%	1%	None
Cost of merchandise...	$ 9,500	$9,500	$9,600	$9,700.00	$ 9,900	$10,000
Interest, insurance, and storage (10% of average inventory)..	$ 500	$ 250	$ 125	$ 62.50	$ 50	$ 25
Clerical, $5 per order..	$ 5	$ 10	$ 20	$ 40.00	$ 50	$ 100
Total cost for year....	$10,005	$9,760	$9,745	$9,802.50	$10,000	$10,125

The method of determining quantities to order as explained in the preceding paragraphs can be used effectively when the rate of use of the material is fairly uniform throughout the year. If material consumption varies, or if the consumption is concentrated in a few months of the year, the purchases should be planned for delivery at or before the time when the material will be needed. In such cases the quantities to order cannot be safely based upon past usage. If the standard quantities to order are not revised as conditions change, shortages of many materials will continuously develop. In periods of decreasing usage, inventories are likely to be too large.

The size of the quantity to order is reflected in the inventory of the item. Frequent reorders will result in more rapid turnover, and fewer orders placed will lower the rate of turnover. The costs of procurement increase as the company attempts to turn its inventory more rapidly because more orders must be placed, more invoices checked, more shipments received and inspected, and more payments made. However, carrying charges decrease as turnover is increased because the average inventory on hand is smaller, and carrying charges increase with a slower rate of turnover. The effect is shown graphically in Figure 55. The distance between the base line of the chart and the line *AB* represents the varying costs of procurement with changes in the number of turnovers per year. The distance between the line *AB* and the line *CD*

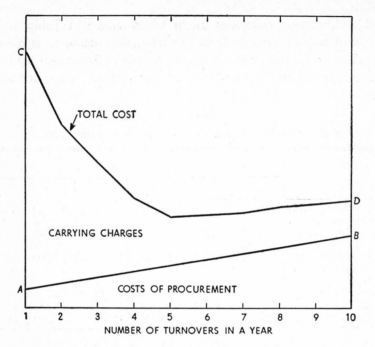

FIG. 55. Varying Costs According to Turnover

represents the carrying charges. The total distance between the line *CD* and the base line represents the sum of the costs of procurement and the carrying charges. The chart indicates that for the item represented in the chart, the lowest cost is achieved when the inventory is turned five times per year.

To determine quantities to order under conditions of varying production, the supervisor of inventory control or some other executive who is familiar with production plans may estimate the probable rate of usage during the next few weeks. This executive authorizes each week the purchase orders currently to be placed. For his use, the person in charge of inventory records prepares a report for each item of materials in stock to show present inventory, weekly usage, and total usage since the beginning of the season or quarter. By reviewing this record, and by making allowance for future production plans, the executive can intelligently plan future purchases and deliveries to meet production requirements.

Reorder Point. In continuous manufacturing, when a few designs are produced on one line or a few lines, the manufacturing department can place a purchase order when the quantity of an item of materials falls to a predetermined level. Normally, the reorder point would be the quantity consumed in production during the period required for delivery by the vendor, plus a margin of safety. To illustrate, assume that 40 days are required for delivery and that the average usage for 40 days is 400 pounds. If the margin of safety is 50 pounds, the order for an additional supply should be placed when the quantity on hand has reached 450 pounds. The margin of safety is designed to provide for fluctuations in the rate of usage and for slight delays in the receipt of the merchandise ordered.

The established reorder point may be observed during periods when usage does not vary greatly from one month to another and stable conditions in the market afford an assurance of deliveries in the time allowed. If the rate of usage varies greatly, or if the market in which the goods are purchased becomes unsettled, the reorder point may be changed. Some companies, following the plan previously explained, provide that an executive who is familiar with production plans review each week the quantities on hand and the current rate of usage to determine the proper time for placing the purchase order.

The Balance of Stores Record. Most companies that handle many varieties of materials find a perpetual inventory record to be desirable. Such a record is called a "balance of stores" or a "stock record." A card record is kept for each size, style, or other variety of materials in stock. The record shows the following information for each item:

Quantity on order.
Quantity reserved for production orders planned ahead.
Quantity received into stock.
Quantity issued from the storeroom.
Quantity available for other orders.
Bin balance.

A form of the balance of stores record is shown in Figure 56. The

STOCK RECORD

PART NO. 18-436   REORDER POINT 150   QUANTITY TO ORDER 200

DATE	REFERENCE NO.	ORDERED	RESERVED	RECEIVED	ISSUED	AVAILABLE	BIN BALANCE
2/6/49	INVENTORY					200	200
2/8/49	P 85		50			150	200
2/10/49	P 83				80	70	120
2/10/49	V 1250	200					
2/12/49	P 85				50	70	70
2/20/49	V 1250			200		270	270

FIG. 56. Balance of Stores Record

method of maintaining the record may be observed by studying the entries made in it. When material is reserved for work planned for future production, the quantity is entered in the column headed Reserved. The amount is also deducted from the balance available. Quantities issued are entered in the Issued column and deducted from the Bin Balance. Receipts are entered in the Received column and added to the Bin Balance. Purchase orders are entered in the Ordered column as memoranda. The quantities on order are not added to the Bin Balance until they are received. For cost accounting purposes the form may be enlarged to show cost prices as well as quantities.

Pricing of Materials Issued. When materials are issued from the storeroom on requisition, their cost is deducted from the inventory balance. Their cost is also entered in the cost accounting records as material cost of goods in process of manufacture. Supplies issued for use in a line or staff department are also deducted at cost from the inventory balance and are recorded as an expense of that department. The cost of the materials or supplies issued may be determined by any one of several methods.

The first-in, first-out method is based on the assumption that the materials first received are the first to be issued. The materials received and charged on each invoice are charged out from the inventory at the price stated on that invoice until the lot has been exhausted. Material issues are then assumed to be issued from the next lot received at the invoice price of the second lot until that lot is exhausted. The units on hand at any time are assumed to be the units last purchased because all issues of materials have been made from the earlier issues.

The last-in, first-out method of pricing is based on the assumption that the last units received are the first to be issued. Materials issued from stock are charged out at the cost of the latest shipment received until that lot is exhausted. The next issues are then made from the next order preceding, provided the materials in that order were not previously issued. This method is designed to charge goods manufactured with the prevailing costs of materials instead of with costs which may have been paid for materials at a much earlier date.

The moving-average method requires that an average unit cost be computed for all units on hand when an order is received into stock. This average price is used to record issues of materials until a new shipment is received, when a new average price is computed. This process is repeated each time an additional shipment is received.

The effect of the method of charging materials depends upon the direction and the extent of changes in prices in the market. When prices are rising, the first-in, first-out method results in charging materials at lower prices than either of the other methods because the materials first purchased were bought at the lowest prices. The result is a lower figure for the cost of goods manufactured or a lower operating expense in the case of supplies. Likewise, this method results in a higher value of the materials in the inventory because the units on hand are assumed to be those last purchased. When prices are declining, the first-in, first-out method gives a higher cost of materials used, a higher cost of goods manufactured, and a lower profit. This method accentuates the effect of fluctuations in profits as prices rise and fall. The amount of fluctuation depends upon the period of time that elapses between the purchase of the materials and their use in production. If a small inventory is carried and materials move rapidly into production, the effect of this method of pricing in comparison with other methods is not great. If the usual inventory constitutes several months' supply, the effect would be substantial.

The last-in, first-out method of pricing tends to keep the cost of materials abreast of current price trends. Materials are priced at a figure that reflects more closely the market conditions at the time they are used in production. Costs tend to advance as selling prices are increased and to decline as selling prices are decreased. The effect is a smaller fluctuation in profit as a result of changes in business prosperity or depression.

The moving average has an effect upon profits and inventory valuation that is intermediate between the other two methods. A practical objection to the moving-average method is that it requires additional clerical work.

QUESTIONS

1. Should the inventory records be kept by the purchasing agent, the cost accounting department, or the person in charge of the storeroom? Justify your answer.

2. What constitutes good management of the stores inventory?

3. Who should be responsible for determining the specifications of materials to be purchased? For determining quantities to order? For the handling of incoming materials?

4. Does the budget or the financial strength of the company enter into the determining of the quantity to order?

5. What expenses are increased when large quantities are ordered each time? What expenses are decreased?

6. Has the development of faster methods of communication and transportation affected buying and inventory practices?

7. How does the method of pricing issues from stores affect the profits and the value of the inventory in a period of rising prices? What is the effect in a period of declining prices?

8. Should a company reserve materials now in the storeroom for use in processing orders planned but not yet started in production? How can such a reservation be made?

9. Should the balance of stores record show both quantities and prices? Why?

10. Should the balance as shown on the balance of stores record indicate the number of units in the storeroom, or should it show the quantity available for future orders?

CASES

66. MATERIALS CONTROL PLAN

The Consolidated Electronics Company manufactures electronic tubes, motors, automatic signaling devices, control instruments for automobile dashboards, and other small instruments. All work is done on contract for the specific order of the customer. Many of the parts are purchased. Materials control is particularly important because purchased materials and parts usually cost about six times the cost of direct labor.

The company has been having considerable difficulty with its materials and parts inventory. Sometimes work in process could not be completed because some of the parts were not available in the storeroom. The shortage of parts resulted in increased costs because of a loss of machine time, wages paid to idle workers, additional supervision, and the necessity for rehandling partially assembled units. Delayed deliveries disrupted customers' schedules and created customer ill will. When orders were placed with vendors to replenish stocks, deliveries were delayed because some vendors might require a lead time of as much as twelve weeks.

When the company attempted to provide for all parts and supplies that might be needed, it accumulated large inventories and reduced the rate of inventory turnover. Some parts were on hand a year or more before they were needed. Inventories remained unbalanced with too much of some items and not enough of others. Foremen attempted to keep their own departments running smoothly by building up reserves of items that might be needed. On several occasions when production was delayed because a part was not available, a supply was later located in some department of the plant. Further imbalance in inventory was created by the acceptance of occasional overruns by vendors who shipped as much as 5 per cent more than the quantity ordered.

To correct the situation, the company established the position of materials control supervisor directly under the plant manager. The supervisor set up a system based upon the use of five forms. One form is a stock record card similar to the usual perpetual inventory record form. A card is prepared for each item in the stockroom to show quantities ordered, receipts, issues, and balance on hand. Prices are not shown on the card because the only object of the control system is to assure that the quantities will be available when needed without being in excess of requirements.

A second form is a receiving and inspection report. It shows quantities received from vendors, the number of items passed by the inspector, and the number of items rejected. Copies of this report are sent to the accounting department, the purchasing agent, the stock control clerk, and the storekeeper.

Another form initiated by the supervisor is the move order. It is used by the foreman who has spoiled, unusable, or excess material or parts of any kind. Foremen are now required to return excess material when a production order is completed and to forward a move ticket with the material. If materials were defective when they were received, they will be returned to the vendor. If defective materials can be reworked in the plant, the plant manager issues a rework order. After the work is completed, the materials are inspected and the results of the inspection are noted on the work order. If the materials are returned to the stockroom, the materials control clerk is notified and he makes the entry for the receipt on the appropriate card.

When a work order is planned, the production control clerk prepares a complete list of all materials and parts that will be needed. He enters on the list the number or quantity of each material or part. A copy of this list is sent to the material control clerk who checks to see that the materials and parts are on hand. He enters the quantities on the stock cards as a reservation for the work order to be issued later. If the materials are not available, he notifies the purchasing agent and the production control clerk. The purchasing agent immediately places an order for any items that will be required.

Once a week the purchasing agent goes through the stock record cards to inspect the quantities on hand and the rate at which an item is being used in production. If the quantity on hand is less than the amount that will be used during the necessary lead time, the purchasing agent places a purchase order for a supply of that item.

In the stockroom, a tag is attached to each bin to indicate the amount of the item on hand. The stockroom clerk adds to the balance any quantities received and subtracts any quantities issued. Once a month, the stock control clerk checks the balances as shown by the stock control cards against the balances as shown by the bin tags. Physical inventories are taken every six months, and the quantities on hand are checked with the bin tags and the stock control cards. Adjustments are made for any discrepancies.

Since the new system was installed, the company has had fewer interruptions to production because of shortages of materials or parts. Foremen have developed a keener appreciation of the need for maintaining production schedules. The hoarding of materials by foremen has ceased to be a problem because the need for hoarding is no longer apparent. Although the new system means more paper work, the management believes that the costs are justified by the results.

Required:

Evaluate the new system as developed by the materials control supervisor.

67. ABC ANALYSIS FOR INVENTORY CONTROL

The Southern Spring and Wire Company carries approximately 2,500 items of materials and parts in stock. The controller has instituted a materials control system based upon the usual plan of balance of stores records, receiving reports, requisitions, reorder points, and predetermined quantities to order. Although the plan requires a great deal of paper work, it has not entirely eliminated shortages and overstocks of certain items. The difficulty is that the lead time of different vendors is not uniform even for the same items, and variations in the rate of production at the Southern Spring and Wire Company sometimes cause unusually large requirements for materials not anticipated by the system of inventory control.

The controller has been studying the plan of inventory control known as the ABC Analysis. This plan provides for the classification of inventory items into three groups, which are designated as A, B, and C. Class A items include the major kinds of materials that are used in large quantities. They constitute a large part of the material cost that goes into the product, and they make up a large part of the materials inventory. Class B items include a larger number of items, but they are less important in materials costs. Class C items include the numerous but inexpensive units of material. They turn very slowly. They are necessary to the production of certain products, but they constitute a small percentage of materials cost.

The controller decided to make an analysis of the items in the inventory of the Southern Spring and Wire Company. He found that 150 items of materials, or 8 per cent of the number of items purchased, accounted for 75 per cent of the total materials cost of the product. These items might be appropriately described as Class A materials. At the other extreme, 1,750 items, or 70 per cent of the total number of items, accounted for only 5 per cent of the total materials cost. These items might be classified as Class C items. The remaining 600 items, constituting 22 per cent of the total number, accounted for 20 per cent of the materials cost. These items were designated as Class B.

The controller decided that the reorder system previously used would be abandoned insofar as Class A items were concerned. Materials falling in this classification would be ordered on an annual contract and scheduled for delivery to the receiving room of the company on a weekly basis. Because the need for the materials was continuous and closely related to the rate of production, most of the materials would be put into production as they were received. Movement through the shop would be watched for delays, "bottlenecks," undue accumulations, and shortages. The reserve supply of Class A items would be kept at a low figure.

As for Class C items, the clerical expenses of ordering, receiving, inspecting, paying invoices, issuing, and accounting were found to constitute a substantial percentage of the total cost of the materials. To reduce such expenses, a sufficient supply for the requirements in production for a period of six to eight months could be economically ordered at one time. The carrying charges on the inventory would be more than offset by the saving in paper work. The perpetual inventory record was also considered unnecessary for Class C items. A supply of each item that would normally be sufficient for use during the reorder period would be tied up in a separate bundle or package or placed in a separate bin. When the storekeeper began to use the reserve stock, he would notify the purchasing agent who would place an order for an additional supply. When any material of the Class C group was received into stock, a fresh reserve supply would be set aside. The cost of Class C materials during any accounting period would be determined by a physical inventory at the end of the period. The value of the ending inventory subtracted from the sum of the beginning inventory and the purchases would give the cost of materials used. This cost would be included in the cost of the goods manufactured as one sum. For cost accounting purposes, the cost would be allocated in the same manner as supplies and other manufacturing expenses.

The records for receipts, issues, and balances on hand of Class B items would be continued in the manner previously used for all materials items. New orders would be placed when the supply on hand dropped to the reorder point. The quantity ordered each time would be the predetermined amount.

Required:

Evaluate the new plan for materials control in comparison with the old plan.

32 Storing
and Issuing
Materials

IF materials and supplies could be received in small quantities at the time they are needed, no storeroom or investment in stores inventory would be necessary. Losses from obsolescence, deterioration, and price declines would be reduced or eliminated; and the turnover of working capital would be increased. But this ideal situation usually is not possible for several reasons, which vary according to the circumstances. In many cases, materials are purchased in large quantities and consumed in smaller amounts. The requirements from day to day are too small for economical purchasing. A reserve supply may also be necessary to assure continuous production when incoming shipments are delayed by transportation, tie-ups because of traffic congestion in railroad yards, the freezing of lakes and rivers in winter, and labor troubles in the plants of vendors. If the product is manufactured to the order of the customer, a supply of various kinds of materials and parts may be carried in stock in anticipation of orders. In other cases, materials may be purchased seasonally and then used in production throughout the year according to a planned schedule. Examples are cotton, corn, tobacco, hides, and lumber. In other industries, the materials may be produced at a fairly uniform rate and then stocked in anticipation of a seasonal demand. Examples are fuel oil and natural gas. Some materials, such as tobacco and flour, are purchased and stored for seasoning before they are processed.

In some cases the production schedules of two or more companies may be so carefully planned and co-ordinated that the maintenance of an inventory of raw materials by the purchaser becomes unnecessary. For example, a fruit canning company may arrange for the delivery of both fruit and containers as they are needed in production. Both fruit and containers may go direct from truck or freight car to the production line. Automobile and electrical appliance manufacturers make the same arrangements for delivery of motors and parts to the assembly plant. To provide for a margin of safety in the making of deliveries according to a definite schedule, the container manufacturer or other supplier may accumulate an inventory of his product in advance of purchase orders. The result is that the problem of inventory management is shifted from the purchaser to the vendor.

RECEIVING AND STORING

The efficient movement of materials and supplies to storage requires a method of checking incoming shipments and moving the materials to shelves or bins. The method of arranging the stores should make economical use of space. Furthermore, the materials should be stored according to a logical plan which would enable the storekeeper to locate quickly any item that is needed.

Receiving Stores. The storeroom manager may best plan for receiving incoming stores if he is advised of the kinds, quantities, and time of receipt. Incoming stores should be counted, weighed or measured, and checked against purchase orders and purchase invoices. Adequate space should be available for receiving and inspecting. Materials should be placed in permanent locations after inspection rather than in temporary locations in bulk storage or in aisles. Handling should be kept at a minimum. Time is saved when the stores can be placed in the shelves in original cartons or in containers in which they will subsequently be issued. Many types of materials and supplies can be stored on pallets or skids and moved by lift truck to permanent storage. Some items may be stored in tote boxes, which interlock when stacked to form a compact, rigid pile. Time can also be saved by making containers self-counting or self-measuring. Such a container is designed to hold a specified quantity, or has markings to indicate quantities.

Use of Space. Good layout is the first essential of the effective use of space. The phases of layout are, first, allocation of the proper amount of space to various uses and, second, effective arrangement. The allocation of space depends upon the size of the storeroom, the kinds of material to be stored, the types of shelves and bins, the height of the ceiling and extent to which vertical storing is possible, and the kinds of equipment used in the handling of materials. The vertical limit for storing is usually considered to be twenty feet. Higher stacking of cartons or pallets creates problems of fire hazards, lighting, and floor loads. If materials are stacked to that height, an aisle width of twelve feet is considered desirable to allow trucks or forklifts to pass each other with pallets or other loads. However, aisles may be no wider than six or seven feet if stacks of materials are less than twenty feet in height.

An effective arrangement in a storeroom which stores small parts provides for receiving and inspecting materials at one end of the room and issuing at the other. The main aisle of the storeroom usually runs lengthwise, with cross aisles at right angles to the main aisle. The width of the aisles depends upon the kinds of material stored and the equipment necessary for moving materials. The main aisle may vary in width from five to ten feet or more. Cross aisles are not as wide as the main aisle. More storage space is available if the rows of shelves or bins extend to the side walls, although such an arrangement is somewhat less convenient and may increase the fire hazard. For economy in the use of space, rows of bins should be placed back to back. A possible storeroom layout is shown in Figure 57.

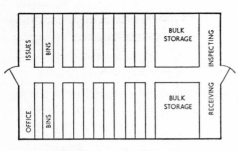

FIG. 57. Layout of Storeroom

Another device for effective use of storage space is flexibility in the sizes of bins. Uniform sizes of bins and shelves would inevitably mean waste space. The use of standard shelving and dividers for bins provides for varying bin sizes, as shown in Figure 58. Some items require drawers for economical storing, some require hooks or brackets, and some require racks of various types.

In the stacking of materials floor loads should be kept within safe limits. At the top of the pile, sufficient space should be allowed to permit the up-ending of cartons when they are removed from the top. The materials should not be stacked so high as to interfere with the proper functioning of the automatic sprinkler system. Fire regulations prohibit stacking to the ceiling.

Method of Storing. In a small storeroom the finding of materials when they are wanted may not appear to be a serious problem; but in a large storeroom, with perhaps 28,000 items, materials and parts

Courtesy of Monarch Machine Tool Co.

FIG. 58. Storeroom Arrangement Showing Flexible Bin System

Note flexibility in distance between shelves and use of dividers.

may easily be misplaced, and additional material may be purchased unnecessarily. The finding of materials should not depend upon the memory of employees. The features of a well-developed plan for arranging stores are as follows:

A system of classification and identification for materials.
A system of identifying and marking storage spaces.
A system of arranging materials in the storeroom.

Four systems of classifying and indentifying materials are used. They are the mnemonic, the numerical, the alphabetical, and some combination of the other three systems.

The word "mnemonic" means assisting or tending to assist the memory. The mnemonic system of classification is especially designed for ease in remembering. The letters used in any symbol are associated with the general classification and name of materials thus designated, and the numbers are associated with the dimensions of the material or the size of the container. While every business may design its own set of symbols to suit its particular requirements, the first letter would usually be "S" to indicate stores; and "W" would indicate worked materials or manufactured parts. The second letter would indicate a general class of stores, such as "P" for paint. The third letter would indicate the class of paint, such as "D" for deck paint. The next letter would indicate the color, as "S" for slate. A numeral might be used to indicate the size of the container. Thus, the symbol S PD¼S would indicate a quart can of deck paint, slate color. A stores classification showing the general classes might be as follows:

CLASSIFIED STORES

S A	Office supplies
S B	Brass and brass products including pipe and fittings
S C	Coal, coke, and other fuels
S D	Wood and wood products
S E	Electrical supplies
S F	Fastenings, bolts, nuts, nails, screws, etc.
S G	Gaskets and packing
S H	Hangers, stands, boxes, bushings, pulleys, and clutches
S J	Gears made of all materials
S K	Chemicals and pigments
S L	Liquid, lubricants, oils, gasoline, and paints
S M	Machine and engine parts for boiler-power and water supply
S N	Metals not otherwise classified
S P	Pipe, pipefittings, and things made from cast iron, wrought iron, and steel
S R	Rubber scrap
S S	Steel, wrought or cast iron, and products made chiefly from same
S T	Tools, implements, and supplies
S U	Building materials, such as cement, quartz, sand, and brick
S V	Abrasives, emery wheels, grindstones, etc.
S W	Wearing apparel
S X	Stores not otherwise classified
S Y	Fibrous and textile materials
S Z	Special parts and supplies for equipment[1]

The mnemonic principle cannot be consistently followed in the classification because the letter which would be appropriate in designating a class of stores may have been used in another part of the classification. The letters "I," "O," and "Q" are usually not used because they may be mistaken for other letters or numbers.

The classification as illustrated is elaborated by the addition of other letters to indicate subdivisions of the main class. For example, one of the subdivisions of the classification S E Electrical supplies is S ES, in-

---

[1] L. P. Alford and J. R. Bangs, *Production Handbook* (New York: Ronald Press Co., 1948), p. 1351. Used by permission.

dicating Sockets and Forks. This subdivision is further classified as follows:

SOCKETS AND FORKS

S ES B	Brass key sockets	S ES P	Porcelain key
	S ES 1B Small		S ES 1P Small
	S ES 2B Large		S ES 2P Large
S ES C	Brass keyless sockets	S ES R	Porcelain keyless
	S ES 1C Small		S ES 1R Small
	S ES 2C Large		S ES 2R Large
S ES H	Hood forks	SES S	Porcelain pull
S ES K	Socket forks		S ES 1S Small
S ES M	Mica sockets		S ES 2S Large
		S ES T	Street hood socket

The principal advantage of the mnemonic system of classification is, as the name suggests, that the symbols are quickly learned and easily remembered. The system has greater flexibility than a numbering system because 23 letters are available as contrasted with 10 numerals or digits. A disadvantage is the necessity for substituting a different letter in case the names of two or more materials begin with the same letter. Furthermore, the designations of new items added to the inventory cannot be listed at the end of the classification but are inserted at a definite place in the list. The problem of adding a new designation for a material is similar to that of including a new word in the dictionary.

In the numerical system of classification and identification, numbers are consistently used to indicate both the principal classes of stores and the subdivisions. In the alphabetical system, letters are used to indicate all classes and groups without regard to the mnemonic feature. A familiar example of a system which combines the numerical and the alphabetical methods is the system of classifying books in a library. A system that is built up without regard to the mnemonic feature may be easier to construct but more difficult to remember. If the items are grouped into classes, the designations for new items would be added at fixed places in the list as they are added in the mnemonic system.

A system of classification and identification may be used for the following purposes:

Indicating materials or supplies to be ordered.
Indicating materials or supplies to be withdrawn from the storeroom.
Indicating materials to be used in the manufacture of the product and in the planning of production.
Arranging stores in the storeroom.

In the arrangement of stores, two methods are used. First, the stores may be arranged according to the system of classification. For example, if the mnemonic system of classification is used, stores designated as S AA would be in the first tier, first bins, in the row adjacent to the first aisle. Stores designated as S AB would be placed in the next bins. Stores would be similarly arranged throughout the storeroom, with stores designated as S ZZ at the far end of the room. When stores are arranged by classification symbols, any item of stores can be located by the symbol, just as a book can be found in the stackroom in the library or an article can be found in the encyclopedia.

Several objections can be made to arrangement by classification symbols. The method is wasteful of space because room must be left at various places for the addition of new items. Unless space is left, the addition of a new type of stores will require the shifting of all stores farther down in the list. Another objection is that many parts and materials require special methods of storing. Heavy materials should be placed in bins near the floor, and light, bulky items should be stored in the higher locations. Extremely heavy items may at times be stored in the basement or even in the yard. Items frequently requisitioned should be stored near the issue window. When the principle of storing according to the classification system is followed, exception must be made for such items.

The second method of arranging stores provides for arrangement by general classes but not strictly according to symbol numbers. When this system is used, new kinds of stores may be put into whatever bin or other space is available. An index that gives the location of the item is maintained in the storeroom. This system, called the "index system," is the method most commonly used.

If the supply of any item in the storeroom is so large that not all of it can be stored in the usual location, the excess supply may be stored on top of a row of bins or located in some other place less accessible to the issue window. Notation should be made on the index card to indicate the location of the reserve supply, and a card should also be attached to the regular bin to indicate the location of the additional supply. However, any deviation from the established system of storing may prove costly. Temporary storage in aisles and odd places can soon disrupt a good system.

PROTECTION AGAINST LOSS

The proper storage of materials requires that the value of the materials be protected against deterioration, fire loss, and damage which might result from improper handling.

Protection against Deterioration. Many types of materials and supplies will deteriorate in quality if they are kept in storage for any length of time. Deterioration may be prevented, first, by carrying small quantities in the inventory and, second, by following the principle of first-in, first-out. Various methods are used to assure that the oldest units will be used first, the exact method depending upon the nature of the materials and supplies. The system of double bins or double storage space provides for two bins or storage spaces for each item of material or supplies. The first order received is placed in the first bin or space, and subsequent orders received are placed in the second bin. Issues are made from the first bin until the first lot is exhausted. Issues are then made from the second bin, while receipts are placed in the first bin. Stores may be rearranged in the shelves or other storage spaces each time a new lot is received, when the old supply is put in front. Issues are taken from the front. This method requires additional handling.

Circular packaged items, such as cans, or rolls of materials, may be stored in gravity-feed racks. The racks resemble a trough and are slightly inclined toward the aisle. As containers are removed from the lower end of the rack, the remaining items roll toward the front to fill the space. Refills are made at the back and upper end of the rack.

Materials in cartons may be stored by the moving-division method. When the first shipment is received, it is stacked in cubical or rectangular fashion upon the floor. Issues are then made from the left side of the stack. When a second shipment is received, a new stack is made to the left of the first, with sufficient space between the two stacks to permit the storage of any additional shipment that may be received. Issues continue to be made from the left side of the first stack until the first shipment is exhausted. Thereafter, issues are made from the left side of the second stack. In this manner the stacks repeatedly move across the area from left to right. The method is illustrated in Figure 59.

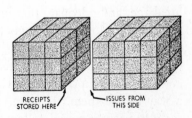

FIG. 59. Storage of Materials to Assure Old Stock Used First

Protection against Damage and Fire Loss. To prevent damage, materials and supplies should be stored with special reference to their requirements as to heat, cold, moisture, dryness, and cleanliness or protection from dust. Bar stock should be supported on racks to prevent bending or springing out of shape. Barrels should be stacked on end and not on the side. Brooms should be stored with the handle end down or should be suspended from hooks. Bags of cement should be protected from the weight of bags piled above them. In some cases, sufficient protection is afforded by placing boards between the layers of bags to distribute the weight. Fragile materials or parts are sometimes stored in boxed pallets or other containers. The containers rather than the materials carry the weight of the items piled above.

Many parts and materials should be stored and removed from racks with care to prevent the marring of polished surfaces. Parts easily damaged may require separate vertical compartments. Finely polished gears are sometimes placed in wax-paper or plastic bags. Special types of cranes or other equipment for lifting and holding material securely may be required for heavy items.

To aid in preventing fire loss in the storeroom, the aisles should be kept clear; bins should be made of steel instead of wood; and highly inflammable materials should be stored in a fire-resistant room with self-closing doors. As further protection against fire loss, fire extinguishers should be placed at convenient locations; and fire regulations should be strictly observed. At all times, good housekeeping is essential in eliminating fire hazards. Despite all precautions to prevent loss from fire, such losses may occur. The stores inventory should be covered by the proper types and amounts of insurance.

Prevention of Waste and Theft. Although the stores may be very valuable, waste in materials and supplies is frequently tolerated, when the mishandling of money is not permitted. Materials may be stored in a careless manner, the storekeeper may not be held accountable for breakage, and adequate precautions may not be taken to prevent theft.

To reduce losses due to poor inventory management, the storekeeper or inventory takers should call the attention of the production planning department to any inactive items which might be used in production; and the person in charge of production planning should attempt to find a way to use them. If materials are obsolete, they should be sold as scrap to prevent complete loss and to make the storage space available. The waste of certain bulk items, such as paint, lubricating oil, and chemicals, may be reduced through purchase in containers of the proper size. Supplies of high unit value should be guarded from pilfering and theft by use of a locked room or closet. It is generally agreed that the balance of stores record should be kept by someone other than the storekeeper, perhaps by a clerk in the cost accounting department. The perpetual inventory record constitutes an independent check on the persons who receive, store, and issue materials and supplies.

Protection against waste and theft also requires that some procedure be designed for assuring a return to the storeroom of materials and supplies withdrawn for use and not used. If it is anticipated that some materials will be returned, such as part of a roll of wire or a steel rod, a record of the withdrawal of the larger quantity should be kept in a temporary file until the unused portion is returned. The return of unused material that was withdrawn in the regular manner is the responsibility of the worker and the foreman. Excessive use of material should be checked by a scrutiny of the cost accounting reports of material costs.

THE ISSUING OF STORES

Two closely related problems that arise when stores are issued pertain to the paper work and physical handling. A proper procedure for issuance requires attention to both problems.

Ease in Issuing. A possible procedure for the issuing of stores is as follows: The requisition is sent to an indexing clerk, who enters after each item listed the location, including the floor, row, tier, and bin number. An order filler takes the requisition, obtains a floor truck equipped with racks and trays, and proceeds from floor to floor or aisle to aisle until the order has been filled. He then pushes the truck to a checking area, where an assistant to the storeroom manager or a group leader checks the material against the requisition. The truck is then taken to the proper department, as indicated by the requisition.

When many orders are for only one or two items, the work of assembling the materials may be facilitated by accumulating the orders for a few hours and then arranging them in sequence by bins for one picker. Some multiple orders may be arranged in sequence, although this procedure is more difficult because one order might call for different items from different parts of the storeroom. Large orders are filled with case lots from the reserve stock wherever possible.[2]

Several arrangements may be made to facilitate the issue of stores, depending upon the kind of material. When the materials are placed in rows of bins, the aisles should be wide enough to permit easy handling of trucks or other equipment. In some storerooms, racks containing bar stock are placed parallel to each other but at a 135 degree angle to the main aisle to permit easy turning of trucks and also to make the contents of the racks visible and accessible. Bar stock is stored with ends toward the aisle from which withdrawals are to be made. Colors

---

[2] Leslie A. Seversen, "More Order Picking with Half of the Work Force," *Factory Management and Maintenance,* Vol. CXI, No. 11 (1953), pp. 138–39.

may be also used to assist in the identification of certain types of stores. For example, a color code may be used to designate the various lengths of molding or other kinds of lumber. A spot of white on the end of a piece might indicate a length of 16 feet, yellow might indicate a length of 14 feet, and blue a length of 12 feet. Colors are also used to identify metal rods of various alloys or any other parts not otherwise readily identified.

The storage and issuance of materials in their original cartons is advantageous if the quantity in a carton is the same as the amount usually requisitioned. Items in case storage are easily counted and issued, and the case protects the materials from scratching or other damage. To facilitate issuance as well as inventory taking, the cartons should be placed in shelves in such manner that the number of cases and the number of items in a case can be determined without moving any cases. Material that is received in bulk may be arranged into standard quantities for issuance and wrapped or boxed before being stored. For example, rags for cleaning are received in bales and issued in five-pound lots. The smaller packages are prepared before the rags are stored.

Plans for issuing various items will vary with the kind of material. Heavy bulky items may be moved by crane, truck, or other special equipment. Heavy bulky stores that are used by only one department are placed in a separate storeroom or storage area near that department. Examples are steel sheets, rolls of heavy brown paper used by a box company, sand used by a glass company, and coal. Materials frequently requisitioned and issued may be stored near the issue window. For some items, a forward stock may be kept near the window and the reserve stock may be kept in a less accessible area. Small parts may be counted and issued by weight. Tables may be prepared to show the weight of any specified quantity of any item. Special scales are also available for counting bulk materials by weight.

Mechanization of storeroom operations is feasible if the company handles a large volume of materials in limited varieties and with cartons of a standard size. The materials may be moved by overhead conveyor, cranes, or other type of equipment. Small parts may be assembled for issue by means of conveyors. The stock clerk removes the materials or parts requisitioned and places them on a conveyor. The conveyor system converges upon the issue window. This method of assembling materials needed for a requisition requires a quick dependable method of communication which reaches all parts of the storeroom. The method also requires a substantial volume of issues, and the turnover of the inventory should be rapid.

Handling and Moving. Many of the principles of materials handling which were discussed in relation to machinery and equipment apply to the handling of materials and supplies in the storeroom. Some types of stores require special types of equipment. Bulky materials of a noncorrosive nature may be moved in self-feeding, self-discharging flow conveyors. Examples are coal, flour, chemicals, wheat, and soybeans. Other types of equipment used for moving materials and supplies to and from storage include cranes, power trucks, hand trucks, gravity conveyors, powered conveyors, and chutes. To reduce the amount of materials handling, some companies equip hand trucks with racks and trays suitable for storage at the workplace. Materials that are withdrawn from stores are placed on the truck in position for use. The truck is then moved to the workplace and left there as a storage receptacle. Materials may also be stored in the storeroom in the containers in which they are later issued.

To reduce the distance for moving materials and supplies after issuance, some companies have established two or more storerooms adjacent to different workplaces. Each storeroom is in charge of an attendant who is under the supervision of the general stores manager. This arrangement is satisfactory provided that the items kept at the various storerooms do not duplicate each other. If the same kind of material is kept and issued at more than one storeroom, care in inventory control is necessary to prevent excessive stocks and the losses incident to large inventories. Inventories are likely to be larger because a reserve supply or margin of safety is kept at each location.

Prevention of Accidents. In most industries the handling of materials is a chief cause of injuries. Among the common types of hazard and injury from materials handling are the following:

Incoming cars or trucks—persons struck by train, automobile, or truck.

Unloading cars or trucks—hands or feet torn, pinched, or crushed; bruises; strains; falls; injury to health from dust, fumes, or chemicals.

Emptying and cleaning tank cars—suffocation or poisoning on entering tanks; burns from acid drips; falls from cars; explosion of inflammable gases; electric shock from extension cords.

Opening baled, crated, or barreled material—cuts and abrasions from sharp edges; nail wounds; strains from lifting; tool wounds.

Piling materials—injuries from falling materials; strains from lifting; falls; foot injuries.

Transporting materials—persons struck by trucks; hands pinched, torn, or bruised under or between articles; articles falling on feet; falls over loose articles.

Handling acids, caustics, volatiles.

Unsafe practices are a frequent cause of accidents. The attempt to move heavy materials by lifting or by hand truck may result in strained muscles or crushed feet or hands. Overloaded or carelessly loaded trucks may cause cartons to fall to the floor. If aisles are narrow, unmarked by lines in safety colors, or crooked, trucks may brush against bins or racks and cause damage or injury to persons. Other causes of accidents are worn or uneven floors, worn crane cables, worn and broken tools, unsafe ladders, wobbly truck wheels, and rickety truck bodies.

To reduce accidents, the causes in each case should be determined and corrected. Situations known to be hazardous should be corrected by such changes as a revision of layout, the provision of proper equipment, and proper maintenance. Mechanical handling should be substituted for manual handling where possible. The selection and training of storeroom personnel should be planned to reduce accidents. Adequate supervision should stress the safety factor when the occasion requires it.

SOME INVENTORY PROBLEMS

Physical inventories are usually necessary to production. Records of quantities on hand are required for the use of executives, for the prevention of waste of materials, and for the preparation of financial statements. The management of the storeroom therefore must give attention to the control of physical inventories and to the records of materials on hand.

Keeping Inventories at a Minimum. One objective of storeroom management is to keep the inventory as low as possible, consistent with continuous production. The manager of the storeroom is not solely responsible for excessive inventories, but he may be of much assistance. He may be able to call attention to slowly moving items or even to suggest the use of other items already carried in stock as substitutes. He may know of needless varieties of items of materials and supplies. If an item has ceased to move because of obsolescence, he may suggest a way of reclaiming it; or he may suggest scrapping it to make space available for other materials. Other suggestions may pertain to possible standardization, eliminating duplication of purchase orders, and avoidance of overstocking. The storeroom manager may be able to offer such suggestions because of his physical contact with the materials and his familiarity with storeroom problems.

Constant Supply. Although good inventory management should keep stores at a minimum, the balances should not be permitted to fall so low that production is delayed for lack of materials. The avoidance of excess quantities requires that careful attention be given to inventory control to assure continuous supply. The balance of stores record is the principal reference; but since it is only a book record, the co-operation of the storekeeper is necessary. To assure that physical inventories are in agreement with book records, the storeroom supervisor should see that incoming shipments are inspected for quantity and quality. Stores should be carefully stored and issued to avoid damage and to assure that all items are of standard quality. The requirement that stores should be issued only on requisition should be consistently observed, and any excess supplies returned to the storeroom from the manufacturing departments should be placed in the proper storage area.

The storeroom clerk may report to the person who keeps the balance of stores record the fact that the supply of an item has reached the reorder point. One method by which the storekeeper may himself observe that the inventory of an item has reached the reorder point is to segregate an amount of an item equal to the predetermined reorder point. The reserve supply may be placed in a separate bin or carton or tied with a string. When the reserve supply is drawn upon, an order should be placed for the purchase of an additional supply.

The system may provide for regular reporting to the balance of stores clerk of the quantity on hand. The exact method of reporting quantities depends on the kinds of stores. Some companies provide for a "bin tag" to be affixed to each bin or shelf and on which is kept a record of the quantity in the bin. The tag shows receipts, issues, and balance. At regular intervals the tags are sent to the balance of stores clerk for comparison of balances as shown by the two records. Another method is to require the person who issues stores from the storeroom to write on the requisition the quantity on hand as shown by the bin tag. When the balance of stores clerk enters the amount of the issue on the perpetual inventory record, he compares the quantity as shown on the requisition with his own record of the balance. Some companies consider the bin tag an unnecessary duplication of the balance of stores record. They rely upon periodical physical inventories for a verification of book balances.

Ease in Taking Inventory. The number of units or the quantity of each item on hand should be determined by physical count at least two times each year. When a count is made, the book inventory should be adjusted to agree with the physical inventory, in case there is a discrepancy. Two methods are used to determine the time for the count of the units on hand. First, the checkers may start at one end of the storeroom and proceed to count the number of units in each bin or other storage space until all items have been inventoried. Second, they may count the number of units when the supply of an item has reached the re-order point. A list of such items would be given the checkers for counting each day. By this method the count is made when the supply is at a low point. The counting, therefore, requires less time than would otherwise be necessary. The disadvantage of this method is that some slowly moving items may not be inventoried at any time during the year, unless special provision is made for them.

Certain methods of storing and issuing are designed to facilitate the taking of the inventory. Supplies and materials stored on shelves should be stacked with labels toward the aisle. Cartons or bales of stores placed on the floor in open areas may be stacked in cubical or pyramid fashion. Cubical storing is preferable because the piles are more easily counted. The number of units in a pyramid may be computed by means of a formula; but the counting is more difficult, particularly after some units have been removed. The advantage of pyramid stacking is the greater stability of the stack. For some kinds of stores, pyramid stacking may be necessary. Cubical storing, if possible, should be in decimal units. For example, if a pile is five or ten units high and five or ten units deep, and if this method is consistently followed, counting is greatly simplified. Although the number of piles cannot be kept at a fixed figure because of receipts and issues, the number in a pile can be kept at a constant figure except possibly for one broken pile.

Issues of materials and supplies should not be taken at random from various piles but should follow a definite plan. For example, issues may be drawn from the top and front of the first pile on the left. All the first pile on the left should be issued before any units are removed from the second pile. The units on hand can then be inventoried by counting the unbroken piles and the number of units in the broken pile on the left. If any cartons are broken when stores are received and inspected, the cartons should be placed where they will be the first to be issued. For liquids kept in drums, such as turpentine, kerosene, and chemicals, a bin tag may be used to record withdrawals and the quantity remaining. To assure that the record of the bin tag is properly kept, the spigot may be locked and issues made only by a responsible person. Similar methods may be used for such bulk materials as rope, wire, and wirecloth.

QUESTIONS

1. Mention situations or industries where an inventory of materials in the storeroom might not be necessary.

2. How has the use of pallets resulted in more effective use of storage space?

3. What factors limit the height of storage areas?

4. What losses and waste may result from lack of planning for the arrangement of stores in the storeroom?

5. Compare the system of classification of stores with the cataloguing of books in a library.

6. What uses are made of the system of classifying stores and designating each class by a symbol?

7. How can methods of storing and issuing materials aid in the prevention of deterioration and loss?

8. Will the posting of guards at the gate prevent pilferage or theft of materials? Can guards prevent the theft of large items?

9. How can workers be required to return unused materials to the storeroom? How can the co-operation of the foreman be achieved in such matters as the prevention of the waste of materials?

10. Should the items in the inventory be counted by the checkers when the supply reaches the minimum, or should all items be counted at regular intervals? Would it be feasible to inventory all items at the end of the year?

11. Should a record of items on hand be kept in the storeroom as a check on the balance of stores record?

12. An overhead conveyor is sometimes used as a "traveling storeroom." What are the advantages of this method?

CASES

68. USE OF STORAGE METHODS TO STABILIZE PRODUCTION

The Union Glass Works, Inc., at Alemeda, California, makes glass containers used by fruit and vegetable canners and soft-drink manufacturers. The company also makes corrugated boxes in which the containers are packed for shipment to the manufacturer. The paper cartons are made according to the specifications of the customer, who uses them to ship the filled containers to his own customers. Fiber shipping boxes carry the name and trade-mark of the canning company or other manufacturer.

The plant manager of the glass company has experienced considerable difficulty in stabilizing production because of the relatively low unit cost of the product and the high cost of storage. Customer demand is greatest during the spring and summer months, and customers prefer not to receive large deliveries in advance of their own production requirements. The container manufacturer has attempted to produce containers in anticipation of customer orders but has found this method inadvisable because of the high cost of storing packages of containers and of removing them when they were needed by customers. Breakage was also high when cartons of containers were piled to great heights by hand labor.

Production has usually been increased during the busy season by putting an additional production line into operation. When a line was started, it was operated twenty-four hours a day; and overtime work could therefore not be used as a method of increasing production. When the expansion of plant capacity seemed to be required because more production lines were needed, the plant superintendent authorized the plant engineer to make a study of the problem.

The plant engineer recommended to the superintendent that lift trucks and pallets be used to store the product. Cartons containing glass containers would be placed on pallets. The cartons would be interlaced to prevent tipping. The lift trucks would be used to place one loaded pallet upon another in the storeroom and to remove them when the customer required delivery. Ceiling heights permitted stacking as high as might be desired. During the late spring and summer when no rain fell in the area, cartons could be stacked in the yard with no protection other than a canvas covering to prevent the accumulation of dust.

Questions:

1. What advantages would the company gain by the proposed plan of production for future delivery?

2. How can the management measure the advantages in terms of monetary savings?

69. NEED FOR MAINTENANCE STOREROOM

When the Woodring Pump Company was first organized, the plant was small; and a careful control of parts used for machine repair was considered unnecessary. When any part was needed, the plant superintendent or the foreman ordered it; and the necessary repairs were made by the employee who operated the machine, with the assistance of the foreman when it was needed. As the volume of work increased and repairs were made more frequently, foremen would often order two or three repair parts when only one was needed. The extra parts were stored in shelves in one corner of the shop, which gradually developed into a storeroom. When a machine was in need of repair, workmen would first look in the storeroom to see whether a repair part was available. If none could be located, an order would be placed for two or three parts; and the extras would be placed in reserve.

Foremen found this method to be unsatisfactory in several respects. A part would frequently be ordered when one was available but was overlooked because it was not quickly located. Reordering a part when one was on hand not only resulted in the purchase of parts not needed but also delayed production. More serious was the fact that no check was ever made on parts that might be needed quickly to prevent delays in production. Although the management trusted its workers, there was the suspicion that occasionally parts were taken by employees for personal use. On some occasions, defective parts removed from machines were placed in the storeroom by mistake. The defects could not be detected by visual inspection; and on several occasions, defective parts were used in making repair work. This caused further labor cost and additional delay.

The plant superintendent decided that the situation could be corrected only by the establishment of a separate storeroom for repair parts, which would be in charge of a responsible storekeeper. However, he was uncertain as to several details. One question was whether the storekeeper should be assigned any additional duties. In the beginning, when repair parts were being catalogued and arranged and inventory cards were being prepared, the full time of one person would be required. Later, the work would require no more than 60 to 75 per cent of the time of one person. The plant superintendent believed that the storeroom should be open at all times during work hours because the time of machine breakdowns could not be anticipated. If any other work was to be given the person in charge, it should be work which could be done at a desk in the storeroom.

Another question concerned the person to be chosen for the new position. Andrew Ramey, assistant storekeeper in the materials storeroom, was a high-school graduate and also the graduate of a business college. He was familiar with all of the details of paper work required, and he was known to be neat and accurate in his work. He had had no experience in the shop itself and was not familiar with the names and numbers of parts. Frank Simmons was another possibility. Simmons was an excellent mechanic. He could tell at once the name of the part required for a repair, and he could identify a part by observation as well as by name. He had attended high school for one year but had no experience in storeroom work. The superintendent was inclined to favor Andrew Ramey for the new position.

Questions:

1. Should the storeroom be open at all times? Should the storekeeper be assigned some other work?

2. Who should be made storekeeper?

PART IX

PLANNING AND CONTROL OF QUANTITIES

33 The Problem of Production Planning and Control

PRODUCTION planning and control includes two major aspects. The first problem pertains to the total volume of production for a month, quarter, or other period of time. An estimate of the total volume is desirable in order that plans may be made for purchasing raw materials, employing and training workers, financing the program, and making other general plans.

The second phase of production planning concerns the planning and controlling of detailed operations from week to week or day to day. This planning makes provision for the production of goods to meet the requirements of individual customers or for the production of specific items to build up the inventory in the storeroom. It prescribes the exact size, color, or other specifications, indicates the number of items, and makes provision for the operations at each workplace or machine. This type of planning and control constitutes the subject of discussion in the present and succeeding chapters.

Development of Production Control. Little advance planning and control of production were necessary during the handicraft stage of production. The master craftsman worked in his own shop and could readily determine the amount of work ahead. When a customer wished to place an order for future delivery, the craftsman estimated the time which would be required for work previously accepted and then indicated a date for completion. If the work ahead became too great, he could decline to accept additional orders. Rush orders were easily handled because the craftsman was familiar with the requirements of all of his customers and could shift from one job to another. The problem was not greatly complicated by the employment of apprentices and journeymen because all of them worked in the same shop under the supervision of the master craftsman.

When machine production was first introduced, the work in many industries was done in the home under a system known as "farming out." A capitalist supplied the materials and sometimes the machines. Work was delivered to the home, where various tasks were performed on a piece-rate basis. Completed work was collected by the capitalist and delivered to the next home, where the next operation was performed. This type of production required some planning, but the system was inefficient because time schedules could not be closely controlled.

When machines were brought together in one building, more detailed planning became necessary. The need for planning increased as the space occupied by the factory expanded and new departments were added. Another factor was the purchase of materials in wider markets and the sale of the product over a wider area. The integration of industry was also a significant development because each business became dependent upon others for parts and materials and in turn supplied parts or materials to other businesses.

Production planning and control was a part of the management work of Frederick W. Taylor. He found that incentive methods of wage payment were ineffective in achieving worker co-operation unless the worker had more work to do as soon as he finished any task. One of Taylor's functional foremen was a route clerk, who had the responsibility for routing the work from one machine to another. Another functional foreman was the instruction card clerk, who determined how the work was to be done and prepared the necessary instructions for the worker. The responsibilities of these two foremen have been enlarged to become the work of the planning or production control department.

Scope of Planning and Control. The management of any activity requires three basic steps. First, plans are made for the work to be done. Second, the plans are put into effect by doing the work or by issuing directions and commands to subordinates to carry out the various steps included in the plan. Third, the work is reviewed to determine the nature of the accomplishment and to revise the plan if necessary. These three steps have been aptly designated as planning, doing, and seeing.[1]

---

[1] This simple but appropriate classification was first used by Alvin Brown, *Organization of Industry* (New York: Prentice-Hall, Inc., 1947), chap. xiii.

The planning phase of production control is usually thought of as consisting of two steps. The first step, which is called "routing," consists of planning what will be done; and the second step, which is called "scheduling," consists of planning when an operation will be started and when it will be completed. The work of doing is usually referred to as "dispatching" because it consists of the issuance of orders to persons who are to do the work. The seeing phase of production control is called "follow-up" and "corrective action." Production control therefore includes four steps: routing, scheduling, dispatching, and follow-up. Corrective action may be thought of as a separate step or as one part of the follow-up.

Each step in production control includes some connotations that are peculiar to this management activity. Routing includes plans for the machine or the workplace where the work will be done, the type of manufacturing operations to be performed, and the quantity that will be produced. It indicates the method by which the product will be made and prescribes the operations for making each part and each subassembly. Routing also includes the determination of the order in which the work will be done. Finally, routing includes determining where the work will be done. The departments that are expected to do the work and also the machines in each department may be specified. In short, routing includes all of the preliminary planning up to the point where the time schedules are established.

In continuous manufacturing where a few products are made in a limited number of designs, the routing should be planned before the plant is laid out. The machines should be installed in the order in which the operations for the manufacture of the product are performed. The methods of materials handling should also be planned with reference to the routing. If this planning has been done, no further attention needs to be given to the routing until the product design is changed when the layout would be changed to conform to the new design. If the plant is laid out by processes or functions, each production order must be separately planned.

Scheduling fixes the time when the order will be completed and the finished product will be placed in the storeroom or shipped to the customer. In continuous manufacturing, the scheduling may not be necessary after the materials are placed in production at the head of the line. With the machines arranged in the order in which the operations are performed, the work is moved along from one workplace to another by conveyor or other method. If the plant is laid out by processes, scheduling becomes necessary in order that each workplace may be supplied with work and an undue amount of work in process will not accumulate at any workplace. Unless the work is moved along according to a detailed plan, the scheduled date for final completion and shipment to the customer may not be met.

Dispatching means the execution of the plans as established in the work of routing and scheduling. It includes the preliminary work of preparation prior to the starting date, as well as the issuance of orders to the manufacturing departments. Before the factory begins work on the product, materials may be purchased, machines may be repaired or set up for the work, workers may be employed or trained, and machine tools may be manufactured or purchased. When work is started, orders

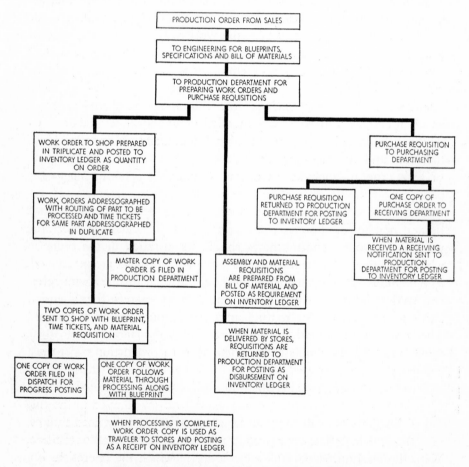

FIG. 60. Flow Chart of the Path of a Production Order

From Fred O. Orthey, "Production Control Based on Improved Inventory Records," *Factory Management and Maintenance,* Vol. CV, No. 12 (1947), pp. 98–99. Used by permission. Production department is synonymous with planning department.

and instructions are issued to workers and to various departments including the storeroom, materials handling, and inspection.

Follow-up includes checking up on the work as it progresses, comparing the progress with the original plans, and taking such corrective action as may be necessary or possible.

The details of the steps in production control vary with the company, the product, and the persons responsible for the planning. The procedure followed by one company is shown in the diagram in Figure 60.

An Illustration of Planning and Control. The four steps in production planning and control may be illustrated by almost any type of activity, such as baking a cake, growing a vegetable garden, making an automobile trip, or building a house. A familiar example is the serving of meals in a cafeteria. The line of customers and their trays corresponds with an assembly line in a factory. Each tray contains a variety of foods chosen by the customer to suit his needs, his preferences, and his purse. The four steps in planning and controlling the service are as follows:

1. A complete meal is planned with choices for each course. The quantities of each type of food are determined, and the methods of cooking and serving each kind of food are planned. These activities constitute the work of routing.

2. The time for beginning each phase of the work is fixed. The complete meal should be ready when the doors are opened for service. It is therefore necessary to determine the hour of the day when each meal will be served and also the hour when service will be discontinued. Since some foods require a longer time for cooking than others, the hour when each type of food will be started in the oven or on the stove should be determined by working back from the time when the first customers are to be served. These activities constitute the work of scheduling.

3. The manager checks on the pantry to determine which foods are on hand and which should be purchased. Instructions are given to the kitchen and dining-room help as to the time for reporting for work. Food is purchased, prepared, cooked, and served according to schedule. These activities constitute the work of dispatching.

4. The serving of the meal may not proceed strictly according to plan. Some of the help may fail to report for work on time. Food may not be available in the market in the necessary quantities or at satisfactory prices. Shortages of some foods may develop because the choices made by customers may not follow the anticipated pattern or because an unusually large number of persons may ask to be served. Some of the food may be rejected because it was not properly prepared. The manager

must therefore be prepared to provide substitutions or to make other revisions of the original plan. This work constitutes follow-up and corrective action.

The cafeteria is used merely to indicate the principal steps in the problem. In fact, production planning is usually much more complicated. To cite a specific example, a plant of the Western Electric Company manufactures over 2,000 different types of electric coils. The planning of the manufacture of a coil requires routing through 2 to 20 operations, and the sequence of the operations lacks uniformity. The weekly output may be 700 orders. The planning department usually schedules about 7,000 operations each week. This planning requires a large amount of detailed work.

Advantages of Production Planning. The planning and control of production is intended to permit the use of machines for as large a percentage of the time as possible and to assure employees steady and continuous employment. When the product is routed through the plant in lots or batches, such as batches of shirts or trousers, the quantities are planned for the continuous operation of the workplaces and for other economies. The reservation of materials for work planned ahead or the planned purchase of needed materials should prevent the interruption of production due to a lack of materials. The planning of parts production may avoid interruption of work due to a shortage of parts on the assembly line.

The planning of production is desirable not only for the reduction of manufacturing costs and the maintenance of good employee relations but also for favorable relations with customers and vendors. Customers benefit from the orderly delivery of finished goods according to schedule. Vendors benefit because they can more effectively plan their own production. Rush purchase orders are avoided when production is planned, and the requirements for materials and purchased parts are anticipated. As explained in relation to inventory problems, the work of the purchaser may be so closely co-ordinated with that of the vendor that containers, parts, and some materials may move directly to the production line without first being put in the storeroom.

Relation to Other Management Problems. The work of production planning and control is affected by virtually all other activities of the enterprise because a primary objective of the business is the production and sale of goods at a profit. It is affected by the location of the plant in relation to the sources of materials and manufactured parts and to the time required for deliveries. It may also affect the mode of transportation, which might be rail, water, or truck. Plant location also affects the choice of a type of building and therefore the plant layout. All these management policies affect the time required for the purchase and delivery of materials into stock and for transfer from one department to another.

The kind of materials-handling equipment in the plant is also an important factor in production planning. Material dropped down a chute, put on a moving belt, or pushed along the line is immediately available at the next workplace. If the work is placed on a hand truck which is later moved by freight elevator to the next floor, allowance should be made for the time required in transportation in planning the load of work at the next workplace. Equally significant is the provision of general-purpose or special-purpose machines. General-purpose machines permit greater flexibility in planning and may make it possible to route work around a bottleneck operation. Machine breakdowns are less disrupting when machines can be used for more than one type of work.

Personnel programs affect production planning because they affect the efficiency of the workers and the speed of work. Important personnel plans and programs are the training program, the employment and induction procedures, and service activities.

The practice of buying or making parts should be considered. During busy years or seasons, some companies buy many parts which they make for themselves at other times. A closely related practice is that of manufacturing for stock in the dull season in anticipation of later demand. When this method is followed, the volume of production in the dull season is equal to the sales plus the amount put into stock. During the busy season the output is equal to the sales minus the amount withdrawn from stock. The stabilization of production is related to guaranteed employment or the guaranteed annual wage.

Other significant management programs which affect production planning are plant expansion; improvement of working conditions; addition of new products; standardization of workplaces, tools, materials, and products; and overtime work.

Departments Affected by Production Planning. The work of production planning and control constitutes a staff or facilitating function. The flow of work from one department to another is planned, and starting and completion dates are fixed by the planning department. The manufacturing departments report the progress of work to the planning department in order that it may take corrective action, if necessary. Planning affects the purchasing department, which places orders for materials to be delivered by the vendor in time for work to be done. The stores department receives the material upon delivery, stores it until it is needed, and issues it for use in production when requisitions are presented. The personnel department uses the production plans or the production budget for the preparation of a personnel budget. Employees are hired, trained, transferred, or laid off in accordance with the plans for production.

The maintenance department co-operates in the production program by periodically inspecting equipment, lubricating machinery, making regular and emergency repairs, and overhauling machinery. The toolroom stores, issues, and repairs the machine and hand tools used in production. Its responsibility is to see that proper tools are available for each task.

Product design is also closely related to planning. The design of the product prescribes the parts necessary to assembly. The product should be designed with reference to the costs involved in routing and scheduling and also with reference to the machines required for processing. In the continuous-process industry, as previously explained, the product design determines the layout. Production time is also affected by the closeness of the tolerances, which affect machine time and may increase the number of defective parts.

The work of inspection is related to production planning because the planning department notifies the inspection department when to inspect and receives reports from the inspector when the inspection is completed. Close inspection may result in the necessity for reworking the product or it may require the placing of a new work order to replace the rejected parts.

The production standards set by motion and time study indicate the probable time that will be required for a task at any workplace. Such standards are used to schedule the work and the moving of the materials. Motion study is a factor in planning because it should reduce the time required for each task.

The sales division supplies customers with estimates of delivery dates which are dependent upon the work of production planning. After the order of a customer has been accepted, inquiries from the customer as to the progress of the order are referred to the planning department.

Production Control Methods. Production control systems are of three types—planning by line departments, systematic planning, and scientific planning. Planning and control by line departments, which is also called "conventional control," represents the minimum of planning. Orders for work to be done are issued by the plant superintendent to the foreman of the first processing department, with no date of completion specified. The foreman plans all work within his department and assigns work to machines and men in whatever way seems best to him. When operations are completed in one department, the foreman has the work transferred to the next department and makes a report of its progress to the general foreman or the plant superintendent. If an order is delayed in production or a customer requests an early delivery, the sales division may report the fact to the plant superintendent, who will check on the status of the work and will attempt to have it completed in time to satisfy the customer. In some companies, expediters are employed to see that preference is given to rush orders. Although this method has produced satisfactory results in many small plants, it may prevent an orderly flow of work and thereby increase costs.

In systematic control, plans for dates of completion of orders are made according to promises given to customers or to dates of delivery to the storeroom for the replenishment of stocks. Progress reports are made to the planning department upon the completion of work at each machine or in each department. The planning department constantly compares the progress of each order with planned completion dates, estimates the time required for subsequent operations, and takes corrective action when necessary.

In complete or scientific control of production, all phases of production are planned by a staff department. The plans should include starting dates in the first department and the completion dates in the last department, as in systematic planning, and they also include schedules for each step in production in the other departments. In planning this work, the planning department uses the results of motion and time studies and the standards established by such studies. In some companies, the planning department may have authority to assign work to each machine and to each worker at each workplace. It may give precedence to a delayed order to bring it up to the schedule. To accomplish its objectives, it may advise the production engineer concerning the specifications for the product and the parts used in manufacture. It may control the balance of stores record, and it may originate requests for the purchase of the needed materials. Tool design, purchase, and repair should also be co-ordinated with the work of production planning.

Centralized or Decentralized Control. When planning and control are centralized, the planning department determines the order of work at each workplace. The worker reports to the planning department when he has finished a task, and he is then assigned to a new task. The foreman is relieved of responsibility for the order of work, and he is free to devote his time to general supervision. However, foremen sometimes object to being deprived of authority in connection with work assignments.

In decentralized control, the central planning department schedules the work to the manufacturing department and determines the date when the work is to be started and completed in each department. The foreman assigns tasks to workers and to machines and sees that the dates prescribed by the central planning department are met. This arrangement permits over-all control of production but leaves considerable authority to the foreman. Many companies that formerly used centralized planning have found decentralized planning to be less expensive and more effective. The trend is toward decentralized planning.

Effect of Method of Manufacture. Methods of production planning and control vary widely because methods of manufacture differ. Production methods are of two general types: first, the production of a variety of products for stock or for orders of customers and, second, mass production or quantity production of one product or a very few products for stock or for shipment directly to customers.

When a company produces a variety of products, several differences in methods of production are possible. The product may be made from a number of materials with standard parts. Examples are stoves, electric fans, radios, and office appliances. It may be made from a small number of materials in a variety of patterns or designs. Examples of this type of product are china, flat silver, costume jewelry, linoleum, and shoes. It may be made from a large number of materials, with each job separately planned. Designs and specifications used for one product may not be used for another. Examples are houses, bridges, ships, and custom-made clothing.

In mass-production industries, two types of operating methods affect the planning. First, some companies produce one product or a few products in quantity; and the customer is expected to purchase the standard products. The specifications of the product are not changed to meet the preferences of individual customers. Examples are ice cream, cement, flour, bread, gasoline, salt, and various chemicals.

Second, some companies make the product in a limited number of designs. Although the customer is permitted in advance of production to choose the design he prefers, he must select one of the standard designs adopted by the manufacturer. Examples of these products are combination breakfasts in a restaurant, certain types of building materials, and automobiles.

Production planning and control also depend upon whether production is of the assembly or the continuous type. Continuous industries are further classified as synthetic or analytical. The assembly industry may be compared with a river having numerous tributaries, with each tributary being fed by smaller streams. The main artery of the river corresponds with the main assembly line in a factory. The tributaries of the river correspond with production lines for the major parts of the product, and the streams feeding the tributaries correspond with the lines for producing parts which are assembled to make the major sub-assemblies. The mouth of the river corresponds with the end of the assembly line. The situation is shown graphically in Figure 61.

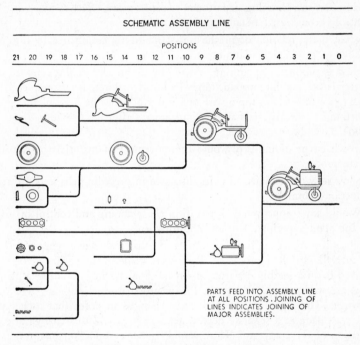

SCHEMATIC ASSEMBLY LINE

POSITIONS

21 20 19 18 17 16 15 14 13 12 11 10 9 8 7 6 5 4 3 2 1 0

PARTS FEED INTO ASSEMBLY LINE
AT ALL POSITIONS . JOINING OF
LINES INDICATES JOINING OF
MAJOR ASSEMBLIES.

FIG. 61. Lines for Assembly of a Product

Reproduced from *Schedugraph,* prepared by Remington Rand, Inc. Used by permission.

The system of production control should be adapted to the requirements of the individual company and its methods of production. No system can be prescribed to meet the needs of all businesses. When the production period is short, a simple system may be satisfactory. When it is long, a more detailed and elaborate system may be necessary. In continuous industries the planning of weekly or monthly output with regular follow-up of production records may be sufficient.

QUESTIONS

1. Compare the need for production planning in the factory system with the need under the handicraft system and the farming-out system.

2. Illustrate the principal steps in production planning with reference to adding a porch to a house. Illustrate by reference to making a trip by automobile.

3. Show the relation of product design and the setting of specifications for the parts to production planning.

4. Show the relation of the decision to buy or make a part to production planning.

5. How is production planning affected by the method by which the plant is laid out?

6. How can the planning department make its plans effective when planning and control is considered a staff function?

7. What is the relation of production standards as established by time study to methods of production planning?

8. How is production planning affected by differences in the point at which the materials are put into production? In bread making, for example, all materials except paper for wrapping are put into process at the head of the line. In candy making, some materials are put into process after the first ingredients have been cooked.

9. In what type of industry would the movement of materials be considered a separate process?

10. Show how the various activities discussed in preceding chapters are related to production planning.

11. Would any company now leave all of the planning and control of production to the plant superintendent and the foremen?

12. The plant of an appliance manufacturer that makes five types of products was formerly laid out by processes. Parts were made in the various departments and moved to an assembly department for the final assembly. The five principal products are washing machine parts, refrigerator parts, jet engine parts, valves, and fittings. The layout of the plant was changed in order that each type of product was made in a separate department. How would this change affect the organization of the company? How would it affect production planning?

CASES

70. PLANNING FOR PRODUCTION

The Jackson and Harper Company manufactures office forms, such as order blanks, invoices, and cost sheets. Each order must be made to meet the specific requirements of the customer. The plant may handle as many as 1,200 orders each month. The plant is organized into five departments—preparatory, press, finishing, receiving and stores, and shipping.

Because of the large number of orders to be handled, considerable difficulty has been experienced in preventing an accumulation of work in process and in meeting promised delivery dates. The control department has designed a single form for production control, which is expected to simplify the procedure. The form consists of an original and a number of copies, in order that all interested departments may receive proper notification of plans and schedules.

In planning for production, the first step will consist of assigning a production order number and typing a production order form. The production order will then be sent to the routing section where the operations necessary for production will be determined, and machines most suited to the work will be indicated. This information will be entered on the form. Next, the production order will be referred to the materials control section, which will calculate the amount of materials that will be needed. If the required materials are not in stock, they will be ordered; and delivery dates will be noted on the production order form. Then the order will be referred to the standards section, which will estimate the probable time required for production at each work station.

Starting and completion dates will now be determined, and the time for each operation will be scheduled. Orders will be listed on a machine-load bulletin board in the order in which they are to be run. A master schedule will also be kept to show starting and completion dates for each order. Each department is to be notified of work scheduled for the department by sending it a copy of the completed production order. Each department will maintain a bulletin board which will provide space for scheduling work at each machine.

Communication between the manufacturing departments and the production control department will be effected by telephone and by personal conferences. Written reports on the progress of work will not be required, but foremen and workers will be expected to maintain the schedules set. In cases of delay, foremen will be expected to determine the cause and correct the situation if possible.

Questions:

1. What manufacturing problems are peculiar to the production of business forms?

2. Why is scheduling especially important in this industry?

3. What is the advantage of the use of a simple form prepared in several copies?

71. PLANNING FOR SPECIAL ORDERS

The Automotive Radiator Company makes radiators for large automobile manufacturers and also for automobile repair shops in the area. Most of the orders are for large quantities of radiators for a few makes of cars, but some orders are for one, two, or three radiators for an earlier model car. The company can supply a radiator for a model of any make for any year, since it has on file the detailed specifications for all makes, including radiators for cars no longer manufactured.

The plant of the company is laid out by processes, since the products are too diverse to permit a production line. The production planning department issues complete instructions to the first department where radiators are started in production. The work is inspected after processing is completed in the department, and a report is sent to the production planning department. A move order is then issued by the production planning department, and the work is then moved in compliance with the order. This procedure is continued as the work moves along from one department to the next. About four weeks are required for the completion of an order.

Since customers are permitted to order one radiator at a time, small orders are frequently received for radiators to be installed in earlier models of cars. Until recently, small orders were handled in the same way as large orders. Customers have protested against the long delay in deliveries as the automobile owner is always in a hurry to have his car repaired and returned to him. Unless a distributor has stocked a radiator in advance which he can supply to the repair shop, a long delay is inevitable.

In practice, the small orders usually require a longer time in production than large orders. A small order might require the resetting of a machine, and both foremen and workers object to frequent changes. Even though an order for one or two radiators might be marked "Rush," workers were inclined to take the long-run standard items first. The company employed expediters to move through the plant and to see that rush orders for small quantities were given priority. Sometimes when two radiators of a kind have been ordered, only one would be delivered to final assembly and inspection. The responsibilty for such an error is not easily placed, as the mistake might have been made by the production control clerk or by operators anywhere along the line. Delays of this kind are very annoying to the customer and the sales division.

To correct the difficulty, the plant superintendent has agreed to use one corner of the plant for the processing of small orders. One machine of each type will be moved from each operating department, and these machines will be set up in a new production line. No paper work will be required except for the one production order for the manufacture of the radiator. All of the processing, inspecting, and transferring of small orders in production will be supervised by one foreman. Under this arrangement, work will be handled more rapidly. The plant superintendent believes that most orders can be completed within twenty-four hours after the instructions are issued to the department.

Required:

Discuss the advantages of the proposed change in layout and the problems that may be created.

34 Routing
and
Scheduling

THE discussion in this and the next chapter relates to production planning and control in diversified manufacturing, where each order is separately routed, scheduled, and dispatched. In a later chapter, planning and control in continuous manufacturing or mass-production industries will be considered. In diversified production, the planning department may consist of four sections, suggested by the four steps in production planning, and control. However, routing is so closely related to the design of the product that it is frequently regarded as an engineering function. A possible organization of a planning department is shown in Figure 62. In this organization, routing is not included.

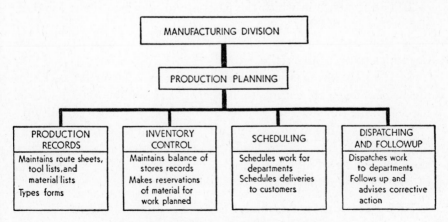

FIG. 62. Organization of Planning Department

This function is assumed to be a part of the work of the design engineer. The control of the balance of stores inventory records is placed under the manager of production planning. Production control is concerned with quantities on hand, on order, and reserved for work planned ahead. It is not especially concerned with unit cost or with the total value of the inventory. For this reason the inventory control function is usually included in the accounting department.

ROUTING

The work of routing in diversified production depends in part upon the nature of the manufacturing processes. In some cases, the product may be made of one piece of material which is fabricated at a number of workplaces. For example, a circular wood saw, as explained in the discussion of plant layout (see page 215) is made of one piece of steel which is cut to size and then subjected to such operations as punching center hole, cutting teeth, sharpening the teeth, and tempering by heat treatment. These operations would be listed on a route sheet, which would also provide other information, such as the specifications of the materials and the workplaces where the work is to be done.

In an assembly industry, the product is made of several parts and subassemblies which are purchased or processed separately and then assembled. Routing indicates the materials and the processes required to make each part and each subassembly. The work of routing may consist of six steps, which are:

1. The parts necessary for the final assembly of the product and also the subassemblies are listed, and their specifications are stated.

2. The sequence in which the parts are to be manufactured and assembled is determined.

3. The materials necessary to the manufacture of each part and the quantities of each material are fixed.

4. The steps or operations necessary to the manufacture of each part are listed. The jigs, cutting tools, gages, and fixtures which will be needed in the manufacture of the product are determined and listed.

5. Forms for use in dispatching are prepared and filed.

6. Provision is made for dividing the order into the proper batches, since the routing of all the material for a production order in one lot or batch may be uneconomical.

Parts Necessary for Assembly. To cite a simple illustration of what the first step involves, the parts necessary for the manufacture of a blackboard eraser would include a wood or fiber back and perhaps five strips of felt, three of which might be black and two white. The parts necessary for the manufacture of a knife might be one large blade, one small blade, a backspring, two strips of steel, two strips of bone, and two rivets. A pair of scissors would require two blades and one rivet.

More complicated products would require a consideration of the parts necessary for subassemblies. For example, a bicycle is composed of a frame, a front wheel, a rear wheel, a seat, a chain, handle bars, and two mudguards. These parts are called "subassemblies" because each is composed of several parts. The wheel, for example, consists of a hub, a rim, a number of spokes, a tire, and an inner tube. The production planning would necessarily take into consideration the fact that some of these parts would be purchased, while other parts would be made in the plant.

Sequence of Parts Completion. An ideal planning and production schedule might make it possible for all parts to reach the assembly line at the exact time they are needed. In most cases, however, this ideal cannot be realized because of delays in delivery of material, machine breakdown, absence of employees, accidents, precedence given to special orders, and failure of employees to meet standards. In some cases the quantities of a part required on the production line are not sufficiently large to permit economical production. The better plan, therefore, may be to produce parts for reserve stock to be withdrawn from the storeroom as needed. The maintenance of a reserve bank of parts at each workplace along the line may be desirable to prevent delays and interruptions.

Materials Necessary. The kinds and quantities of materials that will be required in production should next be determined. If parts are produced and stored in advance of production, the parts are included in the list of materials. The list of parts and materials required for the production of an article is called a "bill of materials." If the product is complicated, such as a typewriter or a computing machine, the bill of materials may include several pages. A part of a bill of materials is shown in Figure 63.

In many cases the bill of materials may be quite simple. Materials for the manufacture of glass bottles to

BILL OF MATERIALS		
NAME OF PRODUCT _SIMPLEX 6 CYL. ENGINE_ MODEL NO._72_		
DRAWING NO. _72560-4_ NO. OF SHEETS _16_ SHEET NO._1_		
PART NO.	UNITS	PART OR MATERIAL
27213	2	BEARING
27335	4	BRACKET
11620	2	HINGE
45601	1	BASE
25219	1	CLUTCH
21702	6	SPARK PLUG
34822	16	BOLT
17109	6	BUSHING
46203	6	CONNECTING ROD
26523	4	HOOK
27117	6	SPRING
25613	4	BEARING
57314	2	RING
		ETC.

FIG. 63. Bill of Materials

From *Management Controller,* prepared by Remington Rand, Inc. Used by permission.

the order of the customer would include only the sand, some chemicals, and coloring matter. Tin cans would require only the coated sheets, some solder, and plastic coating. Candy would require chocolate, sugar, and a limited number of other ingredients. Printed forms require metal for the plates, paper of a designated quality, ink, carbon paper, and shipping cartons.

Operations Necessary. When the flow of work is planned, the order is first routed by departments and then to specific machines. The routing by departments indicates the general steps in production. The procedure is much the same in any business, although the names of the operations and departments will vary. The steps in various industries might be as follows:

> *Machine Shop Operations:* Lathe, mill, shape, drill, grind, inspect, ship.
> *Printing Steps:* Copy, composition, engraving, mats, make-up, client O.K., pressroom.
> *Foundry Operations:* Patterns, cores, flasks, molding, cleaning, inspect, ship.
> *Advertising Steps:* Copy, photo, layout, final copy, client O.K., art, paste-up, printing.
> *Textile Production:* Grilling, combing, drawing, spinning, spooling, ship.
> *Job Shop Operations:* Cut off, mill, drill, weld, plate, polish, assemble, deliver.
> *Publishing Operations:* Editorial, composition, galley, author, illustrations, paging, author, press, bindery.[1]

After each general step in production has been planned, the product is routed to specific workplaces and machines. The detailed operations are listed on an operation ticket which is sometimes used also as a shop travel card to accompany the material as it moves through the plant. The operation ticket shows the following information:

> Part number and name.
> Quantity to be manufactured.
> Operation names and numbers.
> Department and machine numbers.
> Number or specification of tool to be used.
> Estimated time required for each operation.

Space may be provided on the operation ticket for the insertion of the date when each operation is scheduled for beginning and completion. This information is entered later as a part of the work of scheduling. Space may also be provided for entering the number of the operator to whom the work is assigned when an order is dispatched. A form of the operation ticket is illustrated in Figure 64.

---

[1] Adapted from Wassell Organization, Inc., *How to Prevent Mishandling of Orders.*

NUMBER Y 1724	PART NAME COVER FOR WINDOW MODEL						
MATERIAL FB – 30 0.078 X 48 X 120		STANDARD QUANTITY 200					
DEPT. NO.	OPERATION	HOURS PER 100 PARTS	MACHINE NO.	TOOL NO.	DATE	OPERATOR	
	DRAW ABOVE MATERIAL FROM STOCKROOM A FOR DEPT NO.1 DRAW PARTS FROM STOCKROOM B FOR DEPT. NO. 3–1– PD – 2057						
1	SHEAR TO 2–7 16 X48	0.450	310	10 –915			
1	SHEAR TO 1.135	0.500	314	10 – 915			
1	NOTCH END	0.110	312	13 –032			
1	CHANNEL FORM	0.200	376	K-5939			
2	GRIND EDGES	0.500	687	14-686			
3	WELD FILLER	0.500	744	12-144			
3	DRILL 2 HOLES	0.775	253	11– 44			
3	TAP 2 HOLES DELIVER TO STOCKROOM C	0.575	253	8-461			

FIG. 64. Operation Ticket

From *Management Controller,* prepared by Remington Rand, Inc. Used by permission.

The routing to machines may be a flexible arrangement, if many machines are general purpose. Sometimes, several sizes and types of milling machines or lathes, for example, may be available for doing certain kinds of finishing operations. A flat surface on a small casting may be finished by hammer and chisel, file, shaper, facing in a lathe, milling, surface grinding, or broaching. Corrugated paper may be made on a machine that will process wide rolls of paper or narrow rolls, and textile fabrics may be made on wide or narrow looms. Corrugated paper boxes may be stapled by fully automatic machines or at manually operated machines. Chocolates may be hand-dipped, or the chocolate coating may be applied automatically by machine. The method and the machine used in any case will depend upon the exactness of the work required, the time allowed for the work, the work already scheduled for each workplace, and the price at which the product will be sold.

The operation ticket is similar in some respects to the process chart as described on page 224. Both forms list the operations necessary to the manufacture of the product. However, the operation ticket is used in diversified manufacturing where the operating departments must receive detailed instructions as to the work to be done to make a product of a given size, style, color, or other specification. It also indicates quantities to be produced. The process chart is stated in more general terms and indicates only the operations or processes necessary to the manufacture of any product. For example, the process chart for making shoes would indicate only the general steps of cutting the leather, trimming the parts for the lining, sewing, and assembly. The operation ticket would carry detailed instructions for a particular style, size, and color to make a specified number of pairs of shoes.

The processes as listed on the process chart may have been built into the layout, and the work of routing would thereby be simplified. For example, various types of jars and bottles, corrugated paper, or tin cans would usually be made on the same machines, with changes in molds or in machine set-up. The manufacture of cubes of pressed sugar or small cakes of soap in wrappings bearing the name of the customer would likewise be done on the same line as other orders, with only a change in machine adjustment and a change in the roll of paper on the wrapping machine.

Preparation of Forms. Several forms are prepared as a part of the work of routing. The purposes of the forms are, first, to notify a department of the work to be done and, second, to provide a report of work completed. Where many persons are concerned with the work, it is often possible to include on one form the information which may be required by two or more departments. Copies of a form may be prepared in different colors for the use of various departments. For example, the operation ticket may be prepared in seven copies, as follows:

COLOR	USE
1. White	Master standard operation sheet for use by the engineering department.
2. Ecru	Central production order control form. This copy is placed in the master file in the production control department.
3. Green	Departmental production order control form. One copy is prepared for each interested department. Each copy indicates the date the department is to start work on the order.
4. Buff	Traveling production order form. This copy is attached to the material. It is sent to the first department where work is started and it travels with the material as work progresses.
5. Salmon	Material requisition form. This copy is sent to the first interested department which uses it to draw materials from stores when the work is started.
6. Blue	Parts requisition form. This copy is sent to the first interested department which uses it to draw parts from the storeroom when the work is started.
7. Pink	Cost department notification form. This copy is sent to the cost department which uses it to set up the cost record for work in process. The reverse side may be printed to provide space for job costs as the work is done.[2]

---

[2] Remington Rand, Inc. *Management Controller*, p. 21.

The copies of the operation ticket are prepared by the use of mimeograph or other duplicating equipment. All copies of the ticket are referred to the clerk in charge of the balance of stores records, who deducts the quantities required from the available balance. If the material is not available, he holds the forms until it becomes available. A similar procedure is followed for tools and fixtures. The forms are not sent to the departments concerned until materials, tools, and drawings are available and the work has been scheduled. One form that is in common use is the material requisition. This form is sent to the storeroom to authorize the department to which the material is to be sent and indicates the number of the production order.

If the material is moved by crane or truck rather than by conveyor, a move ticket may be used to authorize a worker to move it. This form identifies the material, indicates the quantity, and shows the production order number. It may indicate the sequence of operations, as well as the department to which the work is to be moved next. If a separate move ticket is prepared, the buff copy of the operation ticket, referred to as the "traveling production order form," would not be used.

When the work is inspected by a professional inspector, a special form called an "inspection ticket" may be used to notify him that the work is ready for inspection. This form provides space for recording the number of good pieces, the number of pieces rejected, and the cause of rejection.

The shipping order is a notice issued to the shipping department to ship stated quantities of the finished product to a customer. Provision is made in the form for the recording of partial shipments.

Division of Work into Batches. When the work is routed from one workplace to another, economies may sometimes be effected by sending the material through the plant in batches instead of in a single lot. Examples are articles of clothing such as trousers or dresses, chapters of a book in a printing plant, the printed books in a bindery, and springs for automobile seats or beds. When material is moved in batches, the machines need not be reset for each batch; and a part of the material is forwarded to the next department when an operation is completed, instead of being held until the operation has been completed on all units in the order. The decision as to the most economical quantity in a batch is a part of the work of routing.

The first consideration in dividing the order into batches is the economical unit for materials handling. When material is stored in the storeroom on pallets, the economical size of the unit would be a pallet load. If the material is stacked in cartons, the unit might be one carton or perhaps two or more cartons. In still other cases, the economical unit for materials might be stated in rolls of paper or bundles of steel sheets. The use of the economical lot size facilitates the stacking of material in the storeroom and moving it to the first workplace for processing.

The size of the batch is also affected by the space required by the material and the amount of space available at each workplace. Another factor is the method of internal transportation and the cost of moving small batches. The investment in the inventory of work in process should also be considered. Costs may be increased by holding materials until the operation has been completed on all units. Since the product can be finished and shipped to the customer in shorter time if it is moved in batches, the urgency for getting the work completed would be another factor. The person in charge of routing should also take into consideration the amount of work already planned ahead for succeeding departments. If departments which perform later operations already have all of the work they can do, and if a transfer of the material in batches would only result in an accumulation of work in later departments, no saving would result from the division of work into batches.

The effect of the division of work into batches is shown in the chart in Figure 65. The chart shows that if the work is routed in one batch, it cannot be completed until the end of June. If it is routed in two batches, it can be completed by the middle of May. The time required in production can be further reduced by dividing the work into a greater number of batches.

It should not be inferred that routing in diversified production always provides for the movement of material in batches. In some cases the work of routing includes the grouping of various customers' orders into a single lot to make an economical lot or batch. For example, a candy company owning a factory and a chain of candy stores would plan production in the factory to permit the production of candy for several stores on a single factory order. A bottle company might group orders of customers for bottles to permit the production of one lot of bottles of the same size through one order on the factory. The arrangement would permit the economical operation of the mixing equipment and the tank furnace, provided the bottles are of the same size and color. They need not

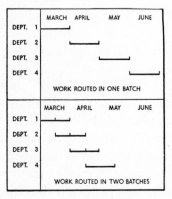

FIG. 65. Effect of Dividing Work into Batches

be the same shape because they are shaped in different molds. A linoleum manufacturer would group orders from sales offices or distributors to permit a large run of linoleum of the same quality and the same pattern.

SCHEDULING

The second step in production planning is scheduling. This step is closely related to routing because routing cannot be completed without reference to the work previously scheduled for each department. Routing and scheduling are often done by one person, and the two steps are performed simultaneously on different production orders. The production planning department may find it necessary to reroute an earlier order to provide for later work. Both the routing and the scheduling may be changed in case of machine breakdown, delayed deliveries of materials, and other emergencies. Each of the first two steps affects the other, and both depend upon dispatching and corrective action.

Nature of Scheduling. Scheduling of work introduces the element of time. It may provide only for starting and completion dates; or it may provide for starting, completion, and transfer dates from department to department. Usually the date of completion or delivery to stock is first determined, and then the date when work is to be completed in any department is determined by working backward from the final completion date. For example, a publisher might schedule a book for publication on April 1. Preliminary steps could then be scheduled as follows:

Delivery to stock, in batches, beginning April 1.
In bindery, in batches, received in bindery February 15 to March 1.
In press, February 1 to Febraury 28.
Correction of plates, set type for index, January 20 to January 31.
Page proof read by author, index prepared, December 15 to January 25.
Preparation of pages and page proof, December 10 to January 15.
Preparation of illustrations, November 1 to December 31.
Galley proof read by author, November 5 to December 31.
Type set, November 1 to December 15.
Editorial, October 1 to October 31.

It will be observed that some operations are planned to overlap in point of time. Galley proof is to be sent to the author before the setting of the type has been completed. Illustrations are to be made while the type is being set. The books are to be sent to the bindery and delivered to stock in batches. The situation is shown graphically in Figure 66.

The diagram in Figure 66 is prepared on the principle of the Gantt chart. The short vertical line to the left of each horizontal line indicates

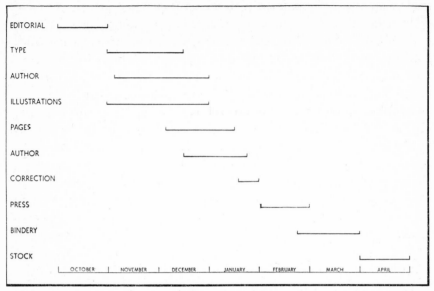

FIG. 66. Scheduling Production

the date when an operation is to be started. The short vertical line to the right indicates the date when an operation is scheduled to be completed. Horizontal spaces represent the time required to complete the processing of the work. The space for one week does not represent the same quantity values for different phases of the work. It may represent pages of manuscript read and marked by the editor, ems of type set by the typesetter, plates prepared, or number of books printed or bound in the designated period of time. The time required for transportation of materials is included in operation time.

Purposes of Scheduling.   The inclusion of the time element in production planning serves a number of purposes for various persons inside and outside the company. Operating departments can use the information pertaining to the amount of work planned to schedule personnel, extra shifts, overtime, machine repair, and other work. Foremen can determine for themselves whether their operations are on schedule. The purchasing department may make its plans for the purchase of supplies, tools, or equipment. The machine shop can know when special fixtures, molds, or tools will be required. The planning department knows at each stage whether an order is on schedule and whether corrective action will be necessary. If a machine or department is becoming overloaded, the fact is known in time to permit rerouting of some of the work, declining additional customer orders, or making other plans.

Satisfactory relations with customers and vendors depend upon scheduling the work and then producing according to schedule. Deliveries may be promised to customers with the assurance that the goods can be delivered on time. A garment manufacturer, for example, who plans to make shirts or dresses for sale in a seasonal market requires assurance that textiles, buttons, and thread of certain specifications will be available when they are needed. Scheduling permits the production plans of one manufacturer to be integrated with the plans of others.

Information Necessary for Scheduling. Before the element of time can be introduced into the planning of work, information should be available to indicate the operations necessary for the manufacture of the product as established by the product design engineer or the person in charge of routing. This information is shown in the operation ticket (Fig. 64, p. 613). The person who schedules the work needs to know the machine capacity and the number of hours a day or week that a machine can be expected to operate. If production depends upon the rate at which a worker can do the work and not upon the speed of machine operations, the standard time for various tasks as established by motion and time study should be available.

The time required for the transportation of the materials from one machine to another is also a factor. For this reason, the person doing the scheduling should be familiar with the plant layout, the distances between machines, and the methods of materials handling. When work is completed at one machine, it may be scheduled for another machine that is conveniently located even though a more efficient machine would be available in another part of the plant. The dates when purchased materials or parts will be available should be known, and a margin of safety is usually advisable. Since all planning is intended to assure that deliveries to stock or to customers will be made at a certain time, the dates when deliveries are wanted should be known.

In estimating machine capacity, the planning department first determines the number of hours per week the machines of each type may be expected to be in operation. The estimate is based upon the number of machines, the number of days per week the plant will be in operation, the number of shifts, and the estimated percentage of efficiency. To illustrate, the computation for engine lathes might be made in the following manner:

Number of lathes in the department	3
Number of labor shifts	2
Hours per shift	8
Number of days of plant operation per week	5
Total number of hours (multiply)	240
Estimated percentage of efficiency	75
Weekly capacity, hours in use	180

When the work previously planned for lathes is converted into the number of hours required to complete the work assigned, the management can determine the length of time which will be required to complete new work and the extent to which the production program is in balance. For example, the results might be as follows:

	No. 36 Lathes	No. 16 Lathes
Number of machines................	3	4
Weekly capacity, hours in use.........	180	240
Average weekly load for next 18 weeks,		
work now scheduled...............	160	230
Surplus weekly capacity..............	20	10

A tabulation of this kind, when continued for the various machines and other workplaces, will indicate when the volume of work scheduled for a machine is nearing machine capacity. It will indicate to the management the need for additional equipment of certain types or possibly the desirability of revising production plans.

The hours scheduled for each machine or workplace may be tabulated by means of a monthly or weekly machine-requirement record, as illustrated in Figure 67. The first step is the preparation of an operation card describing each operation

MACHINE __WG 480__ TYPE _DRILL PRESS_ SIZE _NO. 2_

SCHEDULED MACHINE REQUIREMENTS

DATE	ORDER NO.	JANUARY		FEBRUARY		MARCH		APRIL	
		HRS.	CUM.	HRS.	CUM.	HRS.	CUM.	HRS.	CUM.
12/6	186	60	60						
12/15	190	35	95						
12/28	198	45	140						
1/3	210			40	40				
1/6	215			52	92				
1/8	220					32	32		
MONTHLY CAPACITY (HOURS)			150		140		150		

FIG. 67. Monthly Machine-Requirement Record

as indicated on the operation ticket as shown in Figure 64. The operation cards are then sorted by machines, and the work is scheduled for a definite time of starting and completion. The information is recorded on the monthly machine-requirement record by order number and by month. After the information has been tabulated in this manner, the cards are re-sorted by order numbers and filed for future use in dispatching.

As the scheduled machine-hours are entered on the machine-requirement record, the hours are accumulated in the separate columns. When the accumulated figure for each month or week reaches a predetermined percentage of the total available time for the month, a plastic signal is placed on the card in the monthly column to indicate that the machine is close to being overloaded and that no further orders should be scheduled for that period of time.[3]

---

[3] *Management Controller*, p. 41.

It may be desirable that the work
scheduled for each workplace be
planned by days. This is done by
means of a Gantt chart called a "machine-load chart." The machines are
listed in the spaces on the left margin. The horizontal spaces indicate
the days. Work scheduled for a machine is indicated by lines drawn on

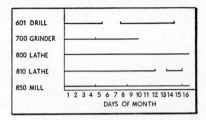

FIG. 68. Machine-Load Chart

the chart for the number of days' work planned. The dates for which
no work has been scheduled are indicated by breaks in the lines. These
spaces will be filled in later as other work is scheduled. The method is
illustrated in Figure 68.

Bulletin Boards for Machine Loads. While a chart is a desirable
method of showing work planned, it lacks flexibility. Changes in schedules made necessary by difficulties arising in production or in the procurement of materials are not easily made on the chart. To provide
flexibility, several types of equipment have been devised. The earlier
type of such equipment was a bulletin board with three spaces for posting operation tickets for work scheduled for each machine. Each space
is equipped with a hook for holding the operation tickets. On the first
hook is placed the ticket for the work now at the machine and in process. On the second hook is placed the operation ticket for work now in
the department and waiting to be done. The tickets for other work
scheduled are placed on the third hook.

The machine load for each machine may also be shown by means of
a pegboard, as illustrated in Figure 69. The machines are listed in the
spaces on the left column. Opposite the designation of each machine
are two rows of holes which are used for the insertion of pegs to indicate the work scheduled. The board is operated on the principle of the
Gantt chart, which means that the horizontal spaces represent the days
of the month. When work is scheduled for a machine, a peg is inserted
to indicate the starting date; and another peg is inserted to indicate the
scheduled completion date. The board indicates the dates for which
no work has been scheduled, as well as the dates of scheduled work.
Operation tickets are filed in pockets on the left side of the board.

The total load scheduled for each machine is indicated by a transparent tape of flexible plastic which is drawn from an opening in the board
adjacent to the machine number and is extended across the board over
the number of horizontal columns that represent the days estimated as
required for the work scheduled. When additional work is scheduled

Courtesy Wassel Organization, Inc.

FIG. 69. Machine-Load Bulletin Board

for the machine, the pegs for the previous order are left unmoved; and additional pegs are inserted to show the new work planned; the tape is then pulled farther to the right to indicate the additional period of scheduled time. In this manner the board is kept up to date and shows at all times the load of work planned for each machine.

Another variation of the bulletin board for scheduling work consists of a row of pockets opposite each machine number, in which are inserted the copies of operation tickets for work scheduled. The pockets are made of sturdy transparent material in which the edges of the tickets are inserted. The edge of each ticket, which is printed in a bright color, is trimmed or cut away according to the number of days or hours which will be required for the work. When it is inserted in the transparent pocket, it indicates the days or hours of scheduled work. Vacant spaces in the pockets represent the time for which no work has been scheduled. The schedule can be revised by shifting the operation tickets in the pocket for each machine.

The method of scheduling machine loads by means of a bulletin board with a pocket for each machine is illustrated in Figure 70. The pockets overlap in such manner that only the edge can be seen. This visible arrangement reduces the space required for the equipment and facilitates reference to the information. It also protects the operation ticket from exposure.

Scheduling the Order. When an order is to be scheduled, the parts list and the operation tickets are taken from the files. The parts list shows what parts are required for assembly, and the operation tickets

Courtesy Remington Rand, Inc.

FIG. 70. Visible Filing System for Machine Loads

show the operations necessary to the manufacture of each part. The person who is scheduling the work next finds out from the balance of stores clerk which parts are available in the storeroom and which parts must be manufactured. In scheduling the manufacture of any part, the clerk refers to the machine-load chart to determine when the machine will be available. If it will be available for more than one period, or if any one of several machines might be used, the most suitable time and the machine best suited to the work would be chosen.

The schedule might be made for the purpose of completing the order at a time that would be satisfactory to the customer, and the clerk would work back from the desired completion date to determine starting and completion dates in each department. If the customer desires delivery at the earliest possible time, the clerk might begin by scheduling the first operation and work through to the last department.

If any machines to be used in the manufacture of the parts are heavily loaded, the clerk might delay the processing in the earlier operations in order that materials or parts may not accumulate at any point with resulting congestion and excessive inventory of work in process. To determine the most economical schedules, the clerk may schedule the operations for the most heavily loaded machine first. He may then project the schedule through the subsequent operations to determine the finish date for that part. He finally estimates the time required for assembly operations and determines the date for the completion of the order.

The production schedule may make provision for possible delays and interruptions in the work. One method provides for banks of materials and work in process at various work stations or machines. For example, if the work for 100 units moves in batches of 10, the work for the first batch at the second machine might not be scheduled to start until the second batch is about due. A slight delay in the processing at the first machine would not require that work be stopped at other machines.

Another method of providing for delays would schedule a machine for something less than 100 per cent of capacity. The loose schedule would permit the department to deliver the work on time to a later department or machine even though a machine may break down, an operator may be absent, or an inexperienced operator is assigned to the work. A loose schedule would also allow some time for rush orders. However, such a schedule would encourage wasteful practices which production planning is intended to avoid.

The scheduled date of completion of each order is entered on a summary sheet of the work which is in process or which has been scheduled. This summary, which is called a master schedule, shows the order number, the description of the product, and the probable date of completion. The master schedule establishes the objective of the production planning department and the operating departments.

The dates for starting and completing the production of each part may be shown graphically by the use of a lead-time chart, as shown in Figure 71. The date set for the final assembly of the product is desig-

LEAD–TIME CHART (SHOWING OPERATIONS TO FOLLOW DUE DATES)															
PART NO.	NOVEMBER														
	1	2	3	4	5	6	7	8	9	10	11	12	13	14	15
1-1					1		0		A			0			
1-2			2		1		0		A			0			
2-1				4		3		2	1			0		A	
3-1	4	3		2		1		0		A		0			
3-2				2		1		0		A		0			

FIG. 71. Lead-Time Chart Used in Scheduling

nated as A-day. Each part is scheduled for completion two days before it will be needed for assembly. The two-day interval will provide for delays and for transportation of materials for short distances. The date for which the completion of any part is scheduled is indicated in the chart as O-day. The dates for completing the various operations necessary to the manufacture of each part are indicated by the figures 1, 2, 3. For example, the figure 1 indicates that, after that date, one operation remains to be performed; and the figure 2 indicates that two operations are to be performed. The figure 0 indicates that all operations have been completed.[4]

The scheduling of production may be illustrated by means of bulletin boards of various types. The spaces across the board represent work orders rather than machines. When the pegboard is used, pegs are inserted to indicate starting and completion dates in the various departments. The scheduling of production orders is also shown by means of a bulletin board with a pocket for tickets showing the operations necessary to the manufacture of each part or each product. The method of operation is the same as that of the bulletin board showing machine loads.

In addition to scheduling machine loads and flow of production orders, the planning department may schedule the delivery of materials into stock and also the production or purchase of tools and other equipment. If materials are to be purchased, the schedule might be made in a manner similar to the following:

```
Date when production is to be started......................April 15
Date when materials should be received, allowing 5 days for
    paper work and a margin of safety......................April 10
Date when material should be shipped by the vendor, allowing
    5 days for transportation..............................April  5
Date when contract should be placed with vendor, allowing
    45 days for shipment...............................February 19
Date when requisition should be placed with the purchasing
    department, allowing 5 days for paper work............February 14
```

Centralized or Decentralized Scheduling. When scheduling is centralized, the planning department schedules the work of each machine, as well as the flow of work from one department to another. When scheduling is decentralized, the planning department schedules the final completion date and the dates for completion in each department. The foreman then assigns the work to individual workplaces and plans to meet the completion dates determined by the general program. The central production control department maintains data for work loads by departments. Each foreman may maintain charts or bulletin boards for machine loads and the flow of production orders within his department.

Adaptations of Scheduling Methods. The methods for scheduling work as developed in manufacturing enterprises may be adapted to many other types of activities. Any person may utilize his time more effectively if he schedules his work and allots his time between the various tasks. In an office the work of each typist or clerk may be scheduled

---

[4] Donald Peddie, "Lead-Time Chart Insures Close Scheduling," *Factory Management and Maintenance,* Vol. CV, No. 9 (1947), pp. 122–23.

in order that the supervisor may know the nature of the work being done by each person and the volume of work which is waiting at each desk. The scheduling may be done by using a sheet of analysis paper, with the names of the office staff listed in the left column. Spaces across the page represent the hours of the day or days of the month. Symbols may be used to indicate rush work, correspondence, duplicating, or other classes of work. By means of such a plan the supervisor may know at all times what persons may be shifted to other types of work in emergencies and what additional help may be needed.

QUESTIONS

1. What activities are so closely related to production planning that they are sometimes placed under the control of the planning department?

2. Name the parts that would be required for a pencil. Name the parts for a brief case.

3. To what extent is the preliminary work of routing performed in connection with product design?

4. Why is the fixing of the sequence of parts completion an important step in routing?

5. What information is listed on the operation ticket? What use is made of the ticket?

6. How is the work of routing affected by the use of general-purpose or special-purpose machines?

7. What costs of manufacturing are increased by the production of a large number of small production orders? Are any costs decreased?

8. A manufacturer who makes radiators to order of the customer for any make of automobile of any year's design sometimes makes three or four when the customer has ordered only one. What are the advantages and the disadvantages of this method?

9. How does the division of the work into batches decrease the cost? When might the orders of several customers be combined to make one large order?

10. Should starting and completion dates be scheduled for each department, or is the scheduling of the beginning of work in the first department and the completion date sufficient?

11. With what machine does the schedule clerk start when he schedules an order?

12. What does the schedule clerk do when he finds that a machine is scheduled for capacity for weeks ahead?

13. If no more materials are available because the plants of vendors are closed by strikes, should the company continue to process the orders already under way, or should it close the plant at once? How are problems of scheduling affected by this decision?

CASES

72. DIVISION OF WORK INTO BATCHES

In a bookbindery, unbound books as they are received from the printing presses are stitched and bound. Six operations are performed—trimming, glueing, stitching, forming, affixing backs, and lettering outside cover. The time required for processing 2,500 books of a certain size and type is estimated for various operations as follows:

Operation Number	Time in Hours
1	10
2	20
3	150
4	40
5	120
6	80

The work can be scheduled in one batch or in several batches. It would also be possible to assign two or more workers to any one operation if necessary to make deliveries at an early date.

Required:

1. Show by means of a Gantt chart the time that would be required if the order is scheduled in one batch.

2. Prepare a chart to show the time required in production if the work is scheduled in five batches.

3. Prepare a chart to show the schedule in five batches for operations 1, 2, 4, and 6. In operations 3 and 5 the work is divided into 10 batches, and it is scheduled for two workplaces.

73. PRODUCTION CONTROL FOR CAPS

Uniform caps are made for chauffeurs, bus drivers, gate watchmen, and various other groups. They are made to order by the Shaeffer Uniform Cap Company in a wide variety of styles and specifications. The company has designed a system to enable the production control department to follow the progress of each lot with a minimum of direction from the central office. When a production order is planned, a set of work orders is prepared in as many copies as there are operations to be performed, plus an extra copy for the dispatcher himself. All copies of the work order, fastened by staples, are sent to the department in which the first operation is to be performed. When the worker has finished the first operation, he tears off the top copy of the work order and hands it to the assistant foreman. If the work is inspected before being moved, the inspector makes the proper notation, removes the copy of the work order, and gives it to the assistant foreman. These copies are picked up twice a day and sent to the dispatcher, who is thus enabled to follow the progress of the work and to take any corrective action that may be necessary.

Work orders do not follow a definite time schedule from one department to another. The dispatcher maintains a master schedule which indicates planned completion dates on the various orders. No corrective action is necessary so long as it appears that the order can be completed on the date required by the customer.

Required:

Evaluate the method of production control used by the company.

35 Dispatching
and
Follow-up

THE phases of production control described in the preceding chapter pertain only to the planning. In routing, the production control department plans the flow of the work from one department or one workplace to another; and in scheduling it determines when the work will be started and when it will be completed. The next step is the carrying out of the plans. To make the plan effective, the orders and instructions must be issued and the progress of the work should be followed. The execution of the plans begins with the procurement of the necessary materials and equipment and the employment or training of the workers in case additional workers will be needed.

DISPATCHING

As soon as a production order is scheduled, steps should be taken to see that the materials will be available when they will be needed. The bill of materials is referred to the balance of stores clerk, who examines the inventory records to see if the necessary quantities are on hand or on order. If the material is available, a notation is made in the Reserved column; and the quantity is deducted from the balance available. The bill of materials is initialed to indicate that the reservation has been made and is then returned to the planning department.

If the materials are not on hand, request may be made to the purchasing department for the procurement of the necessary quantities. However, the request may not be issued immediately if the work is planned for some weeks or months ahead. In some cases the material for several production orders may be economically grouped in a single purchase order. The grouping is accomplished by means of a material-requirement record, as shown in Figure 72. The date for the release of the purchase requisition is determined by the estimated time required for paper work, shipment by the vendor, transportation, and receipt in the storeroom. A similar procedure should be followed for purchased parts and machine tools.

MATERIAL 18-463								
DATE	REFERENCE	JAN.	FEB.	MARCH	APRIL	MAY	JUNE	
11/18	NO. 418			120				
11/20	NO. 422			80				
11/30	NO. 435				200			
12/10	NO. 450				50			
12/21	NO. 260			100				
TOTAL				300	250			
NOW IN STOCK (NOT ALLOCATED)				80				
BALANCE ORDERED				220				
DATE 12/21								

FIG. 72. Material-Requirement Record

Issuance of Orders. The orders are conveyed on the forms which were prepared as a part of the work of routing. One form may carry instructions to all persons who will be concerned with the work, provide for the authorization to do the work, and make provision for the signatures to indicate that the work has been accomplished. An illustration of a form used in planning and controlling production is the operation ticket shown in Figure 64 on page 613. Many companies have found that the use of one form for all dispatching operations greatly reduces paper work, eliminates confusion, and speeds up the flow of work. However, some companies use different forms for workers, inspectors, the storekeeper, and others. In any case, provision should be made for authorizing the necessary activities and providing the appropriate reports.

The issuance of materials or parts from the storeroom is authorized by a requisition for prescribed quantities. The materials requisitioned were previously entered on a bill of materials. For purposes of identification, a copy of the operation ticket may accompany the work in process as it moves from one workplace to another, or a separate identification tag may be used. Instructions as to the nature of the work to be done at each machine are transmitted by means of the operation ticket which authorizes the worker to perform the stated machine or assembly operations. One form of operation ticket is often made to serve as a work order in each department. Several copies of the operation ticket are duplicated in such a manner that certain information is omitted from each copy and only the information required by a department is included in the copy sent to it. A separate form may be used for the inspection order and inspection report, but many companies use a copy of the operation ticket for this purpose. If the materials are heavy or bulky, special handling by the internal transportation department may be necessary. In that case a special order is issued, and a report is made to the planning department when the material has been moved. The transportation is considered as a separate operation and is handled in the same manner as work at the machine. When the product has been completed, a report is made to the planning department that the goods have been received in the storeroom or the shipping room.

Following the Progress of the Work. Many plans have been devised for following the progress of the work and for showing present conditions in some graphical manner. Frequently, a bulletin board is used because it provides flexibility. The pegboard which is used for scheduling may be used for dispatching and for following the progress of the work. When work is started on an order, a transparent colored tape of flexible plastic is pulled out from the left side of the board; and the end of the tape is fastened under the starting date by means of a peg or tack. As the work progresses, the tape is pulled farther out to indicate the extent of the progress or the percentage of work done. For example, if the schedule for the first week calls for 400 units and the output is only 300, the tape is pulled three fourths of the way across the space for the first week. On another order, if the schedule calls for the production of 100 units and production is 110, the tape representing the progress of that order is pulled all the way across the space for the first week and one tenth of the way across the space for the next week. The first order is behind schedule, and the second is ahead of schedule. The current date is indicated by a string drawn across the board from top to bottom. If all orders are on schedule, the tape for each order will extend to the string representing the current date. If no order is ahead of schedule, no tape will extend beyond the string.

When an order is behind schedule, a peg may be inserted to indicate the cause of the delay. Numbers on the heads of the pegs or the colors of the pegs may indicate the cause of the delay, according to an established code. Causes of delay might be lack of materials, machine breakdown, lack of manpower, accident, or failure of a worker to meet standards. When steps have been taken to expedite an order, a peg with a distinctive color or numbered head may be inserted in the line to show that this action has been taken. This procedure shows that further attention to the order is not necessary.

On another type of bulletin board, as has been explained, the scheduled time is indicated by the width of the edge of the operation ticket which is inserted in the groove of one of a series of overlapping pockets. The tickets in one pocket extending the length of the board indicate all work to be done and also the time scheduled for each operation. The progress of an order, as indicated by reports from the shop, is shown by a colored signal which is moved across the board from left to right.

For example, when the shop reports an operation completed on 500 of 1,000 parts of an order which was scheduled to require six days, the signal is moved to show three days' work completed. If such a report has been received after four days have been spent on the work, the order is one day behind schedule. The current date is indicated by a string as in the case of the pegboard. If the colored signal is to the left of the string, the order is behind schedule. If the signal is to the right, the order is ahead of schedule.

Changes in Machine Loads. Some system of keeping machine loads up to date is necessary in order that the dispatcher may know whether work at each machine is proceeding according to plan and whether the machine will be available for the next order at the scheduled date. The usual method is to use a bulletin board which operates on the same principle as the board for recording progress on an order. On the machine-load board the machines are listed in the spaces to the left, and a line across the board indicates the work planned for the machine. Production at the machine is shown by a tape which is pulled from the left side. The distance covered by the tape indicates the amount of work done.

When the board consists of a series of pockets, one pocket is used to show the work planned for each machine. A plastic signal is moved across the pocket to indicate the progress of the work, and a string drawn from the top is used to indicate the date. Work at the machine is indicated as behind schedule or ahead of schedule by the position of the signal in relation to the string.

Communication between Departments. Since the work of routing, scheduling, and dispatching is essentially that of correlating the work of the various departments, the planning department must be in frequent communication with foremen and workers. For this purpose, some companies use a pneumatic tube system. Other companies use the telephone because it affords an opportunity for discussion of problems, but its limitation is that it does not provide a written record and may result in misunderstanding. The teletype is also successfully used in dispatching. By means of this instrument, orders are automatically recorded on receiving machines in the departments to which messages are sent.

FOLLOW-UP

The production control department follows up orders given and must at times revise the schedules because of delays and also because of spoilage and defective work. Regular reports of progress are received and tabulated by the follow-up section. Some companies ask the foreman to prepare a "behind-schedule report" or a "fall-down report" as soon as he realizes that he cannot meet the schedule on an order. This report, which shows the order number and the cause of the delay, is sent to the follow-up section. The form of the report is shown in Figure 73.

In some companies the behind-schedule report originates in the planning department. Delayed orders are spotted by examining the files each day to determine which orders were scheduled to be moved to new locations on the preceding day. If a report of completion has not been received, the order is listed as behind schedule and is described as critical. A report is then prepared which identifies the delayed order and indicates the operation number and the department or machine at which the material was last reported, the operation number and the machine at which the order is overdue, and the number of days overdue. Copies of the behind-schedule report are distributed to the foremen to notify them of the status of such orders. Each foreman reports to his division chief or other line supervisor concerning work listed as overdue in his department. This report indicates the status of each overdue order and the cause of the delay. A copy of the report is sent to the planning department.

BEHIND SCHEDULE REPORT

TO PRODUCTION FOLLOW UP FROM *DEPT. 184*
PRODUCTION ORDER NO. *116* PART NO. *185-358*
SCHEDULED STARTING DATE *3/6* REPORT DATE *3/7*

CHECK REASON:

NO MATERIAL
✓ NO TOOLS
WORKER ABSENT
RECEIVED LATE IN DEPARTMENT
MACHINE OVERLOADED
MACHINE BREAKDOWN
INCORRECT ROUTING
CHANGE IN SPECIFICATION
OTHER REASON

REMARKS

NEW # 8 DRILL ORDERED 3/6

C. SMITH
FOREMAN

FIG. 73. Behind-Schedule Report

The follow-up section may prepare a weekly report summarizing the work load of each type of machine and the changes in machine loads since the date of the last report. The report on machine loads is illustrated in Figure 74. The report is based on the assumption that the plant will be operated for two shifts of forty hours each and that machines are expected to be in use 90 per cent of the time.

SUMMARY OF MACHINE LOADS 6/15

MACHINE	NUMBER OF MACHINES	HOURS AVAILABLE FOR WORK (2 SHIFTS)	LOAD 6/8	NEW HOURS	HOURS USED	LOAD 6/15	WEEKS AHEAD
RADIAL DRILL	6	432	1,680	420	430	1,670	3.8
MEDIUM PLANER	4	288	680	290	286	684	2.3
LARGE PLANER	5	360	1,150	380	360	1,170	3.2
SMALL LATHES	7	504	2,680	560	500	2,740	5.4

FIG. 74. Summary of Machine Loads

Some machines may become overloaded as a result of delays or interruptions or as a result of the rerouting of orders in adjusting production schedules. The situation is noted on the machine-load chart by means of a colored plastic signal or a peg in the case of the pegboard. When the overloaded condition becomes known, appropriate corrective action may be taken by adjusting the schedules of certain orders, by authorizing extra shifts or overtime work, or by other appropriate action. If orders cannot be delivered on time, customers should be notified. In some cases, additional sales orders may be declined until the situation has been corrected.

When parts or finished products are manufactured for stock and placed in the storeroom, the report to the planning department indicates the number of defective products and the number of good pieces. If the total quantity of standard products completed is greater than the number originally scheduled or expected, the overage may be deducted from the number planned on the next order. If the total quantity of good production is less than the quantity needed for stock, the shortage may be added to the number planned on the next scheduled order. In some cases, additional shop orders may be released immediately to cover shortages. When a reorder is necessary, the number of the same parts or products originally scheduled for the next order may be included. A large number of units in the new order may be desirable to provide sufficient quantity for an economical run and to reduce the unit cost due to machine set-up and paper work.

The follow-up section may prepare a report comparing the work done in each department with the amount of work scheduled. The section determines the number of hours originally allotted to the work from the work schedule and the number of hours taken from subsequent reports. The difference between these two is the number of hours of variance from the standard. If the work is still in process, the follow-up section may determine the standard number of pieces per hour and the number of pieces completed. This report would show the following information:

Part number and name.
Operation number.
Department or machine number.
Shift.
Number of pieces completed per hour.
Standard or scheduled number of pieces per hour.

Usually, this report is not prepared for every order but only for those for which performance appears to be unsatisfactory. The report may be of value to the scheduling section in planning future work because it indicates the reliability of standards previously established. It also indicates the orders in progress on which costs will be in excess of standard. Consequently, this report permits the management to take action to correct an undesirable trend in costs before the order is completed and before the final cost figures are available.

QUESTIONS

1. A novelty manufacturing company does not plan completion dates in each department but only the date of shipment to the customer. To each order is attached a sheet of coupons, and when a worker completes an operation, he tears off a coupon and places it in a box. Coupons are collected hourly and taken to the planning department where a notation is made on a master control sheet. Is this method of follow-up satisfactory?

2. A manufacturer of radiators for automobiles employs expediters who move through the plant to locate orders that the customer needs at an early date. The expediter tells foremen to give precedence to any order that is classed as "rush." Is the planning department performing its proper function in staff work?

3. The work of production planning has sometimes been divided into planning, doing, and seeing. What is included in the work of seeing?

4. What reports does the planning department need for purposes of follow-up and corrective action?

5. Where does the behind-schedule report originate? What use is made of the report?

6. Can foremen and workers be expected to report promptly any delays or interruptions to production? If an order gets behind one day, might it be brought up to schedule the following day? Does this problem suggest a reason why the foreman might like a little slack in the work standards that are established by time study?

7. How does the sales division co-operate in handling problems of delayed schedules, machine loads, and rush orders from customers?

8. What corrective action may be taken when the number of items rejected by the inspector is larger than had been expected? How may the problem be handled if the number of rejects is less than expected?

9. Should the original schedule provide for some slack or the accumulation of some banks of parts at the machines to prevent delays in production?

10. In busy seasons, steel companies sometimes produce at a rate that exceeds rated capacity. How is such high production possible?

11. How will careful production planning and control reduce the cost of the product? How will it increase sales of the product?

12. Should the established schedule be changed to satisfy a customer? When might this change be made?

CASE

SCHEDULING WORK IN A GARAGE

The service manager of a garage is responsible for interviewing motorists who bring their cars to be repaired and for making arrangements with them concerning the work to be done. He has designed a form with spaces for entering the name of the owner, the make of the automobile, the year model, the license number, and the time the owner will call for his car. The form also lists the various types of repair work to be done, and usually the service manager indicates the required work by placing a check mark in the appropriate space. Unusual types of needed repairs are noted in extra blank spaces at the bottom of the form.

The service manager finds that the customer asks two questions: "How much will it cost?" and "When can I get the car?" To permit an answer to the first question, the service manager has prepared an estimate of the probable time required for each kind of repair, with an upper and lower time limit for certain types of work for which the required time is uncertain. The garage charges the customer for the mechanic's time at the rate of $3.75 per hour. Parts are charged extra when they are used.

The manager has learned that a trade association of automobile dealers has prepared a booklet in which the various types of repair work are listed, along with a suggested charge for each repair. He finds that his own charges are usually less than those suggested in the booklet. He is contemplating a revision of his prices to conform with the suggested price list.

As for informing the customer when the car will be ready, the manager has devised a chart along the lines of the Gantt chart, with horizontal spaces marked to indicate the hours of the day. One line is to be used to record the work scheduled for each mechanic. When any work is assigned to a mechanic, the scheduled starting and completion times will be indicated by short vertical lines in the appropriate spaces. The number of the repair order will be written in just above the line. When a customer brings in his car for repair work, the manager will refer to his chart to determine when a mechanic will be available. In this way, he will be able to answer both questions of the customer.

Questions:

1. What are the advantages of the system devised by the service manager?
2. What difficulties might he encounter in operating the system?
3. Could the manager safely use the schedule of charges prepared by the trade association, or would he run the risk of violating the antitrust laws?

36 Planning and Control in Continuous Manufacturing

THE system of production planning and control as described in preceding chapters is used in industries that manufacture and sell a variety of products. A company that manufactures a relatively small number of standardized products or a single product in continuous manufacturing cannot use such a system to advantage because too much clerical work is required. Although the four steps of routing, scheduling, dispatching, and follow-up are necessary, the methods of planning and control are adapted to the production requirements.

Characteristics of Continuous Production. A distinguishing characteristic of continuous production is that all products are made by similar operations at the same series of workplaces. The parts are transferred from one department or workplace to another in a continuous flow or in small batches. Work is continued in succeeding departments as the material is received, even though preceding operations have not been completed on the entire quantity. Parts or materials are transferred for succeeding operations or for assembly without being placed in the storeroom for later withdrawal by requisition.

It should not be inferred that all industries manufacturing by continuous and concurrent operations are exactly alike. As explained in connection with the discussion of plant layout, such industries may be either analytic or synthetic. In analytic industries, such as meat packing or oil refining, the work is planned to provide for the fanning out of work in process from the point at which the materials are put into production. In synthetic industries the work is planned to provide for the orderly combining of parts produced on converging production lines which terminate when the finished product emerges in the last department.

Manufacturing enterprises in continuous-production industries may be organized on more than one basis. Some companies set up separate production lines for each principal product and plan separately for each line. An example is a bakery which may have separate production lines for bread, cakes, and other products. Some companies make more than one product on one line by changing machine tools or by adjusting the machine. For example, a linoleum manufacturer may make the product in various colors and designs by using different stencils and different colors in the materials. A can company may make different sizes of cans on the same line with adjustment to machines that slit the sheets, form the bodies, and perform other necessary operations including the testing of the can for leaks. Other products that may be made in more than one variety on a single line are glass jars, bottles, bread, and soap. After the machines on the line have been properly set, the materials are processed in a continuous flow until another change in machine set-up is made and production is started on a new design, size, or other variety of product.

In assembly industries, which operate on the principle of continuous production, the products are not necessarily all alike but may be produced in a number of varieties. For example, automobiles sold under a single trade name may differ in color, types of upholstery, body style, and combinations of accessories. The principal requirements for continuous production in an assembly industry are that the parts are interchangeable, the varieties or sizes of any part are made on the same equipment, and all varieties of the product are moved by the same mode of transportation in the assembly line.

Routing. Routing in a continuous industry is closely related to product design and plant layout. Since the same processes are continuously repeated, the production centers are laid out to perform the operations effectively and to facilitate the transportation of the materials. The production line is not changed as long as the product remains the same and more efficient equipment is not devised. Examples are plants for canning fruits, manufacturing soap, refining sugar, and packing meat.

In the continuous manufacture of a product that consists of a number of parts and subassemblies, such as computing machines or electric fans, the plan for routing the product is also built into the layout. The routing of the product requires attention to the production of the various parts as well as their assembly. After the layout has been arranged to provide for the flow of work, the materials may be started in production in the first department and then moved through to final assembly without interruption.

Preparation for Production. When a new model is to be introduced, the various activities in preparation for production should be scheduled for completion by the date when assembly is to begin. In the automobile industry, the preparatory work includes the following activities:

Engineering and testing.
Manufacture or purchase of tools and dies.
Purchase and installation of machinery and equipment.
Purchase of finished parts and assemblies.
Purchase of crude materials.
Purchase of fabrics.
Purchase of special materials.

Since the time required for completion of the various phases of preparatory work is not the same, some activities should be started at an earlier date than others. In scheduling the deliveries of materials and purchased parts, allowance should be made for the fact that the volume of production may be small when car assembly begins. The volume may be expected to increase gradually as various difficulties in production are overcome and the departments gain momentum. A possible schedule of the basic preliminary work is shown in Figure 75.

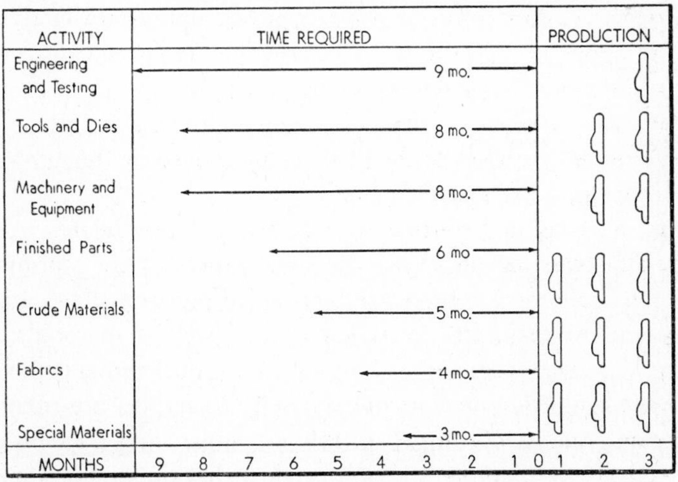

ACTIVITY	TIME REQUIRED	PRODUCTION
Engineering and Testing	9 mo.	
Tools and Dies	8 mo.	
Machinery and Equipment	8 mo.	
Finished Parts	6 mo	
Crude Materials	5 mo.	
Fabrics	4 mo.	
Special Materials	3 mo.	
MONTHS	9 8 7 6 5 4 3 2 1 0 1 2 3	

FIG. 75. Scheduling Preparation for Production

Scheduling Production with Demand. The first question which should be decided in scheduling production is whether the rate of output is to be stabilized from month to month or whether it is to be varied according to fluctuations in the volume of sales. If production can be maintained at about the same rate throughout the year, the company will benefit in many ways. Labor turnover will be decreased because the labor force can be kept busy. Lower labor turnover decreases the cost of employing and training workers and reduces cost in other ways. Moreover, industry is becoming increasingly conscious of its obligations to labor for stabilized employment as well as to stockholders for profits and dividends.

A further advantage of scheduling production with demand is that machinery and equipment would be more effectively utilized. Provision need not be made for peak demand but only for the average monthly output. The need for a smaller amount of equipment would be reflected in decreased building space, heating and lighting costs, and other costs of production.

If the sales volume varies with the season of the year, or the phase of the business cycle, management may not be able to stabilize production by producing during the slack season and storing in anticipation of demand. If the product is bulky, an excessive amount of storage space might be required. Examples of such products are boxes, tin cans, glass containers, cheap furniture, and automobiles. A heavy product may not be easily stored or removed from storage when delivery is requested, although lift trucks and pallets and other types of materials-handling equipment have simplified the problems of storage. Style changes in the clothing industry increase the hazards incident to production in anticipation of demand. In some cases the product may be made according to detailed specifications of the customer. If the raw material is perishable, it must be processed at just the right time. Examples are fruit and vegetable canning and oyster processing. In other cases, the finished product may be perishable and must be produced as needed by the customer. Bakery products are examples.

Many companies that do not produce uniform quantities from month to month do not vary production with fluctuations in sales volume. The increase in sales in the busy months is met partly by increasing the rate of output and partly by drawing upon the storeroom for stock produced during preceding months of lower sales volume.

Scheduling Monthly Deliveries. In scheduling monthly and weekly production, the first step is to estimate the monthly shipments to customers and the monthly deliveries to stock. These two estimates are not necessarily the same. In estimating consumer demand, the percentage of customers who will order a certain style of body or a certain kind of upholstery, in the case of automobiles, should be determined in order that purchase and production programs may be controlled. The desired production of the finished product might be as shown in Figure 76. This estimate is made in terms of product and not in monetary terms. The estimates embodied in the production program are based upon market conditions in the territorial

MONTH	PRODUCTION PROGRAM					
	MODEL NO. 10		MODEL NO. 20		MODEL NO. 30	
	THIS MONTH	CUM.	THIS MONTH	CUM.	THIS MONTH	CUM.
JANUARY	5,000	5,000	10,000	10,000	7,000	7,000
FEBRUARY	6,000	11,000	12,000	22,000	8,000	15,000
MARCH	6,500	17,500	13,000	25,000	10,000	25,000
APRIL	6,500	24,000	13,000	38,000	12,000	37,000

RECOMMENDED _____ DATE _____
PRODUCTION MANAGER

APPROVED _____ DATE _____

FIG. 76. Estimate of Production

area in which the sales are made and upon the prospects and plans of the business itself. The market conditions pertain to the plans of competitors and competitor industries, the statistics of business conditions, analyses of probable trends of prosperity or depression, and reports of salesmen concerning the conditions within their territories. Another factor is the condition of raw materials markets, price changes, new kinds of materials, and other such developments.

The production schedule also depends upon many developments and contemplated changes within the company. Probably the most significant internal data pertain to the production and sales of various product lines during the preceding year, or the trend for such data may be established by a study of the figures for several years. The prospects for the ensuing year will be affected by advertising plans and changes in the advertising appropriation, the opening of new sales branches or other new sales outlets, changes in the design of the product, and the expansion of the product line. Various changes in the manufacturing division may also be significant, such as increased capacity due to mechanization or automation, improved plant layout, the introduction of production standards as a result of time studies, or new methods of materials handling. In some cases, financial plans may affect the ability of the company to finance a larger volume of production.

Scheduling Production of Parts and Assemblies. The weekly or monthly schedules of production of parts and assemblies are prepared by computing backward from the monthly production schedules. A chart showing the flow of production from one department to another may be prepared as shown in Figure 77. This chart shows that if tanks are to be completed on the assembly line on December 10, the steel for the motor generator should be in the steel mill on August 13. Steel for

FIG. 77. Scheduled Production

From *Automotive War Production*. Reproduced by permission of Automobile Manufacturers Association.

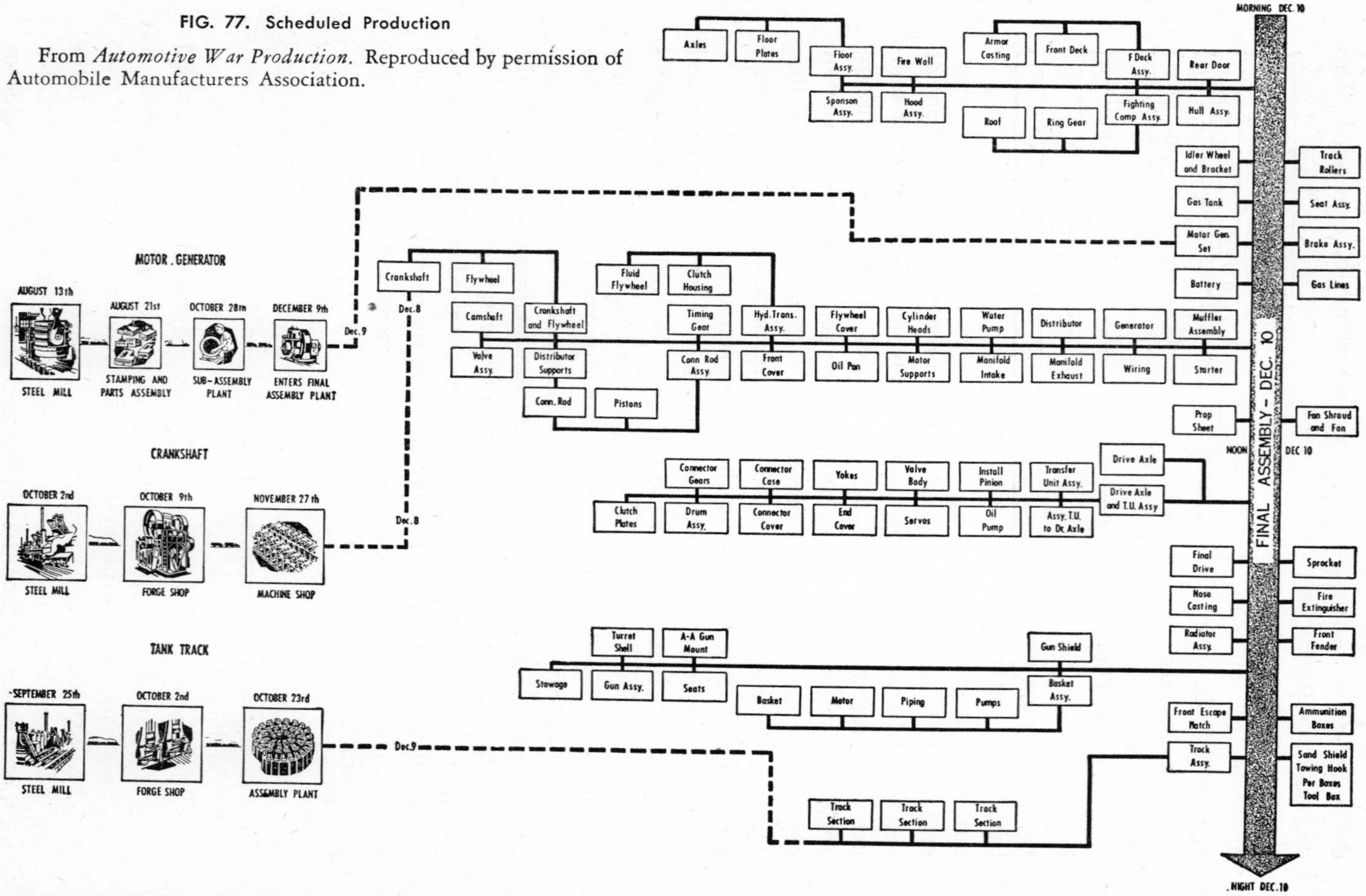

the crankshaft should be in the steel mill on October 2, and steel for the tank track should be in the steel mill on September 25. The flow of the materials for each of the various parts is timed throughout each of the succeeding departments. If production of 400 tanks is planned for December, the motor generators for that number of units should be processed by the steel mill in August. The steel for the crankshafts for December production need not be processed in the steel mill until October.

The Factory Float. The factory float is the amount of inventory in process of production at any one time. It includes materials being processed, materials being transferred from one workplace to another, and materials in temporary storage awaiting fabrication or transfer. In accounting, the float is usually referred to as "goods-in-process inventory."

The amount of the float may be stated in terms of a certain number of days or weeks of production. For example, if the steel that is put into production on August 13 does not emerge as finished product until December 10, it is in process 119 days (including Sundays and holidays). By the time the steel is completed in production, other steel equivalent to production for 119 days has been put into process. If production amounts to 50 units per day and 100 pounds of steel are required for each assembly, the float would total $50 \times 100 \times 119$, or 595,000 pounds.

One objective of production planning is to keep the float as low as possible. If the float is greater than necessary for continuous production, the result is idle capital, possible deterioration, obsolescence of parts in case of changes in design, and crowding of workplaces. The float is reduced by effective plant layout; regular servicing of machines; effective methods of employee selection, training, and motivation; and other management methods. Detailed factors affecting the amount of the float are as follows:

Labor turnover.
Absences and general employee efficiency.
Sunday and holiday work.
Balance in plant layout, preventing delays.
Straight-line layout.
Short moves from one workplace to another.
Type of materials-handling equipment.
Condition of machinery and equipment.
Effective control of materials inventory.
Effective planning and control of production.

Keeping the Factory Float Low. The extent to which management is successful in keeping the factory float low is measured by the ratio of processing time to the total time required in production. For example, if the time spent in processing material in the operating departments is 20 hours and the total time that elapses from the issuance of the material in the first department to the completion of the product is 200 hours, the efficiency is 20/200, or 10 per cent. If the total elapsed time can be reduced to 180 hours, the efficiency is increased to 20/180, or 11.1 per cent. The measurement of efficiency is stated as a formula as follows:

$$\text{Manufacturing cycle efficiency} = \frac{\text{Process time}}{\text{Total elapsed time}}$$

The saving that results from improving manufacturing cycle efficiency depends in part upon the point at which the reduction in elapsed time is achieved and also upon the nature of the process. The saving is usually greatest if the time can be reduced in the final assembly and shipping operations, or in some department near the end of the processing. The reason for the greater saving in later processing is that the investment in work-in-process inventory gradually increases as the work moves from one department to another. If all of the materials are issued in the first department as they might be in making glass jars, boxes, sugar, or flour, the value of the product is increased in later processing as a result only of the expenditure of labor and expenses. If additional materials or parts are added in the later departments, the cost of the product is increased still further. The greater the investment in the product, the greater is the saving that results from improving the manufacturing cycle efficiency.

The saving from increased manufacturing efficiency under varying conditions may be illustrated graphically as shown in Figure 78. In the first chart, costs are shown on the assumption that all materials are issued in the first department and that the cost is increased in later departments only by labor and expenses. The total cost of the product at each stage is represented by the distance between the top line and the base. The last space to the right represents the time required to complete the shipment to the customer. The investment in the product is not increased during this time because shipping expenses represent a part of selling expense. If materials could be processed one week sooner in the first department, the interest saving would be computed on the amount represented by the distance from the top line to the base. If a similar saving in time could be made in the last department and in ship-

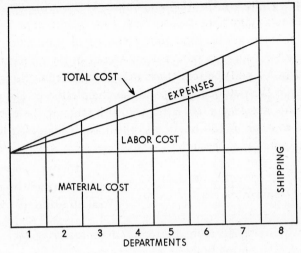

MATERIALS ALL ISSUED IN FIRST DEPARTMENT

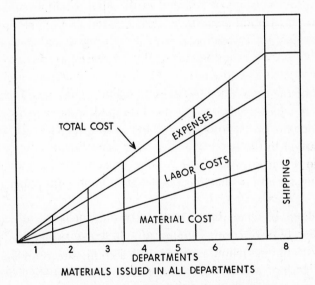

MATERIALS ISSUED IN ALL DEPARTMENTS

FIG. 78. Increase in Cost under Varying Conditions

ping time, the interest saving would be computed on a much larger amount.

The lower chart illustrates the accumulation of cost on the assumption that materials are issued in all departments. In this case, the difference in cost between the first and last departments is much greater. In these charts, no significance should be attached to the relative amounts of the elements of manufacturing cost.

Scheduling Daily Runs. As production nears the assembly stage, the scheduling of production must provide for any permissible variations in product design. In the automobile industry the distributor, in response to requests of customers, may be permitted to specify colors, body style, upholstery, and certain accessories. In each case the customer is required to choose from a limited number of varieties offered by the manufacturer. A car may be made in 8 color combinations, 2 kinds of upholstery, 3 body styles, and 3 combinations of accessories. These combinations make possible 144 varieties ($8 \times 2 \times 3 \times 3$). Since the varieties cannot conveniently be carried in stock, the most economical plan is to schedule production in order that automobiles will leave the production line with the proper specifications. The scheduling is done by means of a daily run sheet, as shown in Figure 79.

DAILY RUN SHEET				
DATE_____				
DISTRIBUTOR	COLORS	BODY STYLE	UPHOLSTERY	ACCESSORIES
W.C. RICE, DALLAS	# 4	# 1	# 2	# 1
R.W. SMITH, PEORIA	# 8	1	2	2
G.C. ARTHUR, TOLEDO	# 3	2	1	1
ETC.				
APPROVED_____ PRODUCTION MANAGER :				

FIG. 79. Daily Run Sheet

Copies of the daily run sheet are distributed to the head of each production line which feeds into the main assembly line. The sheet is used to determine the order in which fenders, wheels, bodies, and other parts are forwarded in the line. The time required for any part to be fabricated before reaching the main assembly line is known, and the progress of any car along the line can be definitely determined from the schedule.

The manner of scheduling after the daily run sheet has been prepared may be seen by reference to Figure 80. This chart does not show the schedule of any one manufacturer but is a composite chart based upon the experience of a number of companies. The chart shows that a car which is to be finished at 2:20 P.M. on Friday will start on the final assembly line at 1:00 P.M. on the same day. The rear assembly will be started on Monday at 8:00 A.M., while the gear assembly will be started at Monday noon. Other assemblies are timed to start in a similar manner. However, the production of each part need not be timed as precisely as the chart seems to indicate because many parts are interchangeable and will fit into the assembly of any automobile along the line. Such parts are planned only in the necessary quantities. They may be

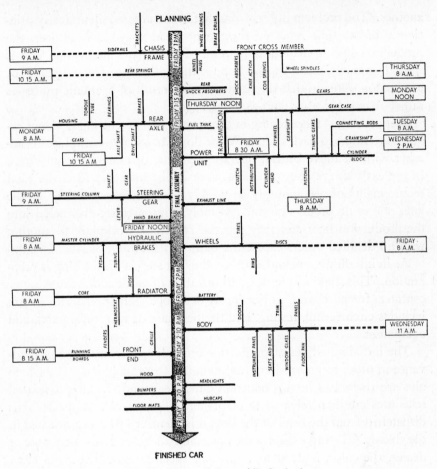

FIG. 80. Timing of Automobile Production

Reproduced from *Automobile Facts*. Used by permission of Automobile Manufacturers Association.

stored in bins at each station, or they may be moved to workplaces by overhead conveyor.

In some industries the time required for production is much shorter than in the automobile industry. In most companies, however, scheduling consists of both long-range and short-run planning. In the baking industry, for example, long-range planning requires that machinery, equipment, storage space, shipping facilities, and inventories of materials be planned in order that quantities of the product may be balanced with daily and weekly fluctuations in demand. The flow of work should be planned each day in order that employees may report for work as the product moves forward from one stage of production to another. The problem differs from that in the automobile industry principally in the time required for the production cycle. Moreover, the production line is cleared at the end of each day's production and is started from the head of the line on the following day. Methods of production differ in that the product is the result of synthetic processes rather than fabrication and assembly.

Dispatching. Dispatching in continuous manufacturing does not require attention to each order. Work flows from one workplace to another without move orders, operation tickets, or material requisitions. In the early stages of production, work is dispatched to meet the total requirements of the monthly or weekly production schedules. In the later stages of production and assembly, the parts are channeled into the production line; and they proceed from one workplace to another with no detailed orders except the daily run sheet.

As in intermittent manufacturing, the first step in dispatching is preparation. This step includes the authorization of work and the making of contracts for purchases, as previously described. The preparation work includes engineering, testing, and the purchase of materials, parts, and equipment.

The initial schedules of production are prepared many months in advance in order to permit long-run planning for production. The schedules are revised as final production dates near, and weekly production schedules are then released to plants and departments. As each car is dispatched from the head of the line, it is identified by a tag attached to the chassis. The tag indicates the name and address of the distributor or dealer, the color, body style, and other specifications. Except in cases of accident, machine breakdown, or other interruption, the car advances without further direction from the planning department through the stages of assembly, inspection, and shipment.

Follow-Up. Dispatching is followed by periodical reports of accomplishment, comparison, and corrective action when necessary. The reports may show the results of all phases of the purchasing and production program. The report of the purchasing agent would show contracts authorized to be placed and contracts actually made. It would show for each month the materials which were scheduled for delivery into stock and the actual deliveries. Any delays in the deliveries of materials are promptly reported to the planning department, and the production program is revised when necessary.

The production of each plant or each department is reported weekly, and the volume of production is compared with the schedule. This report might be prepared in the form shown in Figure 81. This type of report shows the amount of the float or work-in-process inventory at the beginning of the week, the work placed in production, the work completed, the scrap, and the balance in process at the end of the week.

Standards are available to the managemnt for determining the success of each manager regarding the amount of work started, the amount completed, the scrap, and the balance in process.

Another report that may

WEELY PRODUCTION REPORT					
DEPARTMENT _18_			FOREMAN _J. SMITH_		
WEEK BEGINNING	IN PROCESS FIRST OF WEEK	PLACED IN PRODUCTION	COMPLETED	SCRAP	IN PROCESS END OF WEEK
2-2	500	600	540	10	550
2-9	550	650	660	5	535
2-16	535	640	645	8	522
2-23	522	635	630	4	523

FIG. 81. Weekly Production Report

be prepared is a monthly report comparing actual production with scheduled production. This report is illustrated in Figure 82.

MONTHLY PRODUCTION REPORT							
						DATE	
MODEL	APRIL		MAY		JUNE		TOTAL
	ACTUAL	SCHEDULED	ACTUAL	SCHEDULED	ACTUAL	SCHEDULED	ACTUAL	SCHEDULED
X-445	41	40	45	40	39	40	125	120
X-448	80	85	85	85	90	85	255	255
X-541	30	35	33	35	35	35	98	105

FIG. 82. Monthly Production Report

The reports and charts presented in the present chapter should be regarded only as illustrative. They are designed to indicate the general nature of such reports and the types of information needed by management for the control of production.

QUESTIONS

1. A sugar refining company refines the raw sugar through a series of operations until the product nears completion. It then diversifies its operations to produce granulated sugar in boxes and bags, brown sugar, confectioner's sugar, and lump sugar in cube shape. Some cubes are specially wrapped to meet the requirements of customers, and some granulated sugar is packed in small bags. Should this industry be classified as continuous or diversified?

2. In continuous manufacturing, are all products on a line of the same design? Answer with reference to automobile production.

3. A glass manufacturer produces to the order of the customer by changing the molds on the forming machine. After the molds have been set up, the machines run continuously until the bottles for the customer have been made. How should these manufacturing operations be classified?

4. How do the steps in production planning in continuous manufacturing differ from the same steps in diversified manufacturing?

5. Is the nature of the work changed by the fact that the production line may be cleared at the end of the day and a new run started at the head of the line the next day, as in bread making?

6. What are the advantages of scheduling production at a uniform rate throughout the year regardless of sales demand? What additional costs might be incurred? Might the company lessen the degree of fluctuations by producing somewhat in excess of current demand during the slack season?

7. Could the manufacturer lessen the extent of the fluctuation by producing a staple item, such as plain white shirts, during the slack season and concentrating on a seasonal item, such as fancy shirts, in the busy season? What problems might be encountered by this plan?

8. What expenses are incurred when the factory float is too high? How may the size of the factory float be reduced?

9. How does the factory float affect the plans for the changing of the design of the products?

10. In continuous manufacturing, what control is exercised over production after the parts are started at the head of the line?

11. How can an automobile manufacturer keep the lines moving if the bodies come through in the wrong order and a body of the wrong color is lowered into position over a chassis?

12. What daily and monthly reports are needed for control in continuous-process industries, such as automobiles or bakery products?

CASES

75. USE OF LABOR POOL

The Holt Appliance Company regularly employs about 800 men and women. Its manufacturing operations consist of various machining operations, painting, assembling, and testing. Some of the departments have been troubled with excessive absenteeism, and the foremen have had difficulty in making substitutions for employees who fail to report for work. After discussion of the problem at a conference between the plant superintendent, the foremen, and the personnel manager, it has been decided that a labor pool would be established under the supervision of a pool manager who would report to the plant superintendent.

According to the plan, a pool of twenty-five persons of varied experience would be available on call from any foreman to replace absentees in any department and to meet other emergencies. In employing workers from the pool, the employment department would seek to find persons who could do any one of several types of work. However, the pool manager would attempt to learn the qualifications of each person in the pool and to send the same persons continuously to any one department for a given type of work as far as that was possible. It was agreed that foremen would be required to give initial instruction in some cases, but it was hoped that members of the pool would in time be able to develop facility in several kinds of work.

To keep the members of the pool occupied when they were not on call from an operating department, the production planning department was asked to assign certain types of special work which was not required to meet a close schedule. Such work would include handling goods returned by customers, packing shipments for export, maintenance, and production of parts for stock in anticipation of future orders.

Members of the pool would have first preference in transfers to operating departments for filling vacancies or newly created jobs. They would be paid a guaranteed hourly rate when working under the pool manager and would be paid for substitute work at the going rate for that type of work. An advantage to persons working under the direction of the pool manager would be that they could learn a variety of types of work and could shift to new positions to break monotony.

Questions:

1. What would be the advantages of the proposed plan?

2. Would workers like to be members of the pool?

3. What does the proposed plan indicate concerning the simplification of tasks in industry?

76. FILLING ORDERS OF CUSTOMERS

The first delivery of mail at a large mail-order house is received at 5 o'clock in the morning. The mail is immediately weighed to determine the probable number of customers' orders. This estimate is possible because the company has learned that, on the average, each pound of first-class mail brings a certain number of orders. By means of similar relationships the company can estimate the probable number of pounds of mail and orders to be received in each of the two later deliveries for the day. This information enables the company to assign the proper number of clerical workers to handle the work at the various stations along the route of the order.

In the mail department, letters are opened; the cash is removed and recorded; and orders are classified by method of payment, such as cash, C.O.D., and time. Orders are sent to the order-reading department, where orders are read and any special requests, such as time of delivery, are noted. The method of shipment, which might be parcel post, freight, express, or truck, is determined. Orders are classified as "singles" if all merchandise is ordered from a single department or as "multiples" if the merchandise comes from more than one department. Next, in the index department the name-and-address stencil of a customer is removed from the file, and package labels are prepared. A customer record, on which is entered the date and value of the order, is kept. This record is used for keeping mailing lists up to date.

In the entry department the description and price of the merchandise are checked, and a separate sheet is prepared for each item on a multiple order. Each order is then scheduled to be delivered to the packing and shipping department at a certain time in the day. The time is stenciled on each order and also on each entry sheet. The purpose of the scheduling is to enable all items of merchandise on any one order to arrive at the packing station at the same time. The entry sheets are then sorted by merchandise departments, and they are forwarded to the appropriate department or section of the storeroom. The customers' orders are sent to the packing department.

In the merchandise departments, which together constitute the stockroom, the merchandise as specified on the entry sheets is taken from the bins, inspected, and placed on a moving belt at a time which assures delivery to the packing department at the scheduled time. Moving belts on each floor carry the merchandise to a gravity chute which terminates in the packing room. By means of the customer's order and the entry sheets accompanying the merchandise, the clerk in the packing room assembles the merchandise for each order, wraps it, and prepares it for mailing. If any item is out of stock, the entry sheet for that item is also sent to the packing room, where a refund check, or a notice that the missing item will be sent later, is prepared for inclusion in the customer's shipment.

Required:

1. Explain the purpose of each step in filling orders.

2. Compare the method of filling orders with production planning in diversified production.

PART X

FINANCIAL
PLANNING
AND
CONTROL

37 Budgetary Planning and Control

THE budget is a co-ordinated financial plan for a business enterprise. It includes estimates of sales, production, purchases, labor costs, expenses, and financial operations. Its purpose is to plan, co-ordinate, and control the activities of various divisions and departments of the business.

The budget may be partial or complete. A partial budget is a financial plan for one or a few activities. For example, the partial budget might provide for advertising expense, product research, a production program, or plans for the expansion of plant facilities, without including expense budgets for each department. When budgets are first introduced in a business, the expenses of a few departments may be budgeted on a trial basis. As foremen and other persons come to know the advantages of operating on a budget, the plan may be gradually extended to other departments. When the budget is confined to a limited number of departments, it is a partial budget.

A complete budget is a financial plan for all the activities, including sales and finance. It is an estimate of both income and expenses. It provides for the expansion of plant facilities and the procuring of funds through bank loans or the sale of corporate securities, and it consists of separate departmental budgets and a master budget. The master budget summarizes and consolidates the data included in the departmental budgets.

NATURE OF THE BUDGET

The budget estimates are stated in dollars and cents. In some cases, supplementary estimates are prepared in other terms. Estimates of sales and production are usually made in terms of units of product. Purchases may be estimated in units of material, as well as in monetary terms. The labor budget may indicate the number of workers required in addition to labor cost.

Relation of the Budget to Management. The budget is a significant tool of management. When the budget estimates are formulated, a general view should be taken of all of the activities of the business for the purpose of maintaining balance. When funds are granted or denied for any purpose, the decision is then made that a particular activity is or is not necessary. The increase or the decrease in the budget allowance of a department means that the activities of that department will be expanded or curtailed. Since the budget may include expense allowances for all departments, it reflects the views of management concerning the value of each activity and the success of each executive.

The budget emphasizes the idea that expenditures for any purpose should be justified by increased income, decreased expenses in another category, increased tangible or intangible assets, or other business or social advantages. The business budget reflects management plans and also serves as an important check on management decisions.

The budget permits the management to give careful consideration to future developments and to choose in orderly fashion the course of action to be followed. Also, it enables the management to take advantage of favorable developments and to prepare for unfavorable developments. For example, if the prospect is for an increase in the volume of business, the company may plan to expand facilities, increase purchase commitments, employ and train more workers, or add new lines of products. If a recession appears imminent, the company might plan to reduce inventories, decrease purchases, postpone the expansion of facilities, and change its employment program. However, the company might wish to offset unfavorable tendencies by increasing its advertising appropriation, introducing a new product, or initiating some other program for increasing sales. Since the budget makes possible the selection of the most desirable course of action, both unwarranted optimism and undue pessimism may be avoided.

The budget establishes a standard of accomplishment for the various departments, and each department is expected to reach established goals of production and sales with the funds allotted for the purpose. The budget permits each executive to determine for himself whether his performance is satisfactory. If he can produce the quantities of product required by the budget with the allotted funds, he knows he is meeting the standard for his department. In this manner the budget is a means of raising the level of performance throughout the organization. It provides a basis for comparison and corrective action.

Static or Flexible Budget. The static budget is a financial plan which is considered to be fixed and not subject to variation. It is prepared on a monthly, quarterly, or yearly basis. New estimates are made each year because the budget is based upon data that relate to a specific or definite period of time.

The flexible budget provides several estimates of expenses for each manufacturing department and other departments for varying volumes of sales and production. The first estimate establishes a standard of expense on the assumption that the volume of production will be normal. Other estimates of expenses are made for a volume of production that is 10, 20, or 30 per cent below normal. An estimate may also be made for a volume of production of 10 to 20 per cent above normal. Normal production is stated in number of units produced in order that its meaning may be definite. When the foreman knows the current volume of production in any month, he can easily determine which budget figures apply. Some expense allowances are changed as the volume of production increases or decreases, while other allowances do not change with variations in production.

The flexible budget has a marked advantage over the static budget during periods of business uncertainty. It makes a revision of the expense budgets unnecessary when sales and production programs are changed. It is a means of separating budgeting and forecasting. Flexible budgets need not be revised from year to year, unless the prices of supplies or wage rates for labor in a department are changed.

Length of Budget Period. The budget is usually made for one year in advance, although it may be made for a shorter or longer period. In some cases, partial budgets of plant expansion and finance are made for five or ten years or even longer. The budget should cover at least a seasonal cycle, including an off season and a busy season, in order that plans may be made to supply the increased sales demand in the busy season. If goods are produced to the order of customers, the budget period may be relatively short unless customers' orders can be anticipated with a fair degree of certainty. Some companies continuously project the budget twelve months in advance. At the end of each month the current month is dropped from the estimates and the corresponding month next year is added. In this manner the planning always permits each department to make advance commitments for advertising, purchases, and other contracts.

The Budget Officer. Some executive directly responsible to the chief executive is usually placed in charge of the procedure for the development of the budget. This executive may be the controller or the treasurer; but he may hold a position especially created for the budgetary work, such as budget supervisor, budget director, or assistant. The essential requirement is that the person who assists with the budget be coordinate in rank with the major executives and also have the support of the chief executive. The budget officer may be assisted by a committee composed of executives who are thoroughly familiar with conditions throughout the operating departments. The committee is usually composed of the heads of the major divisions.

The entire organization should take an interest in the preparation and operation of the budget. This favorable condition cannot be created as soon as the program is initiated, but it is the result of long and successful experience. A gradual introduction of a budget program is frequently advised in order that general participation and interest may be developed.

PREPARATION OF THE BUDGET

The budget is based upon a plan for the production and sale of goods and services. As a basis of the plan, the results of earlier programs are reviewed and their favorable and unfavorable aspects are considered. Possible changes inside the business and outside the company are also taken into consideration. The plan is developed with reference to the organization. Each division of the business is assigned a part of the program. The amount of money to be spent by each division is estimated. Each major executive knows by reference to the budget the performance expected of him and the cost of his share of the program.

Development of the Estimates. Each major executive may participate in the development of the budget for his division. The head of each division usually prepares the original budget estimate for his division, and he transmits the estimate to the chief budget officer. The budget officer may combine and summarize the estimates to show the total result. He then transmits them to the budget committee, together with information to assist the committee in evaluating the proposed program. When the estimates have been revised or approved by the committee, they become the budget for the ensuing period; and they are transmitted by the budget officer to the various departments for their guidance. Any later revisions are recommended by the budget officer and the budget committee.

The manner in which the proposed budget is to be assembled for submission to the budget committee is prescribed by the chief budgetary officer. The expense estimates for each department should be classified by the nature of the expense, such as wages, supplies, communication, repairs and maintenance, and taxes. Each department should submit its estimates in terms of dollars and cents. In addition, some departments submit estimates in terms of physical units, such as units of product to be sold, units produced, and volume of purchases. The labor budget shows labor costs in dollars and also the number of persons to be employed.

The various estimates are closely related to each other and are integrated to form a consistent, balanced program. For example, the sales estimate is limited by the amount of the product that can be manufactured; and the amount to be manufactured depends upon the amount that can be sold at a profit. Both the sales and the production budgets may depend upon the funds available for financing and the amount of materials that can be purchased. Expenses vary with the rate of production, although they may not increase or decrease in proportion to changes in the volume of output.

Relation of Budget to Control. Although the budget is prepared under the supervision of the controller or other budget officer, the control exercised through the budget is vested in the operating executives. At times, the controller might seem to be controlling the work of the line and limiting its activities. However, as budget officer, he merely performs a staff or facilitating service, and such authority as he exercises is vested in him as a representative of the chief executive. As the chief accounting officer, he possesses a knowledge of the activities of the company, and he may be able to present figures and schedules of income, costs, and expenses within a short time after the need has arisen. In many instances where the controller seems to have power to deny departmental requests for appropriations, he merely acts as adviser to the president or other executive. Control in an organization should always be exercised downward in the scalar chain and not sidewise. Such control may appear to be exerted laterally because the advice of the budget officer is so well supported by financial data that his recommendations are usually accepted by the person who exercises direct or line authority.[1]

---

[1] See Arnold F. Emch, "Control Means Action," *Harvard Business Review,* Vol. XXXII, No. 4 (1954), pp. 92–98.

THE SALES BUDGET

Financial planning usually begins with the estimate of sales because the other estimates depend upon the amount of goods that can be sold. The company would usually determine the amount that can be sold, with allowance for planned increases or decreases in the amount of goods in the inventory. The planned production determines the requirements for personnel, the purchasing program, and the manufacturing expenses. Selling and general administrative expenses usually are budgeted on the basis of sales rather than production.

During periods of materials shortages, the budget would be formulated with reference to the amount of materials and parts that can be purchased because the shortages may limit production, which in turn limits sales. In any case the budget committee should scrutinize the estimates as a whole to see that they reflect current conditions.

Information Needed. The sales estimate can be accurately prepared only after a careful study has been made of conditions within and without the business. The study is begun with an analysis of sales data for two or more years preceding the budget period. The sales information should be available in the same form as the sales estimate. For example, if the volume of sales of two or more products is to be estimated, sales information for the products in prior periods should be available. The sales data should include information for two or more years for the purpose of determining trends and seasonal or cyclical fluctuations. Such trends may be particularly significant for new products or products whose consumer appeal is increasing or decreasing.

Changes in business programs and expenditures will affect the sales budget. Such changes might include new lines of product to be added, old lines to be dropped, changes in design, and the amount of the advertising appropriation. Any change which affects the volume of goods produced will also affect the amount which can be sold. Production is affected by construction or expansion programs, the installation of an incentive wage system, the number of labor shifts, and various other developments.

Changes that are expected within the industry would also be considered. One company may lose business to, or gain from, its competitors. One industry may also expand at the expense of another. Examples may be found in the transportation, frozen food, and other industries. In estimating its sales volume, each business should consider the plans of competitor companies in the same industry and in competitive industries.

Other significant changes may occur in the market area. For example, the market is affected by such factors as shifts in demand by federal and state governments, the movement of population from cities to suburbs, changes in the age groups of the population, increased international tensions or the easing of tensions, and prosperity or depression in industries which provide employment for customers. If the product is sold to business enterprises rather than to individual consumers, the prosperity of companies in consumer industries should be considered.

Preparation of the Sales Budget. Responsibility for submitting the sales budget to the budget director rests with the sales manager, although he does not necessarily make the first sales estimate. It is usually desirable for the persons who will be responsible for the execution of the budget to assist in making the estimates.

The following procedures for making sales estimates are possible:

1. The sales manager, with the assistance of his research staff, may draw up the sales estimate on the basis of available statistical and economic data. The total sales estimate is assigned as sales quotas to territories, branch sales offices, or individual salesmen. This procedure has the advantage of being based on reliable and perhaps complete statistical information. It is not entirely satisfactory because of the manner in which sales quotas are passed down the line to the various branches of the sales department and to salesmen.

2. Each salesman may be asked to estimate the sales that he believes he can make in his territory. The district sales manager may revise the estimates, which are then submitted to the general sales manager. The estimates for the various districts are combined to determine the total estimated sales. This procedure has the advantage of placing responsibility for execution of the budget upon the district sales managers and the individual salesmen. However, sales estimates made in this manner are likely to be unreliable because the salesmen are not in a position to appraise the prospects of the company and the effects of changes in general business conditions. Some salesmen may set quotas for themselves that are overly optimistic, while others will set quotas that they are certain they can meet with a margin to spare.

3. The estimates may be made in the general sales office and submitted to district sales managers for comment. They are revised in the light of suggestions from men in the field.

Regardless of the manner in which the sales estimate is made, it is closely scrutinized by the chief budget officer and the budget committee. The final estimate should reflect the best opinion of what can and will be accomplished during the budget period.

Importance of Sales Estimate. The figures for estimated sales should represent anticipated performance rather than an easy or a difficult quota for the sales division. The sales budget forms the basic plan upon which other plans will be made. For example, the inventories of raw materials, purchased parts, goods in process, and finished goods are planned with reference to an estimated volume of production and sales. The sales estimate is the starting point for making the financial plan, the estimate of labor requirements, and the expense budgets. The sales executive should not attempt to establish an estimate that can be exceeded and a budget officer should not establish a high estimate merely as a challenge to the sales division.

MANUFACTURING BUDGETS

The manufacturing departments prepare a number of budgets reflecting the performance of the production division in meeting the requirements of the sales program. Such budgets would include goods to be manufactured, raw materials and parts to be purchased, labor to be employed, and expenses to be incurred.

The Production Budget. Some phases of production planning have been considered in preceding chapters. The quantities of each product to be manufactured would be computed by adding the desired inventory at the end of the period to the amount to be sold, and subtracting the inventory at the beginning of the period. The quantities to be manufactured for the entire year would be allocated to weeks and months by making estimates for each week or each four-week period. These figures would represent the quantity to be completed as finished product for delivery to the shipping room or storeroom. The flow of work in process from one manufacturing department to another would be estimated by tracing week by week the amount of product necessary to make the finished product as required by the sales estimate.

In some companies, the production budget may easily be revised from month to month as changing conditions may require, and in other companies such revisions are more difficult. For example, if the product is made of standard materials and parts which are readily available and quickly processed, the production plans may be revised without much difficulty. If it is made of materials that are purchased according to specifications and if the specifications are changed each year or season, the original budget estimate may limit the quantity to be sold in a season or it may require special sales effort to avoid losses on inventory at the end of a season.

Purchases Budget. This budget establishes the plan for the purchase of materials and parts required by the production budget. The purchases estimates are therefore directly dependent upon the estimates contained in the production budget. On the basis of purchases estimates, the purchasing agent may make the purchase contracts. In some companies, however, the purchases are made on the basis of inventory records and the established reorder points. When purchases are made in this manner, the purchases budget is useful principally as a means of financial planning.

Plant and Equipment Budget. This budget shows the additions to be made to the plant, the new equipment to be purchased during the budget period, and also the units to be scrapped or sold. When the expansion or replacement of plant facilities is planned through the budget, the management is usually required to survey carefully all requests and to make the expenditures where they will be most beneficial to the company. Since the plant and equipment budget shows changes in the investments in fixed or capital assets, the funds authorized for expenditure in this budget do not represent current expenses. Large capital expenditures are usually planned over a number of years; and commitments are made after consideration of the long-range trend of business, costs, and money-market conditions. Decision must also be made, in many companies, to buy or to make certain types of equipment.

Maintenance Budget. The maintenance of buildings and equipment is very important because neglect can mean increased expenses in the future. In slack times, maintenance may be neglected because of the pressure to economize. In busy times, maintenance may be neglected because materials and labor are high in price and perhaps difficult to purchase and because repairs might slow production. However, repairs should not be neglected in either good times or poor times. The maintenance program has been considered in Chapter 12. The budget should provide funds for the various types of maintenance work as explained in that chapter, such as the following:

1. Periodic repair or service work, including lubrication.
2. Preventive inspection to assure that equipment is functioning properly and to determine when repairs are needed.
3. Repair work, the need for which is discovered by preventive inspection.
4. Repair work made after machinery or equipment has failed to function. Emergency jobs should be held to a minimum by preventive inspection. They are usually limited to superficial repairs.

The Labor Budget. The budget of labor requirements is based upon the production budget, which shows the number of units of product to be manufactured each month. The amount of labor needed for production depends upon, first, the volume of production and, second, the policy of retaining or laying off men in the slack season. The labor budget is prepared separately for each department, and it shows the number of employees needed each month and the labor cost in dollars. The personnel department uses the labor budget to determine the number of persons to employ. It makes a computation similar to that shown in Table 5:

TABLE 5

DEPARTMENTAL LABOR ESTIMATE

Number on payroll at beginning of month 40
Estimated separations:

Quits	2
Discharges	1
Transfers and promotions	1
Retirements	0
On leave	1
Other causes	0
Total Separations	5
Net	35
Required for production program	42
Difference to be met by transfer or hiring	7

Manufacturing Expense Budget. Manufacturing expenses are budgeted separately for each department. If flexible budgets are prepared, the estimates will show the amount of each expense at stated percentages of normal production, which might be 100, 90, 80, 70, and 60 per cent. The amount of each expense at varying levels of production depends in part upon the nature of the expense, which might be variable, semivariable, or fixed. Variable expenses increase or decrease directly in proportion with changes in output; semivariable expenses vary with changes in output but not in corresponding percentages. Fixed expenses do not change with variations in the volume of production so long as additional plant facilities are not necessary. This classification must be accepted with some degree of caution, however, for few expenses fall clearly within any one of the three classes.

The difficulty of classifying expenses into three groups can be seen from an analysis of the expenses of manufacturing departments. One important group of expenses includes the salaries of foremen, assistant foremen, clerks, inspectors, and various staff personnel. Although salaries are relatively fixed, they may be reduced by layoffs and reductions in pay if the financial situation requires it. Under some conditions salary expenses may be increased by the employment of additional people and by salary adjustments. Although depreciation of buildings, machinery, and equipment is largely a matter of time, the expense is also affected by the amount of wear and tear and the maintenance program. Expenses that are more definitely in the fixed category include property taxes, fire insurance, and boiler and explosion insurance. Expenses that vary to some extent with the volume of production are losses on defective work, bonuses for overtime, heat and light expense, and telephone and telegraph expense.

The effect of varying rates of production upon expenses depends in part upon the program of the management for dealing with the prospect of increasing or declining business. For example, a proposed increase in sales volume might be met by purchasing certain parts usually manufactured, adding a labor shift, increasing production by overtime work, providing additional facilities for production, or increasing efficiency by the mechanization of certain tasks. Each of these policies will affect expenses in a different manner.

The research budget was discussed in Chapter 15 (p. 283). It is one of the most difficult to control because the results are indefinite and long delayed. The budget should indicate the amounts to be spent on each major research project; and the amounts should be further classified as salaries, supplies, equipment, taxes, depreciation, building costs, and other expenses. An additional sum may be appropriated, to be spent in any way the research manager desires.

THE EXPENSE BUDGETS

Several budget estimates may be made for selling and general administrative expenses. The number of the estimates will depend upon the organization of the sales and other divisions as shown by the organization chart. A separate estimate should be made for the expenses of each operating division, such as advertising, sales, and controllership.

Planning for Advertising Expenses. The advertising budget and the sales budget are closely related because increased advertising expense should result in increased sales. The problem in the budgeting of advertising expense is to determine the most profitable relationship between advertising and sales. An increase in advertising expenses beyond a certain point becomes unprofitable. The total amount to be spent for advertising is subject to control by the budget committee.

The advertising expense budget is prepared by the advertising manager, who is usually under the supervision of the general sales manager. His recommendation as to the method of spending the advertising allowance and the media to be used is usually approved by the budget committee because the final responsibility for results rests upon him.

Selling Expense Budget. One group of expenses pertains to the management of the main sales office and branch sales offices, including salaries, supplies, rent of office space, depreciation of equipment, taxes, and insurance. Another group of expenses pertains to the salesmen, such as salaries and commissions, traveling expense, entertainment of customers, samples, and communication. Another group of expenses covers transportation of the product, such as trucking and delivery expense, freight-out when paid by the seller, and freight-in on returned sales. The expenses incurred in warehousing and storage are also included in the selling expense budget. These expenses include heat and light, depreciation, taxes, insurance, salaries, and clerical expense.

The selling expense budget, like the advertising expense budget, raises the problem of determining the most profitable expenditure. Some items of selling expense can be increased with profit to the company; but, beyond a certain point, additional expenditures are not justified by the increase in sales. The selling expense budget is prepared by the sales manager and revised or approved by the budget committee.

Administrative Expense Budget. This budget is prepared by the controller or possibly the office manager, depending upon the nature of the organization. It includes the estimates for the expenses of the accounting, statistical, credit and collection, and general administrative offices. Bad debts expense is also included under this heading. The general administrative expenses do not vary in proportion to changes in the volume of sales. Because of the familiarity of the controller or office manager with operating methods and statistical reports, the administrative expense budget is usually subjected to little revision by the budget committee. Actual expenses do not vary greatly from the estimate.

BUDGET SUMMARIES

The various budget estimates should be integrated to reflect the operations of the entire program. Two summaries may be prepared to show the effect of the separate budgets upon the operation of the enterprise. They are the cash budget and the estimated financial statements.

Cash Budget. From the other budgets, together with certain supplementary information, an estimate of cash receipts and cash disbursements is prepared. To the balance of cash and marketable securities on hand at the beginning of any month are added the cash receipts and cash sales, accounts and notes receivable, dividend and interest income, proceeds of long-term financing, sales of property, and other sources. In this estimate, allowance is made for the time allowed customers in making payment on credit sales and also for cash discounts. In the estimate of cash disbursements, allowance is made for the variations between the expenses for each month and the cash disbursements. For example, bad debts and depreciation, although expenses, are excluded from the estimates of cash disbursements. Insurance, taxes, and royalties appear in the monthly expense estimates but are not paid on a monthly basis. The monthly forecast of cash might be prepared as follows:

MONTHLY CASH FORECAST

Balance at beginning of month (cash and marketable securities) ....

Receipts:
    Cash sales ....
    Collections of accounts receivable........
    Collections of notes receivable ....
    Sales of properties......................
        Total ....
        Total Balance and Receipts..........

Disbursements:
    Expenses ....
    Income taxes ....
    Plant facilities ....
    Interest ....
    Dividends ....
    Other ....
        Total ....

Balance at end (including marketable securities) ....

Additional requirements:
    Cash required, to be borrowed from banks
    Available for payment of bank loans and other purposes......................

Estimated Financial Statements. The budgets make it possible to prepare an estimated profit and loss statement for the coming year and an estimated balance sheet showing the financial position at the end of the year. The estimated statements are prepared with the aid of a device known to accountants as a "work sheet." In the first two money columns are entered the ledger account balances as of the beginning of the year. The summarized budgets for the year are then entered as a series of adjustments. For example, the amount of sales on account is entered as an increase in Accounts Receivable and an increase in Sales. The collections of accounts receivable are entered as an increase in

Cash and a decrease in Accounts Receivable. Expenses paid in cash, as shown in the expense and the cash budgets, are entered as Expenses and as a decrease in Cash. This procedure, which is familiar to all accountants, is continued until the information shown in all the budgets has been entered. From the estimated financial statements prepared in this manner, the budget committee can see the total effects of the proposed program.

EXECUTION OF THE PLAN

The preparation of the budget is only the first step in the program. The success of the budget requires follow-up and control. The accounting department should establish an account classification corresponding to the form of the budget estimates. An account should be opened for each budget allotment, and all expenditures should be classified and entered to show the total expenditure under each classification. Monthly reports should be prepared by the accounting department to show for each income or expense item (1) the amount for the current month, (2) the amount for the same month last year, (3) the budget estimate, and (4) the amount for the current month over or under the budget. Such reports should be prepared soon after the close of each month; and copies should be furnished to department heads, foremen, and other persons in the management.

All significant variations from the budget should be investigated to determine the cause. Some variations may be due to salary or wage changes authorized by the management or to changes in the cost of supplies in the market. Others may be caused by inefficiency. All executives, including the foremen, should be given some incentive to encourage them to meet the budget estimates. The reward might consist of a word of praise, a letter of commendation, a higher merit rating, or a monetary bonus.

Effect upon People. Although the budget is prepared in dollars, units of product, inventory items, and machinery and equipment, it cannot be separated from the people who are affected by it. The budget puts pressure upon the people in an organization because it establishes production goals which must be reached with a limited expenditure for materials, labor, and expenses. Because the budget establishes a standard against which the accomplishments of people are measured, it tends to arouse a certain amount of resentment. Foremen and executives at the lower levels dislike the idea that standards will be raised when accomplishments have been increased or expenses have been lowered, and they may therefore withhold their best efforts to prevent the establishment of more difficult standards during the next month or year. They tend to become suspicious of moves to increase the production budget and to tighten the financial budget. Such feelings cause foremen to favor foremen's unions or clubs as a means of lessening pressure upon themselves. Foremen may look favorably upon labor unions, which may register complaints with management when pressures are passed on to workers. As expenses are incurred, foremen may question the propriety of making certain charges against their departments, particularly in those cases where allocation of expenses becomes necessary.

To assure the success of the budget, middle or top management should work with lower level supervisors to elicit their support. Executives may make budget talks to explain the proposed plans. They may use the expense and cost information to hold additional meetings from time to time. If supervisors fail to meet the budget, they should not be excused, but the reasonableness of budget standards and restrictions should be explained. To gain acceptance and support for the budget, the person in charge of the plan should be skilled in conference techniques and in human relationships as well as in financial management.[2]

Advantages of Financial Planning. When properly operated, the budget should improve management methods in many respects. Executives give careful attention to various possible courses of action and choose the course which will result in the greatest benefit. Errors in management are discovered and corrected.

The program of various departments is kept in balance. Expansion and increased expenditures are authorized for departments that can use the additional funds to best advantage. Departments that are over-expanded may be curtailed, and executives who are not properly placed may be transferred or given training to improve. The activities of the business, such as finance, purchasing, production, and sales, are properly co-ordinated. Co-operation between departments is encouraged.

The executives acquire a greater knowledge of the business and of other persons within the company. Information is made available for the rating of foremen and other executives. A proper method of approach to business problems is developed within the organization. Executives learn to give careful study to any situation before rendering a decision.

Limitations of Financial Planning. Budgets have not always been regarded as successful. The failure of budget programs has usually been

---

[2] See Chris Argyris, "Human Problems with Budgets," *Harvard Business Review,* Vol. XXXI, No. 1 (1953), pp. 97–110.

due to poor management. The difficulty has been that too much was expected in too short a time with too little attention by executives throughout the organization. Not much can be expected when the department heads prepare the budget by taking last year's figures and changing them a little to make them look reasonable and when the current year's reports are merely prepared and filed away. The budget should not be regarded as a time-consuming device or as just another report. It should be regarded by all executives as essential to the success of the enterprise. The full benefits should not be expected immediately. The value of the budget will increase as the management acquires experience in using it.

QUESTIONS

1. How does the budget aid in business management?

2. Is the budget principally a financial plan or a means of control? Is the attitude of the foreman toward the budget the same as the attitude of the top executives? Explain.

3. Why is the budget a better financial standard than the record of performance last year?

4. If a partial budget is made, which items of income and expense would be budgeted?

5. Do the budget items represent goals or limitations upon expenditures?

6. What is the function of the controller and of the chief executive in the preparation of the budget?

7. What estimates in the budget should be stated in nonfinancial terms?

8. Where would a company start in the preparation of a budget?

9. Why is the year the most desirable period for making a budget? Would the year sometimes be too long or too short a period?

10. How does the cash budget differ from the budget for sales, costs, and expenses?

11. What information may be gained from the estimated balance sheet and the estimated profit and loss statement?

12. Show the relation of the plan for the various activities, the budget, the organization of the enterprise, and accounting system, and the financial reports.

CASES

77. BUDGETING MANUFACTURING COSTS

A shirt manufacturing company makes two product lines, which are designated as dress shirts and fancy shirts. Budget plans are made by conferences between top executives, including the vice-presidents in charge of manufacturing, sales, finance, merchandising, and purchasing. For the six months beginning on September 1, the budget committee has estimated that the company can make and sell 12,400 dozen dress shirts and 10,000 dozen fancy shirts.

The cost of materials and supplies for dress shirts is estimated to be $1.00 per shirt, and the cost for fancies is estimated at $1.25. Workers are paid on piece rates, which total 75 cents per shirt for either type of shirt. Manufacturing expenses are estimated to be one third of labor cost, or 25 cents per shirt. Selling and general administrative expenses are estimated at $80,000 for the period of six months.

The dress shirts are sold to retailers for $2.50 each and the fancies at $3.50.

Required:

Prepare a statement for the six-month period.

78. DESIRABILITY OF A BUDGET

Ritchey and Mansfield operate a plumbing and heating contracting business. They install equipment in residences, office buildings, apartments, and other structures on contract. They maintain a storeroom of heating and plumbing supplies which averages about $50,000. Some supplies are purchased for each contract, and some are drawn from the regular stock. Last year, their contracts totaled $325,000. Materials and supplies cost $140,000 for the year. The average number of employees on the payroll was 25, and labor cost was $120,000. Expenses, not including salaries of the partners, were $31,000.

The partners have never prepared a budget. Plans are made from one month to the next, and bank loans are arranged as they are needed. Repayments of loans are made when money is available, and renewals of loans are arranged if funds are not available for payment. Mr. Ritchey believes that substantial economies could be realized by the use of a budget of income. expenses, and costs and also cash receipts and disbursements. Mr. Mansfield is unable to see any advantages of a budget in a business of this kind. He thinks that the firm must take business when it can get it and that planning would be too uncertain to be of any value.

Required:

Explain the advantages of a budget in this kind of business.

38 Planning
and Control
through Costs

JUST as all activities in the plant come to a focus in planning and controlling the volume of production, so the financial results of all activities in production are reflected in the cost of the product. All of the expenses of the various departments, both operating and facilitating, are incurred for the benefit of production and should eventually be reflected in the cost figures. Likewise, the expenses incurred in the various horizontal levels in the production division from the supervisor upwards should be prorated or apportioned in some manner and charged to cost. An effective control of manufacturing operations therefore requires attention to cost figures and the manner in which they are determined. The discussion of cost information in the present chapter is designed to show the way that cost is determined and also the uses that may be made of the cost figures. It is not intended to indicate the detailed methods of organizing and operating a cost accounting system.

NATURE AND USES OF COST INFORMATION

Cost data should not be regarded merely as a report of performance in preceding months or years. The information concerning costs should be related to future plans, policies, and practices. It should be compiled in such detail that it is useful to management in evaluating performance and in increasing efficiency.

Some Uses of Cost Data. Cost information serves many of the purposes of management. The accountant uses cost figures to determine the value of the inventory of finished goods and work in process of manufacture at the various work stations at the end of the month or year. Inventory figures are required in the preparation of the statement of the cost of goods manufactured and sold, the profit for the period, and the closing balance sheet. Although financial statements are required for various purposes, such as reports to directors, stockholders, and creditors, the detailed cost data can be useful to management in many other ways.

Cost information is used in determining selling prices when a company must bid on a contract without knowing what the bids of others will be. Cost information also affords a valuable check on the determination of the selling price of one size or grade of a line of products in relation to the prices of other sizes or grades in the same line. However, the product must usually be priced in relation to prices asked by competitors for similar products in the market. A manufacturer cannot ordinarily fix his selling price by computing his cost and adding what he regards as a fair margin of profit.

When management finds from its cost data that certain products are being sold at a loss or at a small margin of profit, it may be able to discontinue their production and to concentrate on the profitable items. Even though the unprofitable items may be continued in order to retain the profitable business, management can put its major sales effort behind the profitable items. The same considerations apply to unprofitable sales territories or branch offices.

Cost information is designed to inform management of the departments or the manufacturing processes where costs are excessive and to permit the proper steps to be taken to increase efficiency. It should provide the data to permit management to determine whether material costs are excessive because too much material was used or the purchase price was too high; whether labor costs are out of line because the worker spent too much time on the work; or whether processing costs in the manufacture of any product are more than they should have been.

Kinds of Cost Systems. Cost systems are of several kinds because the needs of businesses and industries differ. The two principal types of cost systems are, first, the process cost system which is used in continuous-production or mass-production industries and, second, the job-order or production-order cost system which is used in diversified production.

The process cost system is used to determine the total cost of operating each department or each process in manufacture. The average cost at each stage of production is determined by dividing the cost of operating the department by the number of units produced. Total average cost per unit is determined by adding the average costs at the various stages of production or the average costs in each department. For example, raw sugar is refined by a series of steps which start with removing molasses, reducing the crystals to syrup for purifying, filtering, crystalizing, cleansing, drying, and packaging. Because the sugar flows continuously from one operation to the next, costs can be figured only by dividing the cost of each operation by the number of pounds processed. Similar methods of computing costs are used in such industries as food processing, bread baking, and soapmaking.

The production-order cost system is designed to determine the cost of each unit or each lot of product manufactured. This system is usually preferred to process cost accounting, provided that separate costs can be determined without too much clerical expense. The method is especially suited to companies making products of large dollar cost to the specific order of customers. Examples of such products are bridges, buildings, industrial filters, and ships. It is also used by manufacturers who make a large quantity of items of relatively low unit cost to the order of the customer, such as books, shirts, dresses, glass or tin containers, and machine parts. In some cases, production-order cost accounting is used to determine the cost of items manufactured for stock.

Production-order cost systems are not all operated in the same manner. The types of such systems are as follows:

1. A *historical cost system* shows the actual costs during the present or the preceding month or year.

2. A *standard cost system* shows the cost of the product according to a predetermined standard and the amount by which actual cost differs from the standard. The standard costs may be recorded in the accounting records; or the actual or historical costs may be recorded in the accounts, and the standard cost may be used only for comparative purposes. Standard costs are sometimes called "predetermined costs."

3. An *estimated cost system* shows the costs as estimated by management and the amount by which the actual historical cost varies from the estimate. Estimated costs are usually recorded in the accounting records. Estimated cost differs from standard cost in that the estimated cost is what management thinks the cost actually will be, while the standard cost is what the cost would be if all waste could be eliminated and no mistakes were made by workers or management.

Elements of Cost. The manufacturing cost of any product is the sum of materials, labor, and manufacturing expenses. Material cost is the cost of purchased items entering into the product and becoming a part of it, such as the lumber in a table or the cloth in a shirt. Materials are to be contrasted with the supplies, which are used in the factory but do not become a part of the product. Labor cost is the amount paid workers whose time is spent in fabricating, transporting, painting, finishing, polishing, assembling, or otherwise working directly on the product. The time spent on a task can be clocked, and the amount of the labor cost to be charged to the product can be definitely determined. Material cost plus labor cost equals total prime cost or direct cost. Manufacturing expenses include those costs that are not incurred for the benefit of any one production order or unit of product. They are incurred for the benefit of the entire factory or possibly for the benefit of some one department. Because manufacturing expenses cannot be identified with any one production order or any specific units of the product, they must be prorated as a cost of the various units manufactured. Manufacturing expenses were explained in the preceding chapter in the discussion of the budget.

DETERMINING THE COST OF A UNIT OF PRODUCT

The discussion of cost information in the present section pertains to the production-order method, which shows detailed costs. In diversified production, each production order accumulates costs of materials, labor, and expenses as it moves from one work station or one machine to another. The cost data are recorded in each department, and the information is collected and tabulated by the cost accountant.

Determining Material and Labor Cost. The cost of material to be included in the cost of a production order is not particularly difficult to determine. When materials are requisitioned from the storeroom, the number of the production order is indicated on the requisition. After the cost has been entered by the balance of stores clerk, the requisition is forwarded to the cost accounting department, where the amount is entered on a cost summary, or cost sheet, which is kept for each production order. The quantity of material used in production is definitely known; and the unit cost of the materials may be determined from the balance of stores record by the first-in, first-out method, by the last-in, first-out method, or by the moving-average method.

Labor cost is determined from a labor time ticket, which is prepared in the department where the work is done. The ticket shows the time the work was started, the time when the work was completed, and the elapsed time. The payroll section of the cost department determines the labor cost by multiplying the time taken by the labor rate per hour, or by multiplying the number of pieces by the rate per piece. The principal difficulty in determining labor cost is in deciding the method of entering such items as social security taxes for direct labor, bonus paid for overtime and holiday work, paid vacations, provision for pensions and retirement, and payments for idle time due to delays in production. Although such items are theoretically a part of direct labor cost, many companies treat them as manufacturing expenses. The method of charging them to expense is easier and simpler because manufacturing expenses are not charged to any product but are allocated over the various products. Such expenses as payments made during vacations cannot readily be charged against any one product or the order of any one customer.

Purposes of Manufacturing Expense Accounting. A large part of the difficulty in cost accounting arises in dealing with manufacturing expenses. This fact can be seen from the objectives in accounting for manufacturing expenses. One objective is to determine the total of each class of manufacturing expenses, such as supplies, indirect labor, supervision, depreciation of machinery and equipment, property insurance, and heat, light, and power. This information is valuable to the management in comparing expenses from month to month or from year to year. It is also used in the preparation of the profit and loss statement.

Cost accounting reports also show the amount of expense incurred by each department, both line and staff. This information is necessary in order that each department may be held accountable for its expenses. The classification of expenses by departments is also necessary to the operation of a budget. In cost accounting, the two types of departments are usually called "manufacturing departments" and "service departments."

Another purpose of expense accounting is to determine the cost of service rendered by each facilitating department. Such departments as standards and methods, personnel, repairs and maintenance, production control, inspection, and power do not manufacture the product directly but they assist in its manufacture by rendering a service to the manufacturing departments. After the cost of operating such a department has been determined, the cost of the service rendered to each manufacturing department is computed. The total cost of operating each manufacturing department is the sum of the expenses incurred within the department and the apportioned charges. For example, the cost of operating the assembly department is the sum of the expenses incurred in the department plus the costs of the services rendered to it by the various staff or facilitating departments.

Cost accounting reports show the amount of expenses of each manufacturing department that is charged against each unit or each batch of the product passing through the department. Since the expenses of the department are incurred for the benefit of all units of product fabricated in the department, the amounts must in some manner be apportioned to the various units. This problem is one of the most difficult in cost determination.

Allocation of Service Department Expenses. After the expenses of the service departments have been determined for any month or other period of time, they are allocated or apportioned to the manufacturing departments on some basis which is a measure of the actual cost of service rendered. For example, the total power cost may be apportioned on the basis of the amount of power consumed as determined by meter. Factory lunchroom expense in excess of income from meals is apportioned on the basis of the number of employees in a department. Repair and maintenance expenses are apportioned on the basis of actual cost of the repairs as determined by the cost of the materials or parts used and the wages paid to repairmen. In case no other basis for apportionment is available, the expenses of a service department are apportioned on the basis of number of employees or the number of labor hours in the manufacturing departments.

The allocation of service department expenses to manufacturing departments is complicated by the fact that some service departments render services to each other. For example, employees from the power plant use the facilities of the plant cafeteria; and the plant cafeteria uses heat, light, and power from the power plant. The total expenses of each service department include a part of the expenses of the others. This problem is handled in one of three ways, as follows:

1. Disregard the cost of any service rendered by one service department to another, and apportion the total expenses of each service department directly to the manufacturing departments.

2. Distribute first the expenses of a service department that renders service to the greatest number of service departments and receives the least service from the others. Part of the expenses of such a department would be charged to manufacturing departments, and part would be charged to other service departments. From the remaining service departments, select the one that has served the greatest number of others and has received the fewest services; and distribute the expenses in the same way. Proceed in this manner until the expenses of all service departments have been distributed. The expenses of the last service de-

partment will be distributed entirely to the manufacturing departments, since no expenses are charged back to the service departments whose expenses have been distributed.

3. Proceed as by the second method with the difference that when the expenses of the second service department are distributed, some of the expenses may be carried back to the first department, provided it was benefited by services rendered. When the expenses of the third service department are distributed, some of the expenses may be carried back to the first two departments, provided they received services from the third department. When the expenses of all service departments have been distributed, the procedure will have to be repeated because new undistributed balances for the various service departments have been created. This process is continued as many times as necessary to reduce service departmental balances to small amounts. Any remaining balances are then carried directly to the manufacturing departments, and any service rendered by one service department to another is disregarded.

Allocation of Expenses to the Product. The total direct and apportioned expenses of a manufacturing department are allocated to the product manufactured in that department. This apportionment may be made in any one of several ways. By the labor-cost method, the total manufacturing expenses of a department are divided by the total labor cost to determine a ratio or a percentage. This percentage is applied to the labor cost of a production order to determine the expense to charge as a part of the cost of the order. For example, if the expenses of a department total $15,000 and the labor cost is $20,000, the expenses amount to 75 per cent of the labor cost. If on a given production order the labor cost is $80, the manufacturing expense would be $60. The ratio of manufacturing expense to labor cost is increased by greater mechanization, the installation of materials-handling equipment, and the higher cost of machinery and equipment. Such changes increase the overhead expense and decrease direct labor cost. If a plant is fully automated, the direct labor cost method of spreading overhead expense cannot be used because no direct labor cost is incurred.

If expenses are apportioned by the labor-hour method, the total manufacturing expense of a department is divided by the number of labor-hours to determine the cost per hour. The number of labor-hours spent on any production order multiplied by the cost per hour gives the total manufacturing expense to be charged against the order. The cost per labor-hour is increased by various developments as explained in the preceding paragraph.

Expenses may be charged to an order on the basis of the number of hours of processing time and the cost of operating a machine for one hour. By this method, the expenses of a department are apportioned to the various machines to determine the cost of operating the machine for the month. The cost for the month divided by the number of hours equals the cost for one hour. The number of hours the machine is used in processing any order multiplied by the cost per hour equals the total expense to be charged against the order. Because the workplaces may consist of benches or equipment other than machines, this method is sometimes called the production-center method.

Expenses may be allocated on the basis of material cost. When this method is used, the total material cost is divided by the manufacturing expenses to determine the percentage. The material cost on any order multiplied by the expense ratio equals the expense to be charged against the order. This method has limited application.

The most accurate method of allocating manufacturing expenses is the machine-hour method because it results in charging the expenses to the product on the basis of processing time and the costs incident to time. Other methods indirectly allow for time, but the amount of the expense charged to any product is affected by other factors. For example, the labor-hour method is related to time but is not directly related to processing costs because it does not allow for the cost of operating the machine. The labor-cost method results in a charge which is dependent upon the number of hours of labor, but the expense charge is also affected by the wage rate of the worker. However, the labor-cost method is often used because it requires less clerical expense than any other method.

SOME PROBLEMS OF COST DETERMINATION

Cost has different meanings to different people, and cost also varies with the uses to be made of the information. For purposes of managerial use, the concept of cost requires definition. Some possible meanings of cost are explained in the following paragraphs.

Costs Based on a Predetermined Rate of Production. The cost of the product could be computed by apportioning the manufacturing expense each month over the units produced during the month. However, this method would usually result in fluctuating costs because the months do not have the same number of working days and also because expenses do not vary directly with the rate of output. A unit cost which varies from one month to another because of varying rates of production is not usually considered a true cost. The effect of seasonal variations upon cost is eliminated by computing the cost over a longer period, such as a year. The total manufacturing expense for the year is apportioned to the units produced during the year by one of the methods previously explained.

The most accurate method of computing the overhead expense to charge as a part of the cost of a production order might be to wait until the end of the year when the total expense and the total production would be known. However, management cannot wait until the end of the year to know the cost. Therefore, the expenses and the production are usually estimated in advance; and a predetermined expense rate is computed at the beginning of the year. This rate is used throughout the year to determine the proper amount of expense as each order is completed.

When a predetermined expense rate is used, the amount of expense apportioned to all production orders probably will not exactly equal the actual expense. If the actual expense exceeds the amount apportioned, the difference is the underapplied expense. This amount is usually regarded as the cost of idle time or as a loss due to the low volume of production. However, some accountants recommend that the underapplied expense be apportioned to all production orders completed during the year by computing a supplementary rate of expense apportionment.

If the expense entered as a cost on the various production orders exceeds the actual expense, the difference is the overapplied expense. Since the cost is overstated in comparison with actual expenses, the difference is usually treated as a deduction from the total cost of goods manufactured. However, the cost of the various production orders might be recomputed.

Cost Based on Normal Rate of Output. In the preceding paragraphs, it has been assumed that the predetermined expense rate is computed on a basis which was intended to apportion the total expense over the production for a year. This method of computing costs would cause the cost per unit to fluctuate with changes in the volume of production from one year to another. To illustrate, assume that a company manufactures only one product. The production, the manufacturing expense, and the manufacturing expense per unit over a period of five years have been as shown in Table 6.

The total cost per unit would include materials and labor in addition to the manufacturing expense as shown in Table 6. If these costs remain the same throughout the five-year period, the total costs might be as shown in Table 7. In this illustration, it is assumed that the material and labor cost is $20 per unit.

TABLE 6

VARYING EXPENSES PER UNIT OF PRODUCT WITH CHANGES IN VOLUME OF OUTPUT

Year	Number of Units Produced	Manufacturing Expense	Manufacturing Expense per Unit
1	50,000	$ 760,000	$15.20
2	60,000	780,000	13.00
3	90,000	810,000	9.00
4	70,000	784,000	11.20
5	50,000	760,000	15.20
Total..............	320,000	$3,894,000	$12.11

Table 7 shows that the unit cost decreases with an increase in the rate of production and increases with a decrease in the rate of production. Cost figures which fluctuate in this manner may be misleading to the management. Therefore, the cost per unit may be figured on what is considered to be a normal or an average rate of output. In the illustration given, the average manufacturing expense per unit might be as-

TABLE 7

CHANGES IN TOTAL COST PER UNIT WITH CHANGES IN VOLUME OF OUTPUT

Year	Material and Labor Cost	Expense (per unit)	Total Unit Cost
1	$20.00	$15.20	$35.20
2	20.00	13.00	33.20
3	20.00	9.00	29.00
4	20.00	11.20	31.20
5	20.00	15.20	35.20
Average..........	$20.00	$12.11	$32.11

sumed to be $12.11; and the total cost per unit each year might be considered to be $32.11. Over the five-year period the total expense charged on all orders would equal the actual expense, although in some years the expense would be overapplied and in other years it would be underapplied.

The normal rate is determined by selecting some year which is considered normal or average. The manufacturing expense per unit in that year is used as the expense per unit each year. If expense is distributed by the labor-cost method, the normal rate is computed by determining the ratio of manufacturing expense to labor cost in the normal year.

The unit cost of the product as determined by the methods described should be regarded as estimated rather than as exact. Such a unit cost can be of much value to management, provided that its limitations are recognized.

Standard Cost. A predetermined standard is sometimes established for each element of cost at each stage in production and also for the total cost. For materials, the standard would indicate the estimated amount of each kind of material and the cost per pound or other unit. For labor, the estimate would show the number of hours in each department or at each workplace, the hourly rate, and the total cost in each department. The standard for expenses in each department would indicate the number of hours of machine time or the number of labor-hours, the standard rate, and the total expense. When all of the cost elements are accumulated, the standard should indicate the proper cost of all elements for an order and for each unit of product.

The standard cost shows what the cost should be if the right kinds of materials are used in the right amounts with a minimum of waste or scrap. It shows what the labor cost would be if the work is assigned to workers who are properly trained to do the work and who are paid the usual rates. The standard expense is based upon the standard rate per hour at the machines best suited to process the materials. A cost in excess of the standard may be due to inefficiency or to unusual circumstances inside or outside the company.

When a standard cost system is used, the actual costs and the variances from the standard may be recorded in the accounting records, or the variances may be tabulated for statistical reports. Standard costs may require a substantial amount of work if the company produces a varied product line and the manufacturing process is of short duration. The clerical work may be performed by accounting clerks or by machines. If a machine is used, the standard costs are put into the machine at any time they are computed. The actual costs can be recorded from day to day as the work is done. The machine will compute and record the variances. The information is made available sufficiently early to permit management to take the proper corrective action.

Differential Cost. By differential cost is meant the increase in cost which will result from an increase in production. To illustrate the significance of differential cost, assume that a manufacturer receives an offer to purchase 1,000 units of his product for $2.50 per unit. The prospective purchaser is a chain store or mail-order house whose sales are made under private brand or trade name and do not affect the other sales of the manufacturer. The cost accountant prepares a cost summary which shows a unit cost of $3.00. The statement is as follows.

```
Materials ($1.00 per unit)............................$ 5,000
Labor ($1.00 per unit)...............................  5,000
Expense .............................................  5,000
                                                      -------
   Total Cost of 5,000 Units.........................$15,000
   Unit Cost ........................................ $3.00
```

This statement indicates that cost is in excess of the proposed sales price of the additional 1,000 units. The accountant is requested to show what the costs would have been if the additional 1,000 units had been produced. This statement shows a unit cost of $2.85, as follows.

```
Materials ($1.00 per unit)............................$ 6,000
Labor ($1.00 per unit)...............................  6,000
Expense .............................................  5,100
                                                      -------
   Total Cost of 6,000 Units.........................$17,100
   Unit Cost ........................................ $2.85
```

The cost per unit is still in excess of the proposed selling price, and it therefore seems that the manufacturer should reject the offer. However, total costs are increased only by $2,100, while income is increased by $2,500. On the basis of differential cost rather than average unit cost, the proposed sale appears to afford a profit. Before the decision is made to make and sell the additional 1,000 units at $2.50 per unit, the manufacturer should consider the possible effect on the market, his ability to finance the additional production, and the possibility of legal liability under the Robinson-Patman Act, which prohibits discrimination between customers.

Differential cost might be a factor in the plans of the management for adding a new product to the line or for dropping a product. If a new product will pay its "out-of-pocket" costs and contribute something toward the overhead expenses, it might constitute a desirable addition to the line. The decision to add the product would be affected by other considerations, such as the prestige of the wider line, the effect upon jobs within the company, and the possibility of increased sales for the new item in later years. Similar considerations would affect the proposal to drop an item that pays its direct costs and makes a contribution to the overhead. The possible effect upon people within the company sometimes results in the carrying of unprofitable lines when they should be dropped.

Total Cost. The total cost of all units produced may be as significant as unit cost. To illustrate, assume that a manufacturer produced 6,000 units at a total cost of $17,100 and that selling and administrative expenses totaled $6,000. If he sold the product for $3.80 per unit, his profit and loss statement would be as follows:

```
Sales (6,000 units at $3.80)......................        $22,800
Cost of goods sold:
    Materials ($1.00 per unit)..................$6,000
    Labor ($1.00 per unit)......................  6,000
    Manufacturing expense ......................  5,100   17,100

Gross profit .....................................        $ 5,700
Selling and administrative expenses...............          6,000

Loss .............................................        $   300
```

In order to avoid a loss, the manufacturer increased his selling price to $4.00. However, the higher price caused his sales to decrease to 5,000 units, with results as follows:

```
Sales (5,000 units at $4.00)......................        $20,000
Cost of goods sold:
    Materials ($1.00 per unit)..................$5,000
    Labor ($1.00 per unit)......................  5,000
    Manufacturing expense.......................  5,000   15,000

Gross profit......................................        $ 5,000
Selling and administrative expenses...............          5,700

Loss .............................................        $   700
```

The manufacturer has increased his loss by increasing his selling price. This illustration is not intended to show that an increase in selling prices is always poor policy. It indicates only that other factors besides unit cost should be considered.

Replacement Cost. In time of rising prices for materials and labor, replacement cost is a factor in sales policies. Suppose, for example, that a company has in stock 5,000 units which cost $15,000 to manufacture. If the prices of materials and wages paid to employees have increased to such an extent that the cost of replacing the goods would be $20,000, this fact should be considered in pricing.

Opportunity Cost. The management might like to know what profit was sacrificed or lost by using the semifinished products at certain stages for further processing instead of selling them. Stated in another way, management might wish to know what the final product would have cost if the semifinished product had been transferred to a later department at the prices prevailing in the market for such products.

To illustrate the meaning of opportunity cost, assume that a meat-packing plant produces dressed meats, which are used in making cured and canned meat products, at a cost of $5,000. The company could have sold the dressed meats without further processing for $5,500. In determining the profit from subsequent operations, the cost of the material might be considered to be $5,000. However, if the final profit is only $400, the last department is operated at a loss, when opportunity costs are considered. Other examples of opportunity costs are the use of a building in business when it could be rented, the devoting of the owner's time to a business when he could be earning a salary, and the use of materials by a steel company for the manufacture of fabricated products when the steel could be sold in the market. Opportunity costs do not appear in the cost reports, but they affect the decisions of management.

Disseminating Cost Information. Cost data which is made available to supervisors and executives provides an incentive for cost control and cost reduction. To be useful, cost reports should reflect recent performance. Some data are reported monthly, and other data are reported daily, quarterly, or annually. The cost of a production order or of contract work should be reported as soon as possible after the work has been completed. The reports should be sent to all persons who are in a position to make use of them.[1]

A PROGRAM FOR COST CONTROL

The usefulness of cost information depends largely upon the extent to which it is used to reduce, limit, or otherwise control the various activities which give rise to costs and expenses. An effective program for cost control would require, first, that the objectives of the enterprise be determined. Second, standards should be established for judging whether costs are high, low, or average. Third, the data for costs should be collected, tabulated, summarized, and transmitted to management for comparison with the standard. Finally, good performance should be commended or otherwise rewarded, and excessive costs should be brought under control.

The Question of Objectives. The objective of an industrial enterprise is usually considered to be the production and sale of goods and services at a profit. Therefore, the desirability of any expenditure is determined by the contribution that it makes to profit, either long run or short run. The expenditure may increase profit by reducing cost, im-

---

[1] "Audit Guide for Manufacturing," *Factory Management and Maintenance,* Vol. CXVII, No. 12 (1959), p. 58.

proving quality, increasing the rate of output, or improving human relations. The safeguarding of the health and safety of employees is also essential to the stability and growth of the enterprise. Activities may also increase profits by increasing the volume of sales.

A company usually has other objectives besides profit. It may seek to provide steady employment. It may co-operate with the government in its program of national defense. Other objectives may be established to guide the management in its relations with vendors, customers, communities where the plants of the company are located, and other outside groups. Such objectives provide criteria for determining the desirability of any expenditure.

Standards for Costs. The standard costs for materials are established with reference to the specifications for materials. A standard quantity for each product is also desirable. Standard labor costs are established through work measurement and the regular hourly wages or piece rates. Standards for manufacturing expense involve more difficulty, but an approach to the problem may be made through the methods and procedures described in the preceding pages of this chapter. The budget of manufacturing expenses also constitutes a standard for controlling expenses.

The cost information should be summarized in a form that is easily understood. The data should be sent to those persons in the management who are in a position to take corrective action. The information pertaining to costs in a department should be sent to the foreman and also to his supervisor. Expense analyses should be prepared for each manufacturing department. The classification of expenses would conform to the assignment of duties to the positions as shown by the organization chart.

Action on Cost Information. The cost information may show an excessive cost of materials, labor, or expenses. Further analysis is required to determine which material cost is too large and also to trace the higher cost to purchase prices or to quantity used. Labor cost would be traced to the department, the machine, and the worker. Expenses would be analyzed by departments and by amounts charged on an order at each workplace.

Because all activities of the manufacturing division are finally reflected in the cost figures, a high cost may be caused by poor management of any of the activities that have been described in preceding pages. Difficulties may arise because of ineffective organization, poor morale, lack of motivation, poor maintenance, costly layout, poor methods of materials handling, or any other phase of plant management. No easy solution to these problems can be prescribed, but continuous study and research will be necessary.

Management usually emphasizes cost reduction during periods of recession when sales and profits are declining.[2] Attention may first be directed to activities or services that do not directly contribute to a reduction of costs or an increase in sales, such as long-distance telephone calls, travel, entertainment expenses, and gifts to employees and others on special occasions. Some types of executive development programs may be curtailed.[3] Even though the savings from the elimination of some services or expenses is not large, the top executives may attempt to control costs in this manner because the psychological effect upon people throughout the organization may effect other reductions.

Management may also seek to reduce costs by eliminating some jobs or by combining jobs to effect a reduction in personnel. In time of rising prices and profits, positions may have been added which were considered desirable at the time but which were later found not to be essential. Management may decide that certain positions in departments that perform facilitating or staff functions can be eliminated. The contribution that such positions make to profits cannot always be easily demonstrated.

Another phase of costs that may receive attention pertains to paper work. Clerical work throughout all divisions of the organization has increased, partly because of the requirements of the government in connection with income taxes, social security, deductions from pay for bond purchases, and deductions for union dues. Detailed personnel records may be necessary to prove compliance with federal and state labor laws. The amount of paper work caused by such developments has resulted in the installation and use of tabulating equipment and other office machines in many companies.

Various staff activities also necessitate additional paper work. Examples are production standards, cost records and cost reports, inventory control, the accident prevention program, employment procedures, job evaluation, and merit rating. Each such program should be examined from time to time to determine whether it is worth its cost. Such an evaluation is not easy because the total cost can only be estimated, and the benefits may be diffused throughout the organization.

---

[2] See Ernest Schleusener, "18 Ways to Pinch Pennies," *Factory Management and Maintenance,* Vol. CXVI, No. 6 (1958), pp. 113–15.

[3] Edward T. Thompson, "The Cost-Cutting Urge," *Fortune,* Vol. LXVII, No. 3 (1958), p. 118 ff.

QUESTIONS

1. Distinguish between cost, expense, expenditure, and disbursement.

2. How is cost information related to managerial planning and control?

3. How is cost related to selling prices?

4. How does mechanization or automation affect the various elements of cost?

5. A company that makes metal containers installed machines for coating sheets with tin instead of buying sheets already coated at the steel mill. How will this change affect the costs of the container manufacturer and the steel company?

6. A food-processing company that formerly bought its cans installed machines to make the cans it needed. The can-making department was organized under a separate manager, and its transfers of cans to the food-procesesing department were handled in the accounts as purchases and sales. The cans were valued at the price that would have been paid the container manufacturer. How does this method of treatment assist the management of each department and the company as a whole?

7. How is the predetermined expense rate useful to the management?

8. Should a company continue a product line that pays its direct cost and something toward the overhead of the company? The line is carried at a loss when its share of the overhead is included in the cost.

9. If the cost of materials is increased in the market, should the company charge the cost of materials on hand and bought at a lower price at cost or at present market prices? How would the selling price of the product be affected? Does selling price depend upon cost?

10. Under what conditions would opportunity cost data be useful to the management?

11. How is standard cost related to the planning and control of production?

12. Is the cost of the product an estimate, or is it a correct and accurate figure?

CASES

79. PLACE OF THE COST ANALYST IN THE ORGANIZATION

The management of a metal and fiber container manufacturing company found that the profit ratio was declining because of the increasing cost of materials. The controller obtained permission from the president for the employment of a cost accountant in his division, to be given the title of cost analyst. The duty of the cost analyst was to study cost ratios and point out to the foreman of any department the reason for any cost that was out of line. It would then be the responsibility of the foreman to take appropriate action.

The cost analyst found that, under instructions from foremen, workmen in the slitting department were using sheets of metal carrying a heavier coating of tin than was necessary for the manufacture of certain types of cans. For example, sheets that had been purchased for the manufacture of cans for peaches were used in making oil cans or paint cans. The cost was increased because the sheets carrying a heavier coating of tin cost more per square foot. The waste in each sheet

was also increased because the sheets had been designed for the cutting of a different size can.

The cost analyst reported his findings to the foreman of the slitting department
for action. The foreman stated that he was under pressure from the plant superintendent to get out the work and that he had to use such material as was available.
Furthermore, he politely informed the cost analyst that he took orders from no
one other than his own superior officer, the plant superintendent.

The cost analyst reported this situation to the controller and asked for further
instructions. The controller was sure that the situation called for corrective action,
but he could see no advantage in talking to the foreman himself. He decided to
transmit the information to the president of the company for such action as the
president might wish to take.

Questions:

1. What was wrong with the original plan for finding and eliminating excessive costs?

2. Was the controller right in taking the matter to the president?

3. Might the situation have been handled by the controller and the plant superintendent?

4. Did this situation indicate that the planning and purchasing programs
should be revised?

80. EFFECT OF FLUCTUATING VOLUME OF PRODUCTION UPON COST

The Greenway Printing Company, with a plant in Ohio, manufactures college
textbooks for various publishing companies under contract. The publishing companies attempt to release new books during the spring months in order that they
may be available to teachers before the end of the academic year. With this
schedule, teachers may examine the new book before they begin their summer
vacations. Some books are published in the autumn months for classes beginning
in January or February. Because of the nature of the market, the printing company has its peak period of production in the winter months and a somewhat less
busy season in the autumn. During the months between the two peak seasons,
some books are printed, but the machines are idle much of the time.

When any contract for printing is completed, the accountant prepares a statement of the cost, which is submitted to plant executives and to top management.
In March, he prepared such a statement showing the cost of a contract to be
$7,560, while the customer was charged $11,300. The president commended the
plant manager for holding down the costs. In August, the accountant prepared
another statement showing that the cost of a printing contract was $6,450. On this
contract, the customer was charged $5,100. The president was disturbed by this
statement, and he called upon the plant manager for an explanation. The plant
manager told the president that while the statement was correct, it was not alarm-
ing because August was a slack month. The costs appeared to be high, he said,
because the presses had been idle 60 per cent of the time. The few contracts
completed in July and August had to bear a high amount of overhead. He added
that "we have to offset the loss on contracts in summer against the profit on other
contracts in the winter and autumn."

The president asked: "Of what value are our cost statements if we are required to offset the profit on one contract against the losses on others? Can you make up your cost statements in any other way?"

The accountant replied: "Yes, we could compute an average rate of overhead expense as a percentage of labor costs and spread the overhead more evenly throughout the year. The effect of this method would be to charge more overhead during the busy months and less on contracts completed during the off seasons. The percentage of profit on a contract at one time of the year should then be about the same as the profit completed at another season."

The president commented: "A change in the method of computing costs might be helpful. What would be the effect of such a change upon the profits for the year?"

The accountant said: "The profits for the year would be just the same as they are by the present method of allocating overhead. What we really need is some printing contracts to keep the presses busy during the off season. If we could keep the presses busy on other contracts, we could make a profit on those contracts and reduce the overhead now being charged on such contracts as we get during the off season. Perhaps we might get more business for the off season by offering lower contract prices to our present customers."

The president replied: "Suppose you talk to Bill Watson, our sales director, and get his ideas. If you can make any concrete proposals, report back to me."

Questions:

1. Were the statements properly prepared?
2. What should the company do to correct the situation?

39 General
Planning
and Control

IN preceding chapters, various phases of production management have been considered, largely from the point of view of the individual department. The problems considered have included organizational relationships, physical facilities for production, the product line, production standards, wages and incentives, personnel relationships, and financial controls. Remaining for discussion are certain general problems of planning and control of production which relate to the enterprise as a whole.

THE OBJECTIVES OF THE ENTERPRISE

Planning and control of the activities of an enterprise can be effectively accomplished only after the objectives have been determined. The planning is designed to unify the efforts of people in the organization and to direct them toward the accomplishment of the objectives. A company would usually have several objectives, some of which would be private or business objectives and others would be social or public.

Social Objectives. In a system of private enterprise, the government permits a business to produce and sell products and services, to determine the selling prices—provided the management does not monopolize or conspire to restrain trade, and to make a profit—if costs and expenses are kept sufficiently low to permit a profit. Private businesses are also expected to produce the goods and services required by the government for national defense and for ordinary government activities. Because people do not live solely for the satisfaction of their material needs, businesses are expected not only to produce sufficient goods and services for consumers but also to provide the requirements of leisure time and retirement, to permit longer vacations, and to provide the things necessary to self-improvement. The management of a private enterprise cannot afford to neglect the public and social objectives of production, although some companies may produce and sell goods that are physically or morally harmful to the persons who use them. In a system of private enterprise, considerable freedom remains to the manager even though much restrictive legislation has been enacted.

Adaptation to Change. An economic and social system must be able to make improvements in technology and to adapt organization and business methods to the changes. Technical and political developments at home and abroad require changes in methods of organization, manufacturing processes, machines, plant layout, methods of training and development of management personnel and employees, sources of raw materials, and other phases of management. In a system of private enterprise, the government and the public depend upon business managements to make much of the adjustment. If the adjustment is not made or if it is made too slowly, the economy may enter into a period of decline. Business managements, with a certain amount of encouragement and assistance from the government, perform an important function in adapting to change.

The Profit Objective. The necessity for making a profit is generally recognized by labor and the public as well as by management. Business enterprises obtain the capital from the initial investment of the owners and by borrowing. They are expected to earn a return on the investment, and usually the stockholders expect dividends to be paid on the stock. The payment of dividends is not only an obligation incurred by prior issues of stock but also a requirement for future issues at satisfactory prices. The earning of a fair rate of profit requires attention to all phases of costs and expenses, including selling and administrative expenses. The management must also be concerned with the volume of production and sales and with selling prices.

Usually a business does not attempt to earn the maximum rate of profit on the investment, but it is satisfied to earn a fair rate. The meaning of fair rate is not easily determined. However, a fair rate of return on the investment of the owners would probably exceed the interest rate on bonds or bank loans.

A reason that the management might not attempt to earn the maximum rate on stockholder investments is that the management of a corporation is usually separated from ownership. The directors of the corporation are elected by the stockholders, and the directors elect the chief executive and the heads of the major divisions. In many cases, the stockholders are quite numerous, live in various parts of the country, and do not have close and continuous contact with the affairs of the corporation. Profits and dividends may therefore constitute only one of several objectives of the management.

Obligations to Other Groups. A reason for the lack of complete emphasis upon stockholder interests by corporate managements is that good relations must be maintained with various other groups. If the management attempts to squeeze the last dollar from employees, it will be unable to hire the competent workers that it needs, and workers will become undependable and un-co-operative. The management is also required to maintain good relations with labor unions if it is to avoid labor strife, slowdowns, and interruptions to production. People in the management group are also human, and they must be kept interested and properly motivated.

Other groups with whom management must maintain good relations include commercial bankers, investment bankers, investment counselors, vendors who supply materials and parts, marketing agencies, ultimate consumers of the product, the general public, and agencies of the government. The development of good relations with these groups requires attention to profits and the budget, prices and quality of the product, the prompt payment of financial obligations, support for research programs of the government, waste disposal and other aspects of good citizenship in the community, and various aspects of public relations. Many company policies and practices will be affected by the need for good relationships to outside groups.

Establishing Company Objectives. In many companies, the management has not definitely established the objectives of the enterprise. It may have decided that good relationships should be maintained with stockholders and others without defining such terms as fair rate of profit and dividends, a fair price for the product, the quality of the product required by consumers, and fair and equitable treatment of employees. No difficulty may be encountered during periods of prosperity because sales and earnings enable the company to earn a satisfactory rate of profit on a large volume of production and sales while it pays good wages and maintains a stable amount of employment. The difficulties cumulate when the demand for the product declines and reductions in the volume of production and employment become necessary. In most cases the management will modify its program and change its policies to meet the necessities of the situation.

DIFFICULTIES OF ACCOMPLISHING COMPANY OBJECTIVES

In the accomplishment of company objectives, attention is directed to a great many problems which have been discussed in preceding chapters. Such problems lie in all of the functional activities of the enterprise and in all departments. Each level of the organization from executives to workers presents its problems and its difficulties. In the present chapter, attention will be given to some questions which have not been adequately discussed elsewhere. Because executives are somewhat removed from the work level and because their work consists largely of dealing with people, their problems of accomplishing company and social executives fall principally in the area of human relations.

Overemphasis on Profit. If profit is regarded as the sole objective or even the principal objective of the business, the management will fail to achieve certain of the social objectives and may also fall short of the profit objective. An overemphasis on profit may result in a curtailment of services to customers, the elimination of varieties of the product that do not pay their way, and a type of competition that is sometimes designated as "ruthless" or "cutthroat." If the volume of sales falls off in some seasons or periods of recession, an overemphasis on profit might cause the company to lay off production-line employees, to curtail its program of research, or to dismiss staff personnel who do not make a direct and immediate contribution to profit. Another activity that might be curtailed is public relations work that tends to build up the good will of the company and to strengthen its position in the industry. In its handling of many business activities, the management should consider both the service to the public and the long-run effect upon profits. The emphasis upon profit as distinguished from personnel or public service depends upon decisions made by top management.

Attitude of Specialists. In the absence of effective controls by top management, an influence within the organization that may prevent a complete realization of company objectives is the tendency of specialists to look at problems from the limited point of view of their own work in the company. For example, the time-study man may insist upon the setting of work standards for the various tasks regardless of the effect upon the relation of the company to its employees and to the union. He knows that his procedures are correct, and he thinks that every one should conform to the standards set. The engineer sees the need to replace obsolete equipment with new machines that are more efficient even though the replacement might cause workers to be laid off or the cash budget to become unbalanced. The controller may want to reduce expenses in various departments regardless of the effect upon people or the program of the company. Other specialists also tend to look at problems from a limited rather than a company-wide point of view.

Empire Building. A different problem may arise as a result of the efforts of people to enlarge the work of their own departments by employing more people, spending more money for expenses, or otherwise adding to the prestige of their departments. Objections may also be made to proposals to curtail the activities of a department. The advocacy of expansion or the objection to curtailment of activities cannot easily be shown to be unwise because the results of any one activity are not separate from the work of the company as a whole. Furthermore, the top management may hesitate to put changes into effect that are not approved by the department that is most affected by them. As a result, some activities that do not fully pay their way may be instituted and continued after they have ceased to be profitable.

The Play-Safe Attitude. The company may also fail to accomplish its objectives fully because people at various levels in the organization hesitate to make decisions or to develop new programs because they fear they will make a mistake. In a large organization, a person may believe that security in his position requires that he conform to the policies, regulations, and procedures of the company. If he is not clear concerning the policy or the rule that applies in a given situation, he refers the problem to a higher level in the chain of command. As a result, decisions are delayed, opportunities may be lost, and the objectives of the enterprise are neglected.

The top executives may also fail to show initiative in adjusting programs to changed economic conditions. They may take the attitude that security in their positions is gained by playing safe, avoiding the risk of launching new and possibly unprofitable undertakings, and conserving the resources of the company. This attitude is sometimes called "the maginot-line attitude."

The conservative attitude does not characterize many corporate managements. Evidence of a progressive attitude is found in the fact that the entire economic system has been changing rapidly with the development of new products, new materials, new machines, new manufacturing methods, and other innovations. Many large corporations continue to grow in the dollar value of assets, in dollar value of sales, in numbers of plants, in extent of market area covered, and in profits. Large numbers of new enterprises continue to be organized each year.

The effort to play safe is most likely to characterize a management that is nearing retirement because the available time may be insufficient to develop and complete new programs. If a corporation has a succession of presidents who are nearing retirement when they are promoted to the position of chief executive, the management may permit the organization to drift and the company may lose its position of leadership in the industry.

Bureaucracy. In government the attitude of playing it safe and avoiding risks is usually described as bureaucracy. In its proper sense, bureaucracy means government by bureaus, and a bureau is defined as an agency of government whose officers are appointed rather than elected. The bureaucrat is a career executive. Bureaucracy as a form of government may be contrasted with democracy, monarchy, aristocracy, and other forms.

Although bureaucracy may be a desirable form of government, the term has become associated with certain undesirable tendencies in large organizations whether in government or private enterprise. The large size of an organization requires that a scalar chain of several levels be established and that much of the work of directing day-to-day activities be assigned to junior executives and subordinates at the lower levels. The top executives must concern themselves with general problems, such as the development of proper relationships with institutions and persons outside the company, the formulation of general plans and programs, financial planning and control, meeting emergency problems as they arise, and the adaptation of company programs to changes outside and inside the company.

The people at the lower levels in the organization are necessarily guided by instructions communicated to them from top levels. Such instructions include policies, rules, regulations, position descriptions, indoctrination at the time of appointment and later, executive orders and commands, oral communications, and project assignments. While written and oral communications serve a useful purpose in directing and co-ordinating activities, they restrict the freedom of activity of persons throughout the organization and limit them in the right to make decisions. No matter how detailed and specific the instructions to a junior executive may be made, they cannot anticipate all difficulties that will arise. In fact, a specific and detailed set of rules and regulations may serve only to limit the independence of persons at the lower levels.

In a large organization in which the members have voluntarily become associated, recruits can always be procured from the outside. Replacements can be provided by promotions or transfers from other departments. An executive may therefore feel insecure. When he is confronted with a difficult problem, he may attempt to pass it up the line to a superior or sidewise to an associate. This situation gives rise to the two related evils of "layering," and "passing the buck." Conformity to rules, regulations, and procedures is required of persons in the interests of efficiency, but in specific instances conformity may lead to inefficiency.

Personal Objectives. Another difficulty of getting work done through other people arises because both employees and management personnel permit their personal objectives to interfere with the performance of their duties. It will be recalled that Frederick W. Taylor first become interested in the study and experimentation of management methods because workers were not doing as much work as they should. Taylor attempted to improve performance by establishing work standards, improving conditions of work, and instituting a piece rate as an incentive for better work. Workers may permit their personal objectives to interfere with effective performance in many other ways, such as tardiness, absenteeism, failure to maintain quality, and neglect of the care of the machine. Management has devised many ways of dealing with these problems. Some of the techniques for gaining better cooperation have been described in preceding pages.

Although foremen are expected to take the point of view of the company and to seek to accomplish objectives, they may also permit their personal objectives to interfere. Since they are "caught in the middle" between the workers and their supervisors, they may attempt to avoid difficulties and misunderstandings at the sacrifice of the main objectives. To develop better relationships with workers, they may attempt to avoid setting standards too high, to see that work is kept moving, and to reduce friction between workers. To satisfy the management, the foreman may try to help workers meet production standards, to keep waste and scrap within the limits expected, and to see that unfavorable reports are not transmitted from his department to middle management. The accomplishment of company objectives does not necessarily rank first in the foreman's thinking.

The executives of the middle and higher levels of management also have their personal problems which may interfere with the accomplishment of company objectives. Personal problems and objectives of middle management include the desire for coffee breaks, social activities of

the individual and his family, vacations, pleasure trips, and various
other personal interests. If an executive has social obligations that interfere with his business activities, he may attend to his personal affairs
first with the idea that his business affairs can wait.

The difficulties arising from such human relations problems as empire building, the play-it-safe attitude, and personal objectives caused
Henri Fayol to state that an enterprise reaches a limit in its growth and
ultimately becomes unable to compete effectively. The difficulties are not
insuperable, however, and many of the largest corporations in the United
States are known to be more efficient than many smaller ones. Large
size brings economies in the handling of the technical phases of the
work, provided the people in the organization can be properly motivated and their work can be efficiently supervised and co-ordinated.

METHODS OF CO-ORDINATION AND CONTROL

Many methods and techniques are available to the top management
of a corporation for obtaining effective performance throughout the
organization. Most of the methods have been discussed in the preceding chapters. They include a wide span of control to reduce the number of horizontal levels in the organization, the decentralization of
authority to make decisions, the adoption of a statement of objectives
and policies for the guidance of the lower levels of the management,
the development of a budget which serves as a financial plan, and the
use of cost control methods. Some other methods of controlling performance are considered in the present chapter.

Divisional Profit and Loss Statement. A monthly, quarterly, or
annual profit and loss statement may be prepared for each operating
division. Such statements can be prepared if the company is organized
by product lines, operating divisions, or territories with the head of
each division made responsible for the production and sale of a line
of products. In merchandising businesses, such as chain stores or mail-
order houses, operating data for each branch or each territory may be
separately reported. Such data include sales, cost of goods sold, and
operating expenses. Some general expenses that are incurred for the
benefit of the entire organization, such as the expenses of departments
performing staff functions, would be allocated to the operating divisions on an equitable basis. The smaller the unit for which the statements are prepared the more effective they become. The statements
should be prepared soon after the close of the period to which the data
are related, and the statements should be reviewed and discussed

promptly after they are received. The early preparation of statements is now made possible by the use of machines that tabulate, classify, and summarize the basic data.

Cost Information. The various kinds of cost systems and the information they convey have been discussed in the preceding chapter. The most useful data are the standard costs, which may be compared with the actual cost. If the executive knows the proper cost of materials, labor, and expenses for one unit of product or for each 1,000 units of product and then can know the actual cost, he can know which costs are too high, in what departments the excess costs were incurred, and who may be asked for an explanation. As previously explained, the standard cost data may show the quantities of each class of materials, the unit cost, the number of hours of labor, and the labor cost in each department. The estimate of the manufacturing expense per unit should be based upon a normal rate of production in order that costs may not be affected by seasonal or cyclical variations in production which are beyond the control of the foremen or junior executives whose performance management is attempting to evaluate.

The value of cost information for management purposes depends largely upon timeliness. If the information is available soon after the work has been processed in a department or the production order has been completed, the management may be able to take effective corrective action. Later, every one who is concerned with the cost data may be inclined to think that the information is not necessarily representative of conditions now prevailing. With present-day computing machines, the information can be made available without delay.

Use of Statistical Data. Some companies find that the number of units of the product manufactured and sold can be used as a measure of the success of the company. The data should be compared with the number of units sold by the entire industry, and allowance should be made for seasonal and cyclical fluctuations. If each division makes and sells a product in a different price range, the comparison with data for the industry should be made on the basis of information as to price ranges because an increase or decrease in the sales of any one division may be caused by shifts in the preferances of customers.

The data for the units sold should be classified by territories not only because the success of territorial managers may be judged by the sales trend in different territories but also because plans for the future production, advertising, and sales efforts may be made more effectively. The data may also indicate the number of units in the hands of dealers. An increase in dealers' stocks may indicate a need for revising the production schedules for ensuing months. A decrease in the unit sales of an area might indicate the need for more effective sales efforts, a slump in the industrial activity in the area, or an impending recession which may extend to other territories or industries. In using such data, allowance should be made for economic and financial conditions which are beyond the control of any executive within the company. However, the executive who is removed from the operating level because of his position in the scalar chain may use such statistics as one measure of the success of the company as a whole.

Measuring the Effectiveness of Staff. The departments that render a service or that advise with the line do not make and sell a product and therefore cannot be judged by the usual standards. Although the work of the staff should result in reduced cost, increased sales, or better service, the management may have difficulty in determining whether staff service is effective.

Many series of statistical data can be used as measures of the success of staff departments, and some of them have been mentioned in preceding chapters. The success of the research division, for example, is measured in part by the number of new products developed, the sales and profit made on each new product, the total sales of products developed during the last five years as a percentage of the total sales of the company, and the total research expenditures as a percentage of the total sales. The efficiency of the maintenance department may be measured by the amount of downtime of machines, the number and cost of emergency repairs, the results of work sampling studies of maintenance crews, the total maintenance cost, and other such data. The work of accident prevention is measured by the accident severity rate and the accident frequency rate. The work of the employment section is judged by the number of new employees who remain with the company for a stated period of time, the number who are dropped during the usual probationary period, the amount of time spent in interviewing people, the average time of the interview, and the average cost of hiring a new employee. Other data that may be used in judging the success of the personnel program include absenteeism, tardiness, the accident rate for new employees, the separation rate, the time required for a new employee to reach the usual production standards, the number of complaints and grievances, the amount of scrap and waste, and the number and duration of slowdowns and work stoppages. These series of data are intended merely to suggest some of the possibilities. Each company will compile such statistical data as it considers useful, and it will use the data in such way as seems appropriate under the circumstances.

In a large organization, an improvement in any phase of management seldom results from the work of one person acting on his own authority. For example, a reduction in the accident frequency rate might be due to the work of staff personnel, foremen, and workers. The management should therefore give credit to each person who might have contributed in any way to the results.

Profit-Sharing and Bonus Plans. As a positive incentive, profit-sharing and bonus plans are sometimes found to be effective. Profit-sharing plans for employees may provide for monthly, quarterly, or annual distributions of cash or stock in the company. Some companies add a part of the balance available under the plan to the fund that is available for retirement payments. Aside from the accounting difficulties, the principal objections to profit sharing are that payments are made at infrequent intervals, that the amount of a person's share is not closely related to his own effort, and that profits are greatly affected by programs and policies developed by executives rather than by the workers. Conditions outside the company also have an important effect upon the profits.

A better argument can be made for executive retirement and bonus plans. The fact that payments are not made at frequent intervals is not an objection because the results of the work of executives may not be immediately reflected in profits. The causal relationship between the work of the executive and the amount of profits may be close because the executive helps to shape the program of the company. The executive directs such activities as research, plant expansion, budgeting, and reporting. Furthermore, a mistake at the executive level could be costly to the company.

Because of income taxes, many executives receive a bonus that is paid in stock or in warrants to buy stock at a price below the prevailing market price. If the stock is held for a period of six months or more, the executive can report any profit on the sale as capital gain rather than as ordinary income. Most corporations now examine each proposed transaction for its effect upon taxes before a decision is made.

Executives seem to need pension and bonus plans as an inducement to apply themselves to their work and to provide the company with good management. They may desire the financial benefits, or they may value the prestige and social status that such payments give them. Executives are motivated by both financial and nonfinancial incentives just as other people are motivated. The effect of incentives is not easily measured.

Effective Employment of the Work Force. The accomplishment of the social objective of maximum production of goods and services would require that all groups of workers be employed at the kind of work for which they are best suited. When any worker is required to use his time and effort in a job that does not make the best use of his education, experience, and skill, the efficiency of the economy is lowered and production is lessened. Despite legislation which attempts to prevent discrimination, many persons are denied the opportunity to practice certain trades or to enter certain types of employment. Some jobs are regarded as Negro men's jobs, others as Negro women's jobs, and others as white women's jobs. The wage scales vary according to the nature of the employment. The discrimination against certain groups of workers usually comes from the employees rather than the employer. The argument is advanced that the trade or craft would become crowded if all barriers were removed. Workers also fear that persons not accustomed to the prevailing high rates of pay on certain jobs would be willing to work for lower wages and that the wages of all workers on the job would be affected. However, all workers should have the right to work, and industry should have the benefit of their efforts and skill.

The government encourages industry to employ persons who have certain physical limitations, such as the loss of a hand or foot or the lack of vision in one eye. People who have these and other physical limitations are usually called handicapped people. The name is unfortunate because they may be fully capable of doing certain types of work. An employer may hesitate to hire such people because they may be unable to transfer to other types of work in an emergency. Some employers fear that the limitations of such workers may increase accidents and give rise to claims under the workmen's compensation laws.

Older persons constitute another group whose services are not always fully utilized. Some companies base retirement upon age and others base it upon years of service. Some people are retired when they want to work and are able to continue working. After retirement, a person may be transferred to a position that is less demanding. Some retired persons find employment in another organization. A difficulty with the continued employment of older people is that their mental and physical capacities may gradually decline and their retirement then becomes more difficult for the management. The government discourages the employment of older people through social security and tax regulations. A person who continues working after the age of 65 is unable to collect social security payments, and he is taxed on the income earned. He also continues to be taxed for social security. The legislation pertaining to income and social security taxes was enacted in a depression period for the purpose of reducing the number of persons competing for jobs.

Work Stoppages. The social objective of increasing the standard of living through the production of goods and services is partially defeated by work stoppages, strikes, and lockouts. The time of the entire organization and the physical facilities is lost, in some cases for an extended period. Because unions are organized on a nation-wide scale, an industry that is vital to the economy may discontinue production for weeks or months. The legislation now on the statute books affords some protection through an enforced delay of the strike for a few weeks, but it does not provide a solution. Although some workers on strike may find other employment if the strike lasts many weeks, the pay is usually less than the pay on their regular jobs, and their work is less productive.

Strikes cause other costs for the employer and indirectly for the public. The possibility of a strike prevents the employer from making firm commitments for purchases and deliveries to customers. Unnecessary costs are incurred in the stocking of materials in anticipation of a strike, and production may be suspended for lack of materials. Although some of the losses may later be recouped by the strike-bound company, the national losses may not be recovered. Ultimately a way will probably be found to eliminate industrial strife and to prevent the losses caused by such work stoppages. Strikes by employees of public utilities are now illegal under the laws of some states. Employees of the federal government are not permitted to go on strike.

Strikes and slowdowns indicate that the corporation is not an entity insofar as the people are concerned because the organization is divided against itself. The employees do not feel that they really belong to the corporate organization. The management would like to believe that when a strike is called one part of the organization arrays itself against another part. This division constitutes a very serious weakness of the system of private enterprise.

Unemployment. The involuntary unemployment of workers causes a further waste of human and economic resources. Some unemployment is caused by seasonal fluctuations in the volume of production. Seasonal unemployment in some industries can be reduced by careful planning of production by the management. Goods may be produced in the dull season for sale in the busy season. Customers may be induced to accept delivery in advance of the beginning of a season. Advance dating of invoices and the offering of large discounts during the dull season may also increase sales in the off season. Still other methods are possible for some industries.

Some unemployment is caused by cyclical fluctuations in production, and much of this unemployment defies control by the individual manufacturer. Corrective measures will depend largely upon the government. Much has already been done through the long-range planning of government construction projects, the stabilization of consumer purchasing power as a result of social security and other payments to older persons and the unemployed, and expenditures for national defense. These measures are sometimes called "built-in stabilizers."

Unemployment may be attributed to a variety of other causes. Some people are temporarily unemployed because they are changing from one job to another or are moving from one place to another. Some of the unemployed have been laid off because an industry or an area is declining in importance. Some people are on vacation and some do not want work all of the time. Some are unemployable or can obtain work only when the need for workers is great. Some have been discharged for one of several reasons and have not been able to find employment elsewhere. While unemployment causes economic and social losses, the reasons for the unemployment may be found in unavoidable causes that relate to the economic system, the workers themselves, or changes in technology.

MANAGEMENT AS A SCIENCE

As explained in Chapter 1, the phrase "scientific management" originated with the people who had become interested in management after Taylor began his studies at the Midvale Steel Company in 1880. The name became associated with the new methods and the new spirit of management when Taylor published a book by this name in 1911. At that time, the Taylor methods were generally accepted as models for others to follow. In time, however, many people began to question some of the statements Taylor had made and some of the methods he had followed. Consequently, "scientific management" dropped into disuse as a name for current methods and practices. The question may therefore be raised whether management can properly be regarded as a science.

Management as a Body of Principles. The persons who conducted the early studies in management hoped that principles could be established that would be of general application. They hoped that ultimately the principles would encompass all of the work of management. However, this objective was not accomplished because so much depends upon the manager, his attitude toward the worker, and his ability to gain worker co-operation. A technique or a method that can be successfully used by one person may prove to be impractical when it is used by another under different circumstances. Moreover, management methods and techniques should be changed to conform to developments in technology, changes in the composition of the work force, the higher educational levels of the workers, changes in the national and international situation, and other developments. However, the principles of all sciences are subject to new interpretations and modifications as new discoveries are made. The necessity for change does not invalidate the claim that management is a science.

Continuous Research as an Attribute of Science. Science is characterized by investigation and research in an effort to discover new principles or new applications of established principles. The fact that Taylor conducted a number of research studies partly explains his willingness to accept the name of scientific management as the name of the new system. He contended that his studies had established a science of shoveling and a science of handling pig iron. He thought that other types of work could be developed in the same way. Gilbreth attempted to find "the one best way," first in bricklaying and later in other types of work. He also attempted to find the proper intervals for rest periods, the best way for the worker to spend his time during rest periods, and the best way to overcome the effects of necessary fatigue. He experimented with types of chairs, the proper kind of clothing, and the principles of motion. The Hawthorne studies during the 1920's and the 1930's also demonstrated the methods of doing research work in management and the difficulties of interpreting the results.

During the decade of the 1960's and later years, management will be confronted with new situations for which previous experience will afford only a partial guide. New studies and new points of view will be required for working out new solutions and new methods. The steps in such studies can be summarized as follows: first, define the problem and collect the pertinent facts as they exist; second, analyze the facts and identify the controlling factors; and third, apply constructive thinking to arrive at a solution to the problem and the course of action to be followed.

Much of the research in the field of management has consisted of a review of the literature in the subject, the conducting of interviews, the sending out of questionnaires to executives or managers, and the collecting of statistics for the purpose of establishing a trend which can be projected into the future. These methods continue to be valuable for determining facts and principles that have been successfully applied. However, these methods of conducting research cannot be expected to establish guiding principles that can be followed in a future that is characterized by change. New studies must be made of particular situations as they develop.

Willingness to Accept New Ideas. Although a scientist should hold to the established principles in his field of interest, he should also be willing to adapt his principles to new situations and to accept entirely new ideas. Upon occasion, the scientist should be willing to scrap cherished ideas that are found not to conform to the facts. Since management is relatively new as a field of study, the accepted methods and techniques have resulted largely from experience. Research and controlled experimentation have been conducted only on a limited scale in a few areas of activity. Much work remains to be done before management can be developed into a science.

SUCCESS OF MANAGEMENT IN ACCOMPLISHING OBJECTIVES

The objectives of management, as previously suggested, are both private and public or social. The private objectives pertain to the earning of a profit for the owners while the needs of persons within the company are met. Private objectives include also the maintenance of satisfactory relations with outside institutions with which the company deals. The social objectives pertain to the production of goods and services for the public, including the government. The extent to which business enterprises have attained their objectives requires brief discussion.

Private Objectives. Any conclusion concerning the success of private enterprise in meeting the objectives of the owners and managers will depend upon the period of time to which reference is made. During the decade of the 1930's, many persons concluded that private enterprise had failed to meet the needs of the owners and the persons in the organization of the company. This conclusion was based upon the number of failures and even bankruptcies of corporate enterprise, the foreclosures of mortgages, the lack of employment for the people, and the general economic distress. The causes of the Great Depression of the 1930's were many, and although some managements were at fault, they can hardly be charged with the failures and the losses that were sustained during that period.

The ability of private managements to conduct business enterprises efficiently was demonstrated throughout the decade of the 1950's. Corporations were able to pay the very high income, excess profits, and excise taxes during those years and to earn a satisfactory return for the stockholders. The adequacy of the income that was available to stockholders is indicated by the substantial rise in stock prices and the expansion of corporate assets which was made possible through the funds that were available from profits and the proceeds of the sale of new issues of stock and bonds.

Public Objectives. Except for some periods of depression, the most severe of which followed the crisis of 1929, the public objectives of production of goods and services, full employment, and the development of natural resources seem to have been satisfactorily accomplished. Private enterprise produced the goods and services to meet the requirements of the government during World War II and the Korean War and at the same time adequately met the needs of the civilian population. Business managements have also been able to supply American friends and allies abroad with vast quantities of goods for military and civilian use and for reconstruction. Because managements maintain high productivity in factories, mines, and service facilities, the American worker receives higher real wages than workers anywhere else in the world.

The managements of private enterprises in the United States deserve at least a part of the credit for the high standard of living of the American people. As explained in Chapter 1, managements in the United States readily accepted the methods of machine production, the mass production of parts of standardized dimensions, assembly-line production, and other developments of a technical nature. They took the lead in studying production standards, the causes of fatigue and methods of reducing it, hours of work, and working conditions. While wasteful practices have been continued in many trades and industries, both management and labor are entitled to much of the credit for such advances as have been made.

Corporations in the United States have had the advantage of a wide territorial market which has been unhampered by tariff restrictions. The market has been fairly though not completely free of restraints upon the free flow of trade and commerce between the states. The wide market has been able to absorb large quantities of goods, and business enterprises have been able to attain large size as measured by the number of plants, the number of employees, the volume of production, and the dollar amount of sales. Large size has enabled managements to introduce many economies in both production and sales. Large companies can provide good staff facilities for the rendering of services to the managements of the operating divisions. Business has thus achieved the advantages of large size, and the management has found ways to overcome or to reduce the waste that is often assumed to be associated with large size.

The antitrust laws have required American businesses to retain a measure of competition. Just how effective the antitrust laws have been cannot be definitely determined, but corporate mergers and expansion have not proceeded to the point of monopolizing a commodity or an industry except possibly in local markets. Although some examples of enforced divestiture of a factory or a division can be cited and a few corporations have been dissolved for violation of the law, the mere fact that such action can be taken by the government has usually provided sufficient restraint. Corporate managements usually prefer to observe the antiturst laws and to have their competitors do likewise. Competition between the companies in an industry provides an incentive for good management.

Other Reasons for a High Standard of Living. The inference should not be drawn that management and labor should receive all of the credit for the relatively high standard of living in the United States. The nation was endowed with rich resources, including mineral deposits, forests, arable land, a long coast line with good harbors, and rivers and lakes which provided cheap methods of transportation, power, and water. Prior to World War I, the country was protected by the two oceans and the British navy, and the government was not required to spend large sums of money and manpower for military protection. The energies of the people could be used in the production of the things that were needed by consumers of goods and services.

Perhaps a reason for efficient management and high productivity in the United States may be found in the democratic tradition. The democratic principles were forcefully enunciated in the Declaration of Independence, which may be briefly summarized as follows:

All men are created equal.
They are endowed by their Creator with certain inalienable rights.
Governments are established to protect the rights of the people.
Governments exist with the consent of the governed.

Each of these principles may be subject to certain qualifications or explanations. However, the distance that separated the colonies from the mother country, together with the Anglo-Saxon tradition of law and legal rights, required that the people have considerable freedom in the management of their local affairs. In each community, people concerned themselves with schools, roads, bridges, elections, courts, jury duty, and other affairs of government. The democratic processes were slow, but the people got things done.

Although the democratic principle is not easily reconciled with the delegation of authority from the top to the lower levels of the scalar chain, it has affected many of the practices of management. The country gained its independence through revolt against authority, and the people at present resent arbitrary action, discrimination, and autocratic methods. The democratic tradition has encouraged management to solicit suggestions from employees and persons in the management and to integrate the suggestions into a co-ordinated program. It has helped to increase the self-reliance of employees. It has encouraged the development of managers and executives. Although the precise effect of the democratic principle is difficult to assess, the effect has been significant.

The United States has not developed a hereditary aristocracy with its assumption of superiority of one class above another. The absence of rigid class distinctions has facilitated the promotion of capable people from the ranks to supervisory and executive positions. It has caused subordinates to accept the leadership of any person of demonstrated capacity. This attribute has not always characterized business organizations in certain foreign countries.

The future of the system of private enterprise depends in large measure upon the success of management in meeting new situations and in accomplishing the business and social objectives. Developments will require the adaptation of the organization and the programs of the enterprise to change.

QUESTIONS

1. Contrast the manner in which the economy is adapted to changing conditions in a system of private enterprise with the method of adaptation in a socialist country.

2. Is profit properly regarded as the objective of an enterprise, or is profit the incentive to good management?

3. How could the overemphasis of profit defeat the objectives of management? Illustrate.

4. Is the responsibility of management due principally to the stockholders? Does management ever neglect this responsibility?

5. Is management ever satisfied to earn a fair rate of profit on investment, or does it attempt to earn the maximum rate?

6. Why do persons performing a staff function in an enterprise sometimes neglect the objectives which top management regards as the principal objectives?

7. Why might the chief executive of a company adopt a conservative attitude when he is nearing retirement?

8. Why are the evils of bureaucracy sometimes associated with the officials of government? How can a private corporation avoid the evils associated with bureaucracy?

9. Is the budget principally a financial plan or a method of control? Explain.

10. Does statistical data provide a complete method of keeping top management informed of conditions at the work level?

11. How can the management know that the personnel manager is performing his work effectively?

12. Contrast the effectiveness of bonus plans for executives with the effectiveness of profit-sharing plans for employees.

13. How is research conducted in the field of business management?

14. What is the ultimate source of delegated authority in a business enterprise?

15. How does the existence of the democratic tradition in this country affect the methods and policies of business management?

CASE

81. COMPANY ORGANIZATION AND POLICY

The United Metal Products Company operates a foundry and five metal-working and finishing departments. The board of directors has a membership of twelve persons who are elected by the stockholders for terms of three years. Four of the directors are elected each year.

The organization chart of the company indicates that the president is the chief executive officer. The president has an assistant who is shown on the chart in the same box as the president. These two persons are accustomed to talk frankly with each other about their problems, although they do not talk freely with any other persons in the company. Usually the president asks questions which the assistant answers on the basis of information gained by plant visits, personal observations, informal conferences, and written reports from the major executives and middle management. Recently the following conversation was conducted at luncheon.

PRESIDENT: What do you think of the record that Wales is making as director of the sales program?

ASSISTANT: The sales are holding up very well under his direction, but the explanation seems to be that he handles the large contracts himself. He has just returned from Buffalo with a contract that will assure capacity operation for the next six months.

PRESIDENT: That is good news, though I am afraid that our regular sales force may get discouraged when he gets so many big orders himself. How is my friend Al Summers doing as a salesman?

ASSISTANT: He is recognized as an outstanding salesman. He has been able to get some good orders by assuring the customers an early delivery. When he gets an order, he sees that the customer gets priority in the scheduling of the work, and his orders receive first claim on any raw materials on hand. Of course, the production schedule clerk complains that schedules are disrupted and the purchasing agent claims that he is unable to plan his purchasing program. They all know that Al was a member of the same fraternity as yourself in college, and they are not sure how much interested in him you may be. The thing is, though, Al gets the orders. I know that you have never granted him any special favors.

PRESIDENT: I think that I ought to have a talk with Al. Is our production keeping up with sales orders?

ASSISTANT: Production and sales balance fairly well except for a few items. The production schedule manager plans the production to keep all departments equally busy. The sales division is having some difficulty now moving the 15,000 flat irons that were scheduled for the plant. Last year you know we made 12,000 irons which sales disposed of with considerable difficulty. This year the plant manager requested an increase of 25 per cent in order to keep the men busy and to avoid layoffs. Sales complained about the task of moving so many irons and they may not be able to sell all of them.

PRESIDENT: I know the plant manager is principally concerned with low unit cost and the regularity of employment, but perhaps we make a mistake in permitting the production plan to be made by the people in production. Possibly the estimate of sales volume should be made by the sales division on the basis of what they think they can sell. Or possibly we should have a budget committee or a policy committee to work out the estimate. Anyway I am pleased to see the improvement in the figure for labor turnover.

ASSISTANT: Yes, I think we could well make use of more committees. They could be used effectively for working out a lot of plans, and they could relieve us of the necessity for making so many decisions. However, the improvement in labor turnover can be credited largely to the new policies of the personnel manager. After your last talk with him about turnover, he decided to quit hiring high school and college students in the summer time because they regarded their jobs as temporary. Now he has the interviewers make sure that no people are hired unless they want to come with us permanently. The interviewers ask each applicant why he wants to work for the company, and they attempt to determine from the answers whether the applicant is interested in a permanent job. Of course, we still get some students who claim to have dropped out of school, and later we find that they expect to go back to school in the fall. Some people accuse us of being dollar minded and not community minded in this respect, but we cannot afford to take on temporary workers. True, the work may decline later and we may have to let some people go, but we cannot always plan just how many people we will need.

PRESIDENT: That is true, though we do have a large permanent payroll. How do you think that group of young college graduates is making out?

ASSISTANT: They have adjusted in fine style. They all live in the Stanton Apartments, and they are good friends with each other. Personnel is moving them about the plant and they have been doing good work. They had some difficulty in the foundry because they did not like the dirty work, and the foreman was not sure but that one of them might be in line for his job. In some other departments, they were not received with open arms, and I hear some people refer to them as being on the Executive Special. There is certain to be some jealousy.

PRESIDENT: Yes, I suppose so. I wish we could get everyone to look at such programs from the point of view of the company and not their narrow personal viewpoint. What can we do to get better human relations?

ASSISTANT: You are doing now all that anyone could expect. You have told everyone that your door is always open and that anyone can come to see you at any time. I know that not many employees accept your invitation to come in, and I suppose that this means that they are satisfied with the way things are going, on the whole.

PRESIDENT: What surprises me is the way they pick up little things and magnify them into significant developments. When I came here to lunch with Dr. Van Horn last week, some people seemed to think that I was talking atomic power with him. You know we have been good friends since college days, but I have not yet stopped telling people inside and outside the company that we are not getting into a new research project. What can I do to make people think that I do not work out programs in secret?

ASSISTANT: Of course everyone knows that you have the responsibility for making decisions that affect their everyday lives. John Peters was all set up that you invited him to the board meeting to advise with the advertising budget.

PRESIDENT: Strange to say, I did not invite him. He came to the meeting of the board of directors at the invitation of Mr. Crane, who hangs on as board chairman. I could have given them all of the information they needed to adopt the budget, but after Peters came, I had to let him talk. Well, let's get back to the office.

Questions:

1. What does this conversation indicate relative to the philosophy of the management and the methods used?

2. Comment on the soundness of the methods of the management.

INDEX

Index

A

Ability to pay, 404
Accession rate, 502
Accident frequency, 531
Accident severity, 532
Accidents
　allowance for, in time study, 383
　causes of, 585
　prevention of, 531
Accumulative timing, 373
Accuracy, standards of, 90
Administration, 86
Administrative expense budget, 666
Adolphus, Gustavus, 53
Advertising expense budget, 665
Aggressive interview, 476
Air
　cooling of, 263
　filtering of, 265
　heating of, 263
　movement of, 267
Air-conditioning systems, 263
Alexander the Great, 53
Allied expansion, 39
Allowances, in time study, 383
American Management Association, 20
American Society of Mechanical Engineers, 20, 287
American Standards Association, 551
Analytical industry, 605
Annual improvement factor, 405
Annual wage, 417
Applicants, source of, 471
Application blank, 474
Application, letter of, 474
Applied research, 284
Apprentice training, 510
Aptitude tests, 479
Arbitration, of work standards, 389
Arithmetic average, in time study, 379
Assemblies, scheduling of, 610
Assembly industry, 222
Authority
　to act, 69
　centralized, 75
　delegation of, 35, 88
　kinds of, 69
Autocracy, benevolent, 35
Automation
　effect of, 189, 273
　meaning of, 186

B

Balance
　lack of, 75
　in layout, 214
　in organization, 75
　in work load, 74
Balance of stores record, 566
Bargaining, collective, 407
Bargaining strength, 400
Barth, Carl G., 16
Basic research, 184
Batches, division of work into, 615
Bedaux plan, 425
Behind-schedule report, 633
Belonging, sense of, 124
Benevolent autocracy, 35
Bill of materials, 611
Bin balance, 568
Bin tag, 587
Bins, arrangement of, 576
Blocks, glass, 254
Bloomfield, Meyer, 17
Board of directors, 34
Bonus, Christmas, 435
Bonuses, for executives, 701
Bow-type roof, 170
Break-even point, 154, 189
Brick building, 166
Bricklaying, 13
Broadcasting systems, 271
Budget
　advantages of, 656
　cash, 666
　human problems of, 668
　maintenance, 663
　manufacturing, 662
　operation of, 659
　preparation of, 658
　research, 283
Budget officer, 658
Budget period, 657
Budgeting
　organization for, 657
　purposes of, 655
　relation of, to management, 656, 659
Building
　appearance of, 175
　construction of, 165
　maintenance of, 175

Building—*Cont.*
  multistory, 164
  relation to layout, 221
  relation to lighting, 253
  relation to operating costs, 159, 269
  renovation of, 176
  single-story, 164
  standard design of, 163
Building costs, 144
Building plan, 163
Built-in safety, 172
Built-in stabilizers, 704
Bulletin board, in scheduling, 621
Bureaucracy, 696
Buyer's risk, 553
By-products, 144

C

Cafeteria
  planning in, 599
  plant, 528
Caliper, 330
Cash budget, 666
Catalogues, filing of, 557
Centralized authority, 75
Centralized planning, 603
Chain of command, 70
Change, adaption to, 26, 33, 36
Charts, in inspection, 329
Chemical composition, inspection of, 334
Chiseler, 126
Christmas bonus, 435
Civic values, in plant location, 145
Classification systems, 577
Clerical aptitude test, 479
Climate, in plant location, 145
Cloth, manufacture of, 6
Clubs, employee, 523
Collective bargaining, 407
Color
  in design, 301
  effects of, 258
  inspection for, 334
  of light, 259
  relation of, in lighting, 253
  relation to safety, 259
  uses of, 259
Color distinction, 334
Commercial bribery, 550
Commercial standards, 308
Committees
  authority of, 71
  conditions for success of, 79
  kinds of, 78
  uses of, 79
Commodity theory of wages, 399

Communication
  direction of, 105, 291
  effective, 123
  oral, 103
  written, 71
Communication center, 71
Company housing, 533
Company stores, 528
Company town, 150
Company union, 24
Comparator, in inspection, 333
Complete budget, 655
Conservatism of management, 695
Consultants, 19
Consumer complaints, 314
Consumers' ideas, in design, 302
Container, design of, 305
Continuous manufacturing, 273, 597
Continuous production, 222
Continuous-run method, 372
Control
  budgetary, 655
  cost, 102, 684
  in organization, 70
  in production planning, 595
  relation of inspection to, 323
Control charts, 329
Control group, 23
Control points, 324
Conventional control, 602
Conversational interview, 475
Cooke, Morris L., 17
Co-operative store, 529
Co-ordination, in organization, 62, 71, 76
Correction factor, 381
Cost
  differential, 682
  elements of, 674
  estimated, 385, 674
  historical, 674
  opportunity, 684
  process, 673
  relation of, to price, 673
  replacement, 684
  standard, 674, 682
  total, 684
Cost information, 155, 672, 686
Cost-of-living, 402
Cost of materials handling, 194
Cost reduction, 672
Cost systems, 674
Cost and time clerk, 58
Cost of unemployment, 703
Costs, control of, 686
Counseling of employees, 532
Credit unions, 525
Creeping inflation, 42, 162

Criteria, wage, 401
Cubical storing, 581

D

Daily run sheet, 646
Daily runs, scheduling of, 646
Data processing, 28
Day rate
  advantages of, 414
  disadvantages of, 415
  measured, 416
Decentralization
  in decision making, 75
  of production, 147
Decentralized planning, 603
Decentralized purchasing, 545
Decentralized scheduling, 625
Decision making, an executive function, 29, 69
Defective work, allowance for, 383
Defects, correction of, 322
Degrees, in job evaluation, 442
Delays, allowance for, 383
Delegation of authority, 35, 69, 88
Deliveries, scheduling of, 549
Democratic tradition, 708
Demotion, 497
Dennison, Henry S., 17, 18
Depreciation, of machinery, 202
Design
  of container, 305
  development of, 306
  lag of, 305
  phases of, 302
  problems of, 300
  of product, 299
  timing of changes in, 312
Designs
  addition of, 313
  elimination of unprofitable, 315
  pressure for adding, 313
Developmental research, 285
Dexterity test, 479
Differential cost, 682
Diffusion of light, 251
Dimensions
  inspection for, 330
  standards of, 306
  variances in, 307
Direct lighting, 255
Directors, of a corporation, 34
Discharge, of employees, 499
Discipline, 499
Dispatching, in production control, 629, 648
Diversity of product, 313
Division of labor, 276
Dust removal, from air, 265

E

Earned authority, 69
Education, of executives, 92
Efficiency men, 21
Efficiency wage, 430
Effort rating, 381
Electronic controls, 186
Electronic data processing, 28
Element times, 371, 379
Elements of a task, 369
Emerson efficiency wage, 430
Emerson, Harrington, 17, 430
Empire building, 694
Employee relations, index of, 465
Employees
  comfort of, 172
  counseling of, 532
  handbooks for, 463
  opinion surveys, 128
  publications for, 124
  selection of, 20, 474
  services for, 520
  training of, 20, 507
Employment agencies, 472
Employment department, 18
Employment procedure, 474
Engineering
  department of, 107, 137
  emphasis on, 22
  function, in design, 311
  human, 355
Equipment; see Machinery
Equipment budget, 663
Estimated cost, 674
Estimated financial statements, 153, 677
Examination, physical, 482
Exception principle, 88
Exceptional observations, in time study, 379
Executives
  development of, 93
  education of, 92
  point of view of, 87
  training of, 93
  work of, 85
Expansion
  of plant, 173
  of product line, 313
Expendable pallets, 200
Expense
  applied, 679
  manufacturing, 676
  selling, 666
Experimental group, 23

F

Facilitating function, 62
Factor comparison, 441

Factor in production, labor as, 40
Factory float, 643
Farming out, system of, 596
Fatigue
    allowance for, 383
    relation of, to color, 258
    relation of, to monotony, 276
Fatigue study, 276, 348
Fayol, Henri, 26, 86
Feedback, 186
Feiss, Richard A., 17, 508
Filing systems, 557
Financial aids, to employees, 523
Financial planning, 655
Financial policy, 41
Financial rewards, 413
Financial standards, 90
Financial statements
    estimated, 153, 667
    relation of, to plant location, 153
Fire hazard, 167, 173
First-in, first-out method, 568
Flat organization, 34
Flat roof, 169
Flexibility
    in budgets, 657
    in layout, 220
    in policies, 32, 42
Float, factory, 643
Floor inspection, 329
Floors, types of, 169
Flow process chart, 224, 349
Follow-up, in production control, 602, 643,
    648
Foot-candle, 251
Foremanship, functional, 58
Foremen
    co-operation by, 52
    part of management, 105
    rating of, 113
    recognition of worker by, 126
    relation to personnel department, 459
    relation to production control, 602
    relation to working conditions, 101
    training of, 108
    unions of, 111
    work of, 100
Formal questioning interview, 475
Fringe benefits, 533
Fully automatic machine, 184
Function, 57
Functional design, 304
Functional organization, 57, 58
Funds, source of, 42

G

Gages
    kinds of, 325
    uses of, 332

Gang boss, 58
Gantt, Henry L., 10
Gantt chart, 12, 241
Gases, removal of, 265
General lighting, 255
General-purpose machines, 189
General staff, 53
Gifts, acceptance of, 550
Gilbreth, Frank B., 13, 344, 347, 350
Gilbreth, Lillian M., 13, 344, 347
Glare, 251
Glass blocks, 234
Grading interview, 475
Grievance, 459
Group hospitalization, 521
Group life insurance, 522
Group piece rates, 425
Guaranteed annual wage, 417

H

Halsey plan, 420
Hand-to-mouth buying, 554
Hardwood floors, 169
Hathaway, H. K., 17
Hawthorne experiments, 23
Heating systems, 263
Highway, location on, 140
Historical costs, 674
Hobbing machine, 183
Hopkins, Ernest M., 17
Horizontal co-ordination, 78, 291
Horizontal expansion, 39
Hoxie, Robert F., 18
Human engineering, 355
Human relations, 87, 110, 128
Humidity, 264

I

Idle time, 12
Improvement factor, 405
Incandescent lighting, 256
Incentive wage systems, 429
Indirect lighting, 255
Induction, to the job, 483
Industrial district, 149
Industrial park, 149
Industrial relations, 407
Industrial standards, 308
Inflation
    effect of, 42, 203
    problem of, 42, 162
Insecurity, of workers, 122
Inside sources, of applicants, 471
Inspection
    of equipment, 236
    management of, 335

Inspection—*Cont.*
  methods of, 330
  purposes of, 59, 322
  sampling, 27, 327
Inspection ticket, 615
Instruct, how to, 513
Instruction card clerk, 58
Insurance, for employees, 522
Integration, 38
Interchangeability of parts, 6, 310
Internal faults, 335
Interruptions, allowance for, 383
Interview
  counseling, 532
  employment, 475
  exit, 500
Inventory
  management of, 561
  taking of, 587
Investigation, personal, 477

J

Jefferson, Thomas, 5
Jethro, 89
Job definition, 439
Job description, 439
Job evaluation, 438
Job ranking, 440
Job shop operations, 612
Job specifications, 440
Jobs, key, 441
Joseph, 3
Joshua, 4

K

Key jobs, 441
Key man in production, 101
Key materials, 554

L

Labor
  attitude toward, 40
  division of, 6
Labor budget, 664
Labor conditions, in plant location, 141
Labor cost, 675
Labor grades, 444
Labor-hour method, 478
Labor scouts, 472
Labor supply, 471
Labor time ticket, 675
Labor unions
  attitude toward job evaluation, 449
  attitude toward piece rates, 426
  company, 24

Labor unions—*Cont.*
  insurance plans of, 522
  relation to machine production, 207
Laboratory inspection, 329
Lamps, types of, 256
Land, cost of, 143
Last-in, first-out method, 568
Lathe, 190
Layoffs, 498
Layout
  changing basis of, 220
  essentials of, 213
  process, 215
  product, 217
  relation to other problems, 221
  revision of, 220, 223
Leadership, in product line, 37
Lease arrangement, 39
Lease or buy, 39, 161, 206
Letter of application, 474
Leveling factor, 381
Levels of authority, 70
Liability of employer, 523
Life insurance, group, 522
Light intensity, 251
Light meter, 252
Lighting
  experiments in, 23
  importance of, 249
  methods of, 250, 253
  relation of building to, 253
Limit gage, 332
Line
  definition of, 50
  departments of, 51
  relation to staff, 62, 64
Linear programing, 28
Lines of promotion, 72, 490
Living costs, 402
Living standards, 708
Localized lighting, 255
Loose standard
  causes of, 388
  correction of, 389

M

Machine loads
  changes in, 621
  report of, 634
  summary of, 621
Machine overhead, 679
Machines
  automatic, 184
  benefits of, 707
  causes of breakdowns of, 239
  design of, 244
  inspection by, 326

Machines—*Cont.*
  invention of, 6
  maintenance of, 235
  number of, per worker, 183
  operations by, 181
  output of, 204
  parts of, 181
  replacement of, 42, 202
  sale or rent of, 39
  selection of, 192, 196
  time-recording, 373
  types of, 182
Maginot-line attitude, 695
Maintenance
  budgeting of, 663
  of buildings, 175
  control of, 242
  of lighting systems, 257
  of machines, 236
  planning for, 238
  scheduling of, 239
Management
  beginnings of, 6
  information for, 673
  of inspection, 335
  of maintenance, 238
  as a science, 10
  task, 9
Management consultant, 19
Manual dexterity, 479
Manually operated machines, 182
Manufacturing cycle efficiency, 644
Manufacturing departments, 676
Manufacturing design, 302, 304
Manufacturing expenses
  accounting for, 676
  budgeting of, 664
Manufacturing methods, development of, 6
Market, nearness to, 138
Market segmentation, 303
Materials
  cost of, 568, 675
  effect of air on, 264
  handling of, 194, 222
  location near source of, 139
  purchase of, 541
  requisitioning of, 568
  storing of, 574
  strength of, 333
Mathematical programing, 28
Maximum inventory, 562
Measured day rate, 416
Measurement gage, 331
Mechanical aptitude test, 480
Mechanization of industry, 5
Median, use of, in time study, 379
Medical services, 521
Merit rating, 493

Methods improvement, 343
Methods time measurement, 386
Micrometer, 331
Mill construction, 166
Milling machine, 191
Minimum inventory, 562
Mnemonic classification, 577
Monitor roof, 170
Monotony, 272
Morale
  definition of, 120
  factors in, 121
  importance of, 120
Moses, 4, 89
Motion model, 14
Motion pictures, in time study, 14
Motion study
  advantages to worker, 352
  contribution of Gilbreth to, 14, 344
  economies of, 351
  objections to, 352
  purposes of, 343, 344
  relation of, to time study, 365
Motions, principles of, 347
Move ticket, 615
Multiple machine interference, 184, 383
Multistory building, 164

N

National Bureau of Standards, 316, 398
Natural laws, 10
Noise, 270
Nonfinancial rewards, 120
Normal output, 680
Normal year, 681
Numerical classification, 577
Numerical filing, 557
Nurseries, provision of, 533

O

Objectives
  company, 461, 491
  personal, 461, 706
  statement of, 515
Observation sheet, 370
Obsolescence, of building, 160
Old-age benefits, 123, 524
On-the-job training, 350, 511
Operation ticket, 613
Operations, in production, 612
Operations research, 27
Opportunity cost, 684
Optical projection, 332
Orders, issuance of, 630
Organization
  functional, 57, 58
  line, 50

Organization—*Cont.*
  line and staff, 53
  meaning of, 33, 49
  need for, 49
  planning of, 79
  principles of, 68
  relation of, to size, 34, 36
  for research, 290
  for time study, 366
Overapplied expense, 680
Overexpansion, of product line, 313
Overhead conveyors, 198
Overhead expense, 676

P

Pallet system, 199
Partial budget, 655
Partial inspection, 327
Parts
  buy or make, 38
  interchangeability of, 6
  scheduling of, 610
  sequence of completion of, 611
Paternalism, 41
Payment of workers
  by the hour, 414
  incentive method of, 431
  piece-rate method of, 424
  relation of, to morale, 121
Pegboard, in planning, 621
Pension plans, 524
Performance rating, 90, 380
Performance tests, 480
Permanent storage, 224
Person, Harlow S., 17
Personal objectives, 121
Personal investigation, 477
Personal needs, allowance for, 383
Personal staff, 54
Personnel department, 460, 516
Personnel policies, 462
Personnel work, evaluation of, 465
Philip of Macedon, 53
Physical examination, 482
Piece rates, 363, 385, 424
Pilot plant, 292
Pitched roof, 170
Planned industrial district, 149
Planning
  for building, 161
  financial, 655
  for maintenance, 238
  for new product, 292
  for production, 595
Planning department, 609
Plant budget, 663
Plant cafeteria, 528

Plant layout; *see* Layout
Plant location, 137
Plant magazine, 526
Plant ownership, 160
Plants, modernization of, 160
Plug gage, 332
Point system, of job evaluation, 443
Policies
  financial, 41
  meaning of, 462
  personnel, 462
  statement of, 463
Powered tools, 237
Prices, rising, 162, 203
Process chart, 224, 349
Product
  dropping of, 40
  increase in number of, 37
  rating of, 323
  research, 282
Product design, 223, 303
Product line, expansion of, 37, 313
Production
  estimate of, 639
  improvement in methods of, 6
  preparation for, 293
  stabilization of, 417
Production control, 595
Production report, 622
Professional inspection, 324
Profile inspection, 332
Profit
  as an objective, 692
  overemphasis of, 694
  sharing of, 433, 701
Progressive layout, 213
Promotion, 72
Public relations, 155
Purchased parts, 541
Purchases
  placing order for, 555
  timing of, 543
  types of, 541
Purchases budget, 663
Purchasing practices, 547
Pure research, 284

Q

Quality
  control of, 283
  inspection for, 321
  maintenance of, 101
  payment for, 323
Quantity
  to manufacture, 562
  to order, 553, 563
Questionnaire, employee, 128

R

Radiant heating, 263
Rating
of employees, 121
of foremen, 113
of product, 323
Reciprocal buying, 550
Recognition, desire for, 126
Recommendations, of applicants, 476
Recreation activities, 523
Reduction of costs, 672
Relative bargaining strength, 400
Reorder point, 562, 566
Replacement cost, 684
Requisition
for employment, 474
for materials, 566, 630
Research
control of, 293
co-ordination of, 238
in management, 705
organization for, 290
types of, 284
Research budget, 293
Research project, life of, 295
Responsibility
assignment of, 70
relation to authority, 70
Rest periods, 276
Retirement plans, 524
Rewards
financial, 91
nonfinancial, 91
in training courses, 516
Rising prices, effect of, 42, 162, 203
Risk taking, by management, 695
Roofs, 169
Routing, 610
Rowan plan, 421
Rules, concerning discharge, 500

S

Safety
in buildings, 172
built-in, 172
measures of, 585
relation of machinery to, 193
training in, 514
Safety colors, 259
Sale-and-lease-back arrangement, 161
Sales budget, 661
Sampling
in inspection, 327
of purchased items, 553
work, 356
Scalar chain, 70

Scheduling
of maintenance, 239
of production, 617
Science, management as, 10, 704
Scientific management, 7, 10, 704
Seasonal variations, 419
Security, of workers, 122
Segmentation of markets, 303
Selling expense budget, 666
Semiautomatic machines, 183
Semiworks, 292
Seniority, 495
Separation rate, 502
Service departments, 227, 677
Set-up man, 58
Shop overage and shortage, 634
Shop steward, 388
Simplification, 315
Single-story building, 164
Situational testing, 480
Size, problems of, 36
Skill, rating for, 381
Small-town location, 146
Smoke, removal of, 265
Snapback method in time study, 372
Social obligations, of a company, 691
Social relationships, of workers, 125
Social status, 124
Sound systems, 271
Sources of supply
of materials, 547
of workers, 471
Space comprehension, 479
Space, effective use of, 214
Specialists, attitude of, 694
Special-purpose equipment, 192
Special staff, 54
Specifications, 306, 552
Speculative buying, 554
Stability, 32, 42
Stabilizers, built-in, 704
Staff
authority of, 54
development of, 35, 53
effectiveness of, 700
kinds of, 54
relation of, to line, 54, 62, 107
Standard cost, 674, 682
Standard element times, 384
Standard quantities, 562
Standardization of product, 6
Standards
commercial, 308
industrial, 308
judgment by, 90, 243
production, 56, 364

Statement of profit and loss
estimated, 677
in plant location, 153
Static budget, 657
Statistical data, uses of, 699
Statistical methods, in inspection, 327, 553
Status, 124
Steep organization, 34
Steward, union, 388
Stop watch, in time study, 369
Storeroom layout, 576
Stores
classification of, 577
issuing of, 583
receiving of, 575
Strikes, cost of, 703
Suburban location, 146
Suggestion systems, 529
Superhighway, location on, 148
Surgical benefits, 521
Synthetic industries, 222
Systematic planning, 603

T

Task and bonus plan, 12
Task system, 9
Taxes
in plant location, 144
relation to leasing, 163
Taylor, Frederick W., 7, 20, 125
Teamwork, development of, 694
Temporary storage, 224
Termination report, 501
Testing, situational, 480
Tests
in inspection, 330
for workers, 20
Therbligs, 345
Thompson, Sanford E., 16
Tight work standard, 388
Time-recording machine, 373
Time study
allowances in, 383
beginning of, 363
criticism of, 390
making of, 367
relation to motion study, 365
uses of, 363
Time-study man, 366
Time ticket, 675
Timing of purchases, 543
Tolerances, 307
Total cost, 684
Towne, Henry R., 7
Trade tests, 479
Training
of foremen, 108
of workers, 350, 507

Transfer of employees, 489
Transportation facilities, 139
Turnover, labor, 501

U

Underapplied expense, 679
Unemployment
costs of, 418
reduction of, 704
Union steward, 388
Unions
of foremen, 111
policy of, concerning machines, 207
relation of, to management, 41
Unit cost, 675
Unprofitable designs, elimination of, 315
Unsafe practices, 586
Upgrading, 514

V

Variances, 306
Varieties of product, 313
Vendors
relations with, 547
selection of, 548
Vertical co-ordination, 52
Vertical integration, 38
Vestibule training, 509
Visual inspection, 325
Voluntary inspection, 325
V-shaped roof, 170

W

Wage criteria, 401
Wage determination, 398
Wage differentials, 141
Wage level, 403
Wage systems, 413
Waste disposal, 143, 144
Water supply, 143
Western Electric Company, 23
Whitney, Eli, 6
Williams, Whiting, 22
Windowless factories, 269
Wood-frame construction, 165
Work centers, 219
Work cycle, 272
Work force
changes in, 489
utilization of, 702
Work measurement, 362
Work simplification, 354
Work standards
arbitration of, 389
setting of, 362
Work stoppages, 703

Workers
  attitude of, toward machines, 87, 274
  complaints of, 104
  effect of attitude of, 120
  incentives for, 701
  inspection by, 324
  motivation of, 121
  security of, 122

Workers—*Cont.*
  selection of, 475
  treatment of, 40, 102
Working conditions
  improvement of, 249
  relation of, to wages, 405
  responsibility of foreman for, 101
Workplace arrangement, 348

This book has been set in 12 point and 10 point Garamond Intertype, leaded 1 point. Part and chapter numbers and titles are in 24 point Futura Medium. The size of the type page is 27 by 46½ picas.